SPREAD SPECTRUM COMMUNICATIONS

Volume III

ELECTRICAL ENGINEERING
COMMUNICATIONS AND SIGNAL PROCESSING

Raymond L. Pickholtz, Series Editor

Anton Meijer and Paul Peeters
Computer Network Architectures

Marvin K. Simon, Jim K. Omura, Robert A. Scholtz, and Barry K. Levitt
Spread Spectrum Communications, Volume I

Marvin K. Simon, Jim K. Omura, Robert A. Scholtz, and Barry K. Levitt
Spread Spectrum Communications, Volume II

Marvin K. Simon, Jim K. Omura, Robert A. Scholtz, and Barry K. Levitt
Spread Spectrum Communications, Volume III

William W Wu
Elements of Digital Satellite Communication: System Alternatives, Analyses, and Optimization, Volume I

William W Wu
Elements of Digital Satellite Communication: Channel Coding and Integrated Services Digital Satellite Networks, Volume II

Also of interest:

Victor B. Lawrence, Joseph L. Lo Cicero, and Laurence B. Milstein, editors
IEEE Communication Society's Tutorials in Modern Communications

Wushow Chou, Editor-in-Chief
Journal of Telecommunication Networks

SPREAD SPECTRUM COMMUNICATIONS

Volume III

Marvin K. Simon
Jet Propulsion Laboratory

Jim K. Omura
University of California

Robert A. Scholtz
University of Southern California

Barry K. Levitt
Jet Propulsion Laboratory

COMPUTER SCIENCE PRESS

Computer Science Press
1803 Research Boulevard
Rockville, Maryland 20850

1 2 3 4 5 6 Printing Year 89 88 87 86 85

Library of Congress Cataloging in Publication Data
Main entry under title:

Spread spectrum communications (V.III)
Bibliography: p.
Includes index.
1. Spread spectrum communications—Collected works.
I. Simon, Marvin.
TK5102.5.S6662 1985 621.38′0413 84-4959
ISBN 0-88175-015-8 (Vol. III)
ISBN 0-88175-017-4 (Set)

VOLUME III
CONTENTS

PART 5 SPECIAL TOPICS

VOLUME I CONTENTS

VOLUME II CONTENTS

PART 3 OTHER FREQUENCY-HOPPED SYSTEMS

PREFACE

Not more than a decade ago, the discipline of spread-spectrum (SS) communications was primarily cloaked in secrecy. Indeed, most of the information available on the subject at that time could be found only in documents of a classified nature.

Today the picture is noticeably changed. The open literature abounds with publications on SS communications, special issues of the *IEEE Transactions on Communications* have been devoted to the subject, and the formation of an annual conference on military communications, MILCOM, now offers a public forum for presentation of unclassified (as well as classified) papers dealing with SS applications in military systems. On a less formal note, many tutorial and survey papers have recently appeared in the open literature, in addition to which presentations on a similar level have taken place at major communications conferences. Finally, as further evidence we cite the publication of several books dealing either with SS communications directly or as part of the more general electronic countermeasures (ECM) and electronic counter-counter measures (ECCM) problem. References to all these forms of public documentation are given in Section 1.7 of Chapter 1, Volume I.

The reasons behind this proliferation can be traced to many sources. While it is undoubtedly true that the primary application of SS communications is still in the development of enemy jam-resistant communication systems for the military, a large part of which takes place within the confines of classified programs, the emergence of other applications in both the military and civilian sectors is playing a role of ever-increasing importance. For example, to minimize mutual interference, the flux density of transmissions from radio transmitters often must be maintained at acceptably low radiation levels. A convenient way of meeting these requirements is by spreading the power spectrum of the signal before transmission and despreading it after reception. This is the non-hostile equivalent of the military low-probability-of-intercept (LPI) signal design.

Another instance where SS techniques are particularly useful in a non-anti-jam application is in the area of multiple-access communications wherein many users desire to share a single communication channel. Here the assignment of a unique SS sequence to each user allows him or her to simultaneously transmit over the common channel with a minimum of mutual interference. This often simplifies the network control requirements to coordinate users of the available channel capacity.

Still another example is the requirement for extremely accurate position location using several satellites in synchronous and asynchronous orbits. Here, satellites transmitting pseudorandom noise sequences modulated onto the transmitted carrier signal provide the means for accomplishing the required range and distance determination at any point on the earth.

Finally, SS techniques offer the advantage of improved reliability of transmission in frequency-selective fading and multipath environments. Here the improvement stems from the fact that spreading the information bandwidth of the transmitted signal over a wide range of frequencies reduces its vulnerability to interference located in a narrow frequency band and often provides some diversity gain at the receiver.

At the heart of all these potential applications lies the increasing use of digital forms of modulation for transmitting information, which itself is driven by the tremendous advances that have been made over the last decade in microelectronics. No doubt this trend will continue, and thus it should not be surprising that more and more applications for spread-spectrum techniques will continue to surface. Indeed the state-of-the-art is advancing so rapidly (e.g., witness the recent improvements in frequency synthesizers boosting frequency hop rates from the Khops/sec to the Mhops/sec ranges over SS bandwidths in excess of a GHz) that today's primarily theoretical concepts in a particular situation will be realized in practice tomorrow.

Unclassified research and developments in spread-spectrum communications have reached a point of maturity necessary to justify a textbook on SS communications that goes far beyond the level of those available on today's market. Such is the purpose of *Spread Spectrum Communications*. Contained within the fourteen chapters of its three volumes is an in-depth treatment of SS communications that should appeal to the specialist already familiar with the subject as well as the neophyte with little or no background in the area. The book is organized into five parts within which the various chapters are for the most part self-contained. The exception to this is that Chapter 3, Volume I dealing with basic concepts and system models is a basis for many of the other chapters that follow it. As would be expected, the more traditional portions of the subject are treated in the first two parts, while the latter three parts deal with the more specialized aspects. Thus the authors envision that an introductory one-semester course in SS communications to be taught on a graduate level in a university might cover all or parts of Chapters 1, 3, 4, 5 of Volume I, Chapters 1 and 2 of Volume II, and Chapters 1 and 2 of Volume III.

In composing the technical material presented in *Spread Spectrum Communications*, the authors have intentionally avoided referring by name to specific modern SS systems that employ techniques such as those discussed in many of the chapters. Such a choice was motivated by the desire to offer a unified approach to the subject that stresses fundamental principles rather than specific applications. Nevertheless, the reader should feed confident that the broad experience of the four authors ensures that the material is practically significant as well as academically inspiring.

In writing a book of this magnitude, we acknowledge many whose efforts should not go unnoticed either by virtue of a direct or indirect contribution. Credit is due to Paul Green for originally suggesting the research that uncovered the material in Chapter 2, Volume I, and Bob Price for tireless sleuthing which led to much of the remarkable information presented there. Chapter 5, Volume I benefitted significantly from the comments of Lloyd Welch, whose innovative research is responsible for some of the elegant sequence designs presented there. Per Kullstam helped clarify the material on DS/BPSK analysis in Chapter 1, Volume II. Paul Crepeau contributed substantially to the work on list detectors. Last, but by no means least, the authors would like to thank James Springett, Gaylord Huth, and Richard Iwasaki for their contribution to much of the material presented in Chapter 4, Volume III.

Several colleagues of the authors have aided in the production of a useful book by virtue of critical reading and/or proofing. In this regard, the efforts of Paul Crepeau, Larry Hatch, Vijay Kumar, Sang Moon, Wei-Chung Peng, and Reginaldo Polazzo, Jr. are greatly appreciated.

It is often said that a book cannot be judged by its cover. The authors of *Spread Spectrum Communications* are proud to take exception to this commonly quoted cliche. For the permission to use the historically significant noise-wheel cover design (see Chapter 2, Volume I, Section 2.2.5), we gratefully acknowledge the International Telephone and Telegraph Corp.

Marvin K. Simon
Jim K. Omura
Robert A. Scholtz
Barry K. Levitt

To

Sidney, Belle, Anita, Brette, and Jeffrey Simon
Shomatsu and Shizuko Omura
Lolly, Michael, and Paul Scholtz
Beverly Kaye

for a variety of reasons known only to the authors

Part 4

SYNCHRONIZATION OF SPREAD-SPECTRUM SYSTEMS

Chapter 1

PSEUDONOISE CODE ACQUISITION IN DIRECT-SEQUENCE RECEIVERS

One of the primary functions of a direct-sequence (DS) spread-spectrum (SS) receiver is to despread the received pseudonoise (PN) code. This is accomplished by generating a local replica of the PN code in the receiver and then synchronizing this local PN signal to the one which is superimposed on the incoming (received) waveform. Multiplication or remodulation of the incoming signal by the synchronized local PN code replica then produces the desired despreading process.

The process of synchronizing the local and received PN signals is ordinarily accomplished in two stages. Initially, a coarse alignment of the two PN signals is produced to within a small (typically less than a fraction of a chip) residual relative timing offset. The process of bringing the two codes into coarse alignment is referred to as *PN acquisition*. Once the incoming PN code has been acquired, a fine synchronization system takes over and continuously maintains the best possible waveform alignment by means of a closed loop operation. The process of maintaining the two codes in fine synchronism is referred to as *PN tracking*. In this chapter, we focus our attention on techniques and their performance for accomplishing PN acquisition. Chapter 2 deals with the companion problem of PN tracking.

1.1 HISTORICAL SURVEY

If one searches through the literature which discusses PN acquisition techniques, the common denominator among almost all the methods is that the received and local PN signals are first multiplied[1] to produce a measure of correlation between the two. This correlation measure is then processed by a suitable detector/decision rule and search strategy to decide whether the two codes are in synchronism and what to do if they're not. The

[1] The word "multiplied" is used here in the broadest sense allowing for the possibilities of active or passive, analog or digital, time continuous or time discrete correlation operations. The specific differences among these various forms of multiplication will be partly responsible for the classification of PN acquisition systems to be discussed shortly.

differences between the various schemes depend on (1) the type of detector (and decision strategy) used, which, in turn, is dependent on the form of the received signal and the particular application at hand, and (2) the nature of the search algorithm which acts on the detector outputs to reach the final verdict.[2]

All known detectors for PN acquisition systems, in one form or another, fall into two basic categories, namely, *coherent* or *non-coherent*. By far the most common found in acquisition systems for DS/SS receivers is the non-coherent detector which, for example, might be comprised of a band-pass filter centered at the frequency of the received carrier upon which the PN signal is direct modulated, followed by a square-law envelope detector,[3] an integrate-and-dump circuit which operates over a finite time interval, and a simple threshold device [1]. The reason why the non-coherent detector is most commonly found is that the despreading operation typically takes place ahead of the carrier synchronization function; thus, at the point in time at which PN acquisition is to be accomplished, the carrier phase must be assumed to be unknown.

Consideration has also been given in the literature to PN acquisition systems which operate under the assumption that the receiver is capable of determining good estimates of the carrier phase and frequency shifts brought about by the propagation delay and Doppler produced by the transmission channel, in which case, the carrier can be "demodulated" prior to PN despreading. In these instances, the PN acquisition system can employ a coherent detector which typically might consist of a low-pass filter (possibly implemented as an integrate-and-dump circuit) followed by an optimum Bayes detector [2], [3] or instead just a simple threshold device [4], [5].

It is convenient insofar as our discussion is concerned to perform a further classification of detectors for PN acquisition schemes depending upon whether they are of the *fixed* or *variable* integration time type. Within the category of *fixed* integration time detectors, one can further subdivide them into single dwell [1], [6] and multiple dwell types [7], [8] depending, respectively, upon whether the detector's decision is made on the basis of a single (suitably processed) fixed time observation of received signal plus noise or many such observations (not necessarily independent of one another). Depending upon the duration of the observation, or equivalently, the time allotted to make a decision, relative to the PN code period, single dwell time detectors can be further differentiated according to whether they utilize partial or full period code correlation. The multiple dwell detectors differ from one another in the way in which the additional observations are

---

[2] Much of the ensuing discussion on classification, as well as the unified approach presented in Sections 1.4 through 1.6, is based on the theory as formulated by Polydoros [38], Polydoros and Weber [14], and Polydoros and Simon [39].

[3] An envelope detector followed by a square-law device.

used to *verify* the temporary decision made based on the first observation alone.

More specifically, since all of the detector structures of interest make decisions based on a threshold comparison test of one form or another, following a threshold exceedance of the first dwell (integration) output, the additional dwells in combination with threshold testing are used in accordance with a specified *verification algorithm* to produce a final decision on whether the code phase position under test corresponds to true synchronization. This verification mode of operation of the detector structure typically falls into one of two categories. In the type of multiple dwell acquisition system discussed by DiCarlo [7], [8], a code phase position is immediately rejected or dismissed as corresponding to an incorrect synchronization condition as soon as *any* dwell output fails to satisfy its threshold exceedance test. All other types of verification modes of operation, often referred to as *search/lock* strategies [9], employ algorithms which require repeated threshold testing of a given dwell output or use a majority logic type of decision on the total set of multiple dwell threshold tests (coincidence detectors).

Finally, the category of variable integration time detectors is reserved for those cases where the dwell time, here being the time for a continuously integrated stochastic process to exceed a threshold, is a random variable. As such, the various PN acquisition systems that contain a variable integration time detector typically employ the classical method of *sequential detection* [10] which finds its roots in the detection of radar signals [11].

The next classification of detector structures is in accordance with the rate at which decisions are made on each code phase position under test. High decision rate detectors, such as those used in *matched filter* (passive correlation) PN acquisition systems [12], [13], refer to those structures that make their decisions on the out-of-sync code phase offsets between incoming and local codes at the PN code chip rate or an integer multiple of it. Low decision rate detectors, which employ active correlation, make these same decisions at a rate significantly slower than the code chip rate. As such, many of these structures employ little or no verification.

To complete our classification of detector types, we further categorize them according to the criterion used for deciding between in-sync and out-of-sync hypotheses, e.g., Bayes (minimum average risk), Neyman-Pearson (minimum probability of an error of the second kind—missed detection—for a given probability of an error of the first kind—false alarm), etc.

A summary of the above classification of the structure of detectors used for PN acquisition purposes is illustrated in Figure 1.1, which was originally suggested in [14]. A more detailed discussion of the various forms of the structures themselves and how they fit into the overall acquisition scheme will follow shortly.

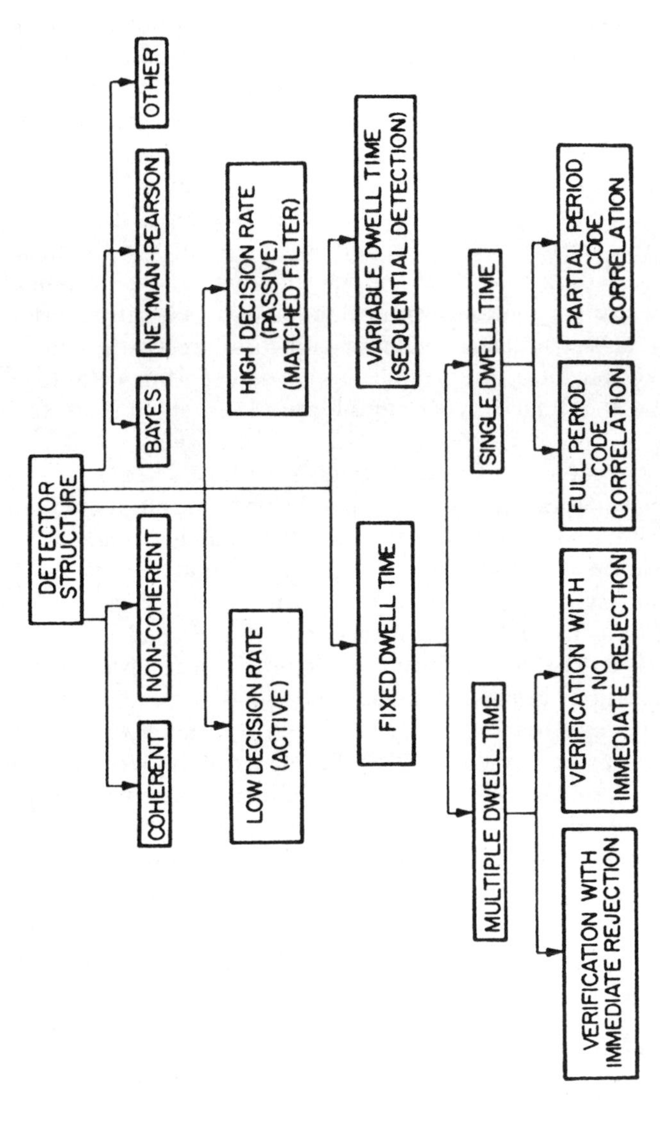

Figure 1.1. Structure of detectors for acquisition purposes (reprinted from [38]).

Not unlike the classification of detector types, the classification of acquisition schemes according to search strategy follows a tree structure [14] (see Figure 1.2) where many of the categories produce the next level of the tree by a simple dichotomy. Perhaps the simplest, at least conceptually, of the search techniques on the first level of the hierarchy is the *maximum-likelihood* algorithm. In its strictest form, the algorithm requires that the input PN signal be correlated with all possible code positions (or perhaps fractional code positions) of the local PN code replica. The correlations are assumed to be performed in parallel and as such the corresponding detector outputs all pertain to the identical observation of received signal plus noise. The correct PN alignment is chosen as that local code phase position which produced the maximum detector output. In a less strict version, the maximum-likelihood algorithm[4] can be implemented in a serial fashion (see Figure 1.3). Here the input PN signal is serially correlated with all possible code positions (or perhaps again fractional code positions) of the local PN code replica and the corresponding detector outputs stored. At the end of the test, the correct PN alignment is again chosen as that local code phase position which produced the maximum detector output. Such a brute force acquisition procedure, whether implemented in parallel or serial form, clearly has the advantage that a definite decision will be made after only a single examination of all code phase positions, or a single search through the entire code period. Thus, multiple examination of each code phase position or multiple searches through the code are avoided by this procedure. However, this rudimentary advantage is overwhelmed by the obvious disadvantage that a decision cannot be reached unless every code phase position has been examined or until the entire code period has been searched. For long codes, as are required in spread-spectrum systems with large processing gain, complexity of the parallel implementation or the time to search the entire code and thus reach a synchronization decision in the serial version is often prohibitive.

Another scheme, which dates back more than two and a half decades, was first introduced by Ward [4] and is based on a sequential estimation[5] of the shift register states of the PN generator. In particular, the RASE (Rapid Acquisition by Sequential Estimation) system of Figure 1.4 makes its best estimate of the first n received PN code chips (n is the number of stages in the code generator) and loads the receiver sequence generator with that estimate, thus defining a particular initial condition (starting state) from which the generator begins its operation. Since a PN sequence has the

---

[4] Note that the serial implementation of the maximum-likelihood algorithm is not true maximum-likelihood since the various hypotheses (code phase positions) are tested using different observations of the received signal.

[5] This should not be confused with the method of sequential detection [10] associated with variable integration time acquisition systems.

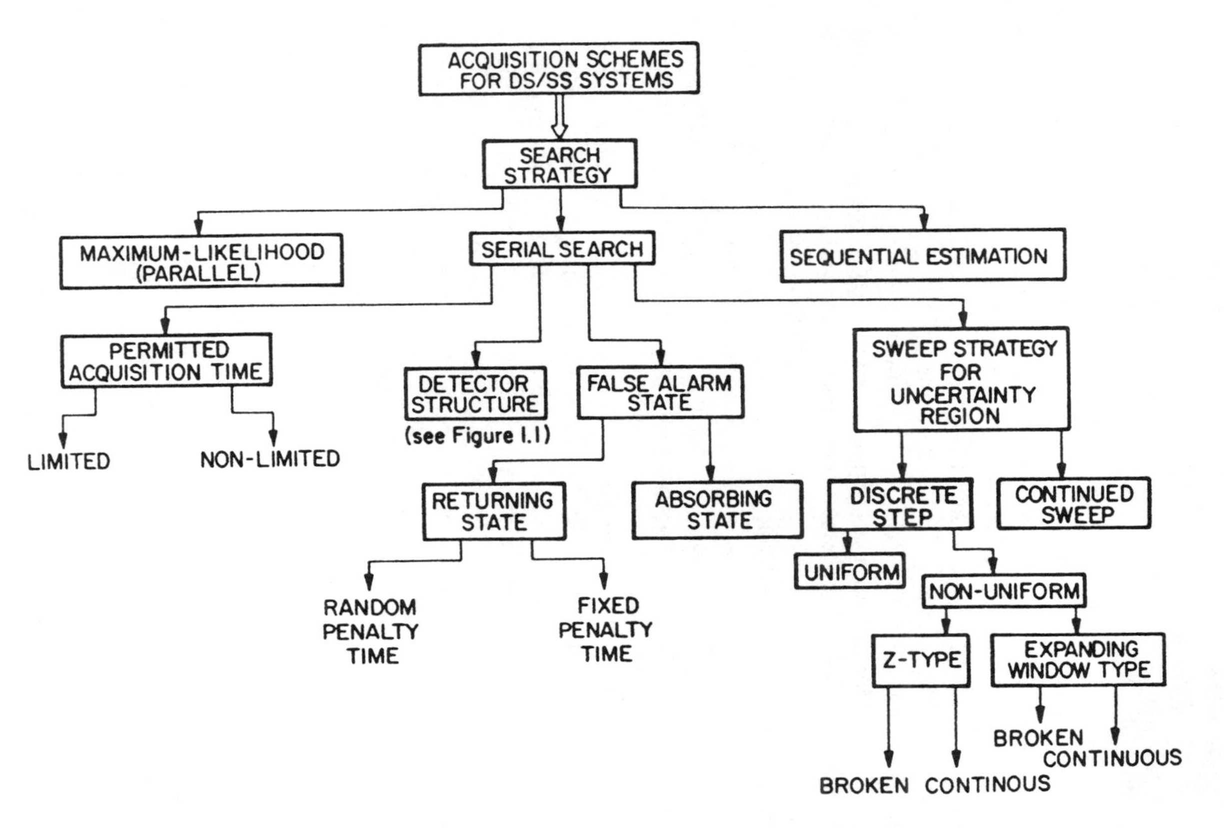

Figure 1.2. Classification of acquisition schemes (reprinted from [38]).

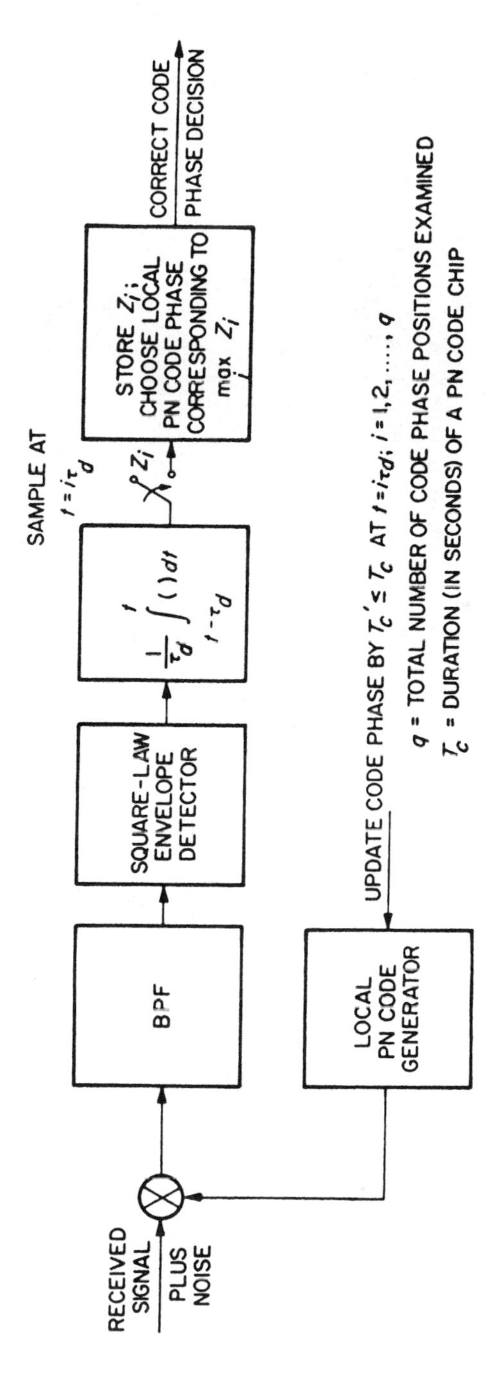

Figure 1.3. A serial realization of the maximum-likelihood search technique.

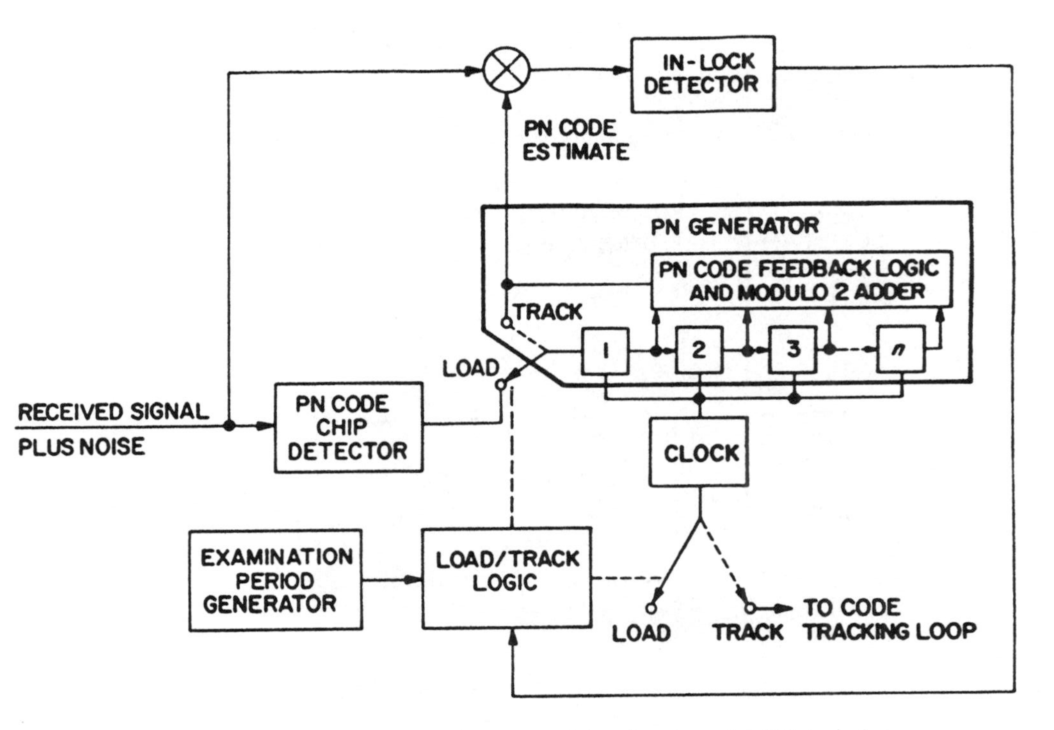

Figure 1.4. A rapid acquisition by sequential estimation (RASE) technique.

property that the next combination of register states depends only on the present combination of states, if indeed this present combination is correct (i.e., all *n* input chips are correctly estimated), all the following states can be predicted based on the knowledge of only this initial condition. Such is the manner in which the RASE maintains synchronization once it has been determined that the *n* detected chips provide the correct starting position, i.e., from that point on it no longer needs estimates of the input code chips. Until such time, however, the local PN shift registers must be periodically, at a rate determined by an examination period generator, loaded with new estimates where the decision when to stop the reload procedure is based upon a threshold crossing of an in-lock detector. The test statistic upon which this in-lock detector makes its decision is the cross-correlation of the input code with that produced by the local PN generator whose shift register contents correspond to the present estimate of the input state. Once it is determined that a correct estimate was made, the lock detector threshold crossing inhibits further reloading of the local shift register. This register is then closed within the PN tracking loop which is responsible for maintaining code phase from that time on.

At this point, several features of the RASE system are worthy of note. Clearly, since the success of this acquisition scheme depends on the ability to make credible estimates of the received PN code chips in the presence of noise, for a PN modulated carrier as an input signal, the estimation process would consist of a simple demodulation and hard-limiting detection of this signal in the same way that one would demodulate and detect any PSK data stream.[6] As such this scheme falls into the class requiring *coherent* detection and is thus of limited use in most spread-spectrum applications. Nevertheless, it warrants discussion since it does have the advantage of being a rapid acquisition technique for *moderate* input signal-to-noise ratios, and in fact, when compared with the simplest serial search (stepping correlator) system to be discussed next, it offers significant improvement in acquisition time even for signal-to-noise ratios down to -15 dB [4]. Despite its rapid acquisition capability, the RASE technique has the drawback of being highly vulnerable to noise and interference signals. The reason for this vulnerability stems from the fact that the estimation process is performed on a chip-by-chip basis and as such makes no use of the interference rejection capabilities of PN signals.

A modification of the RASE system, which was given the acronym RARASE (Recursion-Aided Rapid Acquisition Sequential Estimation), was reported more than a decade later by Ward and Yiu [5]. Here additional estimated code chips are summed to form a sync-worthiness indicator (SWI)

---

[6] In the original version of the RASE as suggested by Ward, the incoming signal was an unmodulated PN waveform and the code chip estimator consisted of a low-pass filter followed by a limiter.

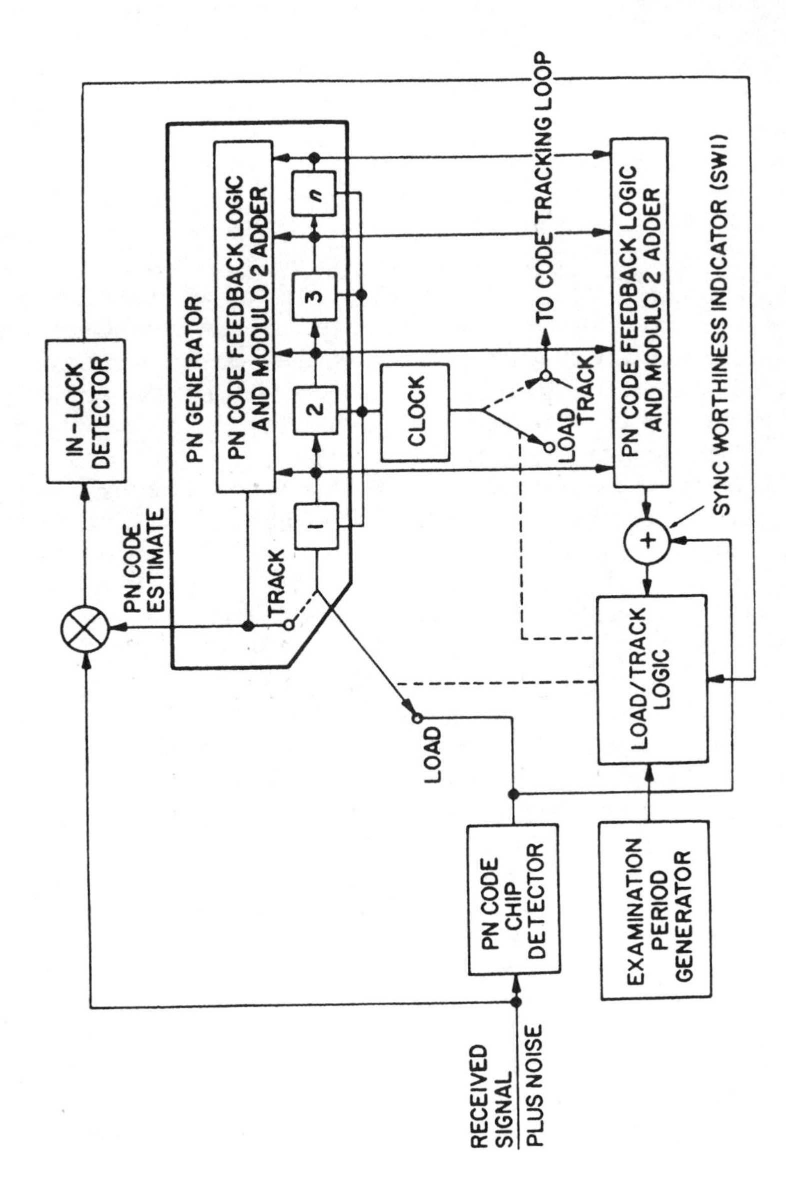

Figure 1.5. A recursion-aided rapid acquisition by sequential estimation (RARASE) technique.

which is used along with the in-lock indicator to determine when the n-stage shift register should switch from a reload to a tracking condition (see Figure 1.5). When compared with the basic RASE system which uses only a simple in-lock detector, the RARASE system was shown [5] to achieve an acquisition time reduction by a factor of 7.5 for a PN code of length $2^{15} - 1$ (15 stage shift register). Other modifications of Ward's initial RASE system have also been investigated [15], [16] which use the recursion relation of the PN code to improve the initial n-chip estimates. For example, Kilgus [15] suggests obtaining a number (η) of independent estimates of each of the n chips and making a majority logic vote among all η estimates to determine the initial n-chip load of the local shift register. Alternately, Pearce and Ristenblatt [16] suggest a threshold decoding type of estimator similar to that used for block codes. Finally, Alem and Weber [2] suggest replacing the simple threshold decision contained within the in-lock detector of the RASE system with an optimum Bayes detector based on the first two statistical moments of the decision random variable, which is assumed to be Gaussian distributed.

Historically, the serial synchronization of pseudonoise signals as introduced by Sage [17] was reported one year earlier than the RASE system. In this original version, a serial search was performed by *linearly* varying the time difference between the PN modulation on the incoming carrier and the PN waveform generated at the receiver with a *continuous* decision process determining when synchronization was achieved. Such a system is also referred to in the literature as a *sliding correlator* PN acquisition circuit [12], [18], [19]. Since the test for synchronization was based on the crossing of a threshold by the output of either a coherent or non-coherent detector, when compared with the serial realization of the maximum-likelihood technique discussed earlier, this scheme trades off shorter acquisition time (i.e., the search can terminate anywhere within the uncertainty region rather than having to wait till the end of the code period) against reduced accuracy in detection of synchronization.

When compared with Ward's sequential estimation technique, the serial search technique, as mentioned, will yield shorter acquisition time for input signal-to-noise ratios less than approximately -15 dB. Although at first glance -15 dB input SNR might seem unusually low, PN spread-spectrum communication systems which operate at, or below, this value are becoming increasingly common. The primary reason for this is that with modern technology we can now produce devices capable of handling the rapid switching rates needed to generate the high chip rate codes required for large processing gain. The need for a high code chip rate carries with it the attendant requirement of a compatibly high detector input bandwidth, which in turn results in a low input SNR. Since in addition to the above considerations serial search techniques have the advantage of being easy to implement, their application, particularly in SS receivers, is becoming increasingly popular. Although Sage's original analysis applied to the case where the input signal was a carrier direct-modulated only by the PN code, the technique is easily extended to include the case of angle-modulated (such as that produced by data modulation) carriers in which the non-coherent detector would include a post-detection filter between the envelope detector and threshold comparison [19].

In more recent years, the trend has been to accomplish the variation of the time difference between the incoming and local PN waveforms by a discrete stepping process wherein the phase of the local PN code is, at uniform increments in time, advanced (or retarded) by a fixed amount (typically a fraction of a chip). This time-discrete sweep of the uncertainty region can be accomplished by a uniform (unidirectional) search from one end of the region to the other, as in the case of no *a priori* information about the received PN code phase, or by a non-uniform search typically starting in the region of highest code phase certainty and expanding as a function of time to regions of lesser certainty. Such *expanding window* serial search strategies [20]–[24], or the simpler *z*-type search strategies [24], are well suited to applications where the length of the code makes it not feasible to search the whole code and thus some *a priori* information about the code phase must be provided by other means.

Continuing our subclassification of search strategies, we can distinguish two different philosophies with regard to the time elapsed before reaching the final acquisition state. In one case, the search is allowed to proceed as long as is necessary to achieve acquisition with the given fidelity criterion, although it is clearly desirable to accomplish this state as fast as possible. Such serial search techniques are classified as having *non-limited* permitted acquisition time and are typically employed in applications where information modulation is always present in the received waveform. Serial search strategies with *limited* permitted acquisition time are characteristic of DS/SS systems where information modulation commences to be transmitted only after PN code acquisition has been ensured. In such applications, a fixed time is usually allotted to achieve code acquisition, and furthermore this achievement must be accomplished with high probability.

The final classification of serial search strategies is in accordance with the way in which the false alarm event (state) is handled. Analogous to radar terminology, a false alarm in serial search PN code acquisition occurs when the detector (including the verification mode if it exists) erroneously decides that an in-sync condition has occurred and proceeds to direct the appropriate logic circuitry to initiate PN code tracking. Under normal circumstances, an erroneous entry into the tracking mode of operation will be detected (by the code loop lock detector) and after a given amount of time (referred to as the *false alarm penalty time*), which, in reality, is a random variable but is often mathematically modelled as being fixed, the system will return to the acquisition mode and continue searching where it last left off. Such a recoverable false alarm state is referred to as a *returning* state. Occasionally, entry into the false alarm state is catastrophic in that the system cannot recover from this event. In this instance code acquisition is completely lost and thus this type of false alarm state is referred to as *absorbing*.

In the remainder of this chapter, we shall focus our attention on the serial search strategy subclass of DS/SS acquisition schemes since, as previously mentioned, these are most attractive in the low signal-to-noise ratio environments in which these systems normally operate. We begin with a detailed discussion of the simplest of the uniform stepping, serial search techniques, namely, the *single dwell* system where a single detector is used to examine each of the possible waveform alignments for a fixed period of time in a serial fashion until the correct one has been located [1]. A recent application of such a system was the code acquisition portion of the S-band despreader aboard the Space Shuttle Orbiter System [25]. In the succeeding sections we discuss the theoretical acquisition time and acquisition probability performance of such a system along with all of the practical considerations required to apply the results. Following this, we shall return to our introductory classification of PN acquisition systems to discuss and give the performance of the conventional *multiple dwell* serial search system with immediate rejection verification mode [7], [8]. Next, we will present a unified approach [14] to serial stepped search acquisition with fixed dwell times in which the previously discussed single dwell and multiple dwell schemes appear as special cases. Another special case of this general approach is the rapid acquisition matched filter system whose behavior and performance are the subject of the following section. The treatment of fixed dwell time systems is completed with a discussion of some optimum PN sync search procedures and sweep strategies for applications where the *a priori* probability density function of the uncertainty region is not necessarily uniform [20]–[24], [26]. Here again the unified approach of [14] along with its equivalent circular state diagram are invaluable in assessing the acquisition performance of these non-uniform stepping strategies [24]. Next comes a combination of analytical and computer simulation results [27]–[30] pertaining to the performance of variable dwell time systems based on the classical method of sequential detection. Finally, as a bridge to the next chapter, we conclude with a discussion of the handover process between acquisition and tracking including some suggestions for search/lock strategies [9], and a brief consideration of parallel search.

1.2 THE SINGLE DWELL SERIAL PN ACQUISITION SYSTEM

Consider the simple model of a single dwell serial PN acquisition system illustrated in Figure 1.6. Since our interest is in the case where the PN code is acquired without knowledge of the carrier phase, the model employs a standard type, non-coherent (square-law) detector. Briefly, the received signal plus noise is actively correlated with a local replica of the PN code

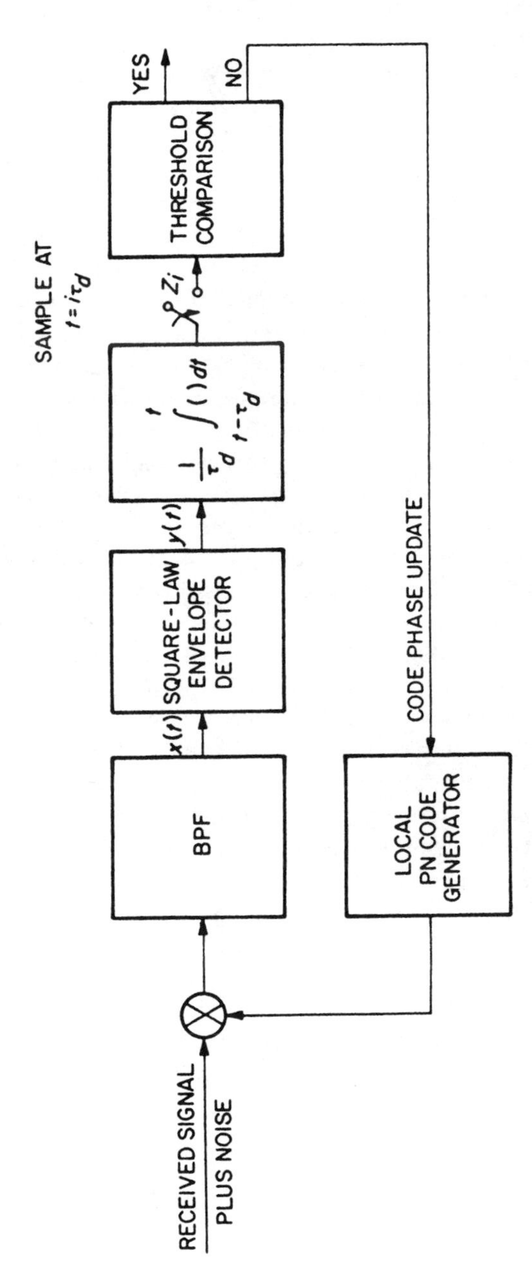

Figure 1.6. Block diagram of a single dwell time PN acquisition system with non-coherent detection.

and then passed through a band-pass (pre-detection) filter. The filter output is then square-law envelope detected with the detector output being integrated for a fixed time duration, τ_d (the "dwell time"), in an integrate-and-dump (I & D) circuit (post-detection integration) and then compared to a preset threshold.

An equivalent low-pass version of the single dwell acquisition system is illustrated in Figure 1.7. Here the received signal plus noise is first demodulated by inphase and quadrature carrier reference signals $I(t)$ and $Q(t)$ whose frequency is equal to that of the receiver carrier on which the PN waveform is direct modulated but whose phase is arbitrary. The demodulated and despread signals are now passed through identical low-pass filters which are the low-pass equivalents of the band-pass filter in Figure 1.6. Square-law detecting the filter outputs and summing produces the signal required for post-detection integration and threshold comparison. Although our analysis of the performance of the single dwell system will directly relate to the band-pass representation of Figure 1.6, our primary reason for introducing Figure 1.7 at this point is to allow for comparison later on in the chapter with an analogous configuration of a matched filter type of acquisition system. Also, in a later chapter on synchronization of frequency-hopped signals, we shall again draw a parallel with the low-pass version of the acquisition scheme as illustrated in Figure 1.7.

1.2.1 Markov Chain Acquisition Model

The Markov chain nature of the acquisition model stems from the way in which the integrate-and-dump (I & D) output is processed. In particular, if the I & D output is above the preset threshold, then a "hit" is declared. If this hit represents a true hit (i.e., the correct code phase has been determined), then the system has officially acquired and the search comes to an end. If the hit is a false alarm, then verification cannot be consummated and the search must continue. In either case, we shall assume that the verification is characterized by an extended dwell time (e.g., $K\tau_d$ sec; $K \gg 1$) assumed to be fixed and an entering into the code tracking loop mode. Understanding that a true hit corresponds to a single code phase position and that this can occur only once per search through the code, we can regard the time interval $K\tau_d$ sec as the "penalty" of obtaining a false alarm, since a false alarm can occur on any code phase position. If the I & D output falls below the preset threshold, then the local PN code generator steps to its next position and the search proceeds. Thus, at each test position (aside from the single true code phase position), one of the two events can take place, each characterized by a probability of occurrence; namely, a false alarm can happen i.e., an indication that acquisition has occurred when the PN codes are actually misaligned, with probability P_{FA}, causing a penalty of $K\tau_d$ sec, or no false alarm occurs with probability $(1 - P_{FA})$, resulting in only a single dwell time of τ_d sec—hence, the Markov chain model. Furthermore, at the

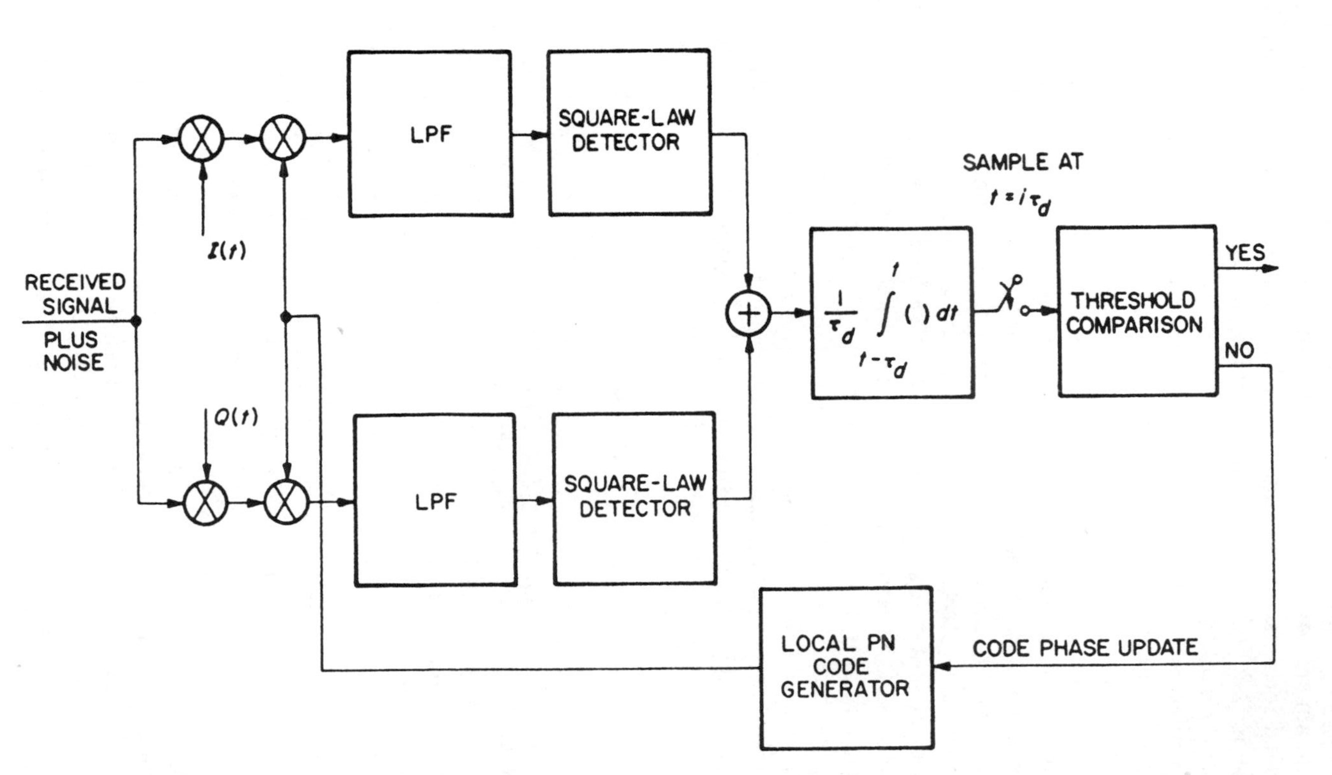

Figure 1.7. An equivalent low-pass representation of the single dwell time PN acquisition system.

true code phase position, either a correct detection can happen, i.e., an indication that acquisition has occurred when the PN codes are indeed aligned, with probability P_D, or no detection occurs, with probability $(1 - P_D)$.

In the absence of any *a priori* information regarding the true code phase position, the uncertainty in misalignment between the received PN code and the local replica of it could be as much as a full code period. Thus for long PN codes, the corresponding time uncertainty to be resolved could typically be quite large. In order to represent a reasonable compromise between the time required to search through this code phase uncertainty region and the accuracy within which the final alignment position is determined, the amount by which the local PN code generator is stepped in position as the search proceeds must be judiciously chosen. It is typical in practice to require that the received and local PN code signals be aligned to within one-half a code chip period ($T_c/2$) before relinquishing control to the fine synchronization (tracking) system. In accordance with this requirement, the time delay of the local PN code signal would be retarded (or advanced) in discrete steps of one-half a chip period and a check for acquisition made after each step. Thus, if $T_u = N_u T_c$ is the time uncertainty[7] to be resolved, then $q = 2N_u$ would be the number of possible code alignments (in serial search parlance, these are referred to as *cells*) to be examined during each search through the uncertainty region. In the more general case where the local code update size is arbitrary, we shall still use q to denote the number of cells to be searched.

The *time to acquire*, T_{ACQ}, i.e., the time to declare a true hit, is a random variable and, in general, depends on the initial (at the beginning of the search) code phase position of the local PN generator relative to that of the received code. The most complete statistical description of this random variable would be given by its probability density function, whose determination would ultimately allow computation of the probability of successful synchronization for the single dwell serial synchronization system. Although the probability of successful synchronization provides the most complete statistical description of system performance, one is often content with measuring performance in terms of the first two moments of the probability density function of T_{ACQ}, namely, *the mean acquisition time*, $\bar{T}_{ACQ}$, and the *acquisition time variance*, σ^2_{ACQ}, both of which come at a considerable savings in computation. Since, historically, the evaluation of $\bar{T}_{ACQ}$ and σ^2_{ACQ} for the single dwell system preceded the evaluation of the probability of successful acquisition for this system, we shall follow the same pattern in our discussions. In this way, the reader is first afforded the insight into the nature of the acquisition process itself which is allowed by

[7]It is convenient to assume that T_u is (or is bounded by) an integer multiple of the code time period pT_c.

computation of the simpler performance parameters $\overline{T}_{ACQ}$ and σ^2_{ACQ}, before being thrust into the complex mathematical developments needed to compute acquisition probability.

Furthermore, to make matters even simpler at first, we shall assume that *no* code Doppler is present in the received PN signal and that the detection probability P_D is constant (time invariant), the latter being equivalent to assuming that only one cell corresponds to a "correct" code alignment. Since the PN code correlation function is triangular over an interval of plus and minus one chip $(-T_c, T_c)$, for a search in increments of $T_c/2$, as is typical, there are, in reality, four[8] cells which correspond to non-zero code correlation. Clearly, the cell corresponding to the largest of these code correlations (nearest to the peak of the triangular correlation curve) would be the one yielding the "correct" code alignment. However, because of the constant P_D assumption, we must appropriately modify the results to be presented based on this assumption so as to apply to the true situation as described above. A discussion of how this is done, based upon a worst case correlation error assumption, will be given in Section 1.2.5. Later on in the chapter, we present a more exact accounting of the effects of having multiple cells with non-zero code correlation.

1.2.2 Single Dwell Acquisition Time Performance in the Absence of Code Doppler

In the absence of *a priori* knowledge concerning the relative code phase positions of the received and locally generated codes, the local PN generator is assumed to start the search at any code phase position with equal probability. Stated in mathematical terms, the probability P_1 of having the signal present (true hit) in the first cell searched is $1/q$, and the probability of it not being present there is $1 - 1/q$. For example, if the number of code chips to be searched is denoted by N_u and the search proceeds in half-chip increments, then $q = 2N_u$ and $P_1 = 1/2N_u$. More generally, if it has been determined that the signal is not present in the first $k - 1$ cells, then the *a priori* probability P_k of finding it present in the k-th cell is $1/(q + 1 - k)$, where $q + 1 - k$ is obviously the number of *remaining* cells to be searched, each possessing an equal probability of having the signal present.

A generating function flow graph for the q-state Markov chain which characterizes the acquisition process of the single dwell system is illustrated in Figure 1.8. As is customary in such flow graphs, each branch is labelled with the product of the transition probability associated with going from the node at the originated end of the branch to the node at its terminating end, and an integer (including zero) power of a parameter denoted here by z. The parameter z is used to mark time as one proceeds through the graph and its power represents the number of time units (dwell times) spent in traversing

[8] If one of the cells corresponds to perfect sync., i.e., the peak of the triangular correlation curve, then there are only three cells which correspond to non-zero code correlation.

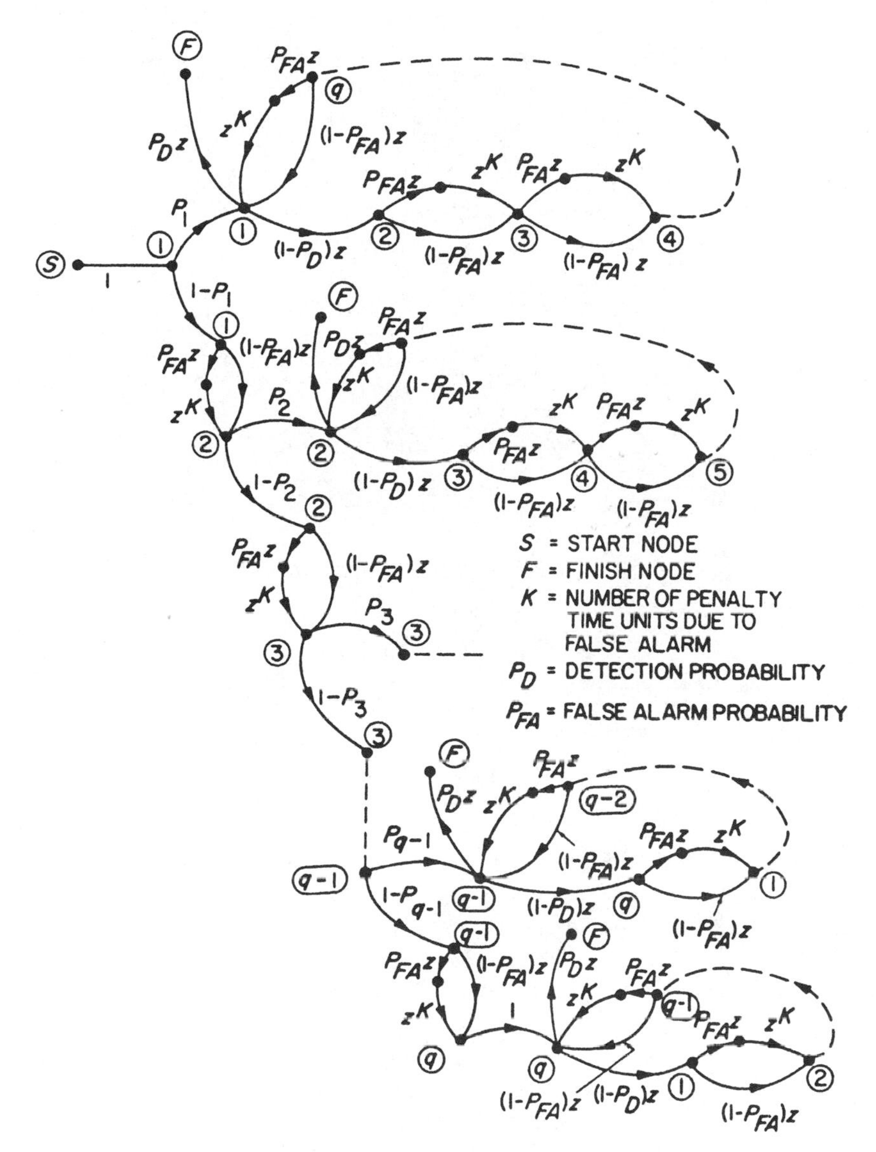

Figure 1.8. Generating function flow graph for acquisition time.

that branch. Furthermore, note that the sum of the branch probabilities (letting $z = 1$) emanating from each node equals unity.

Using standard signal flow graph reduction techniques [31]–[33], one can show that the *generating function* for the flow graph in Figure 1.8 is given by [1]

$$U(z) = \frac{(1-\beta)z}{1-\beta z H^{q-1}(z)}\left[\frac{1}{q}\sum_{l=0}^{q-1} H^{l}(z)\right] \tag{1.1}$$

where

$$\beta = 1 - P_D$$
$$H(z) = P_{FA} z^{K+1} + (1 - P_{FA}) z. \tag{1.2}$$

The mean acquisition time $\overline{T}_{ACQ}$ is obtained by differentiating $U(z^{\tau_d})$[9] with respect to z and evaluating the result at $z = 1$. After some routine algebra, one arrives at the desired result, namely,

$$\overline{T}_{ACQ} = \left.\frac{d \ln U(z^{\tau_d})}{dz}\right|_{z=1}$$
$$= \frac{2 + (2 - P_D)(q - 1)(1 + KP_{FA})}{2P_D} \tau_d \tag{1.3}$$

which for $q \gg 1$ (the case of practical interest) simplifies to

$$\overline{T}_{ACQ} = \frac{(2 - P_D)(1 + KP_{FA})}{2P_D} (q\tau_d). \tag{1.4}$$

The variance of the acquisition time is determined from the first two derivatives of $U(z)$ by

$$\sigma^2_{ACQ} = \left.\left[\frac{d^2 U(z^{\tau_d})}{dz^2} + \frac{dU(z^{\tau_d})}{dz} - \left(\frac{dU(z^{\tau_d})}{dz}\right)^2\right]\right|_{z=1} \tag{1.5}$$

or, since $U(1) = 1$, by the equivalent relation

$$\sigma^2_{ACQ} = \left.\left[\frac{d^2 \ln U(z^{\tau_d})}{dz^2} + \frac{d \ln U(z^{\tau_d})}{dz}\right]\right|_{z=1}. \tag{1.6}$$

Taking the natural logarithm of (1.1) together with its first two derivatives, substituting them into (1.6), and simplifying the resulting algebraic expressions, one obtains (for $q \gg 1$ and $K \ll q$) the desired result, namely,

$$\sigma^2_{ACQ} = \tau_d^2 (1 + KP_{FA})^2 q^2 \left(\frac{1}{12} + \frac{1}{P_D^2} - \frac{1}{P_D}\right). \tag{1.7}$$

We hasten to point out that although Figure 1.6 was drawn for a single dwell system with a non-coherent band-pass detector, the above results apply equally to a single dwell system with a coherent detector, the only difference between the two cases being the interrelation of the parameters τ_d, P_{FA}, and P_D for the detector. This interrelationship, which is essential for computing acquisition time performance, will be discussed later on for the non-coherent band-pass detector.

The above analytical results for the mean and variance of the acquisition time can also be obtained by a simple heuristic approach [34] which, although lacking the mathematical elegance of the Markov chain signal flow graph technique, provides additional insight into the acquisition process in

[9] Note that since the generating function has the property that $U(1) = 1$, we can, if convenient, equivalently differentiate the natural logarithm of $U(z^{\tau_d})$ and evaluate it at $z = 1$.

terms of the underlying tradeoff between false alarm and detection probabilities. As before, we start out with the same basic assumptions, namely, that no *a priori* knowledge of the correct cell's location within the total uncertainty region is available and the cell-by-cell search of the entire uncertainty region is repeated until the correct cell is detected. Although not explicitly stated previously, each cell is assumed to be tested only once during each search of the uncertainty region and the order of the cells in the search is inconsequential.

To make matters simple, we assume at first that during each examination of a cell, the detector is characterized by a constant (time-invariant) detection probability P_D as before, but now, however, a zero false alarm probability. Then, if k (integer) denotes the particular search of the uncertainty region during which the correct cell is *first* detected, then k has the geometric probability density function (pdf)

$$p(k) = P_D(1 - P_D)^{k-1}; \qquad k = 1, 2, 3, \ldots . \tag{1.8}$$

Note that since, by assumption, $P_{FA} = 0$, then the detection probability for each complete search of the entire uncertainty region is equal to the detection probability for the correct cell, namely, P_D. Furthermore, $k - 1$ represents the number of unsuccessful searches of the uncertainty region, each having passed through q cells. Thus,

$$N_u' \triangleq q(k - 1) \tag{1.9}$$

is an integer random variable which represents *the number of cells searched without success of detection prior to the k-th search during which the correct cell will be detected*. Since each of these N_u' cell examinations occupied a single dwell time τ_d,

$$T_u' \triangleq N_u'\tau_d = q\tau_d(k - 1) \tag{1.10}$$

represents the time expired in passing through this unsuccessful series of searches.

The mean and variance of T_u' are readily computed as follows:

$$\begin{aligned} E\{T_u'\} \triangleq \overline{T}_u' &= \sum_{k=1}^{\infty} T_u' p(k) \\ &= q\tau_d \sum_{k=1}^{\infty} (k - 1)P_D(1 - P_D)^{k-1}. \end{aligned} \tag{1.11}$$

Since, by definition, $p(k)$ is a probability density function,

$$\sum_{k=1}^{\infty} P_D(1 - P_D)^{k-1} = 1. \tag{1.12}$$

Furthermore, differentiating both sides of (1.12) with respect to P_D and simplifying gives

$$\sum_{k=1}^{\infty} kP_D(1 - P_D)^{k-1} = \frac{1}{P_D}. \tag{1.13}$$

Thus, combining (1.12) and (1.13) gives the desired result, namely,

$$\bar{T}_u' = q\tau_d\left(\frac{1}{P_D} - 1\right). \tag{1.14}$$

Similarly,

$$\begin{aligned} E\left\{\left(T_u' - \bar{T}_u'\right)^2\right\} \triangleq \sigma_u^2 &= E\left\{T_u'^2\right\} - \bar{T}_u'^2 \\ &= q^2\tau_d^2 \sum_{k=1}^{\infty} (k-1)^2 P_D(1-P_D)^{k-1} \\ &\quad - q^2\tau_d^2\left(\frac{1}{P_D} - 1\right)^2. \end{aligned} \tag{1.15}$$

Differentiating (1.13) with respect to P_D and simplifying by using (1.13) prior to differentiation gives

$$\sum_{k=1}^{\infty} k^2 P_D(1-P_D)^{k-1} = \frac{2}{P_D^2} - \frac{1}{P_D}. \tag{1.16}$$

Finally, expanding the square in (1.15) and substituting (1.12), (1.13), and (1.16) gives the desired result, namely,

$$\sigma_u^2 = q^2\tau_d^2\left(\frac{1}{P_D^2} - \frac{1}{P_D}\right). \tag{1.17}$$

Having now characterized the period of unsuccessful search, we turn our attention to the k-th search interval during which the acquisition process will terminate at the location of the correct cell. Letting m denote this correct cell location, the time required to successfully reach this point from the time the k-th search is initiated is clearly

$$T_s = m\tau_d. \tag{1.18}$$

Since, for lack of any *a priori* information regarding correct cell location within the uncertainty region, m will be uniformly distributed in this region, i.e.,

$$p(m) = \frac{1}{q};\ m = 1, 2, 3, \ldots, q \tag{1.19}$$

with mean

$$\bar{m} = \sum_{m=1}^{q} mp(m) = \frac{1}{q}\sum_{m=1}^{q} m = \frac{q+1}{2} \tag{1.20}$$

and variance

$$\begin{aligned} \sigma_m^2 &= \sum_{m=1}^{q} m^2 p(m) - \left(\frac{q+1}{2}\right)^2 \\ &= \frac{(q+1)(2q+1)}{6} - \left(\frac{q+1}{2}\right)^2 = \frac{q^2-1}{12} \end{aligned} \tag{1.21}$$

then the mean and variance of T_s are respectively given by

$$\bar{T}_s = \left(\frac{q+1}{2}\right)\tau_d$$

$$\sigma_s^2 = \left(\frac{q^2-1}{12}\right)\tau_d^2. \tag{1.22}$$

Finally, the total acquisition time T_{ACQ_0}[10] is the sum of T_u' and T_s with mean

$$\overline{T_{ACQ_0}} = \bar{T}_u' + \bar{T}_s$$

$$= \tau_d\left[q\left(\frac{1}{P_D}-1\right)+\left(\frac{q+1}{2}\right)\right] = \left[\frac{(2-P_D)q+P_D}{2P_D}\right]\tau_d \tag{1.23}$$

and variance[11]

$$\sigma_{ACQ_0}^2 = \sigma_u^2 + \sigma_s^2$$

$$= \tau_d^2\left[q^2\left(\frac{1}{P_D^2}-\frac{1}{P_D}\right)+\frac{q^2-1}{12}\right] \tag{1.24}$$

which for $q \gg 1$ becomes

$$\sigma_{ACQ_0}^2 = q^2\tau_d^2\left(\frac{1}{12}+\frac{1}{P_D^2}-\frac{1}{P_D}\right). \tag{1.25}$$

All that remains is to include the effect of a non-zero false alarm probability on the results in (1.23) and (1.25). Since out of the total of $N_u' + m$ cells searched, k of them are actually correct (one per each of the k searches of the entire uncertainty region), then there is a possibility of a false alarm only on any of the

$$N_{FA} \triangleq N_u' + m - k = q(k-1) + m - k \tag{1.26}$$

remaining cells. Equivalently, N_{FA} is the *maximum* number of false alarms that can occur. If n denotes the actual number of false alarms that occur, each with probability P_{FA} of occurrence, then conditioned on N_{FA}, n has the binomial pdf

$$p(n|N_{FA}) = \binom{N_{FA}}{n}P_{FA}^n(1-P_{FA})^{N_{FA}-n};$$

$$n = 0,1,2,3,\ldots,N_{FA} \tag{1.27}$$

with conditional mean

$$E\{n|N_{FA}\} = N_{FA}P_{FA} \tag{1.28}$$

and conditional variance

$$\sigma_{n|N_{FA}}^2 = N_{FA}P_{FA}(1-P_{FA}). \tag{1.29}$$

[10] The zero subscript is used to denote the fact that we have assumed $P_{FA} = 0$.

[11] It is reasonable to assume that T_u and T_s are essentially independent.

Since for each of the n false alarms a penalty of $K\tau_d$ sec is assessed, then the penalty time due to false alarm is

$$T_p = nK\tau_d. \tag{1.30}$$

Finally, the total acquisition time T_{ACQ} is the sum of T_{ACQ_0} and T_p, i.e.,

$$T_{ACQ} = T_{ACQ_0} + T_p = \left[N_u' + m + nK\right]\tau_d. \tag{1.31}$$

The mean acquisition time is obtained by averaging T_{ACQ} of (1.31). Thus, making use of (1.23) and (1.28), we obtain

$$\overline{T}_{ACQ} = \left[\frac{(2 - P_D)q + P_D}{2P_D} + \overline{N}_{FA}KP_{FA}\right]\tau_d. \tag{1.32}$$

Using (1.26), we have

$$\begin{aligned}\overline{N}_{FA} &= \overline{N_u' + m} - \overline{k} \\ &= \frac{(2 - P_D)q + P_D}{2P_D} - \frac{1}{P_D} = \frac{(2 - P_D)q + P_D - 2}{2P_D}.\end{aligned} \tag{1.33}$$

Thus, substituting (1.33) into (1.32) gives the desired result, namely,

$$\overline{T}_{ACQ} = \left[\frac{2 + (2 - P_D)(q - 1)(1 + KP_{FA})}{2P_D}\right]\tau_d \tag{1.34}$$

which agrees identically with (1.3).

To obtain the variance of T_{ACQ}, we first rewrite (1.26) as

$$N_{FA} = (q - 1)k - q + m \tag{1.35}$$

which for $q \gg 1$ becomes

$$N_{FA} = q(k - 1) + m = N_u' + m. \tag{1.36}$$

Thus, for large q, we may evaluate the conditional second moment of T_{ACQ} as

$$\begin{aligned}E\left\{T_{ACQ}^2 | N_{FA}\right\} &= E\left\{(N_{FA} + nK)^2 | N_{FA}\right\}\tau_d^2 \\ &= E\left\{\left(N_{FA}^2 + 2KnN_{FA} + n^2K^2\right) | N_{FA}\right\}\tau_d^2.\end{aligned} \tag{1.37}$$

Since from (1.28) and (1.29)

$$E\left\{n^2 | N_{FA}\right\} = N_{FA}P_{FA}(1 - P_{FA}) + (N_{FA}P_{FA})^2 \tag{1.38}$$

and from (1.28)

$$E\{nN_{FA} | N_{FA}\} = N_{FA}^2 P_{FA} \tag{1.39}$$

then

$$\begin{aligned}E\left\{T_{ACQ}^2 | N_{FA}\right\} &= \left\{N_{FA}^2 + 2K\left(N_{FA}^2 P_{FA}\right)\right. \\ &\quad \left. + K^2\left[N_{FA}P_{FA}(1 - P_{FA}) + N_{FA}^2 P_{FA}^2\right]\right\}\tau_d^2 \\ &= \left\{N_{FA}^2(1 + KP_{FA})^2 + N_{FA}K^2P_{FA}(1 - P_{FA})\right\}\tau_d^2.\end{aligned} \tag{1.40}$$

Similarly,

$$\begin{aligned} E\{T_{ACQ}|N_{FA}\} &= E\{(N_{FA}+nK)|N_{FA}\}\tau_d \\ &= (N_{FA}+KN_{FA}P_{FA})\tau_d \\ &= N_{FA}(1+KP_{FA})\tau_d. \end{aligned} \tag{1.41}$$

Averaging (1.40) and (1.41) over the distribution of N_{FA} gives the unconditional second and first moments of T_{ACQ}, namely,

$$\begin{aligned} E\{T_{ACQ}^2\} &= \left\{\overline{N_{FA}^2}(1+KP_{FA})^2 + \overline{N}_{FA}K^2P_{FA}(1-P_{FA})\right\}\tau_d^2 \\ E\{T_{ACQ}\} &= \overline{N_{FA}}(1+KP_{FA})\tau_d. \end{aligned} \tag{1.42}$$

Finally, the variance of the acquisition time is obtained as

$$\begin{aligned} \sigma_{ACQ}^2 &= \overline{T_{ACQ}^2} - (\overline{T}_{ACQ})^2 \\ &= \left[\sigma_{N_{FA}}^2(1+KP_{FA})^2 + \overline{N}_{FA}K^2P_{FA}(1-P_{FA})\right]\tau_d^2. \end{aligned} \tag{1.43}$$

In view of the approximation in (1.36)

$$\sigma_{ACQ_0}^2 = \sigma_{N_{FA}}^2\tau_d^2 \tag{1.44a}$$

and

$$\overline{T_{ACQ_0}} = \overline{N}_{FA}\tau_d. \tag{1.44b}$$

Thus, using (1.25) and (1.23) in (1.43) gives

$$\begin{aligned} \sigma_{ACQ}^2 &= \tau_d^2(1+KP_{FA})^2q^2\left(\frac{1}{12}+\frac{1}{P_D^2}-\frac{1}{P_D}\right) \\ &+\tau_d^2\left[\frac{(2-P_D)q+P_D}{2P_D}\right]K^2P_{FA}(1-P_{FA}). \end{aligned} \tag{1.45}$$

Finally, if in addition $K \ll q$, then (1.45) simplifies to

$$\sigma_{ACQ}^2 = \tau_d^2(1+KP_{FA})^2q^2\left(\frac{1}{12}+\frac{1}{P_D^2}-\frac{1}{P_D}\right) \tag{1.46}$$

which is in exact agreement with (1.7).

Although somewhat lengthy, the heuristic derivation of (1.34) and (1.46) is important in that false alarms and missed detections are readily identified in terms of their individual contributions to the mean acquisition time and variance.

1.2.3 Single Dwell Acquisition Time Performance in the Presence of Code Doppler and Doppler Rate

When code Doppler is present, the acquisition time performance of the system of Figure 1.6 is affected in two ways. First, the code Doppler causes the relative code phase between received and locally generated PN codes to be time varying during the dwell time of the integrate-and-dump. This has the effect of increasing or decreasing the probability of detection P_D, depending on whether the code Doppler is causing the relative code phase to increase or decrease. The second and potentially more dominant effect is that code Doppler affects the average search rate. In fact, if the code phase shift caused by the Doppler over a single dwell time is equal to the step size (phase update) of the search, then the average search rate is reduced to zero.

To take both of these effects into account when computing mean acquisition time is indeed a difficult, if not impossible, analytical task. However, it is possible to account for just the effect of Doppler on average search rate in a way which represents an obvious extension of the previous results. Letting Δf_c denote the code Doppler in chips/sec, then the mean search (code phase) update μ in chips is given by [1]:

$$\mu = \frac{N_u}{q'} + \Delta f_c \tau_d + \Delta f_c K \tau_D P_{FA}, \tag{1.47}$$

where[12] N_u/q' represents the search update in the absence of Doppler or, equivalently, the step size of the search in fractions of a chip, $\Delta f_c \tau_d$ is the code phase shift due to Doppler during the dwell time, and $\Delta f_c K \tau_d$ is the code phase shift during verification caused by a false alarm. Thus, replacing q by N_u/μ in (1.4) and (1.7) gives expressions for the mean and variance of the acquisition time in the presence of code Doppler, namely [1],

$$\begin{aligned} \bar{T}_{ACQ} &= \frac{(2 - P_D)(1 + KP_{FA}) N_u \tau_d}{2 P_D \left[\dfrac{N_u}{q'} + \Delta f_c \tau_d (1 + KP_{FA}) \right]} \\ &= \frac{\bar{T}_{ACQ}\big|_{\text{no code Doppler}}}{1 + \dfrac{q'}{N_u} \Delta f_c \tau_d (1 + KP_{FA})} \end{aligned} \tag{1.48a}$$

$$\begin{aligned} \sigma^2_{ACQ} &= \frac{\tau_d^2 (1 + KP_{FA})^2 N_u^2 \left(\dfrac{1}{12} + \dfrac{1}{P_D^2} - \dfrac{1}{P_D} \right)}{\left[\dfrac{N_u}{q'} + \Delta f_c \tau_d (1 + KP_{FA}) \right]^2} \\ &= \frac{\sigma^2_{ACQ}\big|_{\text{no code Doppler}}}{\left[1 + \dfrac{q'}{N_u} \Delta f_c \tau_d (1 + KP_{FA}) \right]^2}. \end{aligned} \tag{1.48b}$$

Since Δf_c can be either positive or negative, depending upon its sign, the code Doppler can either speed up or slow down the search. With regard to

[12] The prime on q is used here to denote the number of cells searched *in the absence of Doppler*.

the magnitude of the code Doppler, we shall assume that $|\Delta f_c|\tau_d(1 + KP_{FA}) \ll N_u/q'$, so that the denominator of (1.48a) and (1.48b) never approaches zero and the search always proceeds in the direction dictated by the code phase update provided by the local PN generator. Finally, note that, when $\Delta f_c = 0$, then $q' = q$ and (1.48a) and (1.48b) reduce to (1.4) and (1.7), respectively as they should.

The way in which code Doppler is accounted for in extending the results of (1.4) and (1.7) to those given in (1.48a) and (1.48b) can also be applied to further extend them to include the effect of code Doppler rate. In particular, one computes the mean search update analogous to (1.47) and again replaces q by N_u/μ in the expression for mean acquisition time and acquisition time variance.

When code Doppler alone was present, we observed that the mean (statistical) search update was time invariant, i.e., the expression in (1.47) characterizes every cell being searched. When, in addition, code Doppler rate is present, the mean search update is now time dependent in the sense that it is now a function of the cell being searched.

In general, the mean search update μ in any given search cell is equal to the nominal search update N_u/q' (typically, 1/2 for half-chip search increments) of the local PN code generator plus the *mean change in phase* of the received code over the search time of that cell.[13] Thus, letting μ_n denote the mean search update in the n-th cell being searched, and $\Delta\dot{f}_c$ the code Doppler rate in chips/sec^2, then from the Markov model previously established for the single dwell time system, we have that

$$\mu_{n+1} = \frac{N_u}{q'} + \Delta f_c\tau_d(1 + KP_{FA}) + \frac{1}{2}\Delta\dot{f}_c\tau_d^2\left[1 + P_{FA}(K^2 + 2K)\right]$$
$$+ n\Delta\dot{f}_c\left[\tau_d(1 + KP_{FA})\right]^2;\ n \geq 0. \tag{1.49}$$

Note from (1.49) that the mean search update is a linear function of the search cell. Because of this dependence on n, we cannot directly replace q by N_u/μ in (1.4) to arrive at a formula for mean acquisition in the presence of code Doppler and Doppler rate. Rather, we should first find the *average mean search update* μ obtained by averaging μ_{n+1} of (1.49) over all q search cells, i.e.,

$$\mu \triangleq \frac{1}{q}\sum_{n=0}^{q-1}\mu_{n+1} \tag{1.50}$$

and then make the above suggested replacement in (1.4). Thus, from (1.49)

[13] We continue to assume, as before, that the code phase derivatives are positive when they are in such a direction as to aid the search (reduce the acquisition time).

and (1.50), we have that

$$\mu = \frac{N_u}{q'} + \Delta f_c \tau_d (1 + KP_{FA}) + \frac{1}{2}\Delta \dot{f}_c \tau_d^2 \left\{ q(1 + KP_{FA})^2 + K^2 P_{FA}(1 - P_{FA}) \right\}. \tag{1.51}$$

Since the total mean search update must correspond to the total number of chips searched, we have that[14]

$$q\mu = \sum_{n=0}^{q-1} \mu_{n+1} = N_u. \tag{1.52}$$

Thus, substituting N_u/μ for q in (1.51) results in a quadratic equation in μ, namely,

$$\mu^2 - \mu\left[\frac{N_u}{q'} + \Delta f_c \tau_d (1 + KP_{FA}) + \frac{1}{2}\Delta \dot{f}_c \tau_d^2 K^2 P_{FA}(1 - P_{FA})\right] - \frac{1}{2}\Delta \dot{f}_c \tau_d^2 N (1 + KP_{FA})^2 = 0. \tag{1.53}$$

Letting

$$\begin{aligned} A &= 1 \\ B &= \frac{N_u}{q'} + \Delta f_c \tau_d (1 + KP_{FA}) + \frac{1}{2}\Delta \dot{f}_c \tau_d^2 K^2 P_{FA}(1 - P_{FA}) \\ C &= \tfrac{1}{2}\Delta \dot{f}_c \tau_d^2 N_u (1 + KP_{FA})^2, \end{aligned} \tag{1.54}$$

then

$$\mu = \frac{B}{2A}\left[1 + \sqrt{1 + \frac{4AC}{B^2}}\right]. \tag{1.55}$$

Finally, substituting N/μ for q in (1.4), with μ defined by (1.55), gives the resulting expression for mean acquisition time in the presence of code Doppler and code Doppler rate, namely,

$$\overline{T}_{ACQ} = \frac{(2 - P_D)(1 + KP_{FA}) N \tau_d}{2P_D\left[\dfrac{B\left(1 + \sqrt{1 + \dfrac{4AC}{B^2}}\right)}{2A}\right]}. \tag{1.56}$$

[14] Here we have made the assumption that $|\Delta f_c|$ and $|\Delta \dot{f}_c|$ are small enough such that $\mu_{n+1} > 0$ for all $n = 0, 1, \ldots, q - 1$ and thus the search proceeds only in one direction, namely, that dictated by the local PN generator code phase update.

Also, the acquisition time variance in the presence of code Doppler and code Doppler rate becomes

$$\sigma_{ACQ}^2 = \frac{\tau_d^2(1 + KP_{FA})^2 N_u^2\left(\frac{1}{12} + \frac{1}{P_D^2} - \frac{1}{P_D}\right)}{\left[\frac{B\left(1 + \sqrt{1 + \frac{4AC}{B^2}}\right)}{2A}\right]^2}. \tag{1.57}$$

Note again that, when $\Delta f_c = \Delta \dot{f}_c = 0$, we have that $B = N/q' = N/q$, $C = 0$, whereby (1.56) and (1.57) reduce to (1.4) and (1.7), respectively.

1.2.4 Evaluation of Detection Probability P_D and False Alarm Probability P_{FA} in Terms of PN Acquisition System Parameters

The formulas for mean acquisition time and acquisition time variance developed in the previous section are all functions of the detection probability P_D, false alarm probability P_{FA}, and dwell time τ_d. Thus, it would appear at first glance that, for specified values of detection probability and false alarm probability, one could arbitrarily select the dwell time to achieve any desired mean acquisition time. Upon closer examination, one realizes that indeed this is not possible with the fallacy lying in the fact that, for a given P_{FA} and pre-detection signal-to-noise ratio, P_D is implicitly a function of τ_d. To place this statement in evidence, we begin by evaluating P_D and P_{FA} in terms of the PN acquisition system parameters for the simple case of no code Doppler or Doppler derivatives.

When signal is present (i.e., the cell being searched corresponds to a sample value on the PN correlation curve), then the input to the square-law envelope detector can be expressed in the form[15]

$$\begin{aligned} x(t) = s(t) + n(t) &= \sqrt{2}A\cos(\omega_0 t + \psi) + \sqrt{2}n_c(t)\cos(\omega_0 t + \psi) \\ &\quad - \sqrt{2}n_s(t)\sin(\omega_0 t + \psi) \\ &= \sqrt{2}R(t)\cos(\omega_0 t + \psi + \theta(t)), \end{aligned} \tag{1.58}$$

where

$$R(t) = \sqrt{(A + n_c(t))^2 + n_s^2(t)}\,;\ \theta(t) = \tan^{-1}\frac{n_s(t)}{A + n_c(t)}. \tag{1.59}$$

[15] To keep the presentation simple, we shall, at this point, ignore partial correlation effects produced by the filtering of the product of incoming and local PN waveforms over less than a full code period. Later in the chapter, we shall present both exact and approximate approaches for accounting for these effects and their significance.

In (1.58), A is the rms signal amplitude,[16] ω_0 the radian carrier frequency, and $n_c(t), n_s(t)$ are band-limited, independent, low-pass, zero-mean Gaussian noise processes with variance $\sigma^2 = N_0B/2$, where N_0 is the single-sided noise spectral density and B is the noise bandwidth of the pre-detection band-pass filter.

The output of the square-law envelope detector in Figure 1.6, in response to the input $x(t)$ of (1.58), is (ignoring second harmonics of the carrier):

$$y(t) \triangleq x^2(t) = R^2(t) = \left(A + n_c(t)\right)^2 + n_s^2(t) \tag{1.60}$$

and has a non-central chi-squared pdf which is given by

$$p(y) = \begin{cases} \dfrac{1}{2\sigma^2}\exp\left[-\left(\dfrac{y}{2\sigma^2} + \gamma\right)\right] I_0\left(2\sqrt{\dfrac{\gamma y}{2\sigma^2}}\right); & y \geq 0 \\ 0; & \text{otherwise} \end{cases} \tag{1.61}$$

where

$$\gamma \triangleq \frac{A^2}{N_0B} = \frac{A^2}{2\sigma^2} \tag{1.62}$$

is the pre-detection signal-to-noise ratio. In the absence of signal, i.e., $A = 0$, (1.61) reduces to the central chi-squared pdf:

$$p(y) = \begin{cases} \dfrac{1}{2\sigma^2}\exp\left(-\dfrac{y}{2\sigma^2}\right); & y \geq 0, \\ 0; & \text{otherwise} \end{cases} \tag{1.63}$$

which characterizes the square-law output in all search cells that contain noise only.

If $y(t)$ is sampled at intervals $T = 1/B$, then these samples are approximately independent, and furthermore, the integrate-and-dump output can be approximated by a summation over these sampled values, namely,[17]

$$Z \triangleq \frac{1}{\tau_d}\int_0^{\tau_d} y(t)\,dt \cong \frac{1}{N_B}\sum_{k=0}^{N_B-1} y(kT) \tag{1.64}$$

where

$$N_B \triangleq \frac{\tau_d}{T} = B\tau_d. \tag{1.65}$$

[16] For the moment, we shall not enter into a discussion concerning the various system losses and gains which enter into the calculation of the effective signal amplitude to be used in predicting true system signal-to-noise ratio behavior. Such a discussion will be given later on in the development.

[17] For simplicity of notation, we assume that $i = 0$ in Figure 1.6 and set $Z_0 = Z$. Furthermore, it is convenient to assume that N_B is integer, although the results which follow are, for large N_B, valid for N_B non-integer.

Using the approximation in (1.64) and the first order pdf's of (1.61) and (1.63), the pdf of Z, namely, $p(Z)$, for signal present is given by

$$p(Z)=\begin{cases}\dfrac{N_B}{2\sigma^2}\left(\dfrac{Z}{2\gamma\sigma^2}\right)^{(N_B-1)/2}\exp\left[-N_B\left(\dfrac{Z}{2\sigma^2}+\gamma\right)\right] & \\ \times I_{N_B-1}\left[2\sqrt{N_B^2\gamma\dfrac{Z}{2\sigma^2}}\right]; & Z\geq 0\\ 0; & \text{otherwise}\end{cases} \tag{1.66}$$

and for signal absent is given by

$$p(Z)=\begin{cases}\left(\dfrac{N_B}{2\sigma^2}\right)\dfrac{\left(\dfrac{ZN_B}{2\sigma^2}\right)^{N_B-1}}{(N_B-1)!}\exp\left(-\dfrac{ZN_B}{2\sigma^2}\right); & Z\geq 0\\ 0; & \text{otherwise.}\end{cases} \tag{1.67}$$

Normalizing Z by $2\sigma^2/N_B=N_0/\tau_d$ or, equivalently, letting $Z^*\triangleq ZN_B/2\sigma^2$, we can rewrite (1.66) and (1.67), respectively, in the simpler form,

$$p(Z^*)=\begin{cases}\left(\dfrac{Z^*}{N_B\gamma}\right)^{(N_B-1)/2}\exp(-Z^*-N_B\gamma) & \\ \times I_{N_B-1}\left[2\sqrt{N_B\gamma Z^*}\right]; & Z^*\geq 0\\ 0; & \text{otherwise}\end{cases} \tag{1.68}$$

and

$$p(Z^*)=\begin{cases}\dfrac{(Z^*)^{(N_B-1)}}{(N_B-1)!}\exp(-Z^*); & Z^*\geq 0\\ 0; & \text{otherwise.}\end{cases} \tag{1.69}$$

The probability of false alarm, P_{FA}, is the probability that Z exceeds the threshold η when signal is absent or, equivalently, in terms of the normalized random variable Z^* and the normalized threshold $\eta^*\triangleq\eta N_B/2\sigma^2$,

$$\begin{aligned}P_{FA}&=\int_{\eta^*}^{\infty}p(Z^*)\,dZ^*=1-\int_0^{\eta^*}\frac{(Z^*)^{(N_B-1)}}{(N_B-1)!}\exp(-Z^*)\,dZ^*\\&=e^{-\eta^*}\sum_{k=0}^{N_B-1}\frac{(\eta^*)^k}{k!}.\end{aligned} \tag{1.70}$$

The detection probability P_D is the probability that Z exceeds the threshold

η when signal is present. Thus, using (1.68) rather than (1.69), we get

$$P_D = 1 - \int_0^{\eta^*} \left(\frac{Z^*}{N_B \gamma} \right)^{(N_B - 1)/2} \exp(-Z^* - N_B \gamma) I_{N_B - 1}\left[2\sqrt{N_B \gamma Z^*} \right] dZ^* \tag{1.71}$$

which, if desired, can be expressed in terms of a generalized Marcum's Q-function.

For large N_B (the case of most practical interest), things become quite a bit simpler. Defining $y_k^* = y(kT)/2\sigma^2$, then from (1.61) and (1.63), the pdf's of y_k^* in the presence and absence of signal are, respectively,

$$p(y_k^*) = \begin{cases} e^{-(y_k^* + \gamma)} I_0\left(2\sqrt{\gamma y_k^*}\right); & y_k^* \geq 0 \\ 0; & \text{otherwise} \end{cases} \tag{1.72}$$

$$p(y_k^*) = \begin{cases} e^{-y_k^*}; & y_k^* \geq 0 \\ 0; & \text{otherwise.} \end{cases} \tag{1.73}$$

Also, from (1.64) and the definition of Z^* in terms of Z, we have

$$Z^* = \sum_{k=0}^{N_B - 1} y_k^*. \tag{1.74}$$

Since, by previous assumption, the y_k^*s are independent random variables, then for large N_B, Z^* is approximately Gaussian distributed with mean $\overline{Z^*} = N_B \overline{y^*}$ and variance $\sigma_{Z^*}^2 = N_B \sigma_{y^*}^2$. The means and variance of the pdf's in (1.72) and (1.73) are well known [35] to be

$$\overline{y^*} = 1 + \gamma; \; \sigma_{y^*}^2 = 1 + 2\gamma; \text{ signal present} \tag{1.75}$$

$$\overline{y^*} = 1; \; \sigma_{y^*}^2 = 1; \text{ signal absent.} \tag{1.76}$$

Thus,

$$\overline{Z^*} = N_B(1 + \gamma); \; \sigma_{Z^*}^2 = N_B(1 + 2\gamma); \text{ signal present} \tag{1.77}$$

$$\overline{Z^*} = N_B; \; \sigma_{Z^*}^2 = N_B; \text{ signal absent.} \tag{1.78}$$

Using the Gaussian assumption, the false alarm probability is

$$\begin{aligned} P_{FA} &= \int_{\eta^*}^{\infty} \frac{1}{\sqrt{2\pi N_B}} \exp\left[-\frac{(Z^* - N_B)^2}{2N_B} \right] dZ^* \\ &= Q\left(\frac{\eta^* - N_B}{\sqrt{N_B}} \right) \\ &\triangleq Q(\beta) \end{aligned} \tag{1.79}$$

where $Q(x)$ is the Gaussian probability integral. Thus, if P_{FA} is specified, β

can be determined. The corresponding detection probability under the same assumption is

$$P_D = \int_{\eta^*}^{\infty} \frac{1}{\sqrt{2\pi N_B(1+2\gamma)}} \exp\left[-\frac{\left(Z^* - N_B(1+\gamma)\right)^2}{2N_B(1+2\gamma)}\right] dZ^*$$

$$= Q\left(\frac{\beta - \sqrt{N_B}\gamma}{\sqrt{1+2\gamma}}\right). \tag{1.80}$$

Combining (1.79) and (1.80) and reidentifying N_B and γ in terms of the system parameters gives the final relation

$$P_D = Q\left(\frac{Q^{-1}(P_{FA}) - \sqrt{B\tau_d}\left(\frac{A^2}{N_0 B}\right)}{\sqrt{1+2\left(\frac{A^2}{N_0 B}\right)}}\right). \tag{1.81}$$

Thus, given P_D, P_{FA}, A^2/N_0 and B, the dwell time τ_d is determined.

Before we use (1.81) and the dwell time determined from it in the formulas derived in the previous section for mean acquisition time and acquisition time variance, several modifications based upon practical considerations must be made.

1.2.5 Effective Probability of Detection and Timing Misalignment

The calculation of detection probability as in (1.71) or (1.80) implicitly assumed that only one cell in the entire search satisfies the "signal present" hypothesis. In actuality, since the PN correlation curve exists over an interval of ± 1 chip around the peak, a system which updates the locally generated code phase, for example, in half-chip increments would yield several cells for which signal could be considered present.

Typically, the system is designed on the basis of the worst case correlation, which for the half-chip update case would correspond to the pair of correlation points one-quarter chip away from the correlation peak. Since the normalized correlation value at these points is 0.75 (relative to a peak of 1), then the *single* signal point calculation of detection probability as in (1.71) or (1.80) would be based on an effective reduction in the nominal signal-to-noise ratio A^2/N_0 of $10\log_{10}(.75)^2 = 2.5$ dB. Since, however, in reality there exist two worst case correlation positions, then the *effective probability of detection* P_D' for use in computing mean acquisition time is computed as

$$P_D' = P_D + (1 - P_D)P_D = 2P_D - P_D^2, \tag{1.82}$$

where the first term in (1.82) represents the probability of detecting signal present on the first correlation point and the second term is the joint probability of not detecting signal on the first correlation point and detecting signal present on the second correlation point. Clearly, for low signal-to-noise ratios (small P_D), the effective detection probability is approximately twice that computed on the basis of a single signal present cell [(1.71) or (1.80)]. In summary, then, the computation procedures would be as follows: For a given P_{FA}, determine β from (1.79). For a specified P_D', find P_D from (1.82), degrade the given nominal value of γ by 2.5 dB and solve for N_B in (1.80). Determine the dwell time from $\tau_d = N_B/B$, where B is the given band-pass filter bandwidth determined by considerations on allowable modulation distortion (to be discussed next). Using P_D', P_{FA}, and τ_d in (1.4) and (1.7), solve for $\overline{T}_{ACQ}$ and σ^2_{ACQ}.

1.2.6 Modulation Distortion Effects

Typically, the PN modulated carrier is also biphase modulated by data. Depending on the ratio of pre-detection filter bandwidth B to data rate R, this data modulation will suffer distortion and an equivalent power reduction as it passes through this filter. The equivalent power reduction factor M_2 is computed from[18]

$$M_2 = \int_{-\infty}^{\infty} S_m(f)|H(j2\pi f)|^2\,df, \tag{1.83}$$

where $S_m(f)$ is the power spectral density of the data modulation and $H(j2\pi f)$ is the equivalent low-pass transfer function of the pre-detection band-pass filter. Thus, the nominal signal power A^2 must be multiplied by M_2 to account for this effect when computing the effective signal-to-noise ratio to be used in the previous detection and false alarm probability computations.

1.2.7 Reduction in Noise Spectral Density Caused by PN Despreading

Multiplication of the equivalent noise process at the PN acquisition system input by the locally generated PN sequence spreads the spectrum of this noise process and simultaneously reduces its effective spectral height into the data filter. Letting N_0' denote this effective noise spectral density, then since the bandwidth of the data (pre-detection) filter is much narrower than that of the PN process, we have that

$$N_0' \cong N_0 \int_{-\infty}^{\infty} T_c\left(\frac{\sin \pi f T_c}{\pi f T_c}\right)^2 |H(j2\pi f)|^2\,df. \tag{1.84}$$

In (1.84), we have assumed for simplicity of the calculation that the PN line

[18] We shall again encounter this equivalent power reduction factor in our discussion of PN tracking loops in the next chapter.

spectrum is approximated by its envelope. Thus, again in computing the effective signal-to-noise ratio of the system, N_0 should be replaced by N_0'.

Finally, summing up the effects discussed in Sections 1.2.5–1.2.7, the effective signal-to-noise ratio γ' in the pre-detection filter bandwidth is given by

$$\gamma' = \frac{A^2 M_2 L}{N_0' B}, \tag{1.85}$$

where M_2 is defined in (1.83), N_0' in (1.84), and L, the loss due to a chip misalignment τ from the correlation curve peak, is given by

$$L = \left(1 - \frac{\tau}{T_c}\right)^2. \tag{1.86}$$

Again, for half-chip search updates, the worse case loss corresponds to $\tau/T_c = 1/4$.

1.2.8 Code Doppler and Its Derivative

When code Doppler and its derivative characterize the received signal dynamics, the timing error between received and local PN codes is not constant over the dwell time of the detection process. This "smearing" effect has a direct bearing on the calculation of the loss due to fractional chip timing misalignment and thus the expression for this loss given in (1.86) requires modification.

Considering the case where the received signal is characterized by code Doppler and Doppler rate, the normalized signal input to the acquisition dwell time integrator in Figure 1.6 is (under the signal present hypothesis):

$$\tilde{s}(t) = \left(1 - \frac{\tau}{T_c} - \Delta f_c t - \frac{1}{2}\Delta \dot{f}_c t^2\right)^2. \tag{1.87}$$

The corresponding normalized dwell time integrator output is

$$\begin{aligned} L &= \frac{1}{\tau_d}\int_0^{\tau_d} \tilde{s}(t)\,dt \\ &= \left(1 - \frac{\tau}{T_c}\right)^2 - \left[\Delta f_c \tau_d + \frac{1}{3}\Delta \dot{f}_c \tau_d^2\right]\left(1 - \frac{\tau}{T_c}\right) \\ &\quad + \frac{\Delta f_c^2 \tau_d^2}{3} + \frac{\Delta f_c \Delta \dot{f}_c \tau_d^3}{4} + \frac{\Delta \dot{f}_c^2 \tau_d^4}{20}. \end{aligned} \tag{1.88}$$

For small Δf_c and $\Delta \dot{f}_c$, the loss L of (1.88) is well approximated by

$$\tilde{L} = \left[\left(1 - \frac{\tau}{T_c}\right) - \frac{\Delta f_c \tau_d + \frac{1}{3}\Delta \dot{f}_c \tau_d^2}{2}\right]^2. \tag{1.89}$$

Using (1.88) or (1.89) in (1.85), one is able to compute, to a first-order approximation, the effective signal-to-noise ratio in the pre-detection filter bandwidth when the received signal dynamics are characterized by code Doppler and its derivative.

Because of the dependence of L on dwell time τ_d, the procedure for ultimately calculating mean acquisition time is more complex but may be summarized as follows:

1. For a given detection probability (P_D'), solve for P_D from (1.82).
2. For a specified bandwidth B and filter type, compute M_2 from (1.83) and N_0' from (1.84). (Actually, carrier and code Doppler affect these computations but we shall assume these are second-order effects.)
3. Using M_2 and N_0' computed in (2) and L from (1.88) or $\tilde{L}$ from (1.89), determine γ' from (1.85) (assume A^2/N_0 is given).
4. Letting $N_B = B\tau_d$, then for a given P_{FA}, solve for β from (1.79), which together with P_D determined from (1) and γ' from (3), allows us to solve (transcendentally) for τ_d from (1.80).
5. Using τ_d as determined in (4), and the given values of P_D' and P_{FA}, calculate $\overline{T}_{ACQ}$ from (4) and σ_{ACQ}^2 from (1.7).

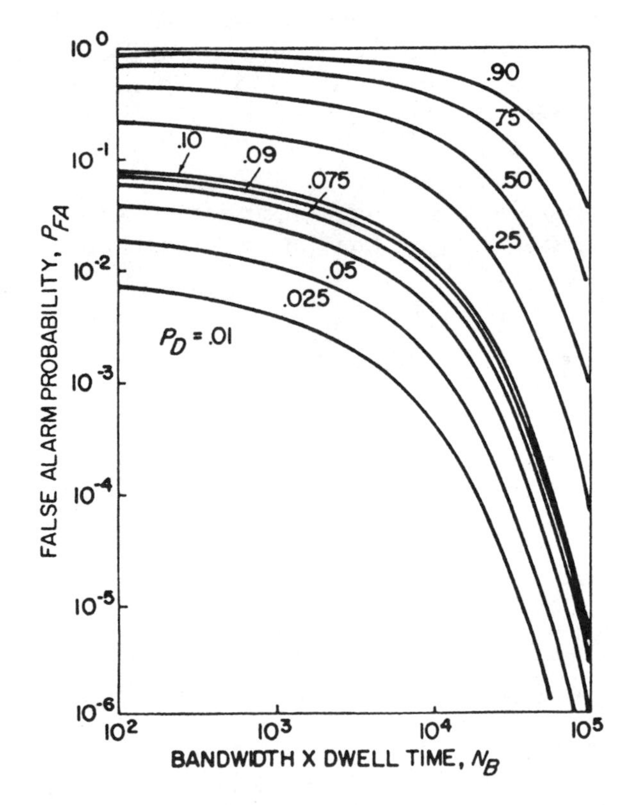

Figure 1.9. False alarm and detection probability performance of non-coherent (square-law) detector; $\gamma' = -20$ dB.

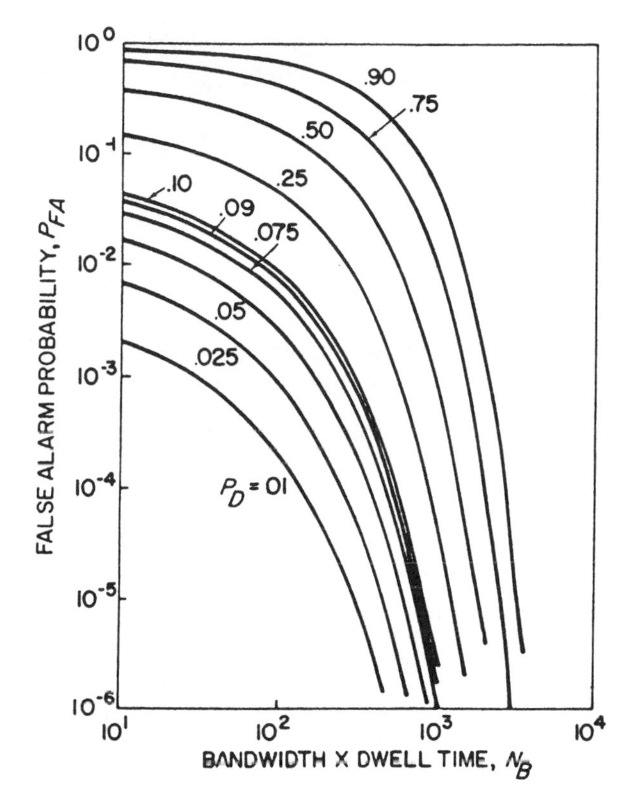

Figure 1.10. False alarm and detection probability performance of non-coherent (square-law) detector; $\gamma' = -10$ dB.

To aid in carrying out step (4), Figures 1.9 and 1.10 illustrate P_{FA} versus N_B with P_D as a parameter for $\gamma' = -20$ dB and -10 dB respectively. These curves are computed using (1.81). Clearly, for fixed P_D and γ', the square-law detector performance improves (P_{FA} decreases) as N_B increases. However, increasing N_B for fixed bandwidth B increases the dwell time τ_d, which acts to increase mean acquisition time.

1.2.9 Probability of Acquisition for the Single Dwell System

A more complete statistical characterization of the acquisition time performance of a single dwell PN acquisition system can be had by considering the *probability of acquisition in k or fewer dwells*. Computation of this cumulative probability requires first obtaining an expression for the probability density function of the number of dwells to obtain successful synchronization [6].

Once again in order to readily gain immediate and exact results, one resorts to the signal flow graph approach which provides the system generating function as in (1.1). Starting with this expression, we first rewrite it in the form of a power series in z, namely,

$$U(z) = (1-\beta)z\sum_{i=0}^{\infty}\left(H^{q-1}(z)\beta z\right)^{i}\left[\frac{1}{q}\sum_{l=0}^{q-1}H^{l}(z)\right]$$
$$= \frac{P_D z}{q}\sum_{i=0}^{\infty}\sum_{l=0}^{q-1}\left[P_{FA}z^{K}+(1-P_{FA})\right]^{i(q-1)+l}(1-P_D)^{i}z^{iq+l}. \tag{1.90}$$

Applying the binomial theorem to the factor involving P_{FA}, the generating function can be rewritten as the triple sum

$$U(z) = \frac{P_D z}{q}\sum_{i=0}^{\infty}\sum_{l=0}^{q-1}\sum_{h=0}^{i(q-1)+l}\binom{i(q-1)+l}{h}P_{FA}^{h}(1-P_{FA})^{i(q-1)+l-h}$$
$$\times(1-P_D)^{i}z^{iq+l+hK} \tag{1.91}$$

In order to proceed further, we must relate the generating function $U(z)$ to the probability of successful synchronization. Recalling (1.31), then

$$N_{ACQ} \triangleq N_u' + m + nK \tag{1.92}$$

is the integer valued random variable which represents the total number of cells that have been examined when successful synchronization (acquisition) occurs. Letting p_j denote the probability that the system acquires on the j-th cell tested, or, in terms of N_{ACQ},

$$p_j = Pr\{N_{ACQ}=j\}; \qquad j = 1,2,3\ldots \tag{1.93}$$

then z has the moment generating function

$$U(z) = \sum_{j=0}^{\infty} z^{j}p_j. \tag{1.94}$$

Thus, equating the coefficients of z^j; $j = 1,2,3,\ldots$ in (1.91) to p_j produces, at least in principle, the desired result.

Determination of these coefficients in (1.91) is possible [7] but quite tedious. To make matters more tractable, but still meaningful, we shall make the assumption that the system acquires within a single search of q cells, or equivalently we impose the restriction $N_{ACQ} < q$. Indeed, if this were not the case in practice, then the serial search synchronization system would give way to the maximum-likelihood system discussed earlier since if all the cells were to be examined there would be no need for a threshold test on each. Returning now to (1.91), we recognize that the restriction $N_{ACQ} < q$ is equivalent to considering only the $i = 0$ term in the summation on i, since the index i represents the number of times that the entire group of cells has been *previously* examined. Thus, $i = 0$ implies that the q cells are being examined for the first time. Making this simplification in (1.91) produces the result

$$U(z)|_{i=0} = \frac{P_D}{q} \sum_{l=0}^{q-1} \sum_{h=0}^{l} \binom{l}{h} P_{FA}^h (1 - P_{FA})^{l-h} z^{l+hK+1}. \tag{1.95}$$

Now making the equivalence between the coefficients of z^j in (1.95) and (1.94) produces, after much simplification, the desired result, namely [6], [7]

$$p_j = \frac{P_D}{q} \sum_{h=0}^{\hat{h}+1} \binom{j-1-hK}{h} P_{FA}^h (1 - P_{FA})^{j-1-h(K+1)};$$

$$\left\lfloor \frac{j}{K} \right\rfloor K + 1 \leq j \leq \min\left\{\left(\left\lfloor \frac{j}{K} \right\rfloor + 1\right) K, q\right\} \tag{1.96}$$

where

$$\hat{h} \triangleq \left\lfloor \frac{\left\lfloor \frac{j}{K} \right\rfloor K}{K+1} \right\rfloor \tag{1.97}$$

and the notation $\lfloor a \rfloor$ represents the largest integer less than or equal to a. Furthermore, the term corresponding to $h = \hat{h} + 1$ clearly has meaning only if $j - 1 - (\hat{h} + 1)K \geq 0$; otherwise its contribution is assumed equal to zero.

The cumulative distribution of N_{ACQ}, namely,

$$P_{ACQ}(j) \triangleq \Pr\{N_{ACQ} \leq j\} = \sum_{i=0}^{j} p_i \tag{1.98}$$

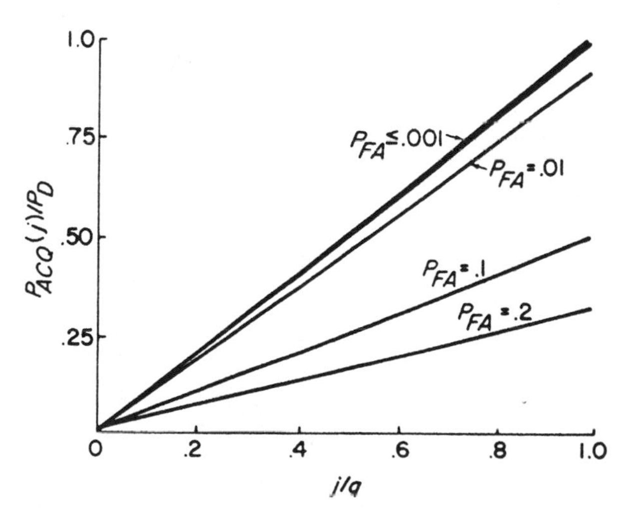

Figure 1.11. Normalized cumulative distribution function for $q = 10^2$, $K = 10$ and various values of P_{FA} (reprinted from [6]).

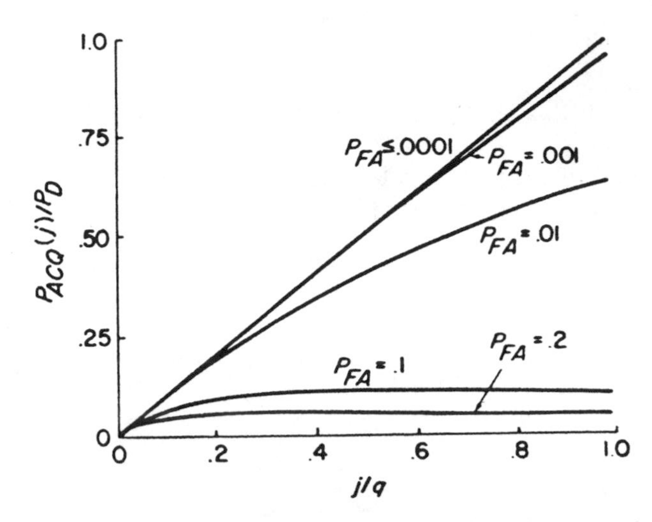

Figure 1.12. Normalized cumulative distribution for $q = 10^2$, $K = 10^2$ and various values of P_{FA} (reprinted from [6]).

represents the probability of acquisition in j or fewer dwells. Although a closed form expression for $P_{ACQ}(j)$ using p_j of (1.96) appears impossible, one can readily obtain numerical results for moderate values of q using digital computation. Figures 1.11–1.14 illustrate the normalized acquisition probability $P_{ACQ}(j)/P_D$ as a function of j/q for various values of q, K, and P_{FA}. In all cases, as P_{FA} goes to zero, we obtain the optimum

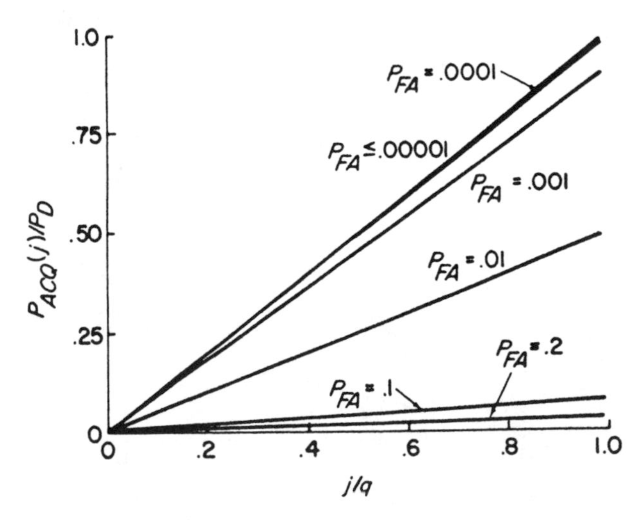

Figure 1.13. Normalized cumulative distribution function for $q = 5 \times 10^3$, $K = 10^2$ and various values of P_{FA} (reprinted from [6]).

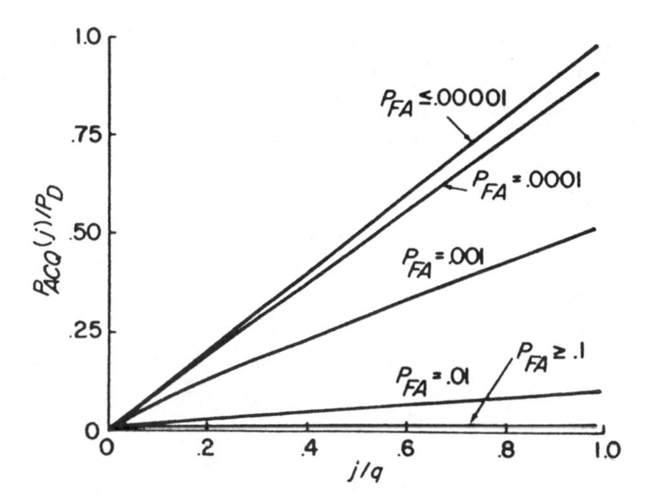

Figure 1.14. Normalized cumulative distribution function for $q = 5 \times 10^3$, $K = 10^3$ and various values of P_{FA} (reprinted from [6]).

performance corresponding to $P_{ACQ}(j)/P_D = j/q$. For a given q, increasing K (the number of dwell penalty time units) requires an attendant decrease in P_{FA} to achieve the same level of performance. In this regard, the value of K is critical in determining the value of P_{FA} which yields near optimum performance.

Before leaving this section we point out that the heuristic approach used to verify the mean time to acquisition and acquisition variance results derived from the flow graph diagram can also be applied here to obtain the acquisition probability behavior. The details are left as an exercise for the reader. As a head start, one can easily show that for $P_{FA} = 0$, convolution of (1.8) with (1.19) gives the probability density function for $N'_{ACQ} \triangleq q(k-1) + m$ as

$$p'_j \triangleq \Pr\{N'_{ACQ} = j\} = \frac{1}{q} P_D (1 - P_D)^j. \tag{1.99}$$

As a final note, we point out the relation of the single dwell system with stepped search discussed here to an equivalent acquisition system using a continuous sweep. In the latter case, the local PN code generator is clocked at a frequency $f_c + \delta f_c$ which differs from the clock frequency $f_c = 1/T_c$ of the incoming PN code by a small amount $\delta f_c \ll f_c$. As such, the epoch difference between the incoming and local PN codes vanishes at instants of time which are $p/\delta f_c$ apart where p is again the period of the PN code in chips. When the input and local codes are actively correlated, the result is a periodic train of "impulses" (triangular pulses of width $2/\delta f_c$) which occur at the instants of vanishing epoch difference. These impulses are detected by means of a non-coherent detection circuit consisting, as we have already seen, of a pre-detection band-pass filter, a quadratic detector, a post-detection low-pass filter, and a threshold device. The first detected "impulse" declares a "hit," sets the local clock frequency to f_c, and activates the tracking loop.

To extend the performance results obtained for the discrete stepping search to the continuous sweep procedure, one must merely equivalence $q\tau_d$ in the former with the time $p/\delta f_c$ to equivalently search one code period in the latter. Furthermore, since KP_{FA} can be written as $(K\tau_d)(P_{FA}/\tau_d)$, then for the continuous system $K\tau_d$ is equivalenced to the false alarm penalty time T_p and in view of the above, P_{FA}/τ_d is equivalenced with the false alarm *rate* $\eta_{FA} = P_{FA}(p\delta f_c/q)$.

1.3 THE MULTIPLE DWELL SERIAL PN ACQUISITION SYSTEM

A generalization of the single dwell serial PN acquisition system is a multiple dwell technique which, by virtue of its additional threshold testing, does not constrain the examination interval per cell to be a constant interval of time. Nevertheless, this scheme falls into the class of fixed dwell time PN acquisition systems as discussed earlier in the introduction in the sense that the variation in integration time is achieved here by allowing the examination interval to consist of a series of fixed short dwell periods (each longer than its predecessor) with a decision being made after each. Allowing the integration time in a given cell examination interval to increase toward its maximum value in *discrete steps*, as per the above, permits dismissal of an incorrect alignment earlier than would be possible in a single dwell system which is constrained to always integrate over the full examination interval. Since most of the cells searched indeed correspond to incorrect alignments, this ability to quickly eliminate them produces a considerable reduction in acquisition time, particularly for long codes.

Consider the N-dwell serial synchronization system illustrated in Figure 1.15. The received PN code signal plus noise multiplied by the local replica of the PN code and the output of the multiplier is applied to each of N non-coherent[19] detectors. The i-th detector, $i = 1, 2, \ldots, N$, is characterized by a detection probability P_{Di}, a false alarm probability P_{FAi}, and a dwell time τ_{di}. These three parameters are for a non-coherent detector, related to each other as per the discussion in Section 1.2.4, in particular, (1.81). On the assumption that the detector dwell times are ordered such that

$$\tau_{d1} \leq \tau_{d2} \leq \tau_{d3} \leq \cdots \leq \tau_{dN} \tag{1.100}$$

[19]Again, as in the single dwell case, the multiple dwell technique can also be used with coherent detectors. In fact, the results in this section are independent of the type of detector used. However, when it becomes necessary to relate the performance to the acquisition system parameters, we shall pursue only the non-coherent case.

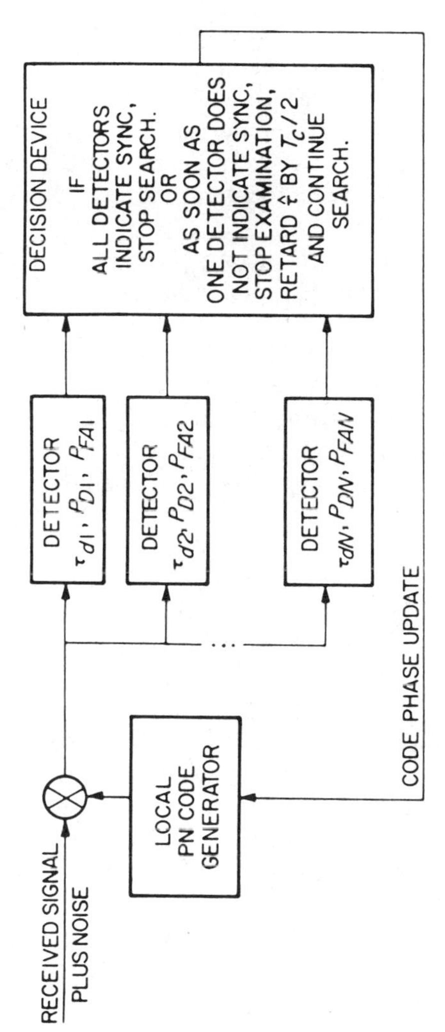

Figure 1.15. The N-dwell serial synchronization system with half chip search.

the decision to continue or stop the search at the present cell is made by sequentially examining the N detector outputs (starting with the first) and applying the following algorithm:

(1) If *all* of the N detectors (tested in succession) indicate that the present cell is correct, i.e., each produces a threshold crossing, then the decision is made to stop the search.

(2) If *any* one detector fails to indicate that the present cell is correct, i.e., it fails to produce a threshold crossing, then the decision is made to continue the search and the time delay $\hat{\tau}$ of the local PN generator is retarded by the chosen phase update increment, whereupon the next cell is examined. Thus, as soon as one detector indicates that the codes are misaligned, the search may move on without waiting for the decisions of the remaining detectors.

Note from the foregoing that the maximum time to search a given cell is τ_{dN}, whereas the minimum time is τ_{d1}. Herein lies the power of the N-dwell system, namely, that most of the cells can be dismissed after a dwell time τ_{dk}; $k \ll N$, whereas the single dwell system requires that each and every cell be examined for a time equivalent to τ_{dN}.

A block diagram of an N-dwell time PN acquisition system using non-coherent detection is illustrated in Figure 1.16. In the form in which the configuration is drawn, all of the N integrate-and-dump circuits initiate their integration at the same instant in time, each one dumping, however, at a later and later time instant in view of (1.100). Thus, because of this overlap in the integration times of the integrate-and-dump circuits, the outputs $Z_1, Z_2, \ldots, Z_N$ represent a set of fully dependent random variables.[20] As such, the probability that Z_i crosses its threshold depends on the probability that Z_k; $k = 1, 2, \ldots, i-1$ crossed their respective thresholds. This fact will be important in what follows later on. In accordance with the search update algorithm, the output of the i-th integrate-and-dump is sampled and compared to a threshold only if all of the previous $i-1$ integrate-and-dump outputs have previously exceeded their respective thresholds. Otherwise, the first integrate-and-dump output to fall below its threshold causes the local code to update its phase and search the next cell thereby resetting all of the integrate-and-dump circuits.

In reality, Figure 1.16 represents only a conceptual implementation of the N-dwell system. In practice, the N integrate-and-dumps would be realized by a *single continuous-time* integrator whose output is sequentially sampled (but not dumped) at time instants $t = \tau_{d1}, \tau_{d1} + \tau_{d2}, \ldots, \tau_{d1} + \tau_{d2} + \tau_{d3} + \cdots + \tau_{di}$ depending, as above, on the outcomes of the first $i-1$ threshold comparisons. This single integrator would again be reset only after a

[20] In [8], an N-dwell configuration is considered wherein the N integrate-and-dump outputs $Z_1, Z_2, \ldots, Z_N$ are independent by virtue of the fact that the i-th integrate-and-dump, $i = 2, 3, \ldots, N$, initiates its integration at the instant in time at which the $(i-1)$-st is dumped.

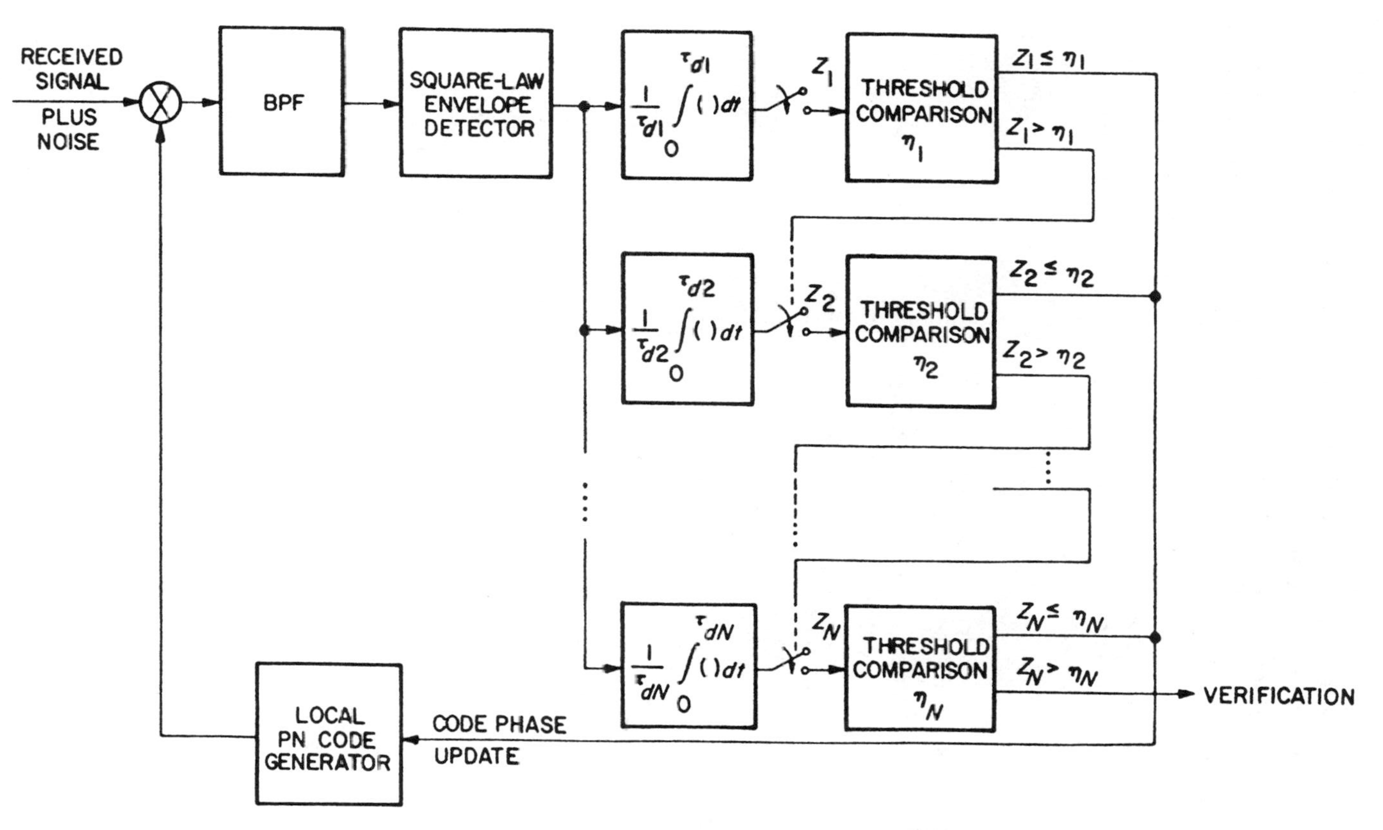

Figure 1.16. Block diagram of an N-dwell time PN acquisition system with non-coherent detection.

decision is made to search the next cell. From the standpoint of functional operation, these two systems are identical. Hence, in what follows we shall not draw any distinction between the two.

In addition to all of the foregoing, one must, as in the single dwell case, characterize the penalty time T_p for a false alarm. This occurs when all N detector outputs exceed their respective thresholds for a cell which does not correspond to the correct code alignment. Regardless of the means for identifying the false alarm (we shall discuss some of these toward the end of the chapter), it is convenient to model T_p as an integer multiple of the *additional* time required by the N-th dwell, i.e.,

$$T_p = K_N(\tau_{dN} - \tau_{d,N-1}). \tag{1.101}$$

1.3.1 Markov Chain Acquisition Model

The procedure for evaluating acquisition performance of the N-dwell system is to once again determine a suitable flow graph model for the process which when reduced results in the system generating function. Since the cell-to-cell or *inter*-cell behavior of the N-dwell system is identical to that of the single dwell system, one should expect that the generating function flow graphs for the two systems would have the same *macro*scopic (coarse) structure. This realization enables one to immediately use the structure of Figure 1.8 for the flow graph representation of the N-dwell system which is illustrated in Figure 1.17.

The *micro*scopic (fine) structure of each of the branches in Figure 1.17 which depicts the *intra*-cell behavior of the N-dwell process, is represented by the series of exploded flow graphs in Figure 1.18. Analogous to Figure 1.8 each branch is labelled with the product of the transition probability associated with going from the node at the originating end of the branch to the node at its terminating end, and an integer (including zero) power of a parameter z_i; $i = 1, 2, \ldots, N$. As before, the parameter z_i is used to indicate the unit time delay as flow propagates along that branch and its power represents the number of such time delay units.

Since Figures 1.17 and 1.18 are to be used to compute a generating function for acquisition time, the z_i's have the following associations: z_1 represents a time delay of τ_{d1}, z_2 a time delay of $\tau_{d2} - \tau_{d1}, \ldots,$ and z_N a time delay of $\tau_{dN} - \tau_{d,N-1}$. Thus z_i; $i = 1, 2, \ldots, N$ represents the additional dwell time one must wait before testing the i-th threshold after the $(i-1)$-st threshold has been tested.

The detection transition probability $P_{Di|i-1}$; $i = 1, 2, \ldots, N$ corresponds to the probability that, for the cell containing signal plus noise, the i-th dwell integrate-and-dump output Z_i exceeds its threshold *conditioned* on $Z_1, Z_2, \ldots, Z_{i-1}$ all having exceeded their respective thresholds. In mathematical terms, letting η_i; $i = 1, 2, \ldots, N$ denotes the i-th threshold; then

$$P_{Di|i-1} = \Pr\{Z_i > \eta_i | Z_1 > \eta_1, Z_2 > \eta_2, \ldots, Z_{i-1} > \eta_{i-1}\}. \tag{1.102}$$

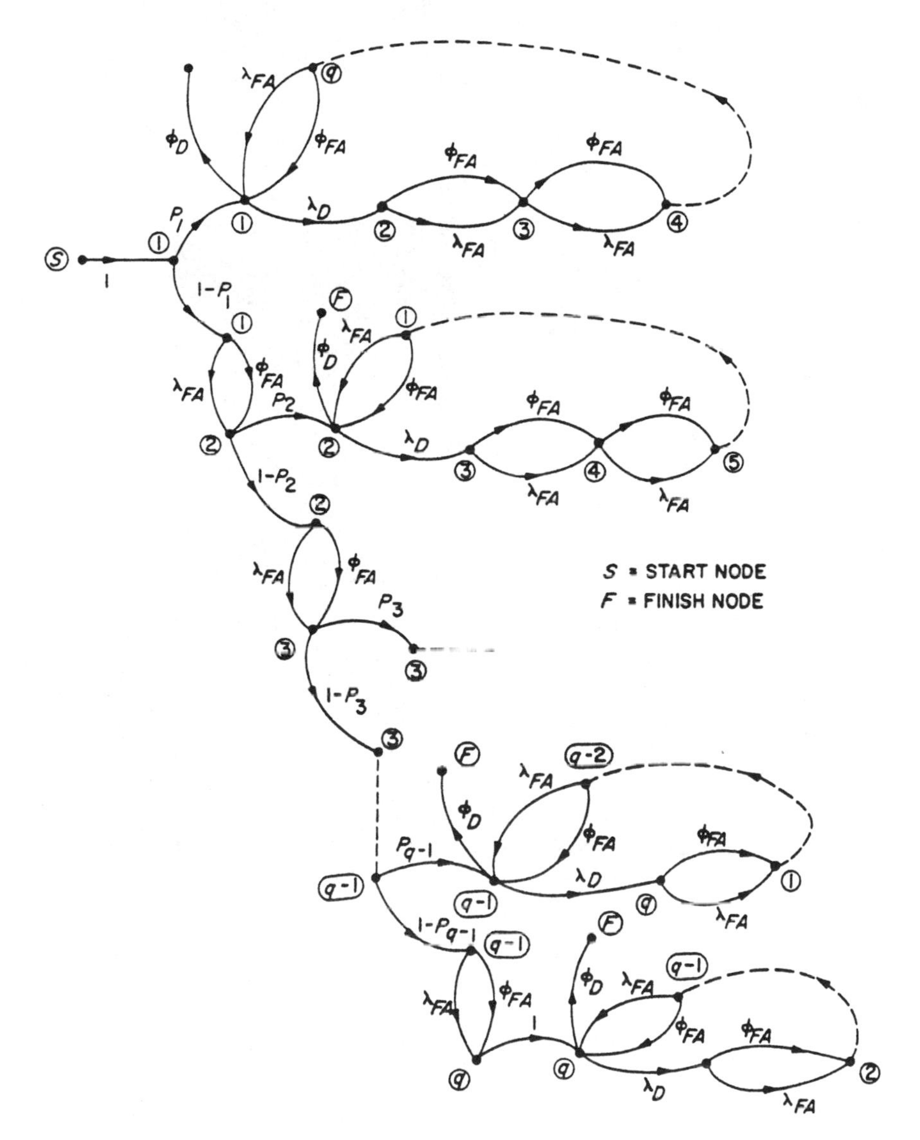

Figure 1.17. Generating function flow graph for acquisition time of the N-dwell process.

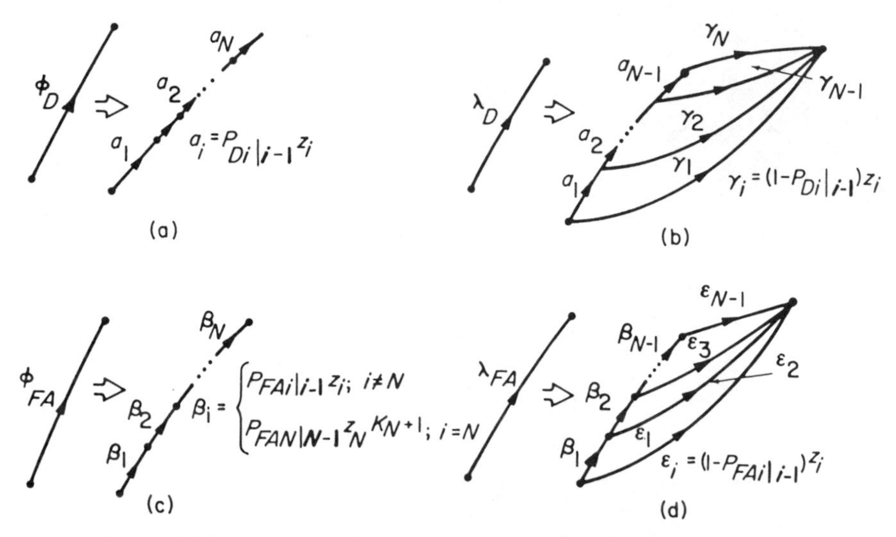

Figure 1.18. Flow graphs for *intra*-cell behavior of N-dwell process.

Similarly, for a cell containing noise only the false alarm transition probability $P_{FAi|i-1}$ is defined identically to (1.102).

With the meaning of the branch labels having been defined in Figure 1.18, the significance of each of the sub-flow graphs (actually a collection of branches corresponding to a single branch in Figure 1.17) is explained as follows. Figure 1.18(a) corresponds to reaching the event of a successful acquisition, i.e., reaching the finish node starting at a node corresponding to the *correct* cell. This event can occur only if *all* of the N integrate-and-dump outputs exceed their thresholds. Hence each node along ϕ_D represents one of the N dwells and the probability P_{ϕ_D} associated with the traversing this entire branch is the system detection probability[21]

$$P_D = \prod_{i=1}^{N} P_{Di|i-1}$$

$$= \Pr\{ Z_1 > \eta_1, Z_2 > \eta_2, \ldots, Z_N > \eta_N \}. \tag{1.103}$$

Figure 1.18(b) corresponds to the event of causing a code phase update, i.e., advancing the search to the next cell starting at a node corresponding to the correct cell. This event will occur if *any* of the N integrate-and-dump outputs fails to exceed its threshold as one progresses through the N-dwell

[21] By definition, $P_{D1|0} = P_{D1} = \Pr\{ Z_1 > \eta_1 \}$.

system. Thus, the probability associated with λ_D is[22]

$$P_{\lambda_D} = \sum_{i=1}^{N}\left(\prod_{k=1}^{i-1} P_{Dk|k-1}\right)(1 - P_{Di|i-1})$$

$$= \Pr\{Z_1 < \eta_1 \text{ or } Z_2 < \eta_2 \text{ or } \cdots \text{ or } Z_N < \eta_N\}. \quad (1.104)$$

Figure 1.18(c) corresponds to a false alarm, i.e., all N integrate-and-dumps exceed their thresholds starting at a node corresponding to an *incorrect* cell. Note that the last sub-branch of ϕ_{FA} has associated with it $Z_N^{K_N+1}$ which represents the additional K_N penalty time units in accordance with (1.101). The probability $P_{\phi_{FA}}$ associated with this event is clearly the system false alarm probability

$$P_{FA} = \prod_{i=1}^{N} P_{FAi|i-1}$$

$$= \Pr\{Z_1 > \eta_1, Z_2 > \eta_2, \ldots, Z_N > \eta_N\} \quad (1.105)$$

where again $P_{FA1|0} \triangleq P_{FA1} = \Pr\{Z_1 < \eta_1\}$.

Finally, Figure 1.18(d) is analogous to Figure 1.18(b) and represents the event of updating the search starting from a node corresponding to an incorrect cell. Again a code search update will occur if any of the N integrate-and-dump outputs fails to exceed its threshold which occurs with probability

$$P_{\lambda_{FA}} = \sum_{i=1}^{N}\left(\prod_{k=1}^{i-1} P_{FAk|k-1}\right)(1 - P_{FAi|i-1})$$

$$= \Pr\{Z_1 < \eta_1 \text{ or } Z_2 < \eta_2 \text{ or } \cdots \text{ or } Z_N < \eta_N\}. \quad (1.106)$$

1.3.2 Multiple Dwell Acquisition Time Performance

With the same standard flow graph reduction techniques [31]–[33] as were used to obtain the generating function for the single dwell system, the flow graph of Figure 1.17 together with Figure 1.18 can be reduced to a single branch whose label is then the N-dimensional generating function for the N-dwell system, namely [7]

$$U(z) = C(z)\left[\frac{1}{q}\sum_{l=0}^{q-1} H^l(z)\right] \quad (1.107)$$

[22] For the $i = 1$ term, we define $\prod_{k=1}^{0} P_{Dk|k-1} = 1$.

where now

$$H(z) = \lambda_{FA} + \phi_{FA} = \sum_{i=1}^{N} \left(\prod_{k=1}^{i-1} P_{FAk|\mathbf{k-1}} z_k \right) (1 - P_{FAi|\mathbf{i-1}}) z_i + P_{FA} z_N^{K_N} \prod_{i=1}^{N} z_i$$

$$C(z) = \frac{\phi_D}{1 - \lambda_D H^{q-1}(z)} = \frac{P_D \prod_{i=1}^{N} z_i}{1 - \sum_{i=1}^{N} \left(\prod_{k=1}^{i-1} P_{Dk|\mathbf{k-1}} z_k \right) (1 - P_{Di|\mathbf{i-1}}) z_i H^{q-1}(z)}. \quad (1.108)$$

With i_n defined as the integer-valued random variable that represents the number of time delay units of duration $\tau_{dn} - \tau_{d,n-1}$ that have elapsed when the final node F is reached (acquisition occurs), the acquisition time T_{ACQ} is given by[23]

$$T_{ACQ} = \sum_{n=1}^{N} i_n (\tau_{dn} - \tau_{d,n-1}). \quad (1.109)$$

With $U(z)$ as the moment-generating function for the joint probability density function $p(i_1, i_2, \ldots, i_N)$, i.e.,

$$U(z) = \sum_{i_1=0}^{\infty} \sum_{i_2=0}^{\infty} \cdots \sum_{i_N=0}^{\infty} z_1^{i_1} z_2^{i_2} \cdots z_N^{i_N} p(i_1, i_2, \ldots, i_N) \quad (1.110)$$

then, analogous to (1.3), the mean acquisition time $\overline{T}_{ACQ}$ is obtained from[24]

$$\overline{T}_{ACQ} = \sum_{j=1}^{N} \left. \frac{\partial U(z^{\Delta \tau_d})}{\partial z_j} \right|_{z=\mathbf{1}}. \quad (1.111)$$

Substituting (1.107) in (1.111) and carrying out the required differentiations of the N-dimensional polynomials $H(z)$ and $C(z)$ gives after much simplification [7]

$$\overline{T}_{ACQ} = \frac{1}{2P_D} \sum_{j=1}^{N} \left[(2 - P_D)(q-1) \times \left\{ \prod_{i=1}^{j-1} P_{FAi|\mathbf{i-1}} + K_N P_{FA} \delta_{jN} \right\} + 2 \prod_{i=1}^{j-1} P_{Di|\mathbf{i-1}} \right] \times (\tau_{dj} - \tau_{d,j-1}) \quad (1.112)$$

[23] For convenience we set $\tau_{d0} = 0$.

[24] The notation $z^{\Delta \tau_d}$ represents a vector whose j-th component, $j = 1, 2, \ldots, N$ is $z_j^{\tau_{dj} - \tau_{d_{j-1}}}$.

which for $q \gg 1$ simplifies to

$$\overline{T}_{ACQ} = \frac{(2 - P_D) q \sum_{j=1}^{N} \left[\left(\prod_{i=1}^{j-1} P_{FAi|i-1} \right) (\tau_{dj} - \tau_{d,j-1}) + K_N P_{FA} \delta_{jN} (\tau_{dN} - \tau_{d,N-1}) \right]}{2 P_D}. \tag{1.113}$$

In (1.112) and (1.113), the Kronecker delta function has the usual definition

$$\delta_{ij} = \begin{cases} 1; & i = j \\ 0; & i \neq j \end{cases}. \tag{1.114}$$

Also, for $N = 1$ (a single dwell system) and $K_1 = K$, (1.113) reduces to (1.4), as it should.

Comparing the forms of (1.113) and (1.4), it is apparent that for the same false alarm penalty time, i.e., $K\tau_d = K_N(\tau_{dN} - \tau_{d,N-1})$, the N-dwell system can yield a smaller mean acquisition time than the single dwell system if

$$\sum_{j=1}^{N} \left(\prod_{i=1}^{j-1} P_{FAi|i-1} \right) (\tau_{dj} - \tau_{d,j-1}) < \tau_d. \tag{1.115}$$

The ability to design the N-dwell system to satisfy (1.115) depends upon the functional relationship between the conditional false alarm probabilities and the dwell times. More will be said about this relationship shortly.

The generating function of (1.107) can also be used to obtain an approximate expression for the acquisition time variance σ_{ACQ}^2 of the N-dwell system. In particular,

$$\sigma_{ACQ}^2 = \sum_{i=1}^{N} \sum_{l=1}^{N} \left. \frac{\partial^2 U(z^{\Delta\tau_d})}{\partial z_i \, \partial z_l} \right|_{z=1} + \overline{T}_{ACQ}(1 - \overline{T}_{ACQ}). \tag{1.116}$$

Taking the required second partial derivatives using $U(z)$ defined in (1.107) and (1.108) and making the assumption of large q, then together with $\overline{T}_{ACQ}$ of (1.113) one obtains after much simplification the relation [7]

$$\sigma_{ACQ}^2 = q^2 \left\{ \sum_{j=1}^{N} \left[\left(\prod_{i=1}^{j-1} P_{FAi|i-1} \right) (\tau_{dj} - \tau_{d,j-1}) + K_N P_{FA} \delta_{jN} (\tau_{dN} - \tau_{d,N-1}) \right] \right\}^2 \times \left(\frac{1}{12} + \frac{1}{P_D^2} - \frac{1}{P_D} \right). \tag{1.117}$$

Again for the special case of $N = 1$ and $K_1 = K$, (1.117) reduces to (1.7).

Once again comparing (1.117) and (1.7) we observe that if (1.115) is satisfied, the N-dwell system yields a smaller acquisition time variance than the single dwell system. In fact, for large q, both $\overline{T}_{ACQ}$ and the standard deviation σ_{ACQ} are directly proportional to the same function $F(N)$ of false alarm probabilities and dwell times, namely,

$$F(N) = \sum_{j=1}^{N} \left[\left(\prod_{i=1}^{j-1} P_{FAi|i-1} \right) (\tau_{dj} - \tau_{d,j-1}) + K_N P_{FA} \delta_{jN} (\tau_{dN} - \tau_{d,N-1}) \right]. \tag{1.118}$$

To proceed further with the evaluation of the first two moments of acquisition time one must relate the *conditional* false alarm probabilities $\{P_{FAi|i-1}\}$ defined in (1.102) to the dwell times $\{\tau_{di}\}$ and the detection thresholds $\{\eta_i\}$. Since, as previously mentioned, the overlap in the integration times of the integrate-and-dump circuits causes the outputs $Z_1, Z_2, \ldots, Z_N$ to be a set of fully dependent random variables, computation of $P_{FAi|i-1}$ involves evaluation of an i-dimensional integral over the joint probability density function $p(Z_1, Z_2, \ldots, Z_i)$. Such evaluations are at best tedious if not altogether impossible.

To circumvent this computational bottleneck, we consider a procedure for obtaining an upper bound on the acquisition performance of the N-dwell system. This will allow direct comparison with the comparable performance of the single dwell system to assess how much improvement can be gained as a function of the number of dwells N. To illustrate the procedure as clearly as possible, we shall first present its details for the simple case of a two-dwell system, i.e., $N = 2$.

Consider that we choose the decision thresholds η_1 and η_2 such that the *unconditional* detection probabilities P_{D1} and P_{D2} are equal, i.e.,

$$P_{D1} = P_{D2} \triangleq P. \tag{1.119}$$

This choice does not necessarily guarantee an optimum decision; however, it allows us to obtain a simple upper bound on performance that will be sufficient to indicate the benefit in going to an N-dwell system.

Next, we note from the law of total probability that

$$P_{D2} = P_{D2|1} P_{D1} + P_{D2|\bar{1}} P_{D\bar{1}} \tag{1.120}$$

where the overbar denotes the complement of the event. For example,

$$P_{D\bar{1}} = \Pr\{ Z_1 < \eta_1 \} \tag{1.121}$$

when signal is present. Since $P_{D2|\bar{1}} \leq 1$ and $P_{D\bar{1}} = 1 - P_{D1}$, then from (1.120),

$$P_{D2} \leq P_{D2|1} P_{D1} + 1 - P_{D1} \tag{1.122}$$

or, using (1.119),

$$P_{D2|1} P \geq 2P - 1. \tag{1.123}$$

Since, from (1.103), the left-hand side of (1.123) represents the system detection probability for the double dwell system, if P_D denotes the system detection probability of the single dwell system and we set

$$2P - 1 = P_D \tag{1.124}$$

then we are guaranteed that the two-dwell system will have an equal or higher detection probability. This in turn implies, from (1.113) and (1.117) an equal or smaller acquisition time mean and variance. Thus, in conclusion, evaluation of (1.113) and (1.117) using (1.124) for the choice of unconditional detection probabilities, i.e.,

$$P = \frac{1 + P_D}{2} \tag{1.125}$$

gives an upper bound on $\overline{T}_{ACQ}$ and σ^2_{ACQ} for the double dwell system.

To proceed further, we note that, analogous to (1.120),

$$P_{FA2} = P_{FA2|1}P_{FA1} + P_{FA2|\bar{1}}P_{FA\bar{1}}. \tag{1.126}$$

Since $P_{FA2|\bar{1}} \geq 0$, then

$$P_{FA2} \geq P_{FA2|1}P_{FA1}. \tag{1.127}$$

The right-hand side of (1.127) represents [see (1.105)] the system false alarm probability for the two-dwell system. Thus, if P_{FA} denotes the system false alarm probability of the single dwell system and we set

$$P_{FA2} = P_{FA} \tag{1.128}$$

then we are guaranteed that the two-dwell system will have an equal or lower false alarm probability. Thus, including (1.128) as a condition on the design will once again produce upper bounds on $\overline{T}_{ACQ}$ and σ^2_{ACQ} as evaluated from (1.113) and (1.117), respectively.

Since, as previously shown, both (1.113) and (1.117) depend on $F(N)$ of (1.118), we shall focus our attention on the evaluation of $F(2)$ using (1.125) and (1.128), or, for equal false alarm penalty times for the single and double dwell systems, the simpler function

$$G(N) = \sum_{j=1}^{N} \left(\prod_{i=1}^{j-1} P_{FAi|i-1} \right) (\tau_{dj} - \tau_{d,j-1}) \tag{1.129}$$

evaluated for $N = 2$. Letting $N = 2$ in (1.129) gives

$$G(2) = \tau_{d1} + P_{FA1}(\tau_{d2} - \tau_{d1}) \tag{1.130}$$

which, from (1.115), when less than τ_d of the single dwell system, will yield an improved acquisition performance.

From the general relationship among false alarm probability, detection probability, pre-detection signal-to-noise ratio, and IF bandwidth-dwell time product for a non-coherent detector (see (1.81)) we can write, for the single dwell system,

$$B\tau_d = f(P_D, P_{FA}; \gamma') \tag{1.131}$$

where A^2/N_0B is replaced by γ', the effective pre-detection signal-to-noise ratio, and $f(\cdot)$ represents the solution of (1.81) for $B\tau_d$. Similarly, for the double dwell system,

$$B\tau_{d1} = f\left(P_{D1}, P_{FA1}; \gamma'\right) = f\left(\frac{1 + P_D}{2}, P_{FA1}; \gamma'\right)$$

$$B\tau_{d2} = f\left(P_{D2}, P_{FA2}; \gamma'\right) = f\left(\frac{1 + P_D}{2}, P_{FA}; \gamma'\right) \geq B\tau_d. \tag{1.132}$$

Then, since by definition $\tau_{d1} \leq \tau_{d2}$, we conclude that $P_{FA1} \geq P_{FA2}$, or in view of (1.128),

$$P_{FA} = P_{FA2} \leq P_{FA1} \leq 1. \tag{1.133}$$

Now, if $P_{FA1} = P_{FA2}$, then $\tau_{d1} = \tau_{d2}$ and from (1.130)

$$G(2) = \tau_{d2} \geq \tau_d. \tag{1.134}$$

Alternately, if $P_{FA1} = 1$ and $P_{FA2} = P_{FA} < 1$, then, from (1.130)

$$G(2) = \tau_{d1} + \tau_{d2} - \tau_{d1} = \tau_{d2} \geq \tau_d, \tag{1.135}$$

which is the same result as (1.134). Clearly, then, for some $P_{FA} < P_{FA1} < 1$, say P_{FA1}^*, there exists a corresponding value of τ_{d1}, namely,

$$B\tau_{d1}^* = f\left(\frac{1 + P_D}{2}, P_{FA1}^*; \gamma'\right) \tag{1.136}$$

which minimizes $G(2)$. Letting $G^*(2)$ denote this minimum value, i.e.,

$$G^*(2) = \tau_{d1}^* + P_{FA1}^*\left(\tau_{d2} - \tau_{d1}^*\right) \tag{1.137}$$

then the ratio $\tau_d/G^*(2)$ is a measure of the minimum improvement in acquisition time and variance of the double dwell system over the single dwell system.

Figures 1.19 and 1.20 are plots of $\tau_d/G^*(2)$ versus P_{FA} with P_D as a parameter and $\gamma' = -20$ dB and -10 dB respectively. We note from these results that for fixed γ' and small P_{FA}, the minimum performance improvement offered by the two-dwell system over the single dwell system improves with increasing detection probability up to a certain point. Beyond that point, $\tau_d/G^*(2)$ decreases with increasing P_D. In fact, as P_D approaches unity, then from (1.125), P also approaches unity, and, from (1.131) and (1.132), τ_{d2} approaches τ_d. Also from (1.81), when P_D approaches unity then P_{FA} tends to unity for any γ' and all $N_B = B\tau_d$. Thus, from (1.133), P_{FA1} also approaches unity, and, from (1.132), τ_{d1} approaches τ_{d2}. Finally, using the above facts in (1.130), we see that $G(2) = G^*(2)$ approaches τ_d or $\tau_d/G^*(2)$ approaches unity.

To generalize the above procedure to arbitrary N, we begin by generalizing (1.119) to become

$$P_{Di} \triangleq P; \qquad i = 1, 2, \ldots, N, \tag{1.138}$$

i.e., all N unconditional detection probabilities are made equal by appropriate choice of the N detection thresholds. Next, following steps analogous to (1.120)–(1.122), it can be shown that the following recursion

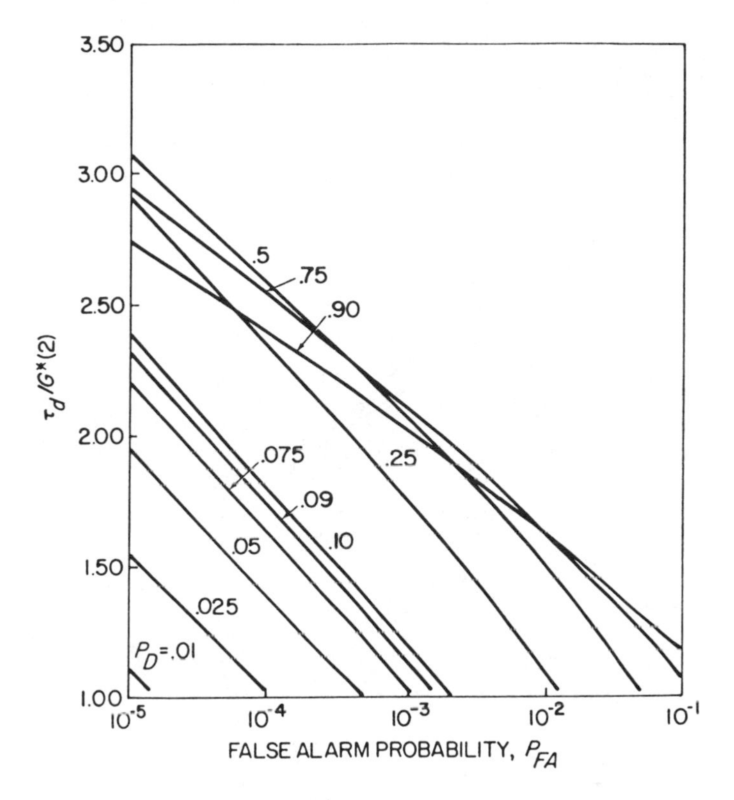

Figure 1.19. Acquisition performance improvement factor for two-dwell system over single dwell system versus false alarm probability with detection probability as a parameter; $\gamma' = -20$ dB.

relation holds:

$$\prod_{i=1}^{N} P_{Di|i-1} \geq P + \prod_{i=1}^{N-1} P_{Di|i-1} - 1 \tag{1.139}$$

Since the left-hand side of (1.139) again represents the system detection probability for the N-dwell system, and the product on the right-hand side represents the same probability for an $(N-1)$-dwell system, starting with (1.123), we may, by induction, arrive at the result

$$\prod_{i=1}^{N} P_{Di|i-1} \geq NP - (N-1). \tag{1.140}$$

Thus, we wish to set

$$P_D = NP - (N-1) \tag{1.141}$$

or

$$P = \frac{N - 1 + P_D}{N}. \tag{1.142}$$

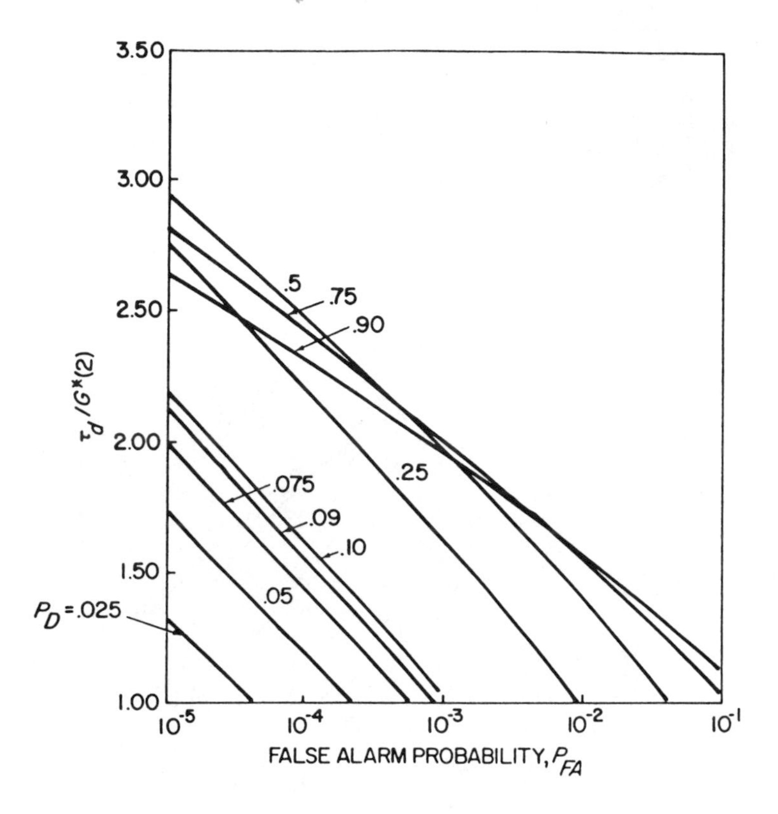

Figure 1.20. Acquisition performance improvement factor for two-dwell system over single dwell system versus false alarm probability with detection probability as a parameter; $\gamma' = -10$ dB.

Similarly, generalizing (1.126), it is simple to show that

$$P_{FAk} \geq \prod_{i=1}^{k} P_{FAi|i-1}; \qquad k = 1, 2, \ldots, N. \tag{1.143}$$

Since the right-hand side of (1.113) with $k = N$ is again the system false alarm probability of the N-dwell system, we wish to set

$$P_{FAN} = P_{FA}. \tag{1.144}$$

Finally, using (1.143) in (1.129), we have

$$\begin{aligned} G(N) &\leq \sum_{j=1}^{N} P_{FA,j-1}(\tau_{dj} - \tau_{d,j-1}) \\ &\triangleq G_u(N). \end{aligned} \tag{1.145}$$

For the non-coherent detector, the analogous relationships to (1.132) are

$$B\tau_{di} = f\left(\frac{N-1+P_D}{N}, P_{FAi}; \gamma'\right); \qquad i = 1, 2, \ldots, N-1$$

$$B\tau_{dN} = f\left(\frac{N-1+P_D}{N}, P_{FA}; \gamma'\right) \geq B\tau_d. \tag{1.146}$$

Again since $\tau_{d1} \leq \tau_{d2} \leq \cdots \leq \tau_{dN}$, we have

$$P_{FA} = P_{FAN} \leq P_{FA,N-1} \leq \cdots \leq P_{FA1} \leq 1. \tag{1.147}$$

For $P_{FA1} = P_{FA2} = \cdots P_{FAN}$ or $P_{FA1} = P_{FA2} = \cdots P_{FA,N-1} = 1$ and $P_{FAN} = P_{FA} < 1$, (1.145) becomes

$$G_u(N) = \tau_{dN} \geq \tau_d. \tag{1.148}$$

Thus, for some set of false alarm probabilities

$$P_{FA} < P^*_{FA,N-1} < P^*_{FA,N-2} < \cdots < P^*_{FA2} < P^*_{FA1} < 1 \tag{1.149}$$

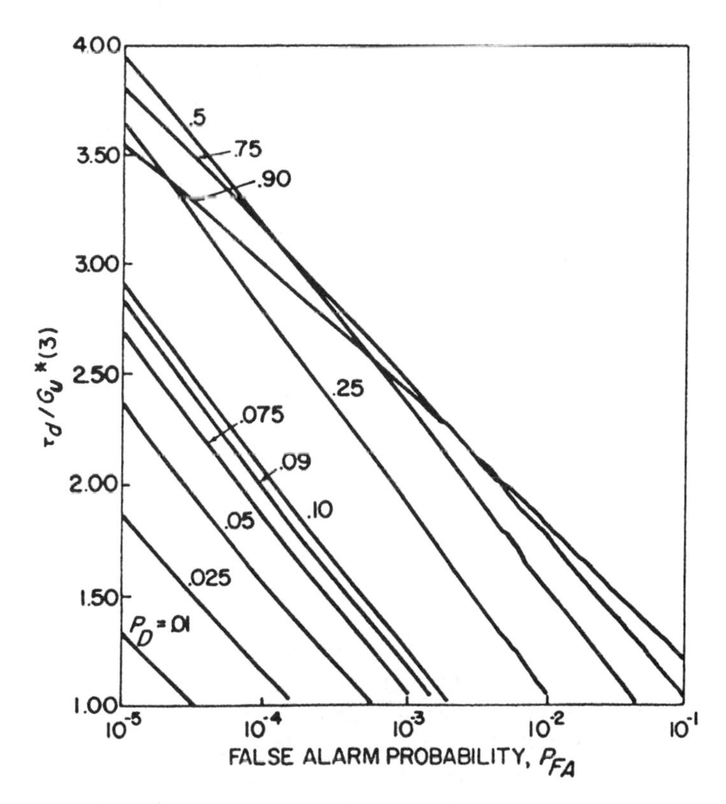

Figure 1.21. Acquisition performance improvement factor for three-dwell system over single dwell system versus false alarm probability with detection probability as a parameter; $\gamma' = -20$ dB.

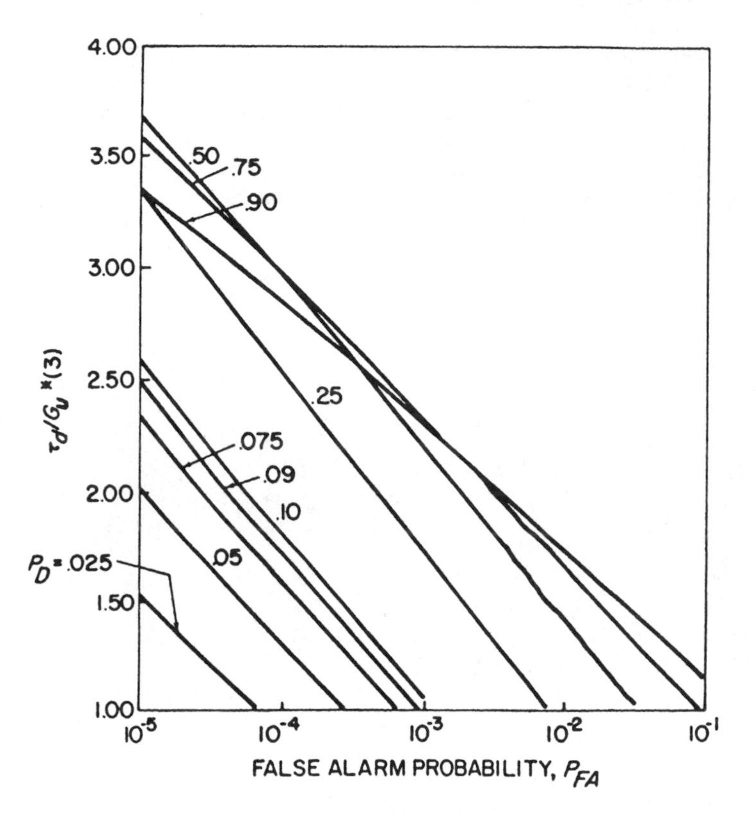

Figure 1.22. Acquisition performance improvement factor for three-dwell system over single dwell system versus false alarm probability with detection probability as a parameter; $\gamma' = -10$ dB.

and corresponding dwell times

$$\tau_{d1}^* < \tau_{d2}^* < \cdots < \tau_{d,N-1}^* \tag{1.150}$$

there exists a minimum of the function $G_u(N)$, namely,

$$G_u^*(N) = \tau_{d1}^* + P_{FA1}^*(\tau_{d2}^* - \tau_{d1}^*) + P_{FA2}^*(\tau_{d3}^* - \tau_{d2}^*)$$
$$+ \cdots + P_{FA,N-1}^*(\tau_{dN} - \tau_{d,N-1}^*). \tag{1.151}$$

The ratio $\tau_d/G_u^*(N)$ is then a measure of the minimum improvement in acquisition performance of the N-dwell system over the single dwell system. Note that obtaining (1.151) requires an $(N-1)$-dimensional minimization. Figures 1.21 and 1.22 illustrate the relative performance improvement results for a three-dwell system ($N = 3$) analogous to those given in Figures 1.19 and 1.20, respectively, for the two-dwell system. Once again as the detection probability P_D approaches unity, the performance improvement ratio $\tau_d/G_u^*(3)$ approaches unity.

1.4 A UNIFIED APPROACH TO SERIAL SEARCH ACQUISITION WITH FIXED DWELL TIMES

We now present a unified approach [14] to predicting the performance of serial search acquisition systems which employ fixed dwell time detector structures. Included as special cases in this generalized approach are the single dwell time system and the multiple dwell time system discussed in Sections 1.2 and 1.3, respectively, as well as a fast decision-rate matched filter acquisition system, which will be discussed in detail in Section 1.5. The restriction of the approach to systems with predetermined and fixed dwell times[25] is based upon the desire to utilize the discrete Markov nature of the imbedded process in such systems to allow application of the flow graph techniques previously demonstrated. We begin our discussion with a description and analysis of a generalized flow graph technique suitable for predicting the acquisition performance of serial search fixed dwell time systems.

1.4.1 The Flow Graph Technique

Consider a generalized serial search system of the type mentioned above where H_1 denotes the hypothesis that the received and local codes are misaligned by less than a code chip (previously designated as a "hit") and H_0 the alternate hypothesis, i.e., the relative alignment is greater than or equal to a chip. The discrete Markovian nature of the underlying process of such a system allows it to be represented by a $\nu + 2$-state flow graph, where $\nu - 1$ of the states belong to the cells corresponding to H_0, and one state (the ν-th) corresponds to H_1. Since, depending on the actual value of relative offset (misalignment) between the codes, up to either $2q/N_u$ or $(2q/N_u) - 1$ cells correspond to H_1 (recall that N_u/q corresponds to the fractional search update in chips), and the total number of cells for H_0 and H_1 combined is q, then ν is determined from either

$$\nu - 1 + \frac{2q}{N_u} = q \tag{1.152a}$$

or

$$\nu - 1 + \frac{2q}{N_u} - 1 = q. \tag{1.152b}$$

These ν states are indexed in a circular arrangement (see Figure 1.23) with the i-th state, $i = 1, 2, \ldots, q - 1$ corresponding to the i-th offset code phase position to the right of the "true" sync position (H_1). The remaining two states are the *false alarm* (FA) *state* and the *correct acquisition* (ACQ)

[25] This excludes schemes based on sequential detection methods, which will be discussed by themselves later on in the chapter.

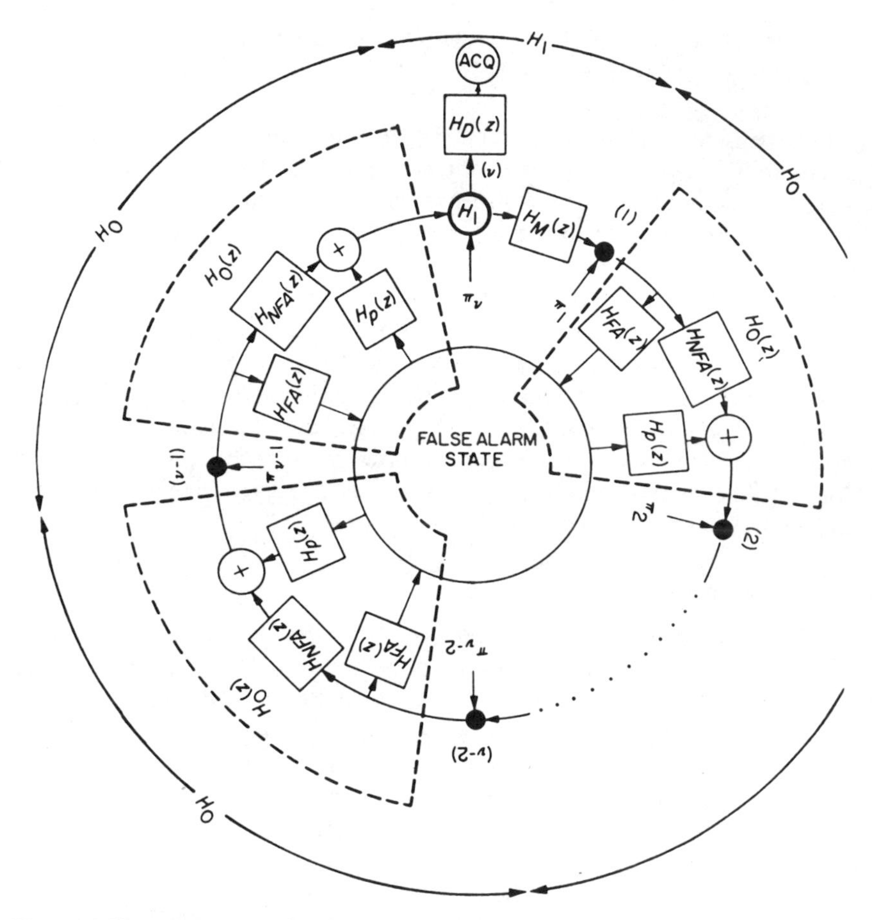

Figure 1.23. A flow graph representation of a generalized serial search acquisition system—the circular state diagram.

state. These are also indicated in Figure 1.23 where it is observed that the acquisition state can be directly reached only from the ν-th (H_1) state, whereas the false alarm state can be directly reached from any of the $\nu - 1$ states corresponding to the offset cells (H_0).

A flow graph model such as that illustrated in Figure 1.23 is an exact representation of the state transition diagram of serial search acquisition systems with no absolute limit on acquisition time. Although we are primarily interested in this class of systems (since their underlying process is indeed Markovian), we shall briefly mention at the conclusion of this section how the above model can be used in the presence of a finite limit on acquisition time.

The first way in which the flow graph model of Figure 1.23 is a generalization of those previously considered is that the *a priori* probability distribution $\{\pi_j;\ j = 1, 2, \ldots, \nu\}$ assigned to the ν states at which the search process can be entered is *arbitrary*. In the absence of any *a priori* information concerning the initial relative position of the codes, the system designer would assign a uniform distribution to the model, i.e., $\{\pi_j = 1/\nu;\ j = 1, 2, \ldots, \nu\}$. This is the case which we have discussed thus far. Another special case of the more general formulation might be a worst case distribution ($\pi_1 = 1,\ \pi_j = 0;\ j \neq 1$) corresponding to an initial relative code position furthest from the correct sync position.

The second way in which Figure 1.23 is a generalization of the previous notions is that each branch of the flow graph is assigned a generalized gain $H(z)$ which characterizes all possible ways by which the process can move along that branch. The significance of the subscripts on these branches is as follows:

$H_D(z)$ = gain for verification of detection
$H_M(z)$ = gain for missed verification of detection
$H_{FA}(z)$ = gain for false alarm occurrence
$H_{NFA}(z)$ = gain for no false alarm occurrence
$H_p(z)$ = gain for penalty after false alarm occurrence

Proper combination of these gains then allows computation of the gain associated with the "generalized" branch between any pair of nodes, e.g.,

$$H_0(z) = H_{NFA}(z) + H_{FA}(z)H_p(z) \tag{1.153}$$

represents the gain in going from node i to node $i+1$ for $i = 1, 2, \ldots, \nu - 1$.

As before, the flow graph representation of the system is used to compute the moment generating function $U(z)$ of the underlying acquisition process. Using standard flow graph reduction techniques, it can be shown [14] that

$$U(z) = \frac{H_D(z)}{1 - H_M(z)H_0^{\nu-1}(z)} \sum_{i=1}^{\nu} \pi_i H_0^{\nu-i}(z). \tag{1.154}$$

For the two special cases of uniform and worst case *a priori* state probability distributions, (1.154) reduces to

$$U(z) = \frac{1}{\nu}\,\frac{H_D(z)(1 - H_0^{\nu}(z))}{(1 - H_M(z)H_0^{\nu-1}(z))(1 - H_0(z))},\ \text{(uniform)} \tag{1.155a}$$

and

$$U(z) = \frac{H_D(z)H_0^{\nu-1}(z)}{1 - H_M(z)H_0^{\nu-1}(z)},\ \text{(worst case)}. \tag{1.155b}$$

The complete statistical description of the acquisition process is obtained by substituting for the various $H(z)$'s in (1.154) the expressions appropriate to the particular configuration at hand and then, as before, expanding the result in a power series in z (see (1.94)). In general, obtaining the complete set of coefficients of this series is a difficult task and approximations must be made in the manner discussed in [7]. Alternately, if one is pleased with the first few moments of the acquisition time, then the relations of (1.3) and (1.6) as applied to $U(z)$ of (1.154) or its special cases in (1.155) are appropriate. In particular, for the mean acquisition time $\overline{T}_{ACQ}$, we obtain from (1.3) and (1.155) the results

$$\underset{\text{(uniform)}}{\overline{T}_{ACQ}} = \tau_d \times \begin{cases} P_{ACQ}\left\{ \dfrac{H_D'(1)}{H_D(1)} + \dfrac{H_0'(1)}{1 - H_0(1)} - \dfrac{\nu H_0'(1) H_0^{\nu-1}(1)}{1 - H_0^{\nu}(1)} \right. \\ \qquad \left. + \dfrac{(\nu - 1) H_M(1) H_0^{\nu-2}(1) H_0'(1) + H_M'(1) H_0^{\nu-1}(1)}{1 - H_M(1) H_0^{\nu-1}(1)} \right\} \\ \quad \ldots \text{if } H_0(1) < 1 \\ \dfrac{1}{H_D(1)}\left[H_D'(1) + H_M'(1) + (\nu - 1) H_0'(1)\left(1 - \dfrac{H_D(1)}{2}\right)\right] \\ \quad \ldots \text{if } H_0(1) = 1 \end{cases} \tag{1.156a}$$

and

$$\underset{\text{(worst case)}}{\overline{T}_{ACQ}} = \tau_d \times \begin{cases} \dfrac{P_{ACQ}}{H_D(1)}\left\{ H_D'(1) + H_M'(1) P_{ACQ} + (\nu - 1)\dfrac{H_0'(1)}{H_0(1)} \right. \\ \qquad \left. \times \left(H_D(1) + H_M(1) P_{ACQ} \right) \right\} \ldots \text{if } H_0(1) < 1 \\ \dfrac{1}{H_D(1)}\left[H_D'(1) + H_M'(1) + (\nu - 1) H_0'(1) \right] \\ \ldots \text{if } H_0(1) = 1 \end{cases} \tag{1.156b}$$

where the primed quantities denote differentiation with respect to z, i.e., $H'(1) = d/dz\, H(z)|_{z=1}$, and

$$P_{ACQ} \triangleq P_{ACQ}(\infty) = U(1) = \sum_{i=0}^{\infty} p_i \tag{1.157}$$

i.e., the probability of acquiring after any number of dwells (see (1.98)). Furthermore, note that in the case $H_0(1) = 1$, (1.154) and (1.157) combine to yield

$$P_{ACQ} = \frac{H_D(1)}{1 - H_M(1)} = 1 \tag{1.158}$$

since it is always true from Figure 1.23 that $H_D(1) + H_M(1) = 1$. Hence the case $H_0(1) = 1$ effectively corresponds to the existence of only one absorbing state, namely ACQ.

Table 1.1
Branch gains for single and multiple dwell systems.

Gain	Single Dwell	Multiple (N) Dwell
$H_p(z)$	z^K	z_N^K
$H_D(z)$	$P_D z$	$\prod_{i=1}^{N} P_{Di\|i-1} z_i = P_D \prod_{i=1}^{N} z_i$
$H_M(z)$	$(1 - P_D)z$	$\sum_{j=2}^{N} \left(\prod_{i=1}^{j-1} P_{Di\|i-1} z_i \right)(1 - P_{Dj\|j-1}) z_j + (1 - P_{D1\|0}) z_1$
$H_{FA}(z)$	$P_{FA} z$	$\prod_{i=1}^{N} P_{FAi\|i-1} z_i = P_{FA} \prod_{i=1}^{N} z_i$
$H_{NFA}(z)$	$(1 - P_{FA})z$	$\sum_{j=2}^{N} \left(\prod_{i=1}^{j-1} P_{FAi\|i-1} z_i \right)(1 - P_{FAj\|j-1}) z_j + (1 - P_{FA1\|0}) z_1$

As simple examples of the application of the unified approach just described, we cite the single and multiple dwell serial search acquisition systems for which the branch gains are shown in Table 1.1.[26] Taking the derivative(s) of these gains as required in (1.56a) and evaluating them with their argument(s) equated to unity produces results identical to (1.3) and (1.112) with $\nu = q$ (i.e., H_1 contains only one cell). Alternately, for the single dwell system with worst case *a priori* probability distribution, we get the additional result

$$\underset{\text{(worse case)}}{\bar{T}_{ACQ}} = \frac{1}{P_D}\left[1 + (q-1)(1 + KP_{FA})\right]\tau_d \tag{1.159}$$

where again we have set $\nu = q$.

As previously mentioned, ν will almost always exceed q in accordance with either (1.152a) or (1.152b). Thus, we now enter into a brief discussion of how to modify the flow graph to account for the fact that the H_1 region actually contains $2q/N_u$ [or $(2q/N_u) - 1$] cells rather than just the single (ν-th) cell shown in Figure 1.23. For example, consider a single dwell system with half-chip search update ($q/N_u = 2$) and let Q_1, Q_2, Q_3, Q_4 denote the four (possibly only three) cells corresponding to the four possible values of relative code misalignment with magnitude less than a chip (i.e., within the triangular correlation curve). Then, the H_1 region of the flow graph expands as in Figure 1.24, where $P_D(Q_i)$; $i = 1, 2, 3, 4$ denotes the detection prob-

[26] For the multiple dwell case, the gains $H(z)$ should actually be written as $H(\mathbf{z})$ where $\mathbf{z}$ is the vector $[z_1, z_2, \ldots, z_N]$. Also, the prime notation in (1.156) now refers to an N-dimensional partial differentiation with respect to the N complements of $\mathbf{z}$ with each component set equal to unity.

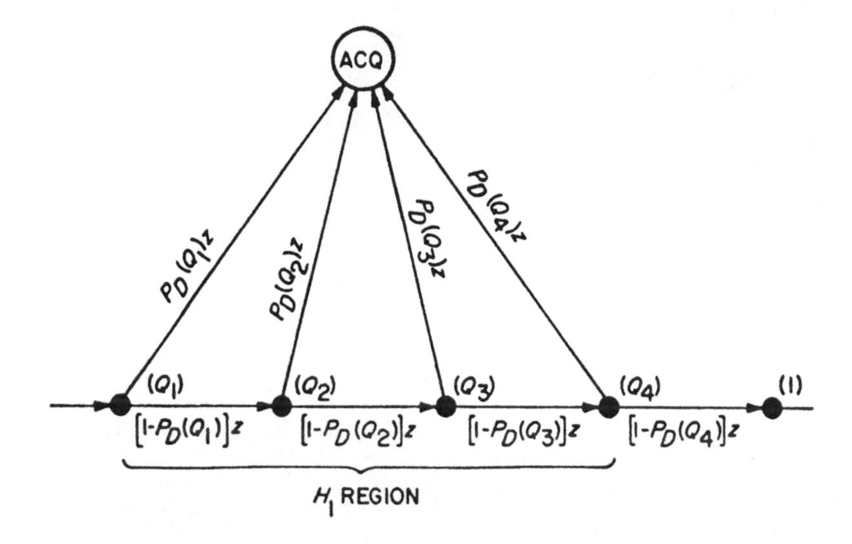

Figure 1.24. Expansion of the H_1 region for a single dwell serial search system indicating the effect of multiple cells with non-zero correlation.

ability evaluated via (1.71) or (1.80) at the relative code misalignment corresponding to Q_i. Thus, instead of the simple entries of $H_D(z)$ and $H_M(z)$ as in Table 1.1, we now have

$$H_D(z) = \sum_{j=1}^{4} \left(\prod_{i=1}^{j-1} (1 - P_D(Q_i)) P_D(Q_j) \right) z^j \tag{1.160}$$

and

$$\begin{aligned} H_M(z) &= \prod_{j=1}^{4} (1 - P_D(Q_j)) z \\ &= \left[\prod_{j=1}^{4} (1 - P_D(Q_j)) \right] z^4. \end{aligned} \tag{1.161}$$

As promised, we conclude this section with a discussion of how to apply the flow graph model to the limited acquisition time case. We recall from the introduction that this case is characterized by the requirement to achieve acquisition (with a given probability) within a finite time, say T_s. Thus, the appropriate performance measure to use here is the probability that the acquisition time T_{ACQ} is less than T_s, which can be calculated by evaluating the cumulative distribution function of T_{ACQ} at T_s. Alternately, if T_s corresponds to J dwells, then we are interested in the probability $P_{ACQ}(J)$

of acquisition in J or fewer dwells as given by a relation analogous to (1.98), which can be evaluated by finding the generating function corresponding to this cumulative probability distribution. Such a generating function is defined by

$$V(z) \triangleq \sum_{j=0}^{\infty}\left(\sum_{i=0}^{j} p_j\right) z^j, \tag{1.162}$$

which can be written in the form

$$\begin{aligned} V(z) &= \sum_{j=0}^{\infty} p_j \sum_{i=j}^{\infty} z^i \\ &= \sum_{j=0}^{\infty} p_j z^j \sum_{i=0}^{\infty} z^i \\ &= \frac{1}{1-z} \sum_{j=0}^{\infty} p_j z^j. \end{aligned} \tag{1.163}$$

Comparing (1.163) with (1.94), we observe that

$$V(z) = \frac{1}{1-z} U(z). \tag{1.164}$$

Since $P_{ACQ}(J)$ is the coefficient of z^J in the power series of (1.162), we can evaluate it with a contour integral analogous to that used to evaluate inverse z transforms, i.e.,

$$\begin{aligned} P_{ACQ}(J) &= \frac{1}{2\pi j} \oint_{\Gamma} \frac{V(z)}{z^{J+1}}\, dz \\ &= \frac{1}{2\pi j} \oint_{\Gamma} \frac{U(z)}{(1-z) z^{J+1}}\, dz \end{aligned} \tag{1.165}$$

where $U(z)$ is given by (1.154) and Γ is a counterclockwise closed contour in the region of convergence of $V(z)$ that encircles the origin.

1.5 RAPID ACQUISITION USING MATCHED FILTER TECHNIQUES

Until now, we have considered only DS acquisition techniques in which the measure of PN correlation was produced by an *active* correlation of the received signal with a locally generated PN reference. For example, in the single dwell serial search system, the received PN signal plus noise was multiplied by the local PN reference and subsequently (after square-law envelope detection to remove the unknown information modulation and unknown carrier phase) integrated for τ_d seconds, the result of which was used to make an acquisition decision by comparison with a threshold. Such a *multiply-and-integrate* type of correlation/detector structure is typified by the fact that the local PN generator is running continuously, and hence, a completely *new* set of $M = \tau_d/T_c$ chips of the received signal is used for each successive threshold test. This poses a basic limitation on the search speed since the local PN reference phase can be updated (slewed) only at τ_d-second intervals (assuming the threshold test fails). Thus, if the search is conducted in $1/N$-chip increments, the search rate $\mathscr{R}_{1D}$ of the single dwell serial search technique is

$$\mathscr{R}_{1D} = 1/\tau_d \quad 1/N\text{-chip positions per second.} \tag{1.166}$$

The search rate of a DS acquisition scheme can be significantly increased by replacing the multiply-and-integrate operation with a *passive* correlator device such as a matched filter (MF). This device can be implemented either as a continuous time or discrete time operation, and with such candidate state-of-the-art technologies as charge coupled devices (CCD's), surface acoustic wave (SAW) convolvers, and discrete time correlators [34], [36], [37].

In the continuous time case, the received PN waveform plus noise is convolved with a fixed finite segment of the PN waveform corresponding to, say, M chips and the continuous time output is tested against a threshold to determine when acquisition has occurred. In this configuration, the input continuously slides past the stationary (not running in time) stored PN waveform replica until the two are in synchronism, at which point the threshold ideally would be exceeded and the local PN generator enabled. Since, as discussed in the introduction, in DS/SS systems the PN spreading waveform is typically biphase modulated on a carrier whose phase is as yet unknown at the receiver, the matched filter acquisition system must be implemented either in a band-pass version (Figure 1.25a) or an equivalent low-pass version (Figure 1.25b). In the former case, a band-pass matched filter is used whose maximum output is detected by a square-law envelope detector. In the latter case, inphase and quadrature carriers with arbitrary phase but known or estimated frequency are used to demodulate the received signal followed by baseband matched filtering of each demodulated signal. The matched filter outputs are then non-coherently combined to produce the desired correlation measure for threshold testing.

Conceptually, the implementation of a matched filter for a finite length PN waveform is most easily visualized in the form of a tapped delay line followed by a passive filter matched to a *single* PN chip waveform (Figure 1.26). To see how this comes about, we recall that a matched filter is generically a passive device that maximizes the signal-to-noise ratio at its output when the signal at its input is imbedded in additive white Gaussian noise. Mathematically speaking, for an input signal $s(t)$ of duration T_o seconds, the impulse response $h(t)$ of the matched filter is given by the reverse of $s(t)$ in its T_o-sccond time slot, i.e.,

$$h(t) = \begin{cases} s(T_o - t); & 0 \le t \le T_o \\ 0; & \text{otherwise} \end{cases} \tag{1.167}$$

Figure 1.25a. A band-pass version of a matched filter acquisition system.

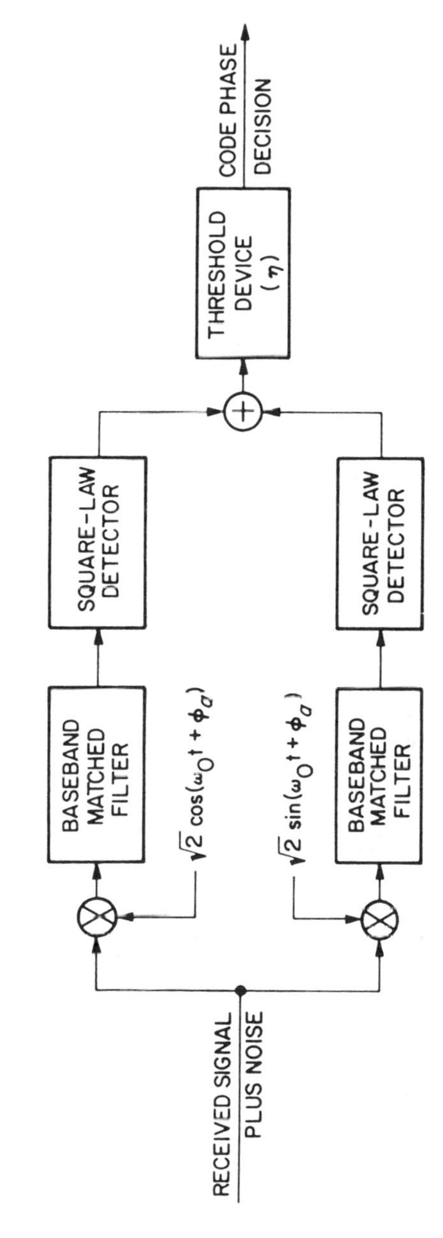

Figure 1.25b. A low-pass version of a matched filter acquisition system.

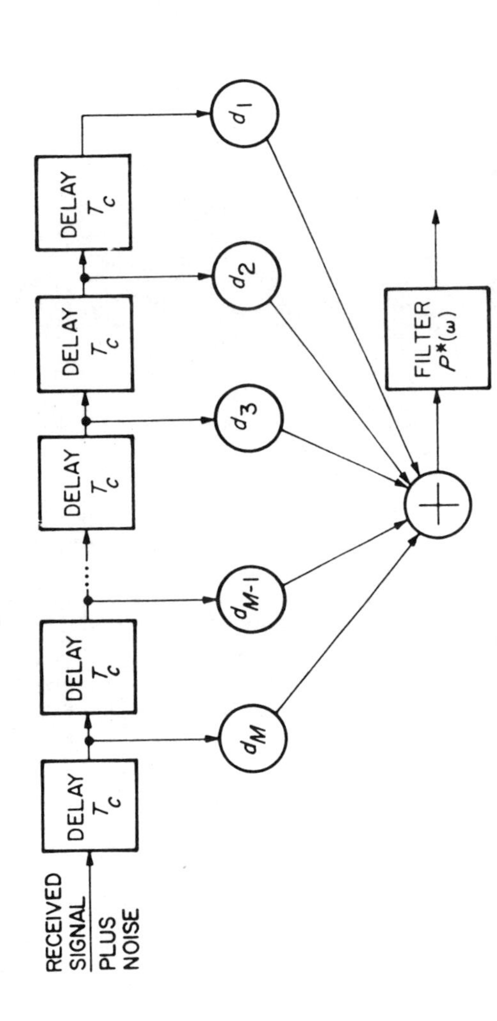

Figure 1.26. A tapped delay line implementation of a matched filter for an M-chip PN sequence.

or in terms of Fourier transforms

$$H(\omega) = S^*(\omega)e^{-j\omega T_o}. \tag{1.168}$$

Suppose now that $s(t)$ corresponds to an M-chip segment of a PN waveform, i.e., $T_o = MT_c$. Then,

$$s(t) = \sum_{n=1}^{M} d_n p[t-(n-1)T_c] \tag{1.169}$$

where d_n is the polarity (± 1) of the n-th chip and $p(t)$ is the basic chip pulse shape. For a baseband matched filter, we would have

$$p(t) = \begin{cases} 1; & 0 \le t \le T_c \\ 0; & \text{otherwise} \end{cases} \tag{1.170}$$

whereas for a band-pass matched filter,

$$p(t) = \begin{cases} \sqrt{2}\cos\omega_0 t; & 0 \le t \le T_c \\ 0; & \text{otherwise.} \end{cases} \tag{1.171}$$

Taking the Fourier transform of (1.169) and substituting its complex conjugate into (1.168) results in

$$H(\omega) = P^*(\omega)\sum_{n=1}^{M} d_n e^{-j\omega(M-n+1)T_c}, \tag{1.172}$$

which has the implementation illustrated in Figure 1.26 as previously stated.

As a prelude to our discussion of the discrete time version of the matched filter acquisition system, consider the output $\tilde{x}(t)$ of the baseband matched filter for an input $x(t)$, i.e.,

$$\begin{aligned}\tilde{x}(t) &= \int_0^{\infty} x(t-\tau)h(\tau)\,d\tau \\ &= \int_0^{T_o} x(t-\tau)s(T_o-\tau)\,d\tau \\ &= \int_0^{T_o} x(t+\zeta-T_o)s(\zeta)\,d\zeta. \end{aligned} \tag{1.173}$$

Of course, for $x(t) = s(t)$, $\tilde{x}(t)$ achieves its maximum value at $t = T_o$, namely,

$$\tilde{x}(T_o) = \int_0^{T_o} s^2(\zeta)\,d\zeta. \tag{1.174}$$

For any other $x(t)$, e.g., a time shift of $s(t)$, and $s(t)$ as in (1.169), we can write (1.173) as

$$\begin{aligned}\tilde{x}(t) &= \int_0^{MT_c} x(t+\zeta-MT_c)\sum_{n=1}^{M} d_n p(\zeta-(n-1)T_c)\,d\zeta \\ &= \sum_{n=1}^{M} d_n \int_{(n-1)T_c}^{nT_c} x(t+\zeta-MT_c)\,d\zeta. \end{aligned} \tag{1.175}$$

Suppose now that we sample $\tilde{x}(t)$ at time instants $t = (M + k/N)T_c$; $k = 0, 1, 2, \ldots$, i.e., at a multiple N of the chip rate. Then

$$\tilde{x}\left(\left(M + \frac{k}{N}\right)T_c\right) \triangleq \tilde{x}_k = \sum_{n=1}^{M} d_n \int_{(n-1)T_c}^{nT_c} x\left(\frac{k}{N}T_c + \zeta\right) d\zeta$$

$$= \sum_{n=1}^{M} d_n \sum_{i=1}^{N} \int_{((n-1)N+i-1)\frac{T_c}{N}}^{((n-1)N+i)\frac{T_c}{N}} x\left(\frac{k}{N}T_c + \zeta\right) d\zeta$$

$$= \sum_{i=1}^{NM} \mathscr{D}_i X_{i+k} \tag{1.176}$$

where

$$X_j = \int_{(j-1)\frac{T_c}{N}}^{j\frac{T_c}{N}} x(\xi)\, d\xi \tag{1.177}$$

and $\mathscr{D}_j$ is the j-th *sub*chip polarity which is related to the n-th chip polarity d_n by

$$\mathscr{D}_{(n-1)N+i} = d_n; \quad \begin{array}{l} i = 1, 2, \ldots, N \\ n = 1, 2, \ldots, M. \end{array} \tag{1.178}$$

Equation (1.176) is in the form of a discrete time correlation that can be implemented either in analog or digital form using a tapped delay line or shift register respectively (see Figures 1.27a and 1.27b). In the latter case, the contents of the shift register which holds the signal samples digitized to one bit and the holding register which permanently contains the fixed segment of the code used for comparison are correlated by comparing them stage by stage, generating a "+1" if the two stages match and a "−1" if they don't, and summing the resulting set of "1's" and "−1's."

Using either the analog or digital correlator of Figure 1.27a or 1.27b as matched filters in Figure 1.25b results in the discrete time version of the matched filter rapid acquisition system. Since for either correlator configuration the outputs occur and are ultimately (after squaring and summing) threshold tested at N times the chip rate, the search rate for this acquisition method is clearly

$$\mathscr{R}_{MF} = N/T_c \quad 1/N\text{-chip positions per second,} \tag{1.179}$$

which is a factor of $N\tau_d/T_c = NM$ faster than that of the serial search technique. This large apparent improvement in search rate, or equivalently, the time to search over the total uncertainty region, is a consequence of the fact that in the MF system, only one *new* fractional $(1/N)$ chip of received signal is used for each correlation test since the prior $NM - 1$ received signal samples are already stored in the tapped delay line or shift register. Because of this fact, however, it would appear that the noise-corrupted correlation values from test to test would be highly correlated because of the $NM - 1$ sample overlap as contrasted to the same test values in the single dwell serial search method which are clearly independent of one another because of the disjoint observations. Nevertheless, it can be shown [14] that, despite the overlap, the underlying acquisition process is still Markov and hence the flow graph model of the unified approach discussed in Section 1.4 can be used to determine its acquisition time performance.

Before proceeding to a discussion of the acquisition time performance, we first complete the description of the system by presenting a method of verification of the threshold crossing event. In particular, the non-coherent correlator/detector structure of Figure 1.25b is followed by a *coincidence*

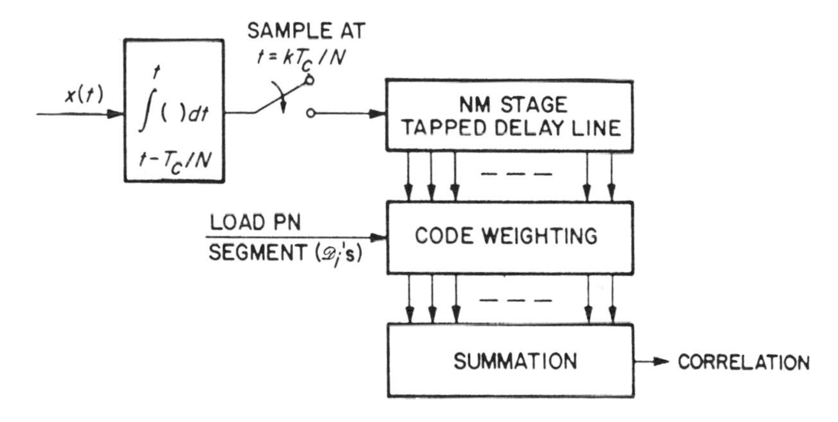

Figure 1.27a. An analog correlator implementation of a matched filter.

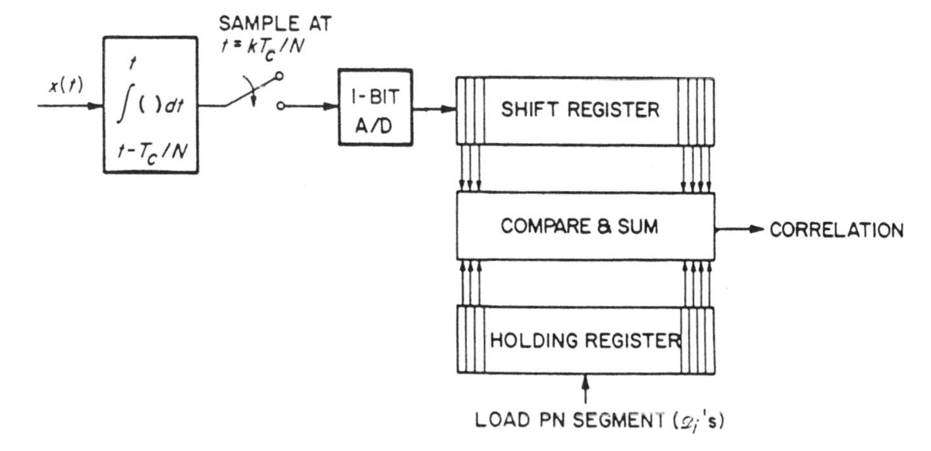

Figure 1.27b. A digital correlator implementation of a matched filter.

detector (CD) whose operation is as follows. Upon a tentative decision of an "in-sync" condition (corresponding to hypothesis H_1), the local PN segment used for code weighting in Figure 1.27a or stored in the holding register of Figure 1.27b is now updated by the local PN generator so that for a specified interval of time, say T_p, the input code and local code segment remain at a fixed relative time offset. During this time interval, the non-coherent correlator/detector continues to make threshold tests; however, to strengthen the reliability of the verification operation performed by the CD these tests are now conducted over disjoint MT_c sec time intervals of the received waveform and are thus statistically independent. If A of these tests are performed in the time interval T_p, i.e., $T_p = AMT_c$, then the rule used by the CD for final acceptance of the H_1 hypothesis is that B out of A of these correspond to threshold crossings. Upon successful completion of this majority logic decision, the tracking loop is activated, whereas upon unsuccessful completion (fewer than B out of A threshold crossings), the local code segment again is held fixed and the search continues.

1.5.1 Markov Chain Acquisition Model and Acquisition Time Performance

The flow diagram for the matched filter acquisition system is a special case of Figure 1.23 where, for the simple case of only one cell leading to the acquisition state ACQ,

$$H_p(z) = 0$$

$$H_0(z) = H_{NFA}(z) = \left[(1 - P_{FA_0}) + P_{FA_0}(1 - P_{FA_1})z^K\right]z$$

$$H_D(z) = P_{D_0}P_{D_1}z^{K+1} = P_D z^{K+1}$$

$$H_M(z) = \left[(1 - P_{D_0}) + P_{D_0}(1 - P_{D_1})z^K\right]z. \tag{1.180}$$

In the above, P_{D_0} and P_{FA_0} denote the detection and false alarm probabilities of the correlation detector (probability of threshold exceedance under H_1 and H_0, respectively) and P_{D_1} and P_{FA_1} are the analogous probabilities of the coincidence detector (probability of B threshold exceedances out of A tests under H_1 and H_0, respectively). Furthermore, since the effective dwell time τ_d (i.e., the time spent in examining each cell under hypothesis H_0 in the absence of a false alarm) in the matched filter system is T_c/N, then equating the false alarm penalty time $T_p = AMT_c$ of the coincidence detector with $K\tau_d = KT_c/N$, gives $K = ANM$.

From (1.180), we observe that $H_0(1) = 1 - P_{FA_0}P_{FA_1} = 1 - P_{FA} < 1$ and thus from (1.154), (1.157), and (1.180),

$$P_{ACQ} = \frac{P_D}{1 - (1 - P_D)(1 - P_{FA})^{\nu - 1}} \sum_{i=1}^{\nu} \pi_i (1 - P_{FA})^{\nu - i} < 1, \tag{1.181}$$

which is also implied by the presence here of an absorbing false alarm state. Such an absorbing false alarm state comes about when the correlation detector produces a threshold exceedance under H_0 and the coincidence detector verifies it with a B out of A majority logic decision producing a termination of the search. For the uniform and worst case *a priori* probability distributions, (1.181) reduces to

$$P_{ACQ} = \begin{cases} \left(\dfrac{P_D}{P_{FA}}\right)\dfrac{1-(1-P_{FA})^{\nu}}{1-(1-P_D)(1-P_{FA})^{\nu-1}} & \text{(uniform)} \\ \dfrac{P_D(1-P_{FA})^{\nu-1}}{1-(1-P_D)(1-P_{FA})^{\nu-1}} & \text{(worst case)} \end{cases} \tag{1.182}$$

and the mean acquisition time under these same conditions becomes

$$\overline{T}_{ACQ} = \begin{cases} P_{ACQ}\left\{(K+1) + \dfrac{\nu(1-P_{FA})^{\nu-2}}{1-(1-P_{FA})^{\nu}}\left[\left(\dfrac{P_{ACQ}}{P_D}\right)P_{FA}(1-P_{FA})\overline{T}_M\right.\right. \\ \left. + \overline{T}_0\left[-(1-P_{FA}) + \dfrac{P_{ACQ}}{P_D}\left((1-P_{FA})^{2-\nu} - (1-P_D)(1-P_{FA})\right.\right.\right. \\ \left.\left.\left. + (\nu-1)P_{FA}(1-P_D)\right)\right]\right\}\tau_d & \text{(uniform)} \\ \dfrac{P_{ACQ}}{P_D}\left\{(K+1)P_D + \overline{T}_M P_{ACQ}\right. \\ \left. + (\nu-1)\overline{T}_0\dfrac{P_D + P_{ACQ}(1-P_D)}{1-P_{FA}}\right\}\tau_d & \text{(worst case)} \end{cases} \tag{1.183}$$

where $\overline{T}_0$ and $\overline{T}_M$ are defined as

$$\begin{aligned} \overline{T}_0 &= (1-P_{FA_0}) + (K+1)P_{FA_0}(1-P_{FA_1}) \\ \overline{T}_M &= (1-P_{D_0}) + (K+1)P_{D_0}(1-P_{D_1}). \end{aligned} \tag{1.184}$$

When the H_1 region contains more than one cell, the flow graph of this region expands as in Figure 1.28, which is drawn for the special case of $N = 1$ (two cells, namely Q_1 and Q_2). Under these circumstances, $H_D(z)$ and $H_M(z)$ of (1.180) are modified to become

$$\begin{aligned} H_D(z) = \Big\{P_D(Q_1) + P_D(Q_2)\big[&(1-P_{D_0}(Q_1))z \\ &+ P_{D_0}(Q_1)(1-P_{D_1}(Q_1))z^{K+1}\big]\Big\}z^{K+1} \end{aligned} \tag{1.185a}$$

and

$$H_M(z) = \prod_{i=1}^{2}\left[(1-P_{D_0}(Q_i))z + P_{D_0}(Q_i)(1-P_{D_1}(Q_i))z^{K+1}\right]. \tag{1.185b}$$

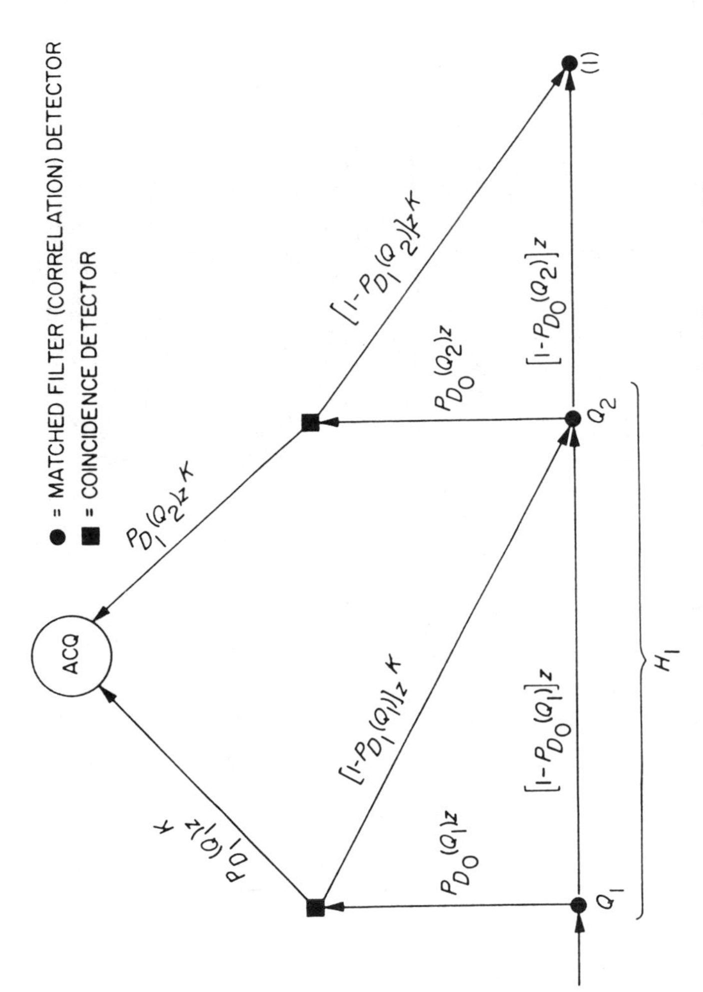

Figure 1.28. Flow graph of the H_1 region for the matched filter acquisition system.

1.5.2 Evaluation of Detection and False Alarm Probabilities for Correlation and Coincidence Detectors

In order to apply the results for P_{ACQ} and $\overline{T}_{ACQ}$ of the rapid acquisition non-coherent receiver as per (1.182) and (1.183), one needs to calculate the detection and false alarm probabilities for both the non-coherent correlation detector (P_{d_0}, P_{FA_0}) and the coincidence detector (P_{d_1}, P_{FA_1}). Computations of this nature were previously performed in Section 1.2.4 for the non-coherent detector associated with the single dwell time acquisition system. While, in principle, the problems are quite similar, we shall soon see that many of the simplifying assumptions made in the previous analysis are not valid here for the matched filter system. Nevertheless, having gone through the details of such an analysis in Section 1.2.4, our presentation here will be brief with emphasis placed on the differences between the two.

First, unlike (1.58), the signal component of the inputs to the square-law detectors in Figure 1.25b is treated as a random variable reflecting the partial correlation effect produced by correlating the input code with the stored reference code over a *finite* time interval which is much less than the code period. In particular, if $\sqrt{2}Ac(t+\tau)$ denotes the input PN code delayed by τ with respect to an arbitrary time reference and $c(t+\hat{\tau})$ denotes the corresponding local reference code, then, when the correlation time MT_c is much less than the code time period pT_c, the correlation

$$C \triangleq \int_0^{MT_c} c(t+\tau)c(t+\hat{\tau})\,dt \tag{1.186}$$

is approximately a Gaussian random variable with mean and variance (conditioned on the hypothesis H_i; $i = 0, 1$) given by [3], [13], [14]

$$E\{C|H_i\} = \begin{cases} MT_c(1-|\varepsilon|); & i=1 \\ 0; & i=0 \end{cases} \tag{1.187a}$$

and

$$\operatorname{var}\{C|H_i\} = MT_c^2 G_i(\varepsilon) = MT_c^2 \begin{cases} \varepsilon^2; & i=1 \\ 1-2|\varepsilon|+2\varepsilon^2; & i=0 \end{cases} \tag{1.187b}$$

In (1.187),

$$\varepsilon = \left(\frac{\tau-\hat{\tau}}{T_c}\right) \pm N_\varepsilon T_c \tag{1.188}$$

denotes the fractional normalized (with respect to a chip) timing offset between the two codes where N_ε is the smallest integer such that ε lies in the interval $(-1, 1)$. Figure 1.29 illustrates the conditional mean and variance of

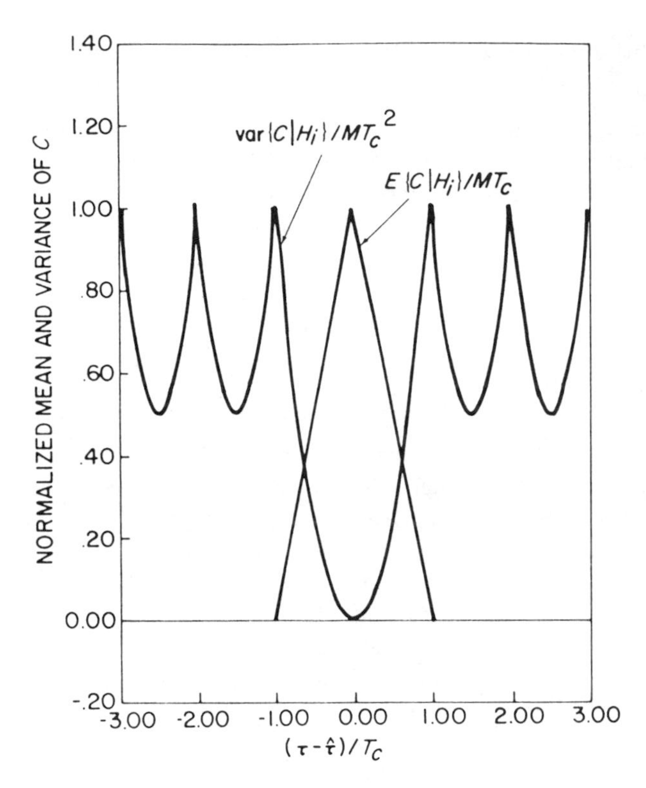

Figure 1.29. The normalized mean and variance of the partial correlation C as a function of the relative timing offset (normalized to the chip interval) between the incoming and local codes.

C for $|(\tau - \hat{\tau})/T_c| \leq 3$. The conditions under which the Gaussian assumption applies to the random variable C have been discussed in Volume II. In short, for $M \ll p$, C behaves like a binomial distribution and the additional constraint $M \gg 1$ causes the binomial distribution to behave like a Gaussian one.

The second difference concerns the validity of the Gaussian approximation to the decision statistic which in the single dwell time system allowed the false alarm and detection probabilities of (1.70) and (1.71) to be replaced by the simpler expressions in (1.79) and (1.80). We recall that the basis for validating this assumption was a central limit theorem argument based on the large values of pre-detection bandwidth–post-detection integration time product $B\tau_d$ typical of the single dwell time system. Since in a fast-decision rate acquisition system, like the matched filter receiver, post-detection integration is not feasible, the central limit argument made previously does not apply here. Instead one must use the exact probability distributions of the decision statistic under hypotheses H_0 and H_1 as determined from the solution to the problem of non-coherently detecting a Gaussian random variable (C) in additive "white" (bandlimited) Gaussian noise. Under certain circumstances, it is possible to simplify matters and obtain results similar to (1.70) and (1.71). Although these simplifications are based on Gaussian approximations to the mixture of two noise processes, one of which is signal dependent [14], it is to be re-emphasized that the assumption of a Gaussian test statistic remains invalid and thus expressions analogous to (1.79) and (1.80) are inappropriate.

1.5.2.1 Exact Results

Defining, analogous to (1.62), the *effective* signal-to-noise ratio γ_i under hypothesis H_i by

$$\gamma_i = \frac{E_c}{N_0} G_i(\varepsilon);\ i = 1, 2 \tag{1.189}$$

where $E_c/N_0 \triangleq A^2 T_c/N_0$ is the chip signal-to-noise ratio and $G_i(\varepsilon)$ is the normalized variance of the partial correlation C as defined in (1.186), then the false alarm probability P_{FA_0} and detection probability P_{D_0} of the matched filter (correlation) detector are given by [14]

$$P_{FA_0} = \sqrt{1 + 2\gamma_0} \int_{\eta^*/\sqrt{1+2\gamma_0}}^{\infty} \exp[-(1 + \gamma_0)y]\, I_0(\gamma_0 y)\, dy \tag{1.190}$$

and

$$P_{D_0} = \frac{1}{\sqrt{1 + 2\gamma_0}} \exp\left\{-\left(\frac{\gamma_1}{1 + 2\gamma_1}\right)\gamma_{pc}\right\} \sum_{k=0}^{\infty} F_k G_k \tag{1.191}$$

where

$$\eta^* \triangleq \frac{\eta}{N_0 M T_c} \tag{1.192}$$

is a normalization of the actual detection threshold η (see Figure 1.125b),

$$\gamma_{pc} \triangleq \frac{(E\{C|H_1\})^2}{\operatorname{var}\{C|H_1\}} = M\frac{(1 - |\varepsilon|)^2}{G_1(\varepsilon)} \tag{1.193}$$

is the signal-to-noise ratio associated with the partial correlation random variable C, and the coefficients F_k and G_k are evaluated recursively as

$$G_{k+1} = (\eta^*)^{k+1}\exp(-\eta^*) + (k + 1)G_k;\ G_0 = \exp(-\eta^*) \tag{1.194a}$$

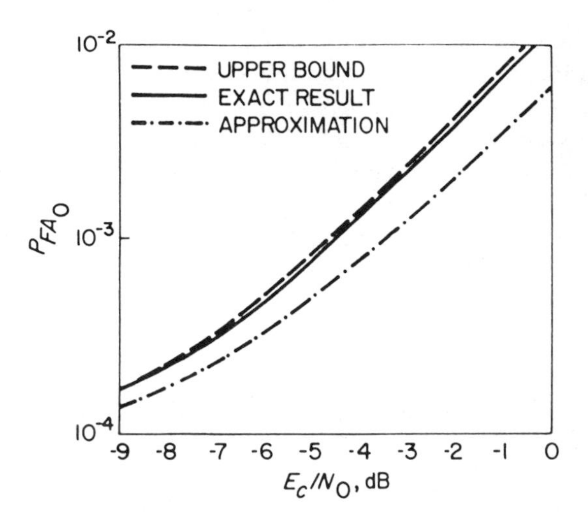

Figure 1.30a. P_{FA_0} versus E_c/N_0 for the matched filter detector with partial correlation ($\varepsilon = 1$, $\eta^* = 10$) (reprinted from [14]).

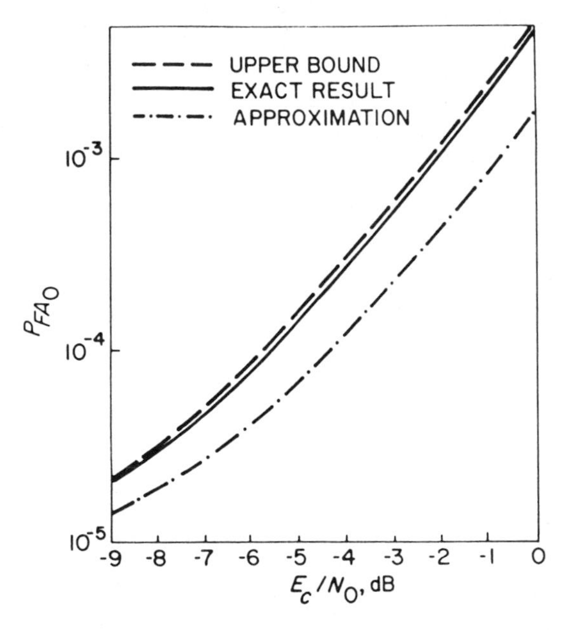

Figure 1.30b. P_{FA_0} versus E_c/N_0 for the matched filter detector with partial correlation ($\varepsilon = 1$, $\eta^* = 12.5$) (reprinted from [14]).

and

$$F_{k+1} = \frac{k + \frac{1}{2}}{(k+1)^2}\left(\frac{2\gamma_1}{1 + 2\gamma_1}\right)F_k + 2E_1E_{k+1}$$

$$E_{k+1} = \frac{1}{(k+1)^2}\left[\left(\frac{2\gamma_1}{1 + 2\gamma_1}\right)kE_k + E_1F_k\right]$$

$$F_0 = 1;\ E_1 = \frac{1}{2}\left(\frac{\sqrt{2\gamma_1\gamma_{pc}}}{1 + 2\gamma_1}\right). \tag{1.194b}$$

Figures 1.30a and 1.30b illustrate P_{FA_0} versus E_c/N_0 for $\varepsilon = 1$ ($\gamma_0 = E_c/N_0$) and normalized threshold values $\eta^* = 10$ and 12.5, respectively. Also shown is an upper bound on P_{FA_0} given by

$$P_{FA_0} \le \sqrt{1 + 2\gamma_0}\exp\left(-\frac{1 + \gamma_0}{1 + 2\gamma_0}\eta^*\right)I_0\left(\frac{\gamma_0}{1 + 2\gamma_0}\eta^*\right) \tag{1.195}$$

which over the region of E_c/N_0 illustrated is very tight. Figures 1.31a and 1.31b are the companion illustrations of P_{D_0} versus E_c/N_0 for $\varepsilon = 0, .5$ and $\eta^* = 7.5$, 10, and 12.5. Also, the matched filters are assumed to integrate over 64 chips.

1.5.2.2 Approximate Results

An approximate approach [14] valid for low E_c/N_0, where the partial correlation "noise" is small with respect to the dominant thermal noise, is to model the quadrature total noise components at the matched filter outputs as independent Gaussian random variables with variance

$$\sigma_i^2 = \frac{N_0}{2}\left[1 + \left(\frac{E_c}{N_0}\right)G_i(\varepsilon)\right];\ i = 0, 1, \tag{1.196}$$

which reflects the additive contributions of the thermal noise and partial correlation "noise" under hypothesis H_i. Under this assumption, the false alarm and detection probabilities of the matched filter detector simplify to

$$P_{FA_0} = \exp\left\{-\frac{\eta^*}{1 + \left(\frac{E_c}{N_0}\right)G_0(\varepsilon)}\right\} \tag{1.197}$$

and

$$P_{D_0} = 1 - \int_0^{\beta}\exp\{-(y + \Gamma)\}I_0(2\sqrt{\Gamma y})\,dy \tag{1.198}$$

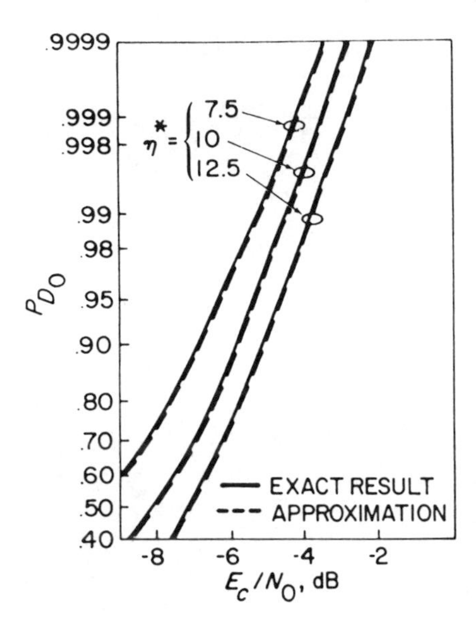

Figure 1.31a. P_{D_0} versus E_c/N_0 for the matched filter detector with partial correlation ($\varepsilon = 0$, $M = 64$) (reprinted from [14]).

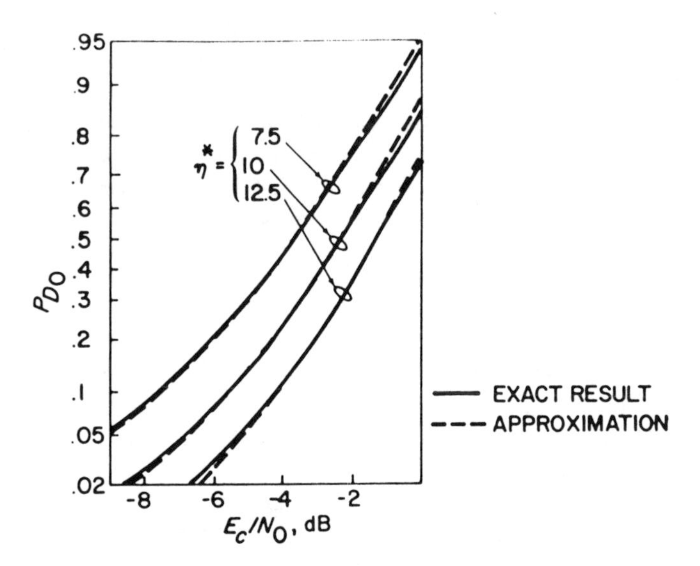

Figure 1.31b. P_{D_0} versus E_c/N_0 for the matched filter detector with partial correlation ($\varepsilon = .5$, $M = 64$) (reprinted from [14]).

where

$$\beta = \frac{\eta^*}{1 + \left(\frac{E_c}{N_0}\right) G_1(\varepsilon)}$$

$$\Gamma = \frac{\gamma_{pc}\left(\frac{E_c}{N_0}\right) G_1(\varepsilon)}{1 + \left(\frac{E_c}{N_0}\right) G_1(\varepsilon)}. \tag{1.199}$$

Equations (1.197) and (1.198), which are in the form of (1.70) and (1.71) respectively with $N_B = 1$, are superimposed (in dotted lines) on the previous exact results in Figures 1.30a, 1.30b and 1.31a, 1.31b. We observe from Figure 1.30 that the approximate analysis of P_{FA_0} is optimistic by about 1 dB, whereas from Figure 1.31 the exact and approximate results for P_{D_0} are in excellent agreement.

It is now a simple matter to compute the false alarm and detection probabilities of the coincidence detector. Since a B out of A majority logic decision with independent testing is governed by a binomial distribution, then

$$P_{FA_1} = \sum_{n=B}^{A} \binom{A}{n} P_{FA_0}^n (1 - P_{FA_0})^{A-n}$$

$$P_{D_1} = \sum_{n=B}^{A} \binom{A}{n} P_{D_0}^n (1 - P_{D_0})^{A-n}. \tag{1.200}$$

1.5.2.3 Acquisition Time Performance

At this point one has all the tools needed to compute the mean acquisition time performance of the matched filter system. For the worst case *a priori* probability distribution, it is possible to make some significant simplifications. The first step in the procedure would be to rewrite the expression for worst case mean acquisition time in (1.183) (valid for a single cell in H_1) in terms of the system parameters, recalling that $K = ANM$ and $\tau_d = T_c/N = T_u/N_u N$ where N_u is the number of chips searched in one pass and T_u is the corresponding time uncertainty. Then, using the approximations $\nu \simeq q = N_u N \gg 1$, $ANM \gg 1$, and the necessary modifications to allow for a multiple cell H_1 region, it can be shown [13] that

$$\frac{\overline{T}_{ACQ}}{T_u} \cong \frac{1 + ANMP_{FA_0} + f_r}{P'_D}, \tag{1.201}$$

which is a very tight approximation to the exact result in the region $P_{ACQ} > .95$ and $qP_{FA} \ll 1$. In (1.201), P'_D is the *detection probability per run* of the multiple cell H_1 region which from (1.185a) is given by

$$P_D' \triangleq H_D(1) = P_D(Q_1) + P_D(Q_2)(1 - P_D(Q_1)), \qquad (1.202)$$

which can easily be generalized for the case of more than two cells in H_1. Note that if $P_D(Q_1) = P_D(Q_2)$, i.e., the fractional offsets for states Q_1 and Q_2 are $\varepsilon = \pm 1/4$, then $P_D' = 2P_D(Q_1) - (P_D(Q_1))^2$, which is identical, as it should be, with (1.82) for the worst case misalignment with half-chip searching. Furthermore, in arriving at (1.201), allowance has been made for the possibility of a reset penalty time T_r ($f_r \triangleq T_r/T_u$ is then the penalty time normalized by the uncertainty time) associated with the time required to realign the codes to the initial phase offset at the start of the search after an unsuccessful sweep of the entire uncertainty region. Clearly, if the uncertainty region corresponds to the full code period as for short codes or specific acquisition preambles, then realignment is automatic and f_r would be zero.

As numerical examples of the application of the foregoing results, Figures 1.32a, 1.32b, and 1.32c illustrate normalized minimum mean acquisition time $\bar{T}_{ACQ}/T_u$ and optimized[27] normalized detection threshold η^* versus chip signal-to-noise ratio E_c/N_0 in dB with N, the number of cells per chip, and M, the number of chips per matched filter integration as parameters. Other parameters assumed were $P_{ACQ} > .95$, a code rate $\mathscr{R}_c = 1/T_c = 512$ kchips/sec, an uncertainty time $T_u = 64$ msec corresponding to $N_u = T_u \mathscr{R}_c = 32767 = 2^{15} - 1$ uncertainty chips, a reset time $T_r = 5$ msec ($f_r = .078$), and best and worst case values of ε. For all cases considered, it was found that $A = 4$ and $B = 2$ (2 out of 4 majority logic decision) was the optimal choice for the coincidence detector, although the performance was relatively insensitive to the actual A and B values as long as A was roughly two times B. Furthermore, we observe that even for an optimized system, there exists a rather sharp "thresholding" effect in the sense that below a certain value of E_c/N_0 the performance degrades rapidly.

1.6 PN SYNC SEARCH PROCEDURES AND SWEEP STRATEGIES FOR A NON-UNIFORMLY DISTRIBUTED SIGNAL LOCATION

Until now, we have assumed that the *a priori* pdf of the signal location across the uncertainty region was uniform, i.e., the correct cell was equally likely to occur in any of the q cells searched in one complete pass. As such, the acquisition system was designed to make complete passes by sweeping (continuously or in discrete steps) across the entire uncertainty region, once

[27] For any E_c/N_0 and fixed M and N, an optimum threshold exists in the sense of minimum $\bar{T}_{ACQ}$.

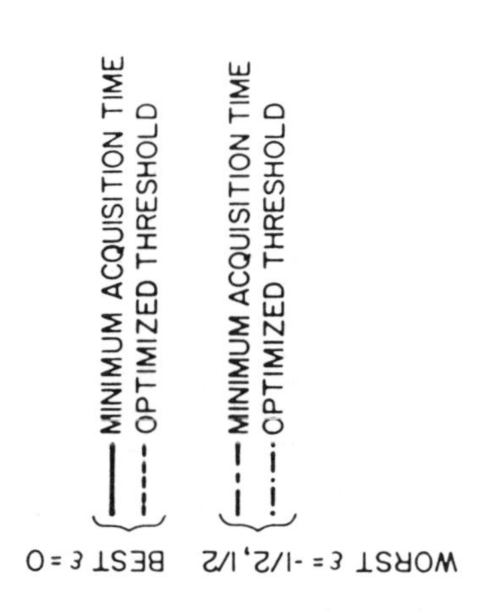

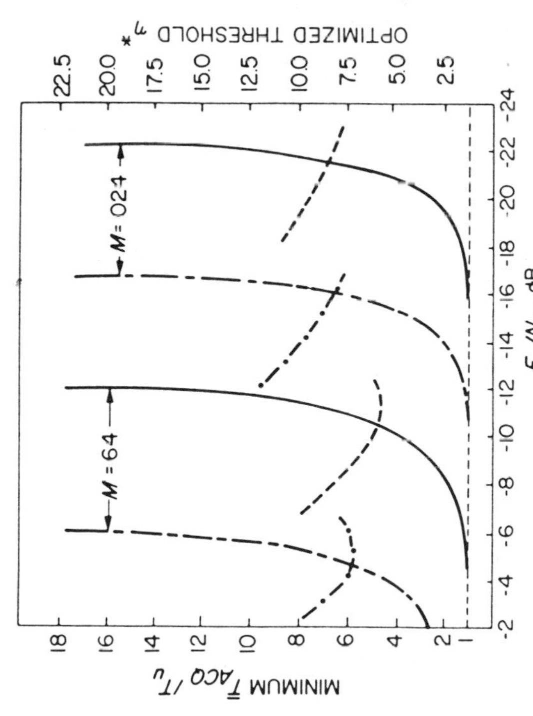

Figure 1.32a. Mean acquisition time versus E_c/N_0; $N = 1$, $A = 4$, $B = 2$, $P_{ACQ} > .95$ (reprinted from [14]).

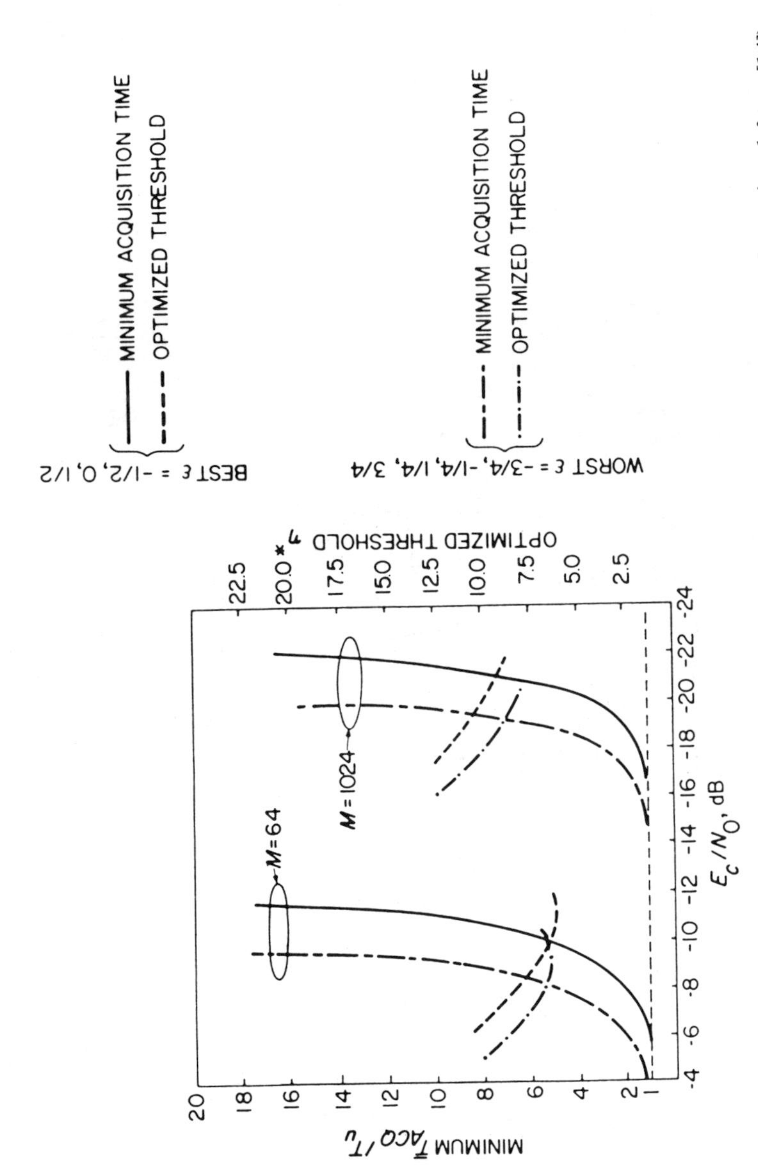

Figure 1.32b. Mean acquisition time versus E_c/N_0; $N = 2$, $A = 4$, $B = 2$, $P_{ACQ} > .95$ (reprinted from [14]).

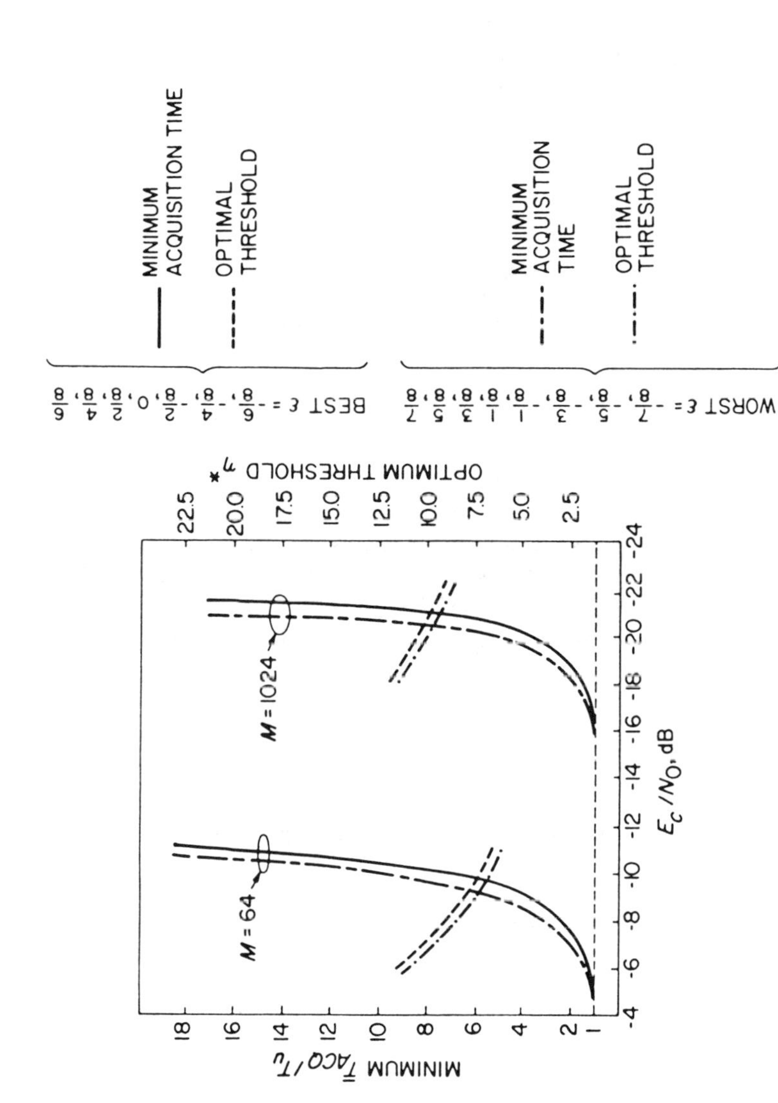

Figure 1.32c. Mean acquisition time versus E_c/N_0; $N = 4$, $A = 4$, $B = 2$, $P_{ACQ} > .95$ (reprinted from [14]).

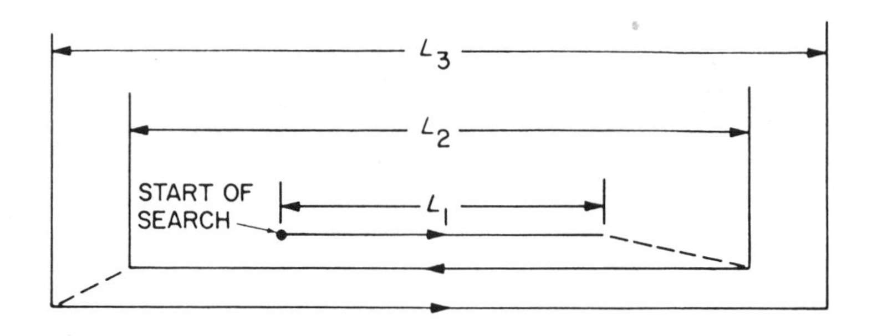

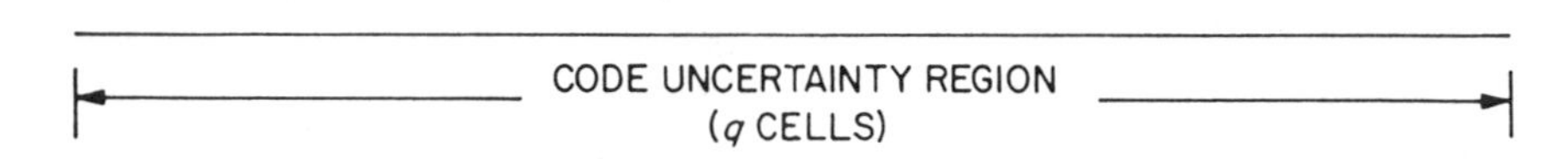

Figure 1.33. A three-window optimized sweep strategy.

per pass, in search of the correct code alignment. When the *a priori* pdf of the signal location is in some sense peaked rather than uniform, then it is more likely to find the correct code phase in the "region" surrounding the peak and one's sweep strategy should be adjusted accordingly. Since, for this situation, full sweeps across the entire uncertainty region would clearly not be the best strategy, one should instead postulate a suitable performance measure, e.g., acquisition time, and proceed to choose a search procedure that optimizes this measure subject to the given system constraints. Indeed, it is intuitively obvious that the number of cells to be searched (and thus the acquisition time) will be reduced by a procedure which begins searching in the region where the likelihood of finding the signal is highest.

1.6.1 An Example—Single Dwell Serial Acquisition with an Optimized Expanding Window Search

As a means of illustration, we shall reduce the scope of the general search problem discussed above by considering first the specific, but practical, case of a single dwell PN acquisition system with a symmetric "expanding window" search centered around the mean of a symmetric, unimodal, *a priori* signal location pdf $\pi_x(x)$ [20]–[24]. An example of such a search strategy for $N_{sw} = 3$ sweeps prior to acquisition is illustrated in Figure 1.33. Let $L_1 \leq L_2 \leq L_3 \leq \cdots \leq L_{N_{sw}}$ denote the lengths (in number of cells) of uncertainty regions to be searched during the N_{sw} sweeps. (We shall set $L_0 = 0$ for convenience). Then if, as before, k (integer) denotes the particular search of the uncertainty region during which the correct cell is *first* detected, then the generalization of (1.8) for the pdf of k is [20]

$$p(k) = P_D \sum_{n=1}^{k} (1 - P_D)^{k-n} [P(L_n) - P(L_{n-1})]; \; k = 1,2,3,\ldots \tag{1.203}$$

where $P(L_n)$ is the probability that the signal location x is within the set L_n, i.e.,

$$P(L_n) = \int_{-L_n/2}^{L_n/2} \pi_x(x)\, dx = 2\int_{0}^{L_n/2} \pi_x(x)\, dx \tag{1.204}$$

with $P(L_0) = 0$ and P_D is still the probability of detection given that the signal is there. Note that for a uniform *a priori* signal location pdf and $L_1 = L_2 = \ldots L_{N_{sw}} = q$ then $P(L_1) = P(L_2) = \ldots P(L_{N_{sw}}) = 1$ and only the $n = 1$ term has a non-zero contribution to the sum in (1.203), whereupon $p(k)$ immediately reduces to the result in (1.8).

Although (1.203) can be formally derived using Bayes' probability rule, it can also be obtained by a simple heuristic argument as follows. Let L_k be divided into k non-overlapping regions, namely, $L_1, L_2 - L_1, L_3 - L_2, \ldots, L_k - L_{k-1}$. Each of these regions represents the additional number of cells searched on a given sweep relative to the previous sweep. By the initiation of the k-th sweep, the region $L_n - L_{n-1}$ has been searched $k - n$ times; $n = 1, 2, \ldots, k - 1$. Thus the *joint* probability of *first* detecting signal in $L_n - L_{n-1}$ and that indeed it was in that region is $P_D(1 - P_D)^{k-n}P(L_n - L_{n-1})$ or, in view of (1.204), $P_D(1 - P_D)^{k-n}[P(L_n) - P(L_{n-1})]$. Since the region $L_k - L_{k-1}$ has not as yet been searched, the joint probability of detecting the signal in this region and that it is indeed there is simply $P_D[P(L_k) - P(L_{k-1})]$. Since the above set of joint probabilities corresponds to mutually exclusive events, (1.203) follows immediately.

To define an optimum symmetric search strategy, we must first define a criterion of optimization along with any additional constraints imposed by the physical system. As suggested earlier, we shall choose as an optimum search strategy that which minimizes the total acquisition time for N_{sw} sweeps where the constraint is to accomplish this minimization subject to a given desired probability of acquiring by the end of these N_{sw} sweeps. Letting $P_{N_{sw}}$ denote this probability, i.e., the probability of acquiring in N_{sw} or fewer sweeps, then since k represents the sweep (search) at which the system is *first* acquired, clearly we would have

$$P_{N_{sw}} = \sum_{k=1}^{N_{sw}} p(k) \tag{1.205}$$

where $p(k)$ is the pdf of k as given in (1.203). Substituting (1.203) into

(1.205) and simplifying yields

$$P_{N_{sw}} = P_D \sum_{k=1}^{N_{sw}} p(L_k)(1 - P_D)^{N_{sw}-k}. \qquad (1.206)$$

Analogous to (1.10), the acquisition time for the first N_{sw} sweeps is[28]

$$T_{N_{sw}} = \tau_d \sum_{i=1}^{N_{sw}} L_i \triangleq \tau_d L_T. \qquad (1.207)$$

Thus, in mathematical terms, the optimization problem can be stated as: For a given P_D and $\pi_x(x)$, choose the search lengths $L_1, L_2, \ldots, L_{N_{sw}}$ so as to minimize L_T with an acquisition probability equal to $P_{N_{sw}}$.

This type of problem is most easily solved by the method of LaGrange multipliers. In particular, the set $L_1, L_2, \ldots, L_{N_{sw}}$ corresponds to the stationary points of the function

$$F = P_{N_{sw}} - \lambda L_T \qquad (1.208)$$

where λ is the LaGrange multiplier (as yet unknown). The stationary points of F correspond to the locations where

$$\frac{\partial F}{\partial L_i} = 0; \; i = 1, 2, \ldots, N_{sw}. \qquad (1.209)$$

Thus substituting (1.206) and (1.207) into (1.208) and performing the required partial differentiations gives

$$P_D(1 - P_D)^{N_{sw}-i} \frac{dP(L_i)}{dL_i} - \lambda = 0 \qquad (1.210)$$

or in view of (1.204)

$$P_D(1 - P_D)^{N_{sw}-i} \pi_x(L_i/2) = \lambda; \; i = 1, 2, \ldots, N_{sw}. \qquad (1.211)$$

For a given $\pi_x(x)$, one can for each i implicitly solve for L_i as a function of λ, say $f_i(\lambda)$. Then λ can, in principle, be eliminated by satisfying the constraint in (1.206), i.e.,

$$P_{N_{sw}} = P_D \sum_{k=1}^{N_{sw}} P(f_k(\lambda))(1 - P_D)^{N_{sw}-k}. \qquad (1.212)$$

Typically, for a given P_D, $P_{N_{sw}}$, and form of pdf $\pi_x(x)$, the solution of (1.212) for λ (and thus L_i: $i = 1, 2, \ldots, N_{sw}$) will exist only for certain values of N_{sw}. To show this, lower and upper bounds on N_{sw} can be obtained as follows. Since $P(L_k) \leq 1$ for all $k = 1, 2, \ldots, N_{sw}$, then from

[28] We assume here, for simplicity, a zero false alarm probability or, equivalently, that the penalty time associated with the occurrence of a false alarm is zero. In the next section, we shall include this effect as part of the more general formulation of serial search systems with non-uniform search strategies following the unified approach discussed in Section 1.4.

(1.212) we have

$$P_{N_{sw}} \le P_D \sum_{k=1}^{N_{sw}} (1 - P_D)^{N_{sw}-k} = 1 - (1 - P_D)^{N_{sw}}. \tag{1.213}$$

Satisfaction of (1.213) with the equality sign gives a lower bound on N_{sw}, namely,

$$N_{sw} \ge \frac{\ln(1 - P_{N_{sw}})}{\ln(1 - P_D)}. \tag{1.214}$$

Similarly, since $L_1 \le L_2 \le \cdots \le L_{N_{sw}}$, then $P(L_1) \le P(L_2) \le \cdots \le P(L_{N_{sw}})$. Hence,

$$P_{N_{sw}} \ge P(L_1)\left[1 - (1 - P_D)^{N_{sw}}\right] \tag{1.215}$$

or

$$N_{sw} \le \frac{\ln\left[1 - \dfrac{P_{N_{sw}}}{P(L_1)}\right]}{\ln(1 - P_D)}. \tag{1.216}$$

Before presenting a specific example of the application of the previous results and the benefits gained therein by using an optimum search strategy, we must first discuss a measure of improvement which can be used in comparing the optimized scheme to the uniform (full sweeps across the entire uncertainty region) sweep scheme. We recall that for a uniform *a priori* cell location pdf, the probability of first acquiring during the k-th full sweep is given by $p(k)$ of (1.8). Thus, for a given desired probability of acquisition $P_{N_{sw}}$, the number N_F of full sweeps (each having q cells) would be obtained from the solution to

$$\sum_{i=0}^{N_F-1} P_D(1 - P_D)^i \le P_{N_{sw}} \le \sum_{i=0}^{N_F} P_D(1 - P_D)^i \tag{1.217}$$

or

$$1 - (1 - P_D)^{N_F} \le P_{N_{sw}} \le 1 - (1 - P_D)^{N_F+1}. \tag{1.218}$$

The solution to (1.218) is easily shown to be

$$N_F = \left\lfloor \frac{\ln(1 - P_{N_{sw}})}{\ln(1 - P_D)} \right\rfloor \tag{1.219}$$

where again $\lfloor x \rfloor$ denotes the largest integer less than or equal to x. Since within a given sweep interval, say the k-th, the cumulative probability of acquisition would be a linear interpolation between the upper and lower bounds of (1.218), the total search length L_{TU} (in cells) for the uniform

Table 1.2
Improvement in acquisition time performance of optimized non-uniform sweep relative to uniform sweep.

	Uniform Sweep		Optimized Sweep			% Reduction in Acquisition Time
	N_F	L_{TU}/σ*	L_i/σ	L_T/σ	I	$(1 - \frac{1}{I}) \times 100$
			$(N_{sw} = 3)$			
$P_D = .25$			2.54	8.83	1.66	40
	2	14.67	2.96			
$P_{N_{sw}} = .5$			3.33			
			$(N_{sw} = 4)$			
			1.19			
			1.93	8.47	1.73	42
			2.46			
			2.89			
			$(N_{sw} = 4)$			
$P_D = .5$			2.63			
			3.53			
	3	20.4	4.24	15.25	1.34	25
			4.85			
			$(N_{sw} = 5)$			
$P_{N_{sw}} = .9$			.56			
			2.42	15.22	1.34	25
			3.38			
			4.12			
			4.74			

*For the uniform sweep case, we assume the search region corresponds to $\pm 3\sigma$, i.e., $q = 6\sigma$.

sweep strategy is given by

$$L_{TU} = q\left\{ N_F + \frac{P_{N_{sw}} - \left[1 - (1 - P_D)^{N_F}\right]}{1 - (1 - P_D)^{N_F+1} - \left[1 - (1 - P_D)^{N_F}\right]}\right. \tag{1.220}$$

or upon simplification

$$L_{TU} = q\left\{ N_F + \frac{(1 - P_D)^{N_F} - (1 - P_{N_{sw}})}{(1 - P_D)^{N_F} - (1 - P_D)^{N_F+1}}\right\}. \tag{1.221}$$

The improvement factor of the optimized sweep strategy over the uniform sweep strategy is then

$$I = \frac{L_{TU}}{L_T} \tag{1.222}$$

where L_T is determined from the solution of (1.211) using the same P_D and $P_{N_{sw}}$.

As an example, consider a truncated Gaussian *a priori* pdf for $\pi_x(x)$. Then, the solution to (1.211) for the optimized sweep lengths can be expressed in the form [20]

$$L_i = 2\sqrt{2}\,\sigma\sqrt{\ln\left[\frac{P_D(1 - P_D)^{N_{sw}-i}}{\lambda\sqrt{2\pi}\,\sigma}\right]}$$

$$\triangleq f_i(\lambda);\ i = 1, 2, \ldots, N_{sw} \tag{1.223}$$

where σ is the standard deviation of $\pi_x(x)$. Using (1.212) to eliminate λ requires solution of the transcendental equation

$$P_{N_{sw}} = P_D \sum_{k=1}^{N_{sw}} (1 - P_D)^{N_{sw}-k}\left\{1 - 2Q\left(\sqrt{2\ln\left[\frac{P_D(1 - P_D)^{N_{sw}-k}}{\lambda\sqrt{2\pi}\,\sigma}\right]}\right)\right\} \tag{1.224}$$

which although impossible analytically can be accomplished numerically on a digital computer for each allowable value of N_{sw}. Several numerical examples were worked out in [20] with the results shown in Table 1.2.

1.6.2 Application of the Circular State Diagram Approach

In Section 1.6.1 we considered the optimization and performance of a particular expanding window serial search strategy as applied to a single dwell acquisition system. This strategy was but one of a class of search strategies that attain improved acquisition performance when *a priori* probabilistic information about the true code sync position is available.

In this section, we generalize these results by allowing for an arbitrary serial search strategy and an arbitrary detector configuration. The approach taken is based upon the circular state diagram method introduced in Section

1.4 as a tool for modelling and analyzing the complete acquisition behavior of straight (uniform) serial search schemes. The advantage of this approach in the application being considered here is that it circumvents complicated combinatorial arguments used in [21]–[23] to characterize the performance of such systems by employing a transform domain description of the stochastic acquisition process. Such a description allows a simple and more systematic evaluation of the generating function of the process using well-known flow graph reduction techniques.

While the method to be described applies to arbitrary serial search strategies, the focus here will be on the two classes of non-uniform strategies depicted in Figure 1.2, namely, the *z-search* and the *expanding window search*. These two classes can be further subdivided into *broken* or *continuous* searches (depending on whether the receiver employs rewinding in order to skip certain cells), and *edge* or *center* searches (depending on where the search and each subsequent sweep are initiated).

Recall from Section 1.4.1 that for a straight serial search, the process can be modelled by a circular state diagram (see Figure 1.23) with $\nu + 2$ states, where $\nu - 1$ of these correspond to out-of-sync cells (hypothesis H_0), one to the collecting state (hypothesis H_1), one to the absorbing correct state (ACQ), and one to the possibly absorbing false alarm state. Along the branches between these various states are found generalized gains $H(z)$ that represent the generating functions of the individual discrete-time detection processes associated with the corresponding paths. Applying standard flow graph reduction techniques to the circular state diagrams then allows evaluation of the moment generating function $U(z)$ of the underlying acquisition process.

To apply this approach to the non-uniform search case, one merely translates the motion of the specific search strategy under consideration into a circular motion along an equivalent circular state diagram analogous to Figure 1.23. To demonstrate how this is accomplished, let us consider first the continuous/center z serial search illustrated in Figure 1.34. Here the search is initiated at the center of the code phase uncertainty region and proceeds following the arrows in the manner shown; i.e., it reverses direction every time the boundaries are reached. Assuming that the location of the true sync state (H_1) is at the shaded cell, the search process will meet it once during each sweep at the dotted positions. We indicate the starting cell by $\nu - k$ where, for the H_1 cell to be in the indicated side, k must satisfy $1 \leq k \leq (\nu - 1)/2$ (for convenience, we assume ν to be odd). Similar diagrams can be drawn for $k = 0$ or $(\nu + 1)/2 \leq k \leq \nu - 1$; however, that will not be necessary due to the symmetry of the problem. Furthermore, we note that since the search is always initiated at the center, π_j should be interpreted as the probability that the central (entrance) cell is not the ν-th (H_1) but the j-th; in other words, π_j stands for the probability that H_1 is actually $\nu - j$ positions to the right (if $j \geq (\nu + 1)/2$) or j positions to the left (if $j \leq (\nu - 1)/2$).

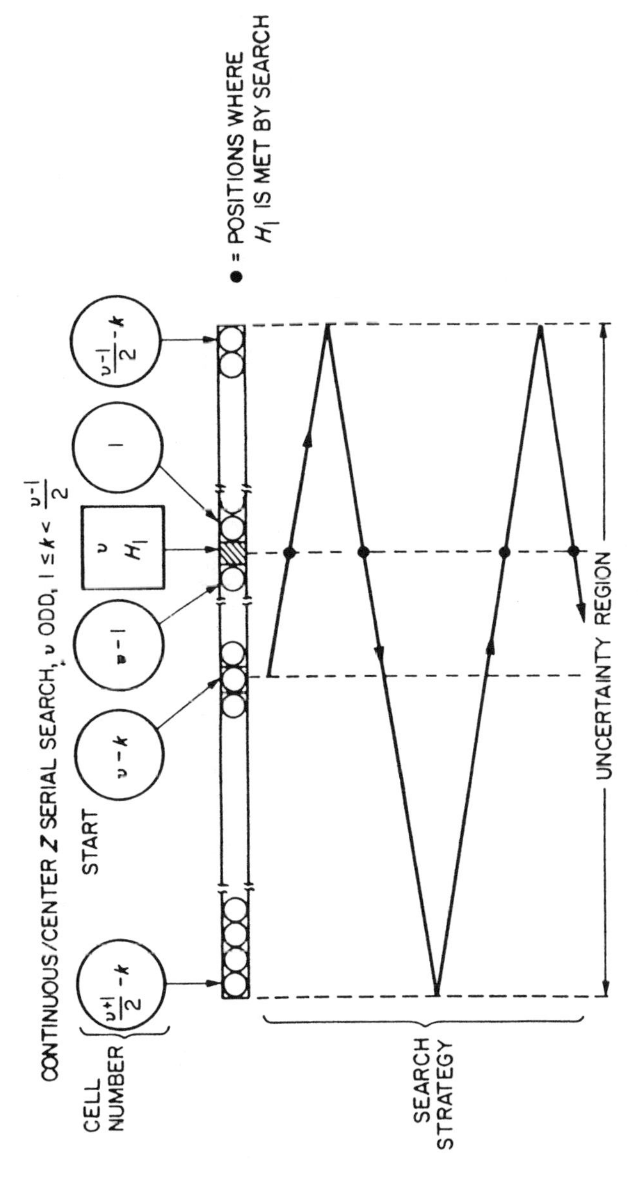

Figure 1.34. Cell numbering for the continuous/center z serial search with $1 \leqq k < (\nu - 1)/2$.

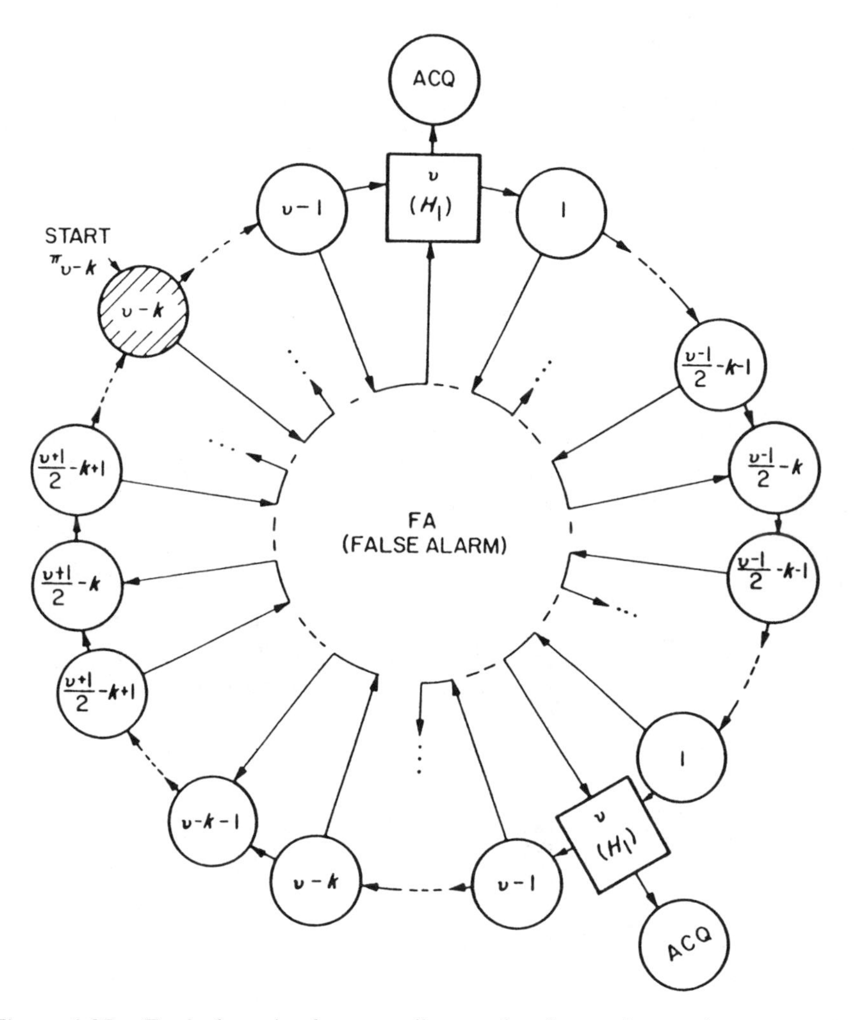

Figure 1.35. Equivalent circular state diagram for the continuous/center z serial search, $1 \leqq k < (\nu - 1)/2$.

Translating the z motion of the search into an equivalent motion along an equivalent circular path leads to the circular state diagram of Figure 1.35, which for purposes of deriving the transfer function $U_{\nu-k,ACQ}(z)$ from state $\nu - k$ to state ACQ can be consolidated into Figure 1.36, which contains two forward paths and one feedback loop. Applying Mason's formula [32] to Figure 1.36 trivially provides the result (for $0 < k < (\nu - 1)/2$)

$$U_{\nu-k,ACQ}(z) = \frac{H_0^k(z)H_D(z)\left[1 + H_M(z)H_0^{\nu-2-2k}(z)\right]}{1 - H_M^2(z)H_0^{2(\nu-2)}(z)}. \quad (1.225)$$

Finally, averaging $U_{\nu-k,ACQ}(z)$ over the *a priori* probability distribution of

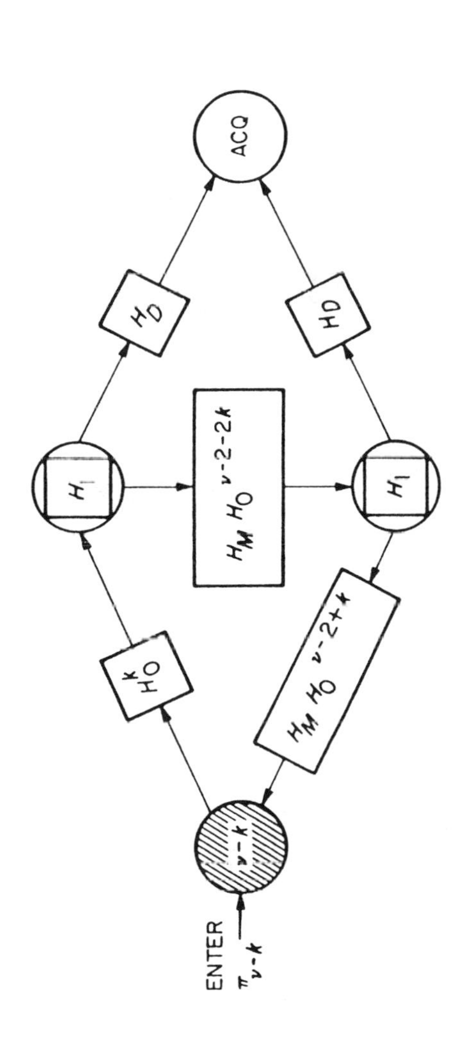

Figure 1.36. Flow graph and corresponding path gains for the continuous/center z serial search entering at node $\nu - k$, $0 < k < (\nu - 1)/2$.

the code phase uncertainty, and taking certain symmetries into account, gives the desired result for the acquisition process generating function $U(z)$, namely,

$$U(z) = \sum_{k=0}^{\nu-1} \pi_k U_{\nu-k,ACQ}(z)$$

$$= H_D(z)\left\{\frac{\sum_{j=1}^{(\nu-3)/2} H_0^j(z)\left[\pi_{\nu-j} + \pi_j H_0^{\nu-1}(z)\right]\left[1 + H_M(z)H_0^{\nu-2-2j}(z)\right]}{1 - H_M^2(z)H_0^{2(\nu-2)}(z)}\right.$$

$$\left. + \frac{H_0^{(\nu-1)/2}(z)\left[\pi_{(\nu+1)/2} + \pi_{(\nu-1)/2}H_0^{\nu-1}(z)\right]}{1 - H_M(z)H_0^{2\nu-3}(z)} + \frac{\pi_\nu}{1 - H_M(z)H_0^{\nu-2}(z)}\right\}. \tag{1.226}$$

Equation (1.226) can be combined with any *a priori* distribution to provide specific results. For example, for the symmetric triangular distribution

$$\pi_j = \begin{cases} \left(\frac{2}{\nu-1}\right)\left[1 - \left(\frac{2}{\nu-1}\right)j\right] & j = 1, \ldots, \frac{\nu-1}{2} \\ \pi_{\nu-j} & j = \frac{\nu+1}{2}, \ldots, \nu-1 \\ \left(\frac{2}{\nu-1}\right) & j = \nu \end{cases} \tag{1.227}$$

which in [22] is used as an approximation to a truncated Gaussian distribution, $U(z)$ of (1.226) becomes

$$U(z) = \left(\frac{2}{\nu-1}\right)\left(\frac{H_D(z)}{1 - H_M^2(z)H_0^{2(\nu-2)}(z)}\right)$$
$$\times\left\{\frac{H_0(z)(1 + H_0^{\nu-1}(z))}{1 - H_0(z)}\left[1 - \frac{2}{\nu-1}\left(\frac{1 - H_0^{(\nu-1)/2}(z)}{1 - H_0(z)}\right)\right.\right.$$
$$\left. - H_0^{\nu-3}(z)H_M(z)\left(1 - \frac{2}{\nu-1}\left(\frac{1 - H_0^{(\nu-1)/2}(z)}{H_0^{(\nu-3)/2}(z)(1 - H_0(z))}\right)\right)\right]$$
$$\left. + 1 + H_M(z)H_0^{\nu-2}(z)\right\}. \tag{1.228}$$

From the generating function $U(z)$ of (1.228), we can obtain the mean acquisition time $\overline{T}_{ACQ}$ by a relation identical to that in (1.3). For example, for a single dwell system, we use the branch gains of Table 1.1 together with the relation of (1.153) in (1.228), whereupon performing the required differentiation and evaluating the result at $z = 1$ gives

$$\overline{T}_{ACQ} = \tau_d\left\{\frac{1}{P_D} + \frac{1 + KP_{FA}}{3P_D(2 - P_D)(\nu - 1)}\left[6\nu^2 - 18\nu + 12 - P_D(6\nu^2 - 15\nu + 9) + P_D^2(2\nu^2 - 4\nu)\right]\right\} \quad (1.229)$$

which for large ν reduces to

$$\overline{T}_{ACQ} = \tau_d\left\{\frac{1}{P_D} + \frac{2(1 + KP_{FA})\nu(3 - 3P_D + P_D^2)}{3P_D(2 - P_D)}\right\}. \quad (1.230)$$

Consider now another variation of the class of z-search strategies, namely, the broken/center z search. This is similar to the continuous/center z, with the exception that the same cells are not searched twice in a row. Instead, when one of the two boundaries is reached, the local code is quickly rewound to the center and the search continues in the opposite direction. Clearly, for *a priori* distributions which are peaked around the center, an improvement in acquisition performance should be expected with respect to the continuous/center z strategy. The magnitude of this improvement will be demonstrated shortly by comparing the mean acquisition time performance of the broken/ and continuous/center z search strategies for the triangular *a priori* distribution. First, however, we present the generating function $U(z)$ for the broken/center z which is obtained from its circular state diagram by steps identical to those used in arriving at (1.226). As in our previous discussions, letting T_r denote the reset penalty time required to rewind the code, $U(z)$ is found to be

$$U(z) = H_D(z)\left\{\frac{\sum_{j=1}^{(\nu-1)/2}\left[\pi_{\nu-j} + \pi_j z^{T_r/\tau_d}H_0^{(\nu+1)/2}(z)\right]H_0^j(z)}{1 - z^{2T_r/\tau_d}H_M(z)H_0^\nu(z)} + \frac{\pi_\nu}{1 - z^{T_r/\tau_d}H_M(z)H_0^{(\nu-1)/2}(z)}\right\}. \quad (1.231)$$

For the triangular *a priori* distribution, (1.231) evaluates to

$$U(z) = \left(\frac{2}{\nu - 1}\right)H_D(z)\left\{\frac{1 + z^{T_r/\tau_d}H_0^{(\nu+1)/2}(z)}{1 - z^{2T_r/\tau_d}H_M(z)H_0^\nu(z)}\left(\frac{H_0(z)}{1 - H_0(z)}\right) \times\left[1 - \frac{2}{\nu - 1}\left(\frac{1 - H_0^{(\nu-1)/2}(z)}{1 - H_0(z)}\right)\right] + \frac{1}{1 - z^{T_r/\tau_d}H_M(z)H_0^{(\nu-1)/2}(z)}\right\}. \quad (1.232)$$

Once again applying the necessary differentiation to arrive at (1.232) the mean acquisition time of a single dwell system, we obtain from (1.232) the result

$$\overline{T}_{ACQ} = \tau_d \left\{ \frac{1}{P_D} + \frac{T_r}{\tau_d} \frac{\left[\left(\frac{\nu - 3}{2} \right) P_D + 2(\nu - 2)(1 - P_D) \right]}{(\nu - 1) P_D} \right.$$

$$\left. + \frac{(1 + KP_{FA})}{(\nu - 1) P_D} \left[\frac{5}{12} (\nu^2 - 2\nu - 3) P_D + (\nu^2 - 2\nu - 1)(1 - P_D) \right] \right\} \tag{1.233}$$

which for large ν reduces to

$$\overline{T}_{ACQ} = \tau_d \left\{ \frac{1}{P_D} \left[1 + \left(\frac{4 - 3P_D}{2} \right) \frac{T_r}{\tau_d} \right] + \frac{(1 + KP_{FA})\nu}{P_D} \left(1 - \frac{7}{12} P_D \right) \right\}. \tag{1.234}$$

To illustrate the improvement in mean acquisition time performance by using a broken/ rather than a continuous/center z search, we can take the ratio of the latter terms in (1.230) and (1.234) since, for large enough ν, the first terms in these equations can be ignored. Thus, to a good approximation

$$\frac{\overline{T}_{ACQ}|_{\text{cont.}}}{\overline{T}_{ACQ}|_{\text{broken}}} = \frac{2(3 - 3P_D + P_D^2)}{3(2 - P_D)(1 - \frac{7}{12} P_D)}. \tag{1.235}$$

Figure 1.37 is a plot of this mean acquisition time improvement factor versus P_D. We observe that the maximum improvement occurs for $P_D = 1$ (absolute probability of detecting the correct cell once it is reached) in which case (1.235) reduces to

$$\frac{\overline{T}_{ACQ}|_{\text{cont.}}}{\overline{T}_{ACQ}|_{\text{broken}}} = \frac{8}{5} = 1.6 \tag{1.236}$$

i.e., a 37.5 percent saving in acquisition time.

In the more general case where the *a priori* probability distribution of the code phase uncertainty is arbitrary (but symmetric), for $P_D = 1$ and ν large, it is simple to show that[29]

$$\frac{\overline{T}_{ACQ}|_{\text{cont.}}}{\overline{T}_{ACQ}|_{\text{broken}}} = \frac{2 \sum_{j=1}^{\nu/2} j\pi_j + \frac{\nu}{2}}{2 \sum_{j=1}^{\nu/2} j\pi_j + \frac{\nu}{4}} \tag{1.237}$$

[29] When ν is large, the assumption of ν odd is inconsequential.

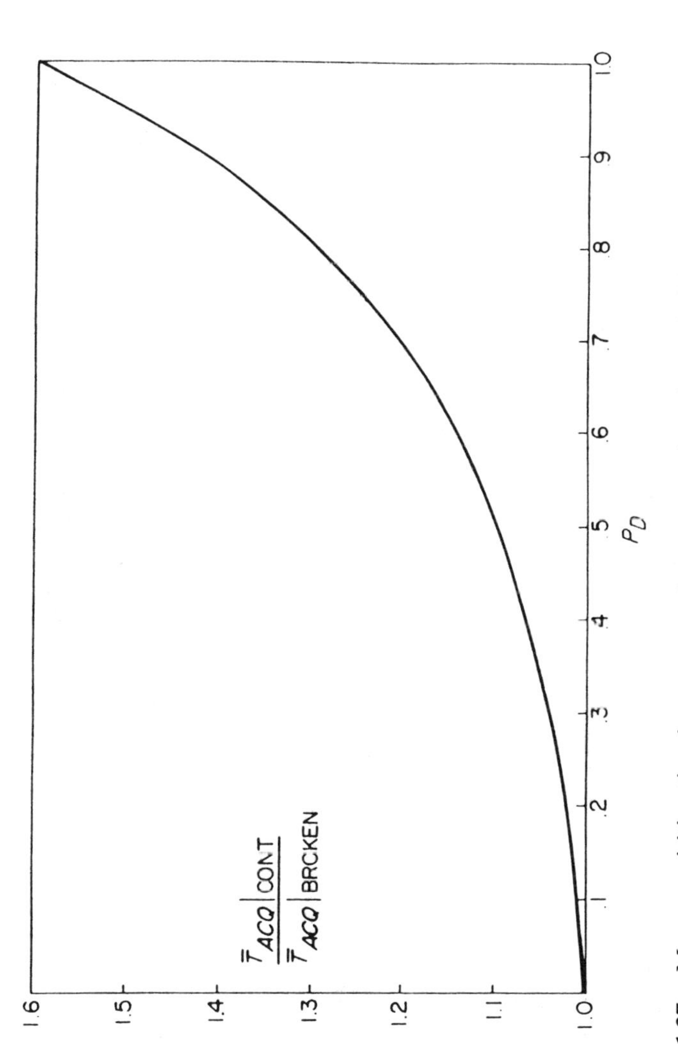

Figure 1.37. Mean acquisition time improvement factor versus detection probability for single dwell acquisition system with triangular *a priori* code phase uncertainty distribution.

which is lower and upper bounded by

$$\frac{6}{5} \le \frac{\bar{T}_{ACQ}|_{\text{cont.}}}{\bar{T}_{ACQ}|_{\text{broken}}} = 2 \tag{1.238}$$

corresponding to the *a priori* distributions

$$\pi_1 = \pi_\nu = \tfrac{1}{2}$$
$$\pi_j = 0; \; j \neq 1, \nu \tag{1.239a}$$

and

$$\pi_{\nu/2} = \pi_{\nu/2+1} = \tfrac{1}{2}$$
$$\pi_j = 0; \; j \neq \nu/2, \nu/2 + 1. \tag{1.239b}$$

Thus, *regardless of the a priori probability distribution of the code phase uncertainty, the broken/center z search potentially offers an improvement of at least* 20 *percent and at most* 100 *percent over the continuous/center z search.* Of course, for $P_D < 1$, these improvements will decrease accordingly.

Finally, we consider the class of expanding window search strategies, two representative cases of which (A and B) are shown in Figure 1.38. The two cases differ in the way the search is continued once the entire uncertainty region has been covered without success. In particular, case A repeats the search starting from the R_1 window,[30] while case B continues by repeating the $R_{N_{sw}}$ window. We note that the strategies analyzed in [21]–[23] constitute slight variations of case B. The equivalent circular state diagrams for the two cases are shown in Figure 1.39. We observe that, after completing the first $R_{N_{sw}}$ sweep, case B is indistinguishable from the continuous/center z search. Furthermore, the diagrams are composed of hexagons with an inscribed R_i; those represent portions of the state diagram which correspond to the partial sweeps R_i; $i = 1, \ldots, N_{sw}$. As seen from Figure 1.38, for each starting cell $\nu - k$ there exists a minimum index j_k such that the first $j_k - 1$ partial windows do not contain the H_1 state, while the remaining $N_{sw} - j_k + 1$ do. This is manifested in Figure 1.39 by the fact that only the hexagons after (and including) the j_k-th can lead to the ACQ state. The portions of the state diagram included in the hexagon R_j can be derived from Figure 1.35 with a proper modification. Typical forms are shown in Figures 1.40a and 1.40b for the two possibilities, i.e., $1 \le j \le j_k - 1$ (Figure 1.40a) and $j_k \le j \le N_{sw}$ (Figure 1.40b). It has been assumed, without loss of generality, that $1 \le k \le (\nu - 1)/2$. Cascading the successive hexagons of Figures 1.40a and 1.40b as per Figure 1.39 will result in the equivalent circular state diagrams for those expanding window search strategies. It is then a matter of systematically following the steps established previously

[30] Note that the radius R_i of the i-th partial window is one-half of the length L_i of the sweep for that window.

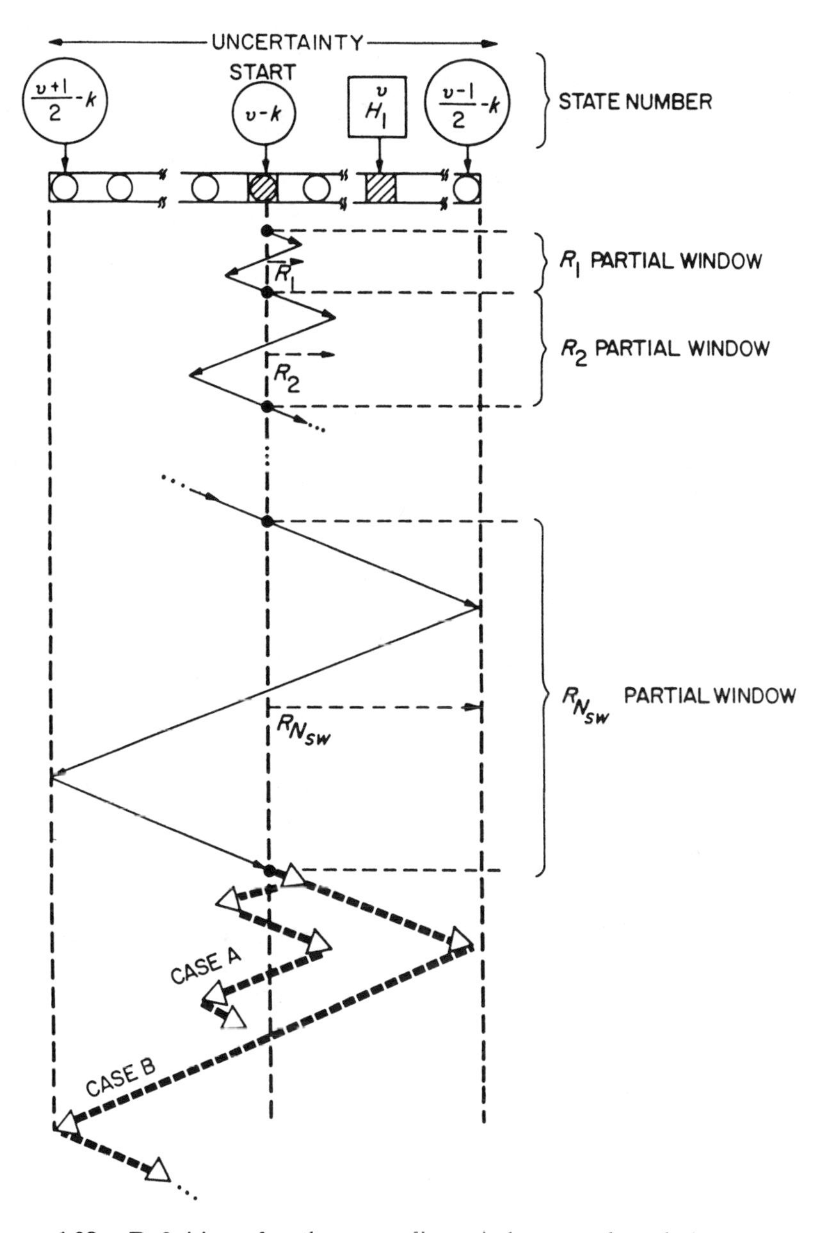

Figure 1.38. Definitions for the expanding window search technique; cases A and B (reprinted from [38]).

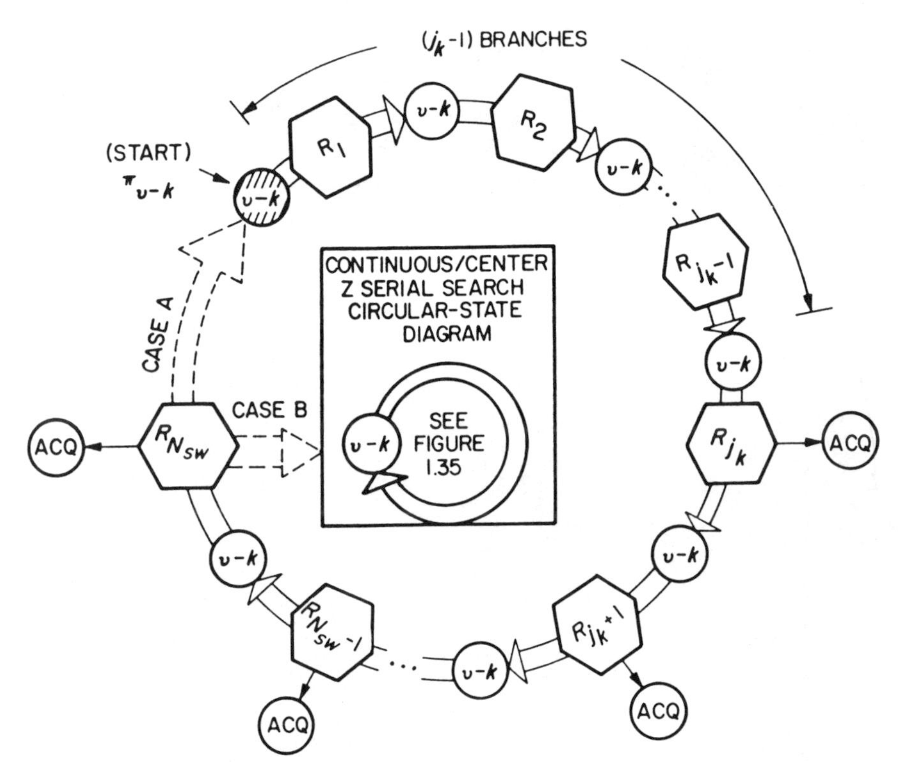

Figure 1.39. Equivalent state diagrams for the two cases A and B of the expanding window serial search of Figure 1.38 (reprinted from [38]).

(i.e., diagram consolidation, gain calculation via Mason's formula, and averaging) in order to arrive at the final expressions of interest. For the two cases A and B, they are given by

$$\text{(Case A)} \quad U(z) = \sum_{i=1}^{N_{sw}} F_1(i) \sum_{j=i}^{N_{sw}} F_2(i,j) \sum_{R_{i-1}+1 \leqq k \leqq R_i} F_3(k,j) \tag{1.240}$$

and

(Case B)

$$U(z) = \left(\frac{H_D(1 + H_0^{\nu}) H_0^{4S(1, N_{sw})}}{1 - H_M^2 H_0^{2\nu}} \right) \sum_{i=1}^{N_{sw}} H_0^{2(N_{sw} - i + 1)} \sum_{R_{i-1}+1 \leqq k \leqq R_i} F_3(k, N_{sw})$$

$$+ \sum_{i=1}^{N_{sw}} H_D H_0^{4S(1, i-1)} \sum_{j=i}^{N_{sw}} F_2(i,j) \sum_{R_{i-1}+1 \leqq k \leqq R_i} F_3(k,j) \tag{1.241}$$

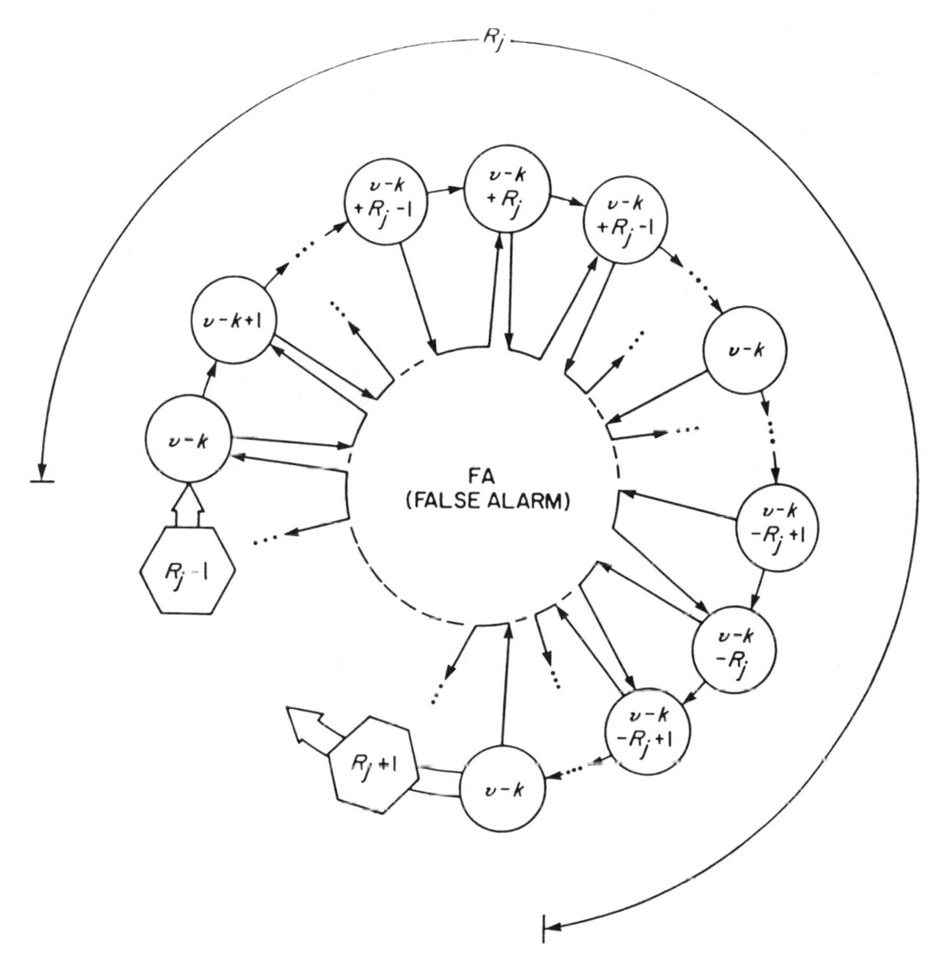

Figure 1.40a. Portion of state diagram corresponding to R_j, expanding window search, $1 \leqq j \leqq j_k - 1$ (reprinted from [38]).

where

$$F_1(i) = \frac{H_D H_0^{4S(1,i-1)}}{1 - H_M^{2(N_{sw}-i+1)} H_0^{4S(1,N_{sw})}} \tag{1.242a}$$

$$F_2(i,j) = H_M^{2(j-i)} H_0^{4S(i,j-1)} \left(1 + H_0^{2R_j}\right) \tag{1.242b}$$

$$F_3(k,j) = \pi_k \left(H_0^k + H_M H_0^{2R_j - k}\right) \tag{1.242c}$$

and

$$S(m,n) = \begin{cases} \sum_{l=m}^{n} R_l, & \text{if } m \leqq n \\ 0, & \text{if } m > n. \end{cases} \tag{1.242d}$$

In deriving the above, the simplifying assumptions were made that the

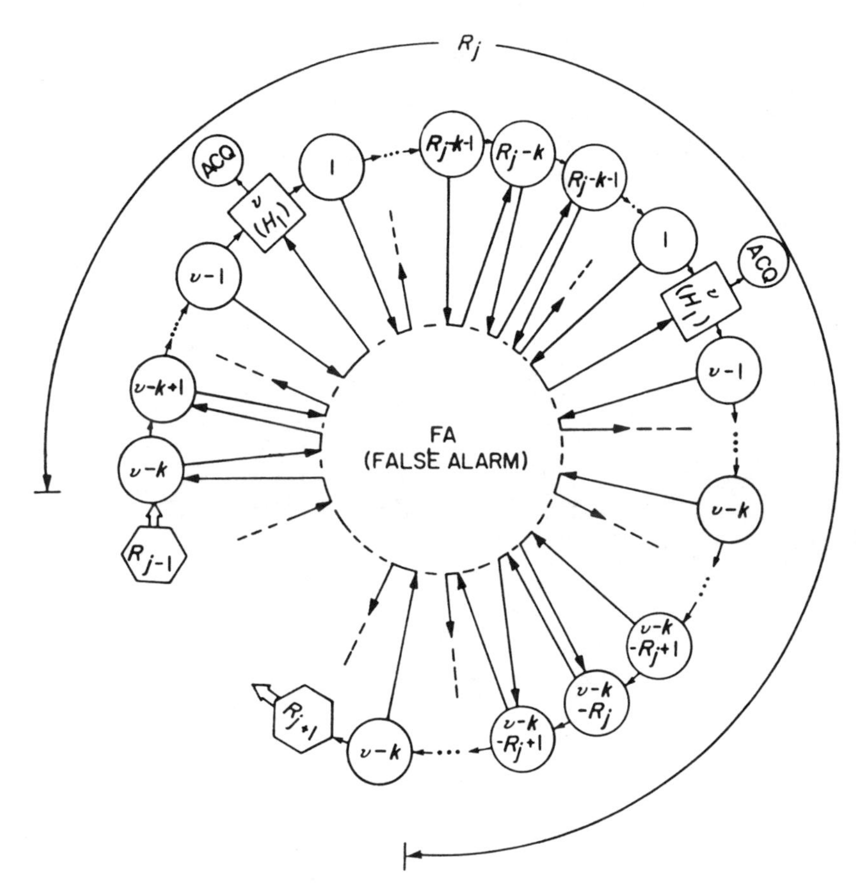

Figure 1.40b. Portion of state diagram corresponding to R_j, expanding window search, $j \geq j_k$ (reprinted from [38]).

a priori distribution is symmetric ($\pi_k = \pi_{\nu-k}$), ν is large, and $R_i \gg N_{sw}$; $i = 1, 2, \ldots, N_{sw}$, all of which are met in practical systems. Also, the dependence of the gains on z has been dropped.

As a particular case of interest, let us consider the "equiexpanding" window search, whereby the radii R_i increase by the same amount of code chips, i.e., $R_i = (\nu/2N_{sw})i$; $i = 1, \ldots, N_{sw}$. Arbitrarily assuming case A, the moment generating function of (1.240) becomes

$$U(z) = H_D \sum_{i=1}^{N_{sw}} \frac{H_0^{i(i-1)\nu/N_{sw}}}{1 - H_M^{2(N_{sw}-i+1)} H_0^{\nu(N_{sw}+1)}}$$
$$\times \sum_{l=0}^{N_{sw}-i} H_M^{2l} H_0^{l(2i+l-1)\nu/N_{sw}} \left(1 + H_0^{(l+i)\nu/N_{sw}}\right)$$
$$\times \sum_{R_{i-1}+1 \leq k \leq R_i} \pi_k \left(H_0^k + H_M H_0^{(l+i)\nu/N_{sw}-k}\right) \qquad (1.243)$$

and, for the single dwell detector, the corresponding mean acquisition time is given by

$$\overline{T}_{ACQ} = \tau_d \left\{ \frac{1}{P_D} + \frac{2(1 + KP_{FA})\nu}{N_{sw}} \sum_{k=1}^{N_{sw}} \frac{E_1(k, N_{sw})}{1 - (1 - P_D)^{2k}} \right.$$

$$\left. \times \left[\alpha(k, N_{sw}; P_D) + \beta(k, N_{sw}; P_D) + \gamma(k, N_{sw}; P_D) \right] \right\} \tag{1.244}$$

where

$$\alpha(k, N_{sw}; P_D) = N_{sw}(N_{sw} + 1)(1 - P_D)^{2k} + (N_{sw} - k)(N_{sw} + 1 - k)\left(1 - (1 - P_D)^{2k}\right) \tag{1.245a}$$

$$\begin{aligned} \beta(k, N_{sw}; P_D) = {} & \frac{1}{2}(N_{sw} + 1 - k)\left(1 - (1 - P_D)^{2k}\right) \\ & + \left\{ \frac{1}{2}[4(N_{sw} + 1 - k) - 1] + \frac{1 + (1 - P_D)^2}{1 - (1 - P_D)^2} \right\}(1 - P_D)^2 \\ & \times \left[\frac{1 - (1 - P_D)^{2k}}{1 - (1 - P_D)^2} - k(1 - P_D)^{2k-2} \right] \\ & - k(k - 1)(1 - P_D)^{2k} \end{aligned} \tag{1.245b}$$

$$\begin{aligned} \gamma(k, N_{sw}; P_D) = {} & \frac{1 - (1 - P_D)^{2k}}{2 - P_D} \\ & \times \left\{ (N_{sw} + 1 - k)(1 - P_D) + \frac{N}{\nu} P_D \frac{E_2(k, N_{sw})}{E_1(k, N_{sw})} \right. \\ & \left. + (1 - P_D)\left[\frac{(1 - P_D)^2}{1 - (1 - P_D)^2} - k\frac{(1 - P_D)^{2k}}{1 - (1 - P_D)^{2k}} \right] \right\} \end{aligned} \tag{1.245c}$$

with

$$E_1(k, N_{sw}) \triangleq \sum_{R_{N_{sw}-k}+1 \le l \le R_{N_{sw}-k+1}} \pi_l; \qquad k = 1, 2, \ldots, N_{sw} \tag{1.246a}$$

$$E_2(k, N_{sw}) \triangleq \sum_{R_{N_{sw}-k}+1 \le l \le R_{N_{sw}-k+1}} l\pi_l; \qquad k = 1, 2, \ldots, N_{sw}. \tag{1.246b}$$

For large ν, it is convenient to replace the discrete *a priori* probability distribution π_k by a continuous distribution corresponding to its envelope $\pi_x(x)$ and evaluate the sums in (1.246) as integrals, namely,

$$E_1(k, N_{sw}) = \int_{(\nu/2)(1-k/N_{sw})}^{(\nu/2)(1-(k-1)/N_{sw})} \pi_x(x)\,dx \tag{1.247a}$$

$$E_2(k, N_{sw}) = \int_{(\nu/2)(1-k/N_{sw})}^{(\nu/2)(1-(k-1)/N_{sw})} x\pi_x(x)\,dx. \tag{1.247b}$$

For the symmetric triangular distribution of (1.227), we have

$$E_1(k, N_{sw}) = \frac{1}{N_{sw}}\left(\frac{2k-1}{2N_{sw}}\right)$$

$$E_2(k, N_{sw}) = \frac{\nu}{4}\left[\frac{3N_{sw}(2k-1) - 2(3k^2 - 3k + 1)}{3N_{sw}^3}\right] \tag{1.248}$$

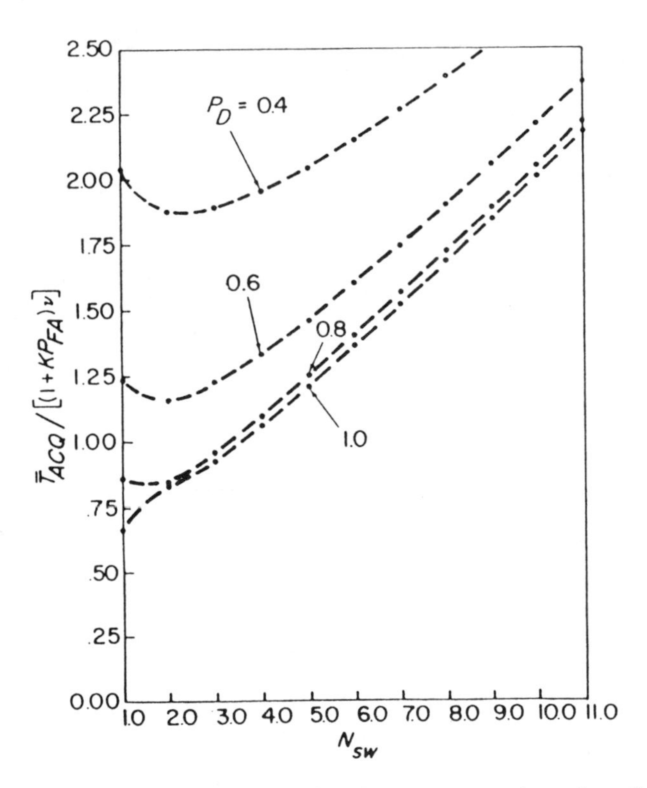

Figure 1.41. Normalized mean acquisition time versus number of partial windows for expanding window search strategy; single dwell system with triangular *a priori* distribution for code phase uncertainty.

whereas for the truncated Gaussian distribution considered in Section 1.6.1

$$E_1(k, N_{sw}) = \frac{Q\left(\frac{\nu}{2\sigma}\left(1 - \frac{k}{N_{sw}}\right)\right) - Q\left(\frac{\nu}{2\sigma}\left(1 - \frac{k-1}{N_{sw}}\right)\right)}{1 - 2Q\left(\frac{\nu}{2\sigma}\right)}$$

$$E_2(k, N_{sw})$$

$$= \sigma\left\{\frac{\exp\left[-\left(\frac{\nu}{2\sqrt{2}\,\sigma}\right)^2\left(1 - \frac{k}{N_{sw}}\right)^2\right] - \exp\left[-\left(\frac{\nu}{2\sqrt{2}\,\sigma}\right)^2\left(1 - \frac{k-1}{N_{sw}}\right)^2\right]}{1 - 2Q\left(\frac{\nu}{2\sigma}\right)}\right\}. \tag{1.249}$$

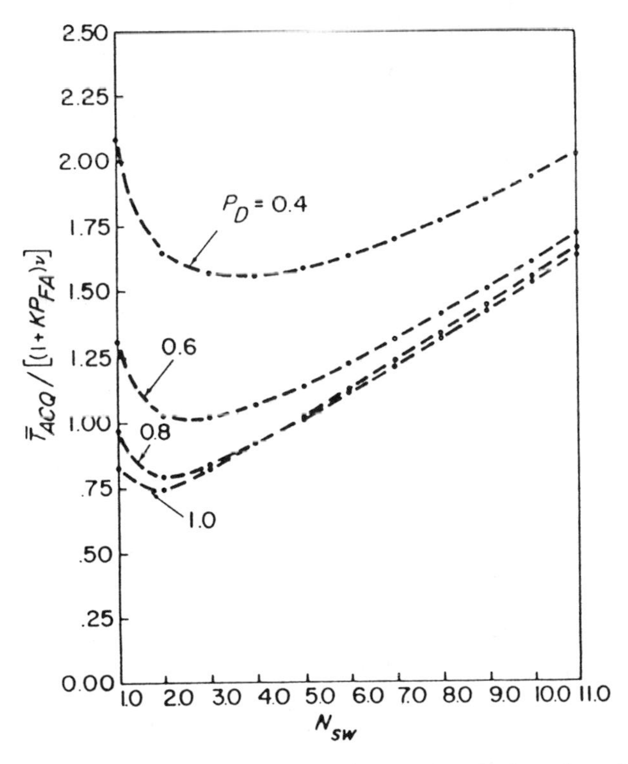

Figure 1.42a. Normalized mean acquisition time versus number of partial windows for expanding window search strategy, single dwell system with Gaussian *a priori* distribution for code phase uncertainty, $\nu/2 = 3\sigma$.

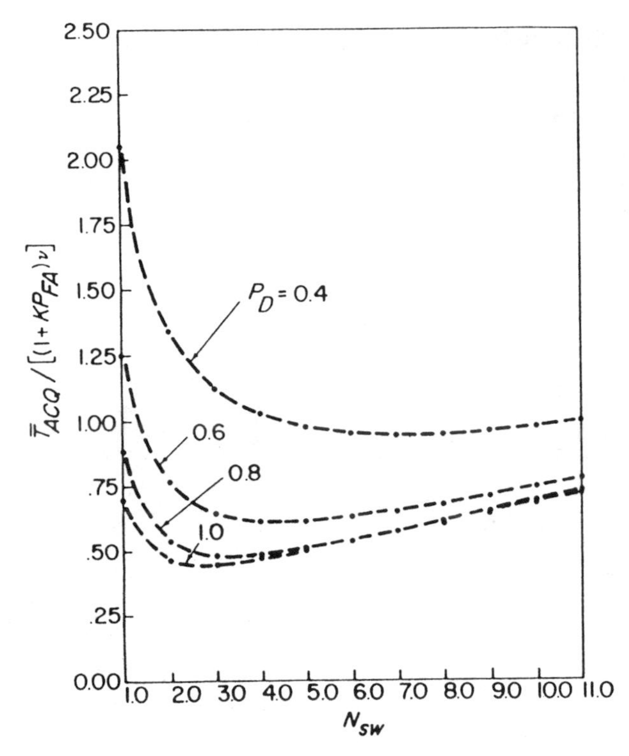

Figure 1.42b. Normalized mean acquisition time versus number of partial windows for expanding window search strategy; single dwell system with Gaussian *a priori* distribution for code phase uncertainty, $\nu/2 = 5\sigma$.

As before, we can ignore the $1/P_D$ term in (1.244) when ν is sufficiently large. Doing so, Figures 1.41 and 1.42a and 1.42b are plots of normalized acquisition time $\overline{T}_{ACQ}/[(1 + KP_{FA})\nu]$ versus the number of sweeps N_{sw} in the uncertainty region with detection probability P_D as a parameter. We observe from these figures that except for $P_D = 1$, there always exists an optimum number of partial windows in the sense of minimizing mean acquisition time. For $P_D = 1$, one window, i.e., a continuous/center z search, is optimum. Furthermore, the more peaked the distribution, e.g., Gaussian rather than triangular, or Gaussian with $\nu/2 = 5\sigma$ rather than Gaussian with $\nu/2 = 3\sigma$, the more there is to be gained by using an expanding window rather than a z-type search. Also, the sensitivity of using more than the optimum number of partial windows decreases as the distribution becomes more peaked.

1.7 PN SYNCHRONIZATION USING SEQUENTIAL DETECTION

We have already made the observation that a single fixed dwell (integration) time PN acquisition system is inefficient from an acquisition time standpoint since its detector spends as much time rejecting a false sync position as it does accepting the correct one. Clearly, if one is to minimize acquisition time, what is needed is a detector that quickly dismisses a false sync position (which occurs in all but one cell per pass through the uncertainty region) but is allowed to integrate over a much longer time interval during the single cell which corresponds to the correct code alignment.

The multiple dwell time system discussed previously was an attempt at accomplishing the above objective wherein the detector integration time was increased in *discrete* steps until the test failed (one output fell below threshold). Thus, for a false sync position, very few steps would be needed (short integration time), whereas for the true sync position, all of the steps would be needed (long integration time).

Another possibility is to allow the integration time to be *continuous* and replace the multiple threshold tests by a continuous test of a single dismissal threshold. Such a variable integration time detector is referred to as a *sequential detector* and the corresponding acquisition system is designed so that the mean time to dismiss the false sync position is much smaller than the integration time of a single dwell system. Thus, since the search spends virtually all of its time dismissing false sync positions, the mean acquisition time of the sequential detection PN acquisition system will be much less than that of the single dwell time system.

To further understand the mechanism by which the above reduction in acquisition time is achieved, we must consider a specific implementation. Consider the serial sequential detection PN acquisition system illustrated in Figure 1.43. Up until the output of the square-law envelope detector, the system operates identically to the single dwell acquisition system of Figure 1.1. Thus, in the absence of the bias voltage b, the output of the continuous time integrator would typically behave as in Figure 1.44a where we have illustrated both the signal plus noise and noise only cases. In particular, the integrator output would follow along the integrated mean of the square-law detector output, which from (1.76) and (1.75) is given by N_0Bt or $N_0B(1 + \gamma)t$, depending upon whether the cell being searched corresponds to a noise only or signal plus noise condition. Equivalently, for both hypotheses, the integrator outputs tend to increase linearly with time but at different slopes. Suppose now that one subtracts a fixed bias voltage b from the signal before integration. Then, if this bias is assigned a value between the means of the square-law detector outputs under the two hypotheses, i.e., $N_0B < b < N_0B(1 + \gamma)$, the integrator output will now tend to *decrease* linearly (with slope $N_0B - b$) when noise only is present, and *increase* linearly (with slope $N_0B(1 + \gamma) - b$) when signal plus noise is present (see Figure 1.44b). If one now chooses a threshold η (of negative value) which causes a dismissal whenever the integrator output falls below it, then the smaller the magnitude of this threshold, the faster the output for the noise only condition will dip below it.

This quick dismissal for the noise only condition is what forms the heart of the sequential detection system and provides the acquisition time ad-

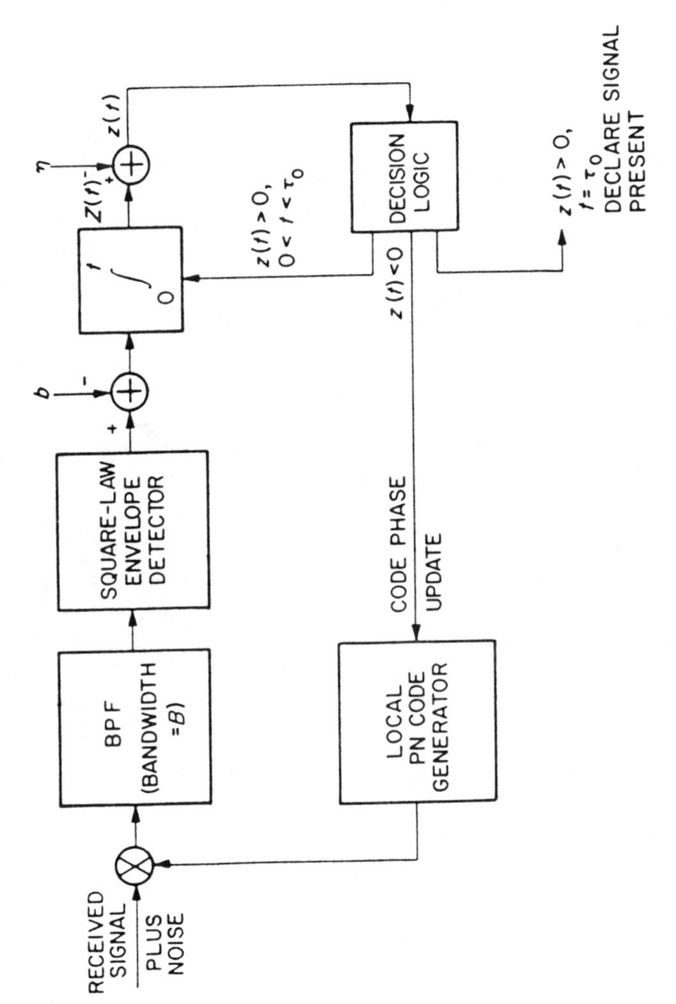

Figure 1.43. A serial sequential detection PN acquisition system with timeout feature.

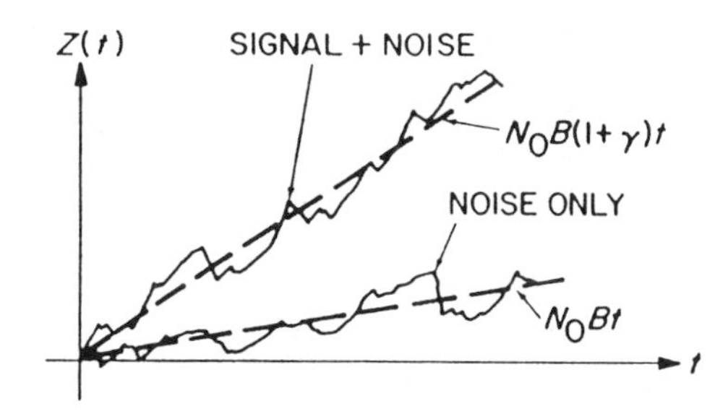

Figure 1.44a. Integrator output with bias voltage absent.

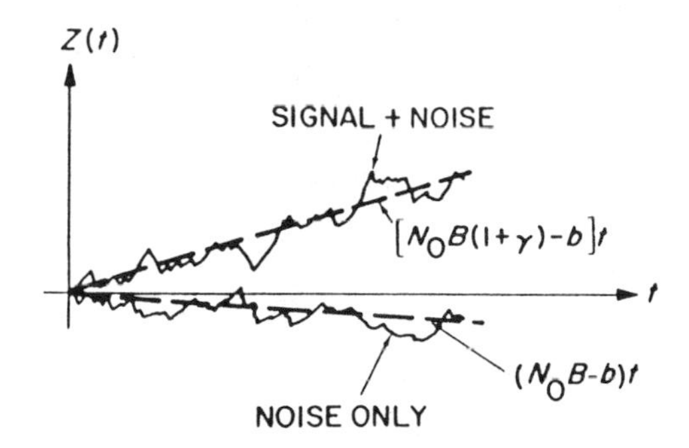

Figure 1.44b. Integrator output with bias voltage present.

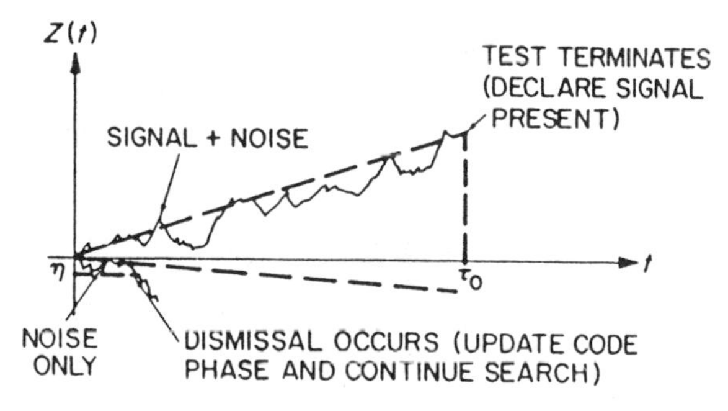

Figure 1.44c. Integrator outputs with threshold dismissal and test truncation.

vantage previously alluded to. Unfortunately, the smaller the magnitude of the threshold, the more likely is the integrator output for the signal plus noise case to also dip below the threshold thus causing a dismissal of the true sync position. Thus, a compromise threshold value must be chosen which allows for a relatively quick dismissal of false sync positions but tends to allow the integrator output for the true sync position to remain above threshold. If this latter event occurs for a designated interval of time, say τ_o, after which the test is terminated (see Figure 1.44c), then the signal is declared present and the cell being searched is declared as the true sync position. The test truncation time τ_o is often referred to as the *time-out* of the sequential detector and in some cases is replaced by a test against a second (positive-valued) threshold. In this instance, the declaration of signal present comes as soon as the integrator output rises above this positive-valued threshold rather than as a result of this output remaining above the lower (negative-valued) threshold for all $0 < t < \tau_o$.

Since the two-threshold sequential detection system is indeed the more classical type in that it represents a direct application of the sequential hypothesis testing originally discussed by Wald [10], we shall discuss its performance first before returning to the sequential detector with the upper threshold replaced by the time-out feature. Another reason for presenting the material in this order is that a good deal more attention (particularly of a theoretical nature) has been paid in the literature to the two-threshold type of system, some of which carries over to the time-out type of system. Unfortunately, both systems are extremely difficult to analyze, and thus, in most applications, one ordinarily relies on simulation results.

1.7.1 A Brief Review of Sequential Hypothesis Testing as Applied to the Non-Coherent Detection of a Sine Wave Signal in Gaussian Noise

Consider the two hypotheses H_0 and H_1 corresponding, respectively, to the application of Gaussian noise only and sine wave signal plus Gaussian noise to a square-law envelope detector as, for example, in Figure 1.45. The equations describing the input $x(t)$ and output $y(t)$ under these conditions are given by (1.58)–(1.60). Furthermore, if $y(t)$ is sampled at a rate $1/B$, then the samples y_k have a probability density function $p_0(y_k)$ given by (1.63) or $p_1(y_k)$ given by (1.61), where the subscript on $p(y_k)$ now corresponds to that on the particular hypothesis being tested.

Define the log-likelihood function

$$\Lambda_k = \ln\frac{p_1(y_k)}{p_0(y_k)} = \ln\left[e^{-\gamma}I_0\left(2\sqrt{\frac{\gamma y_k}{2\sigma^2}}\right)\right]$$

$$= -\gamma + \ln\left[I_0\left(2\sqrt{\frac{\gamma y_k}{2\sigma^2}}\right)\right]. \tag{1.250}$$

Then the sequential *probability ratio* test [27] for the non-coherent detection of a sine wave signal in Gaussian noise sequentially compares the running sum

$$v_i = \sum_{k=1}^{i}\Lambda_k = \sum_{k=1}^{i}\left(-\gamma + \ln\left[I_0\left(2\sqrt{\gamma y_k^*}\right)\right]\right) \tag{1.251}$$

to two thresholds η_1' and η_2' ($\eta_2' < \eta_1'$), where as before it is convenient to talk about the normalized samples $y_k^* \triangleq y_k/2\sigma^2 = y_k/N_0B$. The comparison is made for each $i = 1, 2, \ldots$ until the inequalities $\eta_2' < v_i < \eta_1'$ are not satisfied. Then, if $v_i \le \eta_2'$, it is decided that the signal is not present (dismissal), and if $\eta_1' \le v_i$, it is decided that the signal is present (alarm).

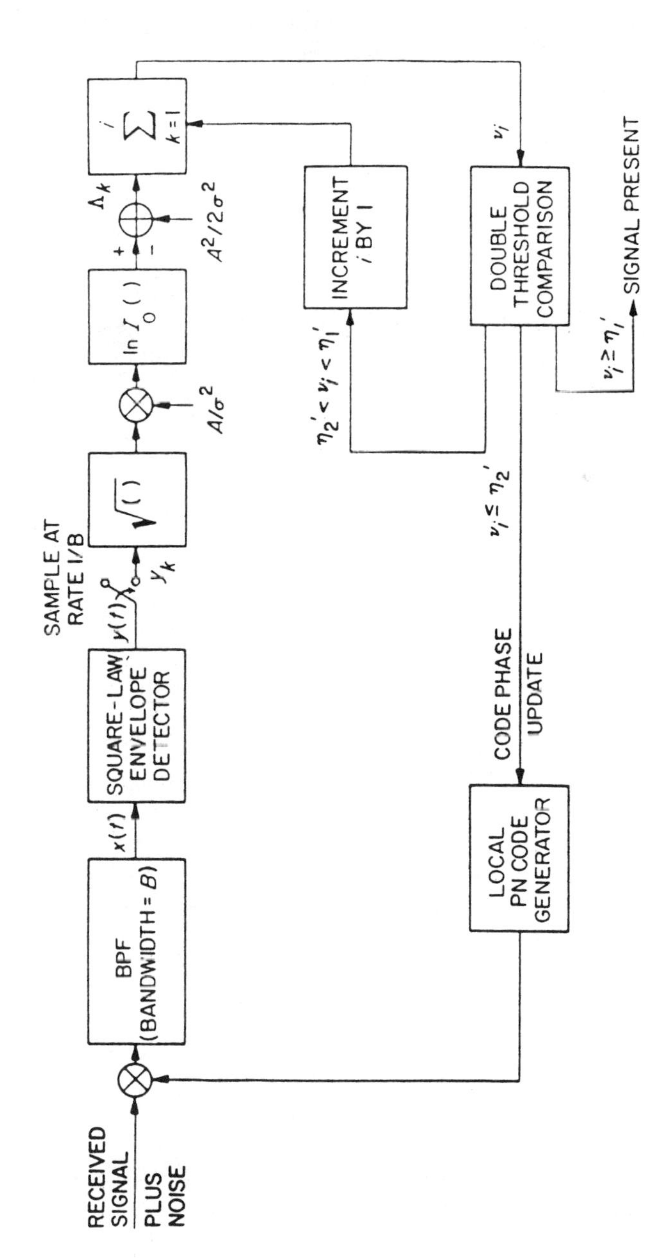

Figure 1.45. Block diagram of a sequential detection PN acquisition system.

Figure 1.45 is a block diagram of the sequential detector with test statistic as in (1.251).

In some discussions of sequential detection, an envelope detector alone is postulated instead of a square-law envelope detector. In this case, the samples of the envelope detector output would have probability density functions

$$p_0(y_k) = \begin{cases} \dfrac{y_k}{\sigma^2}\exp\left(-\dfrac{y_k^2}{2\sigma^2}\right); & y_k \geq 0 \\ 0; & \text{otherwise} \end{cases}$$

$$p_1(y_k) = \begin{cases} \dfrac{y_k}{\sigma^2}\exp\left[-\left(\dfrac{y_k^2}{2\sigma^2} + \gamma\right)\right] I_0\left(2y_k\sqrt{\dfrac{\gamma}{2\sigma^2}}\right); & y_k \geq 0 \\ 0; & \text{otherwise} \end{cases} \tag{1.252}$$

and log-likelihood function

$$\begin{aligned} \Lambda_k &= \ln\left[e^{-\gamma} I_0\left(2y_k\sqrt{\frac{\gamma}{2\sigma^2}}\right)\right] \\ &= -\gamma + \ln\left[I_0\left(2y_k\sqrt{\frac{\gamma}{2\sigma^2}}\right)\right]. \end{aligned} \tag{1.253}$$

Comparing (1.253) with (1.250), we note that the block diagram of Figure 1.45 can be made to apply to the sequential detection system with an envelope detector by simply removing the square root device preceding the multiplication by A/σ^2. This result is intuitively obvious since the tandem combination of square-law and square-root devices following an envelope detector has no effect on its output.

Wald showed [10] that the thresholds η_1' and η_2' are approximately related to the probabilities of false alarm P_{FA} and detection P_D by

$$P_{FA} \cong \frac{1 - \exp(\eta_2')}{\exp(\eta_1') - \exp(\eta_2')} \tag{1.254}$$

and

$$P_D \cong \frac{\exp(\eta_1') - \exp(\eta_1' + \eta_2')}{\exp(\eta_1') - \exp(\eta_2')}. \tag{1.255}$$

Furthermore, the average number of samples $\overline{N}_d$ required to dismiss when signal is not present was shown to be approximately given by the expression

$$\overline{N}_d = \frac{P_{FA}\eta_1' + (1 - P_{FA})\eta_2'}{E\{\Lambda_k\}} = \frac{P_{FA}\ln\left(\dfrac{P_D}{P_{FA}}\right) + (1 - P_{FA})\ln\left(\dfrac{1 - P_D}{1 - P_{FA}}\right)}{E\{\Lambda_k\}} \tag{1.256}$$

where from (1.73) and (1.251)

$$E\{\Lambda_k\} = -\gamma + \int_0^\infty \ln\left[I_0\left(2\sqrt{\gamma y_k^*}\right)\right]\exp(-y^*)\,dy^*. \qquad (1.257)$$

Evaluation of (1.256) is difficult because of the requirement to accurately compute the expectation in (1.257) for each value of γ of interest. Since the integral cannot be obtained in closed form, one can either evaluate it using numerical integration or first expand the $\ln I_0$ function in a power series and compute as many moments of y_k^* as necessary to achieve the desired degree of accuracy. In the case of the latter, approximation of $\ln I_0(x)$ by only the first few terms in the expansion restricts its validity to small values of x or, equivalently, small values of pre-detection SNR.

Another approach based on the small SNR assumption is to make a similar expansion of $\ln I_0(x)$ *directly in the sequential test statistic* of (1.251) and keep only the first few terms. Doing this has the effect of simplifying the detector implementation, which, except when digital processing allows use of a look-up table for $\ln I_0(x)$, is ordinarily difficult. In the next section, we discuss a small SNR sequential test and the corresponding detector performance corresponding to a two-term approximation of the $\ln I_0$ function.

1.7.2 The Biased Square-Law Sequential Detector

Although (1.251) defines a sequential test for the optimum detector, the important case of small pre-detection SNR allows one to simplify this equation into a similar test for an easier to implement (and analyze) detector as follows. When γ is small, the $\ln I_0$ function can be approximated by the first two terms of its power series, namely,

$$\ln I_0(x) \cong \frac{x^2}{4} - \frac{x^4}{64}. \qquad (1.258)$$

Applying (1.258) to (1.251) then gives

$$v_i = \sum_{k=1}^{i}\left(-\gamma + \gamma y_k^* - \frac{1}{4}\gamma^2 y_k^{*2}\right). \qquad (1.259)$$

As suggested in [27], the latter term in (1.259) is further approximated by its expected value when no signal is present. Thus, from (1.76)

$$\overline{y_k^{*2}} = \sigma_{y^*}^2 + \left(\overline{y^*}\right)^2 = 2 \qquad (1.260)$$

and

$$v_i \cong \sum_{k=1}^{i}\left(-\gamma + \gamma y_k^* - \frac{\gamma^2}{2}\right)$$
$$= \sum_{k=1}^{i}\gamma\left[y_k^* - \left(1 + \frac{\gamma}{2}\right)\right] \qquad (1.261)$$

Normalizing v_i by N_0B/γ and recalling the relation between y_k and y_k^* gives the sequential test statistic corresponding to the optimum detector *for small SNR*, namely,

$$Z_i \triangleq \frac{N_0 B}{\gamma} v_i = \sum_{k=1}^{i} (y_k - b) = \sum_{k=1}^{i} Y_k \tag{1.262}$$

where from (1.261) the bias b is given by

$$b = N_0 B\left(1 + \frac{\gamma}{2}\right). \tag{1.263}$$

A block diagram of the small SNR sequential detector is illustrated in Figure 1.46. Identifying (1.262) with Z of (1.64) when $N_B = 1$, one observes that the optimum bias of (1.263) lies halfway between the means of the square-law detector output under the hypotheses H_0 and H_1. Equivalently, for this choice of bias, the integrator output in the presence of the bias voltage will tend to increase linearly when signal plus noise are present at the same rate that it tends to decrease linearly when noise only is present (see Figure 1.44b).

Before proceeding to a discussion of performance, we hasten to point out that for a two-hypothesis test of a sampled random variable, the sequential probability-ratio test is optimum in the sense that, for given P_{FA} and P_D, it requires the minimum average number of samples to produce a decision. For our application, namely, rapid acquisition of a PN sequence in noise, minimizing the average number of samples required is equivalent to minimizing the average dwell time per code phase cell being searched.

Although the sequential probability-ratio test was discovered by Wald in the early 1940's while working on radar detection, an accurate characterization of its performance did not come until many years later. In particular, the integral equation approach of Albert [28][31] was applied by Kendall [29] in 1965 to give exact solutions for the false alarm probability and average test duration of the biased square-law sequential detector in the absence of signal. These results were unique in that they were valid without any restrictions on either the pre-detection SNR or on the thresholds η_1 and η_2. In the next section, we summarize these results beginning with a brief presentation of Albert's integral equation approach.

1.7.3 Probability of False Alarm and Average Test Duration in the Absence of Signal

Let $\{x_i\}$ represent a sequence of observables which form a stationary Markov process with transitions governed by the probability distribution function $F(x_i|x_{i-1})$. Denote by d_i, $i = 1, 2$ a pair of decisions which is to

[31]Actually, Albert's work considered a far more general sequential test than the sequential probability-ratio test of Wald. Our interest, however, is only in Wald's test, which is a special case of Albert's results corresponding to stationary increments in the log-likelihood ratio.

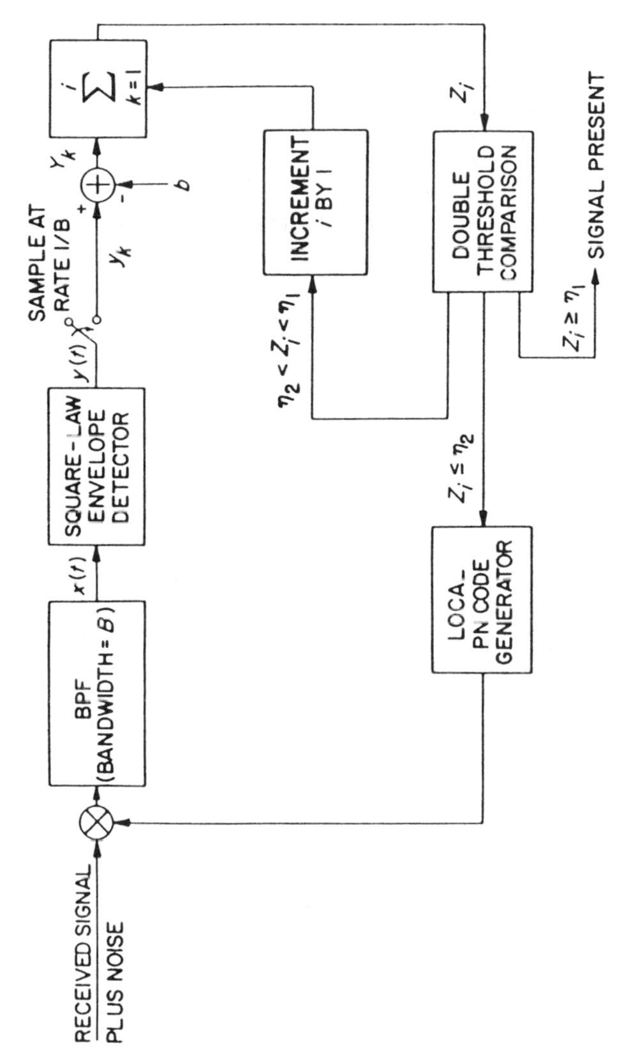

Figure 1.46. Block diagram of a small SNR sequential detection PN acquisition system.

be made about $F(x_i|x_{i-1})$ and d_0 the decision to defer making either d_1 or d_2. The test is conducted by first choosing an arbitrary starting point x_0 (later on we shall set $x_0 = 0$) and making one of the decisions d_i with probabilities $\pi_i(x_0)$, $i = 0, 1, 2$. If either d_1 or d_2 is made the test continues and the element x_1 is drawn using the distribution $F(x_1|x_0)$. Once again one of the decisions is made with the set of probabilities $\pi_i(x_1)$, $i = 0, 1, 2$ and the test either terminates or x_2 is drawn using the distribution $F(x_2|x_1)$. This process is continued until either d_1 or d_2 is made. To guarantee that this occurs with unit probability in a finite number of trials, it must be assumed that there exists an integer M and some $\rho < 1$ such that for all $m \geq M$ the inequality

$$\int_{-\infty}^{\infty}\int_{-\infty}^{\infty}\cdots\int_{-\infty}^{\infty}\prod_{i=1}^{m}\pi_0(x_i)\,dF(x_i|x_{i-1}) \leq \rho \leq 1 \tag{1.264}$$

is satisfied for all x_0.

Using the foregoing model Albert [28] shows that the probability $P_i(x_0)$ that the test ends with decision d_1 or d_2 satisfies the integral equation

$$P_i(x_0) = \pi_i(x_0) + \pi_0(x_0)\int_{-\infty}^{\infty} P_i(y)\,dF(y|x_0) \tag{1.265}$$

and the average test duration (average sample number) $M_1(x_0)$ satisfies the integral equation

$$M_1(x_0) = \pi_0(x_0) + \pi_0(x_0)\int_{-\infty}^{\infty} M_1(y)\,dF(y|x_0). \tag{1.266}$$

For most cases of interest, these integral equations are difficult if not impossible to solve. However, for the non-coherent sequential detection of a sine wave in Gaussian noise using a biased square-law detector, Kendall [29] was able to obtain exact solutions. In particular, the sequence $\{x_i\}$ now corresponds to $\{Z_i\}$ of (1.262), d_1 is the dismissal decision, and d_2 is the alarm decision. Since from (1.262), $Z_i = Z_{i-1} + Y_i = Z_{i-1} + y_i - b$, then, using (1.63),

$$dF(Z_i|Z_{i-1}) = \begin{cases} \dfrac{1}{2\sigma^2}\exp\left[-\left(\dfrac{Z_i - Z_{i-1} + b}{2\sigma^2}\right)\right] dZ_i; & Z_i - Z_{i-1} \geq b \\ 0; & \text{otherwise} \end{cases}. \tag{1.267}$$

Also, the set of decision probabilities $\pi_i(Z_k)$, $i = 0, 1, 2$ is stationary (i.e., independent of k) and given by

$$\pi_0(z) = \begin{cases} 1; & \eta_2 < Z < \eta_1 \\ 0; & \text{otherwise} \end{cases}$$

$$\pi_1(z) = \begin{cases} 1; & Z \leq \eta_2 \\ 0; & \eta_2 < Z \end{cases}$$

$$\pi_2(z) = \begin{cases} 1, & \eta_1 \leq Z \\ 0; & Z < \eta_1 \end{cases}. \tag{1.268}$$

Finally, letting $Z_0 = 0$, then, for $\eta_2 < 0 < \eta_1$,

$$P_{FA} \triangleq P_2(0) = \frac{\exp(-\eta_2'/\gamma)G(-D\eta_2'; Db')}{\exp[(\eta_1' - \eta_2' + b')/\gamma]G[D(\eta_1' - \eta_2' + b'); Db']} \tag{1.269}$$

where we have introduced the normalizations

$$b' \triangleq \frac{\gamma b}{2\sigma^2} = \frac{\gamma b}{N_0 B}$$

$$\eta_i' \triangleq \frac{\gamma \eta_i}{2\sigma^2} = \frac{\gamma \eta_i}{N_0 B}; \; i = 1,2 \tag{1.270}$$

and

$$D \triangleq \frac{1}{\gamma}\exp(-b'/\gamma). \tag{1.271}$$

Also, the function $G(x; c)$ is defined by

$$G(x; c) = 1 + \sum_{n=1}^{N} \frac{(nc - x)^n}{n!} \tag{1.272}$$

where N is an integer chosen to satisfy the inequalities

$$c \leq Nc \leq x \leq (N+1)c. \tag{1.273}$$

By similar methods, Kendall [29] obtains a solution to (1.266) for the average sample number $\overline{N}_d$ which is given by

$$\begin{aligned}\overline{N}_d \triangleq M_1(0) &= \exp(-\eta_2'/\gamma)H[-D\eta_2'; Db'] \\ &+ P_2(0)\{1 - \exp[(\eta_1' - \eta_2' + b')/\gamma]H[D(\eta_1' - \eta_2' + b'); Db']\}\end{aligned} \tag{1.274}$$

where $P_2(0)$ is given by (1.269) and

$$H(x; c) \triangleq (N+1)\exp(-x/\gamma D) - \sum_{n=1}^{N}\sum_{i=0}^{n-1} \frac{(nc - x)^i}{i!(\gamma D)^{i-n}} \tag{1.275}$$

with N still obtained from (1.273). The *average test duration* $\bar{\tau}_d$, for the particular noise only cell under investigation, is simply

$$\bar{\tau}_d = \overline{N}_d/B \tag{1.276}$$

since for the real system the Z_i represent samples taken at a rate $1/B$.

Before presenting numerical illustrations of these results, we point out that with suitable approximations they can be shown to agree with Wald's results [10]. In particular, since Wald's results are approximate in that they neglect the "excess over the bounds," i.e., at the end of the test we have either $Z_i \leq \eta_2$ or $\eta_1 \leq Z_i$, not simply $Z_i = \eta_2$ or $Z_i = \eta_1$, then if the values of the thresholds are such that this effect is negligible, Albert's results simplify to those of Wald. Also, the normalized threshold b' of (1.270) is not required to correspond to the optimum bias of (1.263), i.e.,

$$b' = \gamma\left(1 + \frac{\gamma}{2}\right) = \gamma + \frac{\gamma^2}{2} \tag{1.277}$$

and thus, with Albert's approach, one can study the effect of bias variations on the resulting performance measures. On the other hand, although not previously stated, Wald's result for false alarm probability as applied to the square-law biased detector implies the optimum bias of (1.263) and furthermore is independent of γ [see (1.254)].

Figure 1.47 contains three sets of plots of false alarm probability versus the upper threshold η'_1 with pre-detection signal-to-noise ratio γ as a parameter. The first set of plots corresponds to Wald's result of (1.254). The remaining two sets are obtained from Albert's exact result, i.e., (1.269) with two different biases, namely, the optimum choice of (1.277) and $b' = \gamma$. Perhaps the most striking feature of the exact results is their extreme sensitivity to small variations in bias. For example, when $\gamma = .01$, then from (1.277) we would have an optimum bias $b' = .01005$, which only differs from $b' = \gamma = .01$ by an amount equal to .00005. Nevertheless, the false alarm probabilities for these two bias values are markedly different. A similar situation occurs in Figure 1.48 where the average sample number $M_1(0)$ is plotted versus γ with lower threshold η'_2 as a parameter and the same three situations as in Figure 1.47. Here, Wald's result for the average sample number of a sequential test corresponds to evaluating (1.256) with the $\ln I_0$ function in (1.257) approximated, as previously discussed, by (1.258). Performing the expectation with the aid of (1.76) gives

$$E\{\Lambda_k\} = -\frac{\gamma^2}{2} \tag{1.278}$$

which when substituted in (1.256) results in

$$M_1(0) = -\frac{P_{FA}\eta'_1 + (1 - P_{FA})\eta'_2}{\gamma^2/2} \tag{1.279}$$

where P_{FA} is given by (1.254).

Unfortunately, a similar analysis for the case of signal present is difficult and has not been made available in the open literature. Thus, the relationship among detection probability, pre-detection signal-to-noise ratio, bias, and the two-decision thresholds has not been obtained and, as a result, a complete analytical characterization of the moments of the system acquisition time is not possible.

Another unfortunate situation occurs in regard to the application of Albert's approach to the time-out type of sequential detection system (see Figure 1.43) where the upper threshold is replaced by a maximum time feature. Even in the case of signal absent, there appears to be no valid modification of the basic approach to apply to this situation.

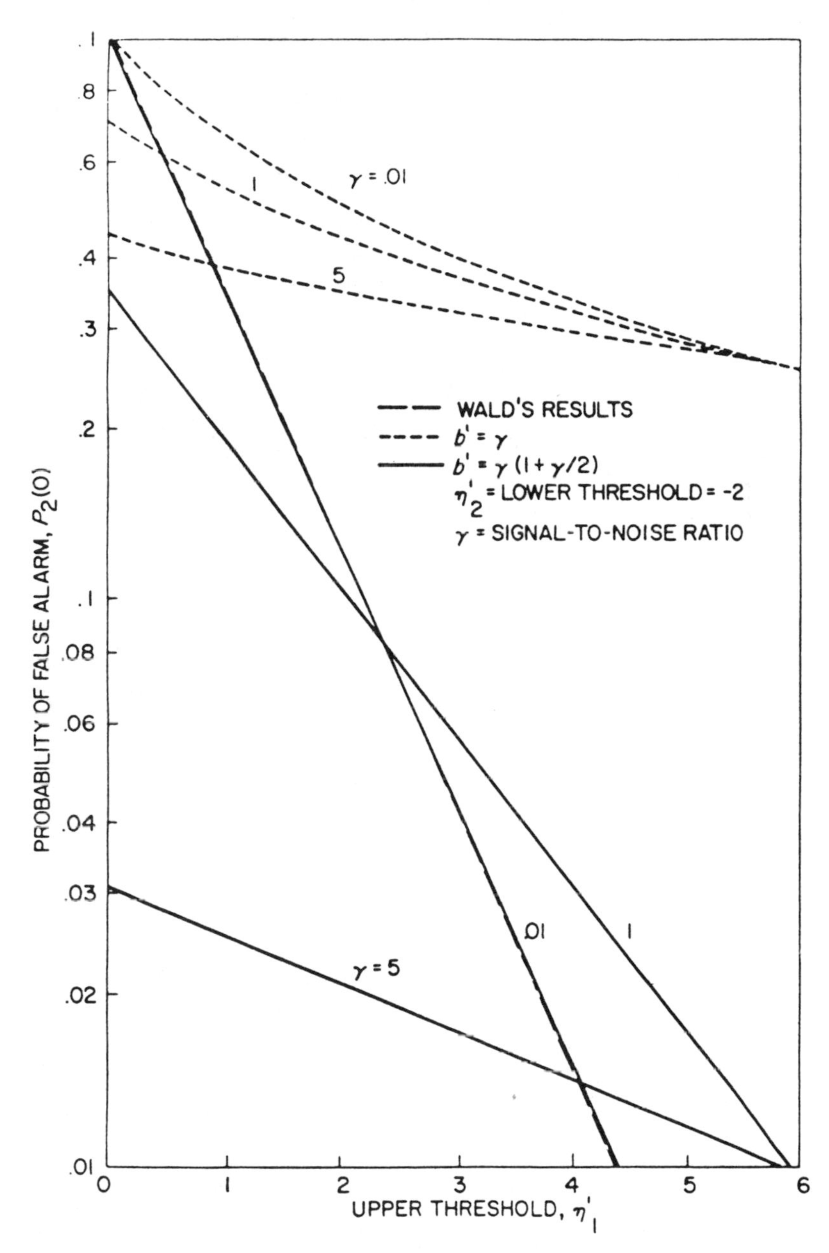

Figure 1.47. Probability of alarm for the biased square-law detector when the signal is not present (reprinted from [29]).

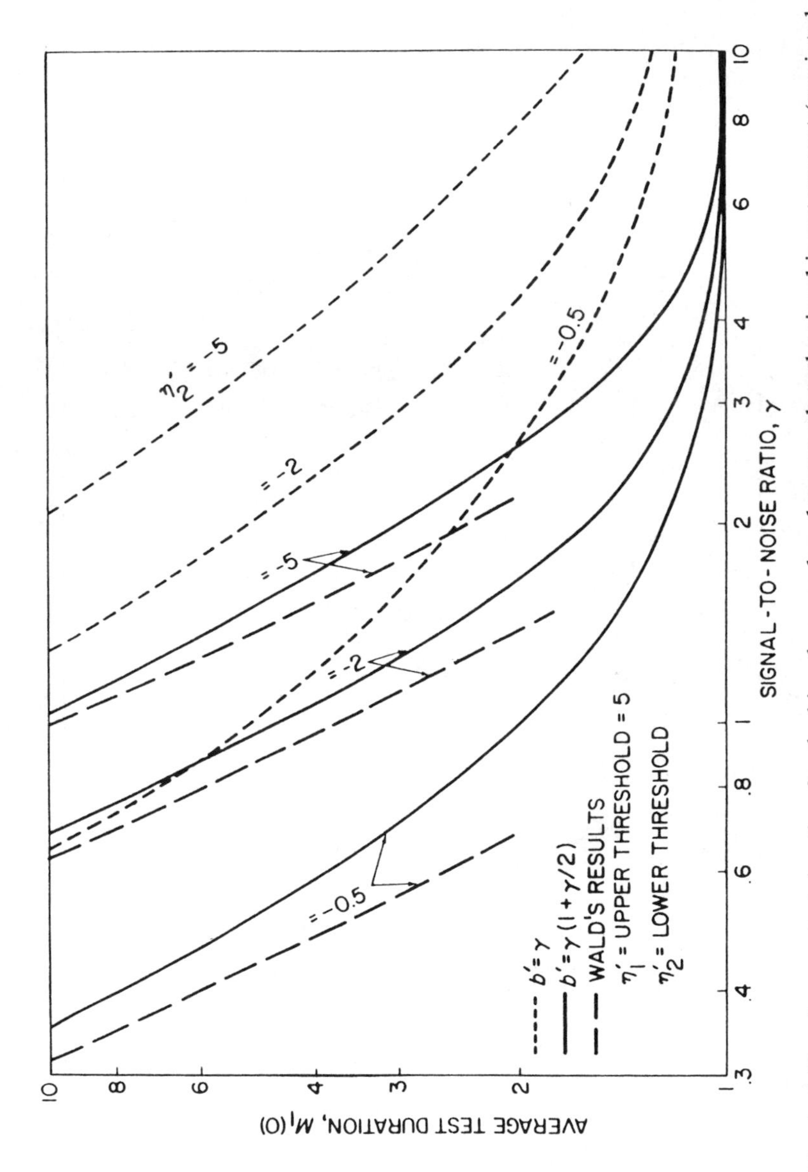

Figure 1.48. Average test duration for the biased square-law detector when the signal is not present (reprinted from [29]).

In view of the foregoing limitations and analytical difficulties, one normally, at this point, turns to a simulation approach. The salient features of such an approach along with typical numerical illustrative results are presented in the next section. Before competely abandoning the analytical approach, however, we recall that Wald's approximate analysis does indeed provide us with a relationship among false alarm probability, detection probability, and the upper and lower detection thresholds [see (1.254) and (1.255)]. Thus, in the region of validity of his approach, i.e., small values of γ and the bias of (1.263), one can combine (1.254) and (1.255) with (1.276) and (1.279) and obtain an expression for the average dismissal time (average test duration for a noise only cell). This relation can then be compared with the fixed dwell time determined from (1.81) for the single dwell system to establish the degree of superiority of the sequential detector.

Thus, we conclude this section with a comparison of the mean search times of the single dwell and sequential detection systems using Wald's approach to analytically characterize the latter. In particular, from (1.254)

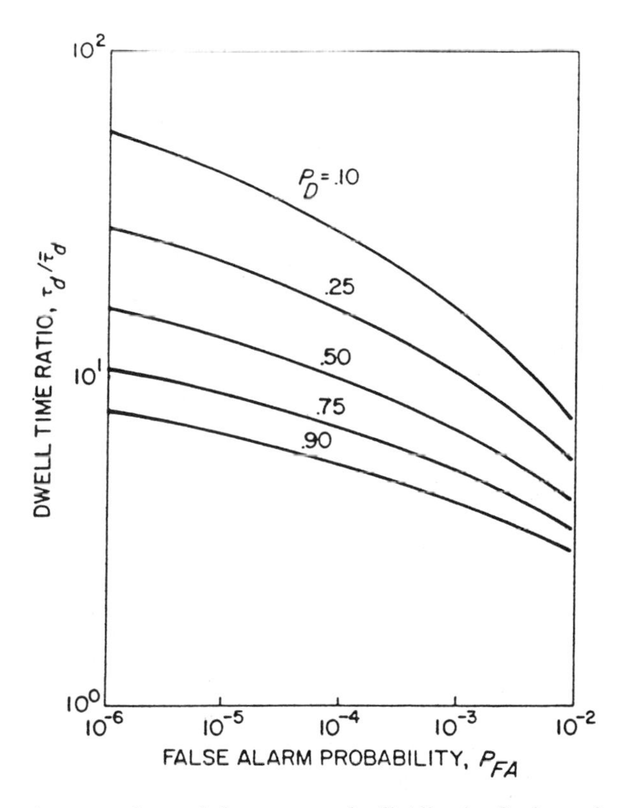

Figure 1.49. A comparison of the average dwell (dismissal) time of a square-law sequential detection system with the dwell time of a fixed single dwell system; $\gamma = -20$ dB.

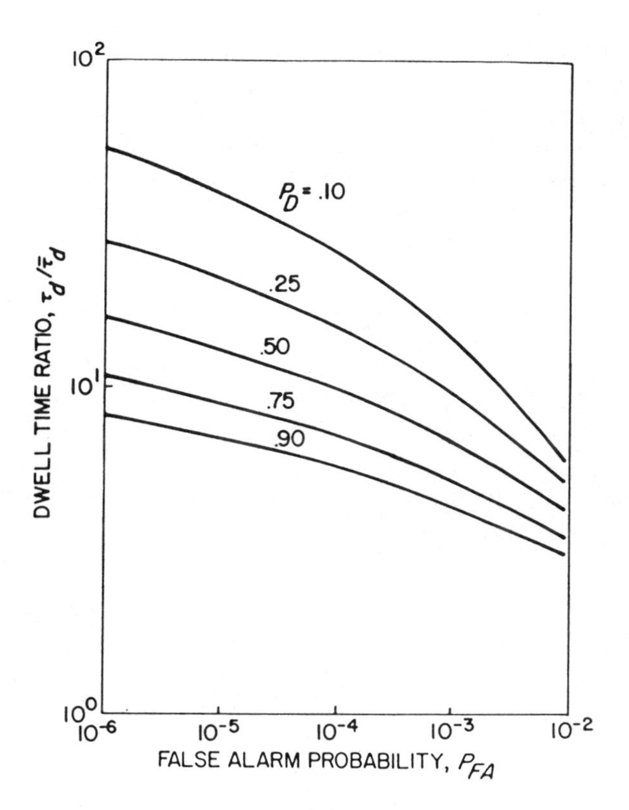

Figure 1.50. A comparison of the average dwell (dismissal) time of a square-law sequential detection system with the dwell time of a fixed single dwell system; $\gamma = -10$ dB.

and (1.255) we obtain

$$\eta_1' = \ln \frac{P_D}{P_{FA}}$$

$$\eta_2' = \ln \frac{1 - P_D}{1 - P_{FA}} \tag{1.280}$$

which when substituted in (1.279) and combined with (1.276) yields

$$B\bar{\tau}_d = -\frac{P_{FA} \ln \dfrac{P_D}{P_{FA}} + (1 - P_{FA}) \ln \dfrac{1 - P_D}{1 - P_{FA}}}{\gamma^2/2}. \tag{1.281}$$

For the single dwell system, solving (1.81) for $B\tau_d$ and, for simplicity, ignoring the prime on γ' gives

$$B\tau_d = \left[\frac{Q^{-1}(P_{FA}) - \sqrt{1 + 2\gamma}\, Q^{-1}(P_D)}{\gamma}\right]^2. \tag{1.282}$$

Figures 1.49 and 1.50 are plots of the ratio $\tau_d/\bar{\tau}_d$ versus P_{FA} with P_D as a parameter and $\gamma = -20$ dB and $\gamma = -10$ dB respectively. A comparison of the two sets of curves reveals their relative insensitivity to the value of pre-detection signal-to-noise ratio γ.

1.7.4 Simulation Results

The final approach for evaluating the performance of a sequential detection system is to simulate the system on a digital computer. Although consuming considerable amounts of computer time, this approach has many advantages over the previously discussed analytical and numerical evaluation techniques. Some of these advantages are as follows:

(1) It allows performance evaluation over a wide range of system parameters, e.g., thresholds, signal-to-noise ratios, false alarm and detection probabilities, etc., merely by changing the program input data.

(2) It is a more "exact" representation of the system behavior. For example, the analytic results presented in the previous two sections originated from consideration of the radar problem where the signal is either "fully on" or not present. In Section 1.2.5 we pointed out that in the spread-spectrum application, the signal may be only "partially on" in that, because of the granularity of the half-chip search step, the signal-present condition occurs at several points along the PN correlation curve. Furthermore, the received PN code is, in general, not synchronous with the local replica so that none of the above signal-present conditions corresponds to fully on; thus, the true signal-to-noise ratio is a random variable that depends on the degree of misalignment between the two codes. Although some approximate analytical modifications were suggested in Section 1.2.5 to try and account for these effects, a simulation can directly model these effects by modelling the code start time as a uniformly distributed random variable between zero and one half of a chip. Simulation results [30] indicate an SNR penalty of about 1 dB due to this random code alignment rather than the pessimistic 2.5 dB suggested in Section 1.2.5 corresponding to a worst case (quarter of a chip) misalignment.

(3) It allows for the consideration of other simplified detector implementations whose performance is either difficult or impossible to evaluate analytically. For example, with a digital implementation, an absolute value detector function might be preferable. Comparison of this implementation with a square-law envelope detector, envelope detector, or the "ideal" detector of Figure 1.45 is then straightforward with a simulation approach.

(4) Finally, the simulation approach is useful in establishing the regions of validity of the various analytical and numerical approximations.

We begin our discussion of simulation results with a comparison of the noise-only behavior of the sequential test for four different detector types. In particular, we examine the variation of false alarm probability and average number of samples to dismiss as a function of bias for:

1. the "ideal" detector (Figure 1.45)
2. the square-law envelope detector (Figure 1.46)

3. the envelope detector (Figure 1.46 with an envelope instead of a square-law envelope detector)
4. the absolute-value envelope detector (Figure 1.46 with an absolute value instead of a square-law envelope detector).

If, for the square-law envelope detector of case (2), the detector output samples y_k are characterized as in (1.60), namely,

$$y_k = (A + n_{ck})^2 + n_{sk}^2 \tag{1.283}$$

where $y_k \triangleq y(kT)$, $n_{ck} \triangleq n_c(kT)$, and $n_{sk} \triangleq n_s(kT)$, then for the envelope detector of case (3) we would have

$$y_k = \sqrt{(A + n_{ck})^2 + n_{sk}^2}\,. \tag{1.284}$$

Similarly, the absolute-value detector model of case (4) would imply

$$y_k = |A + n_{ck}| + |n_{sk}| \tag{1.285}$$

which simulates inphase and quadrature sampling with a large number of quantization levels and the sign bit discarded.

From our previous discussions, it is clear that for all of the above implementations, the sequential test is governed by the choice of three variables, namely, the upper and lower thresholds and the bias. Typically, the upper threshold and bias determine the false alarm probability, P_{FA}, whereas the lower threshold and bias determine the average number of samples to dismiss, $\overline{N}_d$.

Simulation results [30] performed on all four detector types reveal that the false alarm probability is governed by the relation

$$P_{FA} = 0.5\exp(-fT_u) \tag{1.286}$$

where f is a false-alarm rate parameter whose variation with detector type and bias is illustrated in Figure 1.51 and T_u denotes the upper test threshold. The table below relates, for each of the four above cases, the bias and T_u to the analogous parameters previously introduced in this section.

Detector Type	Bias	T_u
Ideal	$\gamma b/2\sigma^2 = b'$	$\gamma\eta_1/2\sigma^2 = \eta_1'$
Square-law	$b/2\sigma^2 = b'/\gamma$	$\eta_1/2\sigma^2 = \eta_1'/\gamma$
Envelope	$b/\sqrt{2}\,\sigma$	$\eta_1/\sqrt{2}\,\sigma$
Absolute-value	$b/\sqrt{2}\,\sigma$	$\eta_1/\sqrt{2}\,\sigma$

From the results in Figure 1.51, we observe that, for the ideal detector, $f = 1$ independent of the bias point, whereas the other detector types have a linear dependence of f on the logarithm of the bias point. This dependence of cases (2), (3), and (4) on bias point could no doubt be removed by a gain normalization of the detector output samples analogous to the A/σ^2 multiplication for the ideal detector (see Figure 1.45). However, the primary purpose of the comparison being to discover the effects of simple implemen-

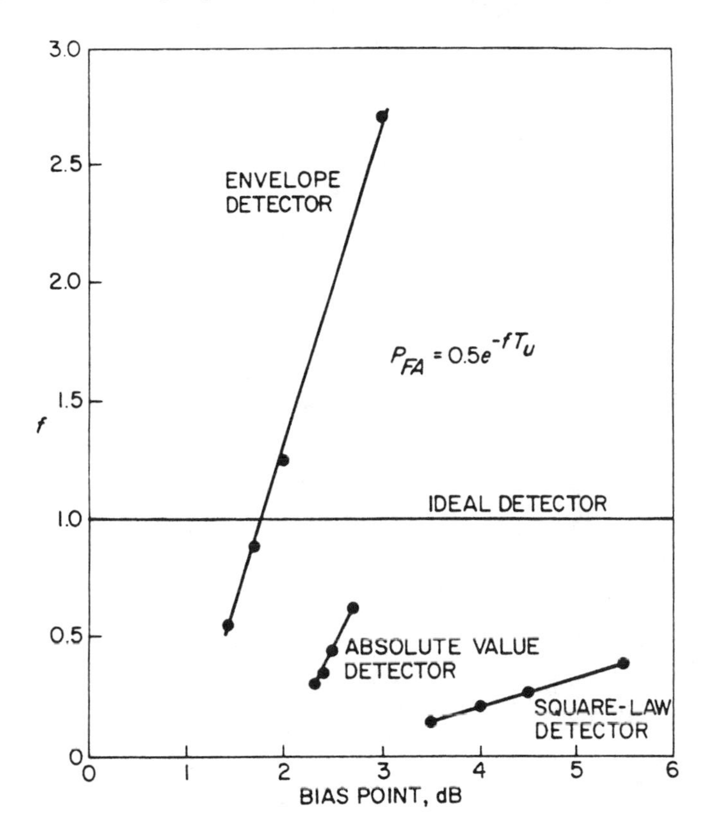

Figure 1.51. Variation in false alarm parameter f with bias point (reprinted from [30]).

tations, such a gain normalization was not introduced into the simulation runs.

Further simulation results [30] performed on the same four detector types produced the following approximate relationship (valid for $\overline{N}_d > 3$) characterizing the average number of samples per dismissal (average sample number):

$$\overline{N}_d = 1.5 - dT_L \tag{1.287}$$

where d is a dismissal parameter whose variation with detector type and bias is illustrated in Figure 1.52 and T_L denotes the lower detection threshold (a negative quantity). Here again T_L is related to η_2 and η_2' in the identical way that T_u was previously related to η_1 and η_1' for the four cases under investigation. Furthermore, the results in Figure 1.52 were generated by setting the bias point to the desired value and then setting T_u to give $P_{FA} = 10^{-6}$ in accordance with (1.286) and the value of f determined from Figure 1.51.

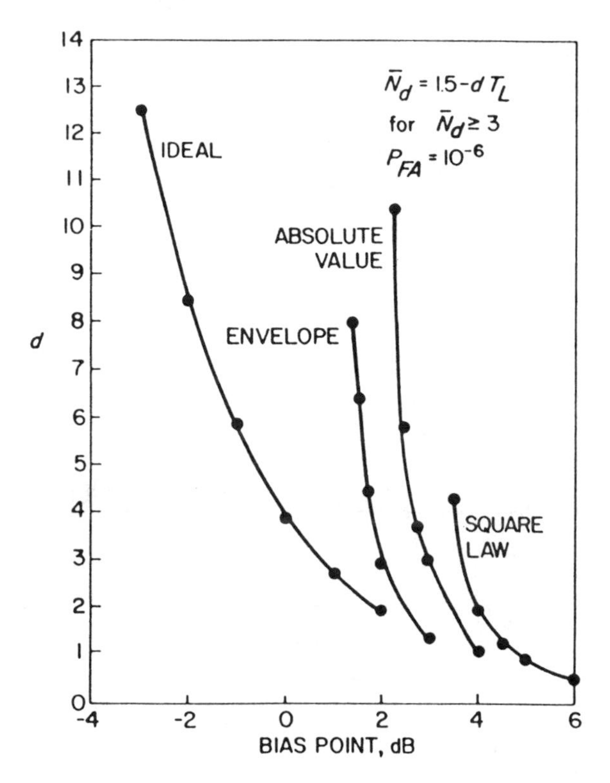

Figure 1.52. Variation of dismissal parameter d with bias point (reprinted from [30]).

In summary, the noise-only simulation results of Figures 1.51 and 1.52 indicate that increasing the bias is effective both in reducing the false alarm probability (except for the ideal detector) and reducing the average number of samples per dismissal.

Simulation results for the signal-plus-noise hypothesis are presented in Figures 1.53 and 1.54, which plot missed detection probability $(1 - P_D)$ versus bias for perfect code phase (operation at the precise peak of the PN code autocorrelation function) and random code phase, respectively. For both sets of plots the pre-detection signal-to-noise ratio γ is chosen equal to 0 dB. Furthermore, for each value of bias point, values of f and d are determined from Figures 1.51 and 1.52, which for $P_{FA} = 10^{-6}$ and $\bar{N}_d = 10.5$ allow calculation of the upper and lower thresholds T_u and T_L from (1.286) and (1.287), respectively. Figure 1.53 reveals the not too surprising result that for each detector implementation there exists an optimum value of bias in the sense of minimum miss probability. Clearly, for the ideal detector with perfect code phase, this optimum bias should theoretically be equal to the pre-detection signal-to-noise ratio, i.e., 0 dB. The simulation results essentially bear this out. What is perhaps surprising, however, is the fact

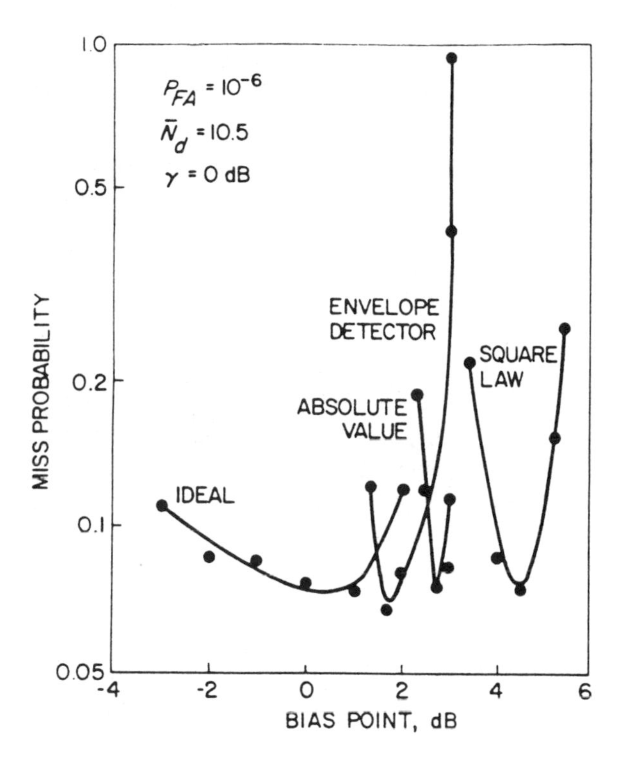

Figure 1.53. Bias points for the various detector types, perfect code phase (reprinted from [30]).

that the ideal detector appears to show no advantage over the other three implementations when all are biased at their respective optimum points. (The fact that the ideal detector minimum appears slightly larger than that for the envelope detector is due to statistical variations in calculating $1 - P_D$ and $\bar{N}_d$).

Another interesting result which may be gleaned from those in both Figure 1.53 and 1.54 is the fact that the ideal detector is much less sensitive to variations about the optimum bias point than the other detectors. This implies more robust performance for the ideal detector in the sense of being more tolerant to parameter variations. This comes as an added bonus to its already optimum behavior in the sense of minimum dismissal time versus miss probability.

A comparison of Figures 1.53 and 1.54 reveals the anticipated results that (1) the optimum bias points are all lower for random code phase, (2) the miss probability is higher for random code phase, and (3) the optimum points are all more sharply defined for random code phase.

Suppose now we assume that the various configurations are designed corresponding to their optimum bias points as determined from Figure 1.54,

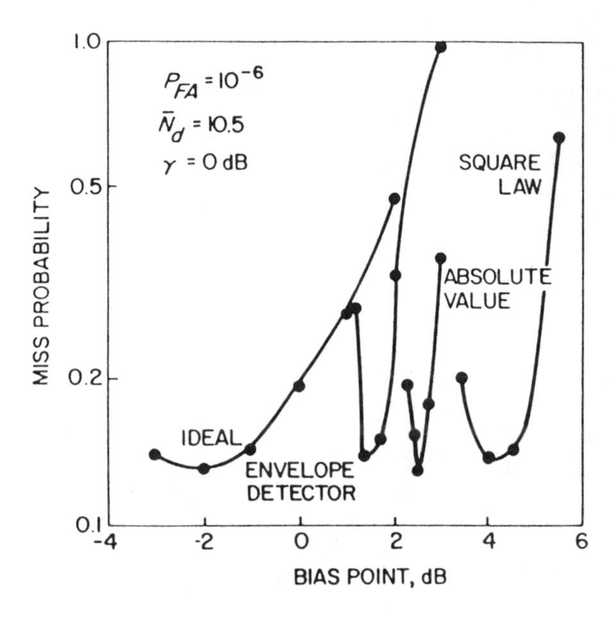

Figure 1.54. Bias points for detectors with random code phase (reprinted from [30]).

namely, -2 dB for the ideal detector, 4.0 dB for the square-law envelope detector, and 2.5 dB for the absolute-value envelope detector. Corresponding to these optimum bias points, upper and lower thresholds can be determined for each configuration from Figures 1.51 and 1.52 and (1.286) and (1.287), assuming P_{FA} and $\bar{N}_d$ are fixed. Then, as the pre-detection signal-to-noise ratio varies about its design point of 0 dB, the miss probability will vary about its design point value (minimum of curves in Figure 1.54) as indicated in Figure 1.55. This portrayal of the variation of miss probability as a function of the predetection signal-to-noise ratio for a fixed design point is often referred to as the "operating characteristic" of the sequential test [11]. To a first-order approximation, the results of Figure 1.55 reveal that the operating characteristic is the same for all four implementations when they are designed with optimized bias.

To wrap up our discussion of simulation results, we now return to the time-out type of sequential detection system introduced earlier in Figure 1.53. Again, this system could be configured with other types of detector implementations as in our discussion of the two-threshold system. However, since the relative performance of these various detector implementations would qualitatively be the same for the acquisition system with the time-out feature as for the two-threshold system, we shall concentrate only on the square-law envelope detector and focus all our attention on whatever behavioral differences occur due to the change in decision logic.

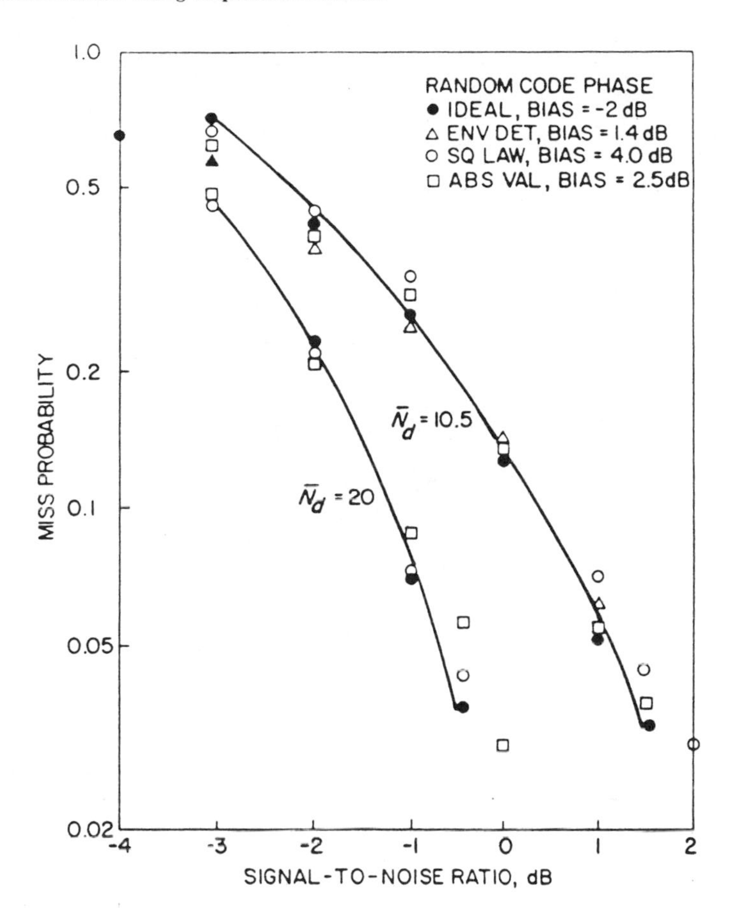

Figure 1.55. Comparison of S/N performance of various detector types at optimum bias point for 0 dB S/N (reprinted from [30]).

Figure 1.56 illustrates the false alarm probability as a function of normalized test truncation time (time-out) $B\tau_o$ for several different values of normalized lower detection threshold η_2/N_0B and normalized bias b/N_0B. The bias values are computed from (1.263) and as such correspond to pre-detection signal-to-noise ratios $\gamma = -17.5$, -15.0, and -12.5 dB. For sufficiently large $B\tau_o$, we observe that P_{FA} decreases exponentially with an exponent whose magnitude increases with increasing bias but is essentially independent of lower threshold. Qualitatively this behavior is analogous to that previously discussed for the two-threshold system with regard to the behavior of false alarm probability versus normalized upper threshold and bias.

Figure 1.57 illustrates the corresponding results for the average sample number $\bar{N}_d$. Again the behavior here is qualitatively similar to that of the

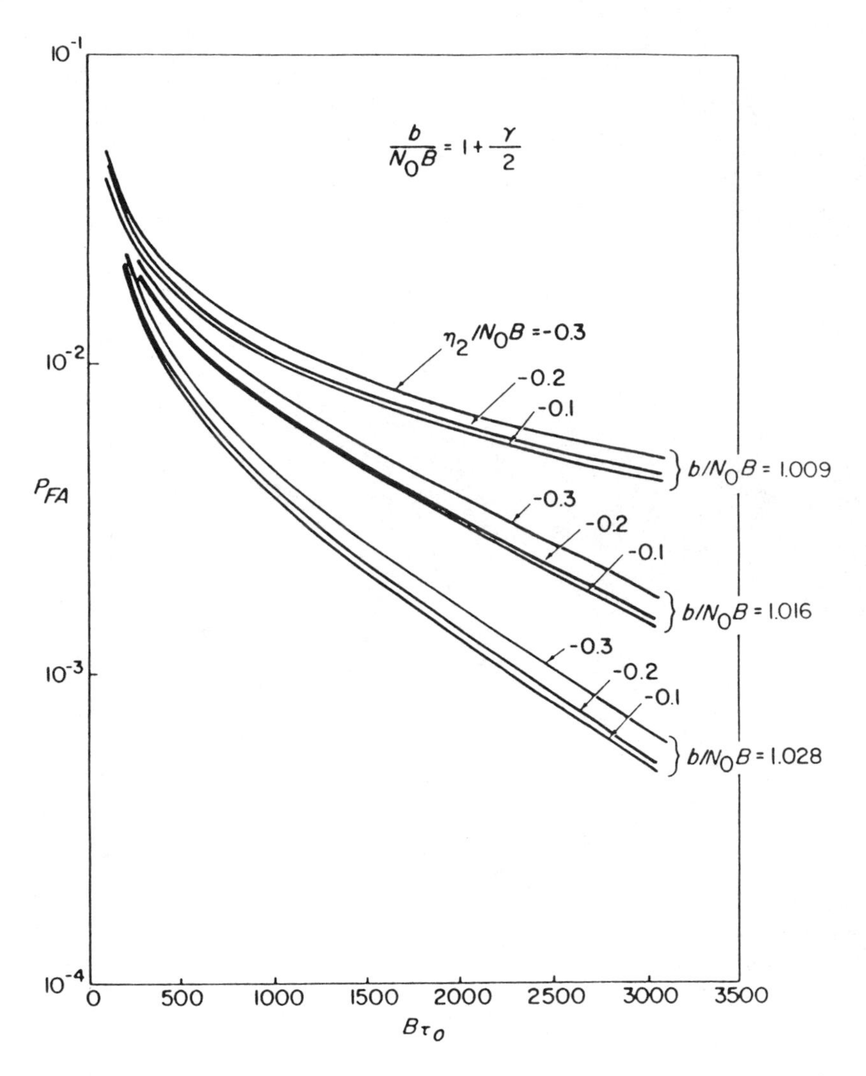

Figure 1.56. False alarm probability versus normalized test truncation time with normalized lower detection threshold and normalized bias as parameters.

two-threshold system in that the average sample number decreases with increasing bias and increasing lower threshold (decreasing $|\eta_2/N_0B|$). Finally, Figure 1.58 illustrates the detection probability versus normalized test truncation time for the same values of normalized lower detection threshold as in Figure 1.56. Here, we observe that detection probability decreases with increasing bias as expected. Furthermore, for small values of $B\tau_o$, detection probability at first decreases but eventually levels off for sufficiently large values of $B\tau_o$. Because of this behavior, it is reasonable to choose the truncation time τ_o to satisfy the requirement on false alarm probability.

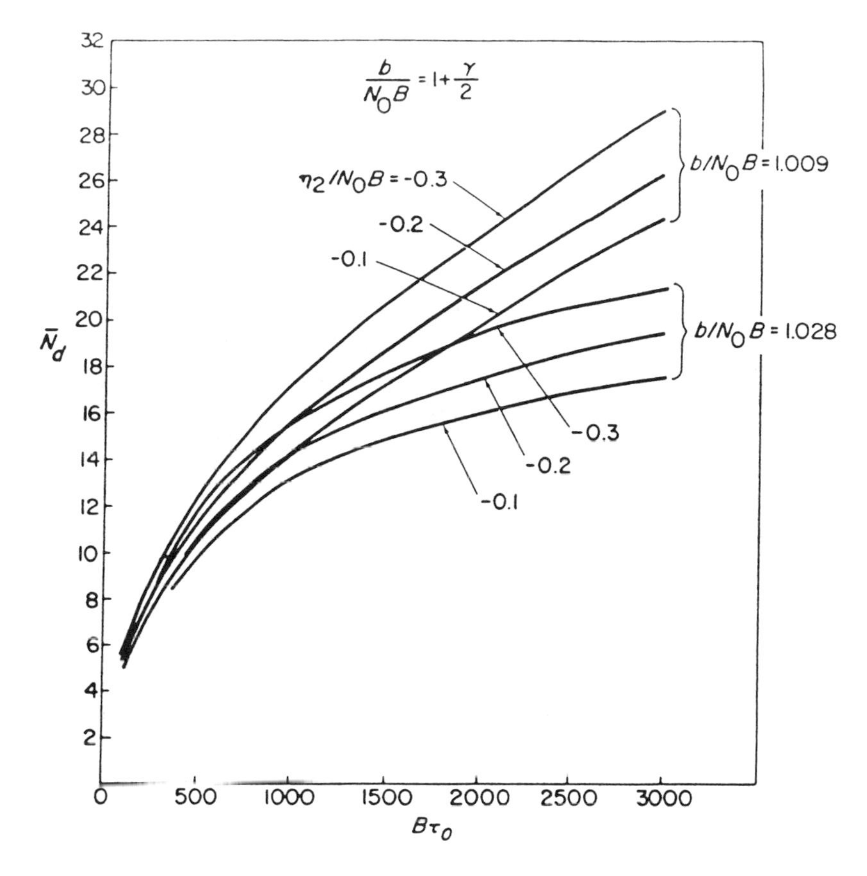

Figure 1.57. Average sample number versus normalized test truncation time with normalized lower detection threshold and normalized bias as parameters.

1.8 SEARCH / LOCK STRATEGIES

In this final section, we discuss the behavior and performance of the receiver's *search/lock strategy* (SLS) whose primary function is to logically control the transition from the *search mode* of operation (coarse PN acquisition) to the *lock mode* of operation (PN tracking). The intermediate state as represented by the above transition from coarse acquisition to tracking is often referred to as *fine PN acquisition*. In effect, it yields a verification of the validity of a "hit" produced by the search algorithm before turning control over to the tracking loop. A secondary function of the SLS is to continuously monitor the receiver while in its lock mode of operation so as to determine when a loss of synchronization has occurred thereby requiring reinitiation of the search mode.

In selecting an SLS, conflicting requirements on the dwell time per test of a code phase cell must be compromised. Since rapid acquisition is desirable,

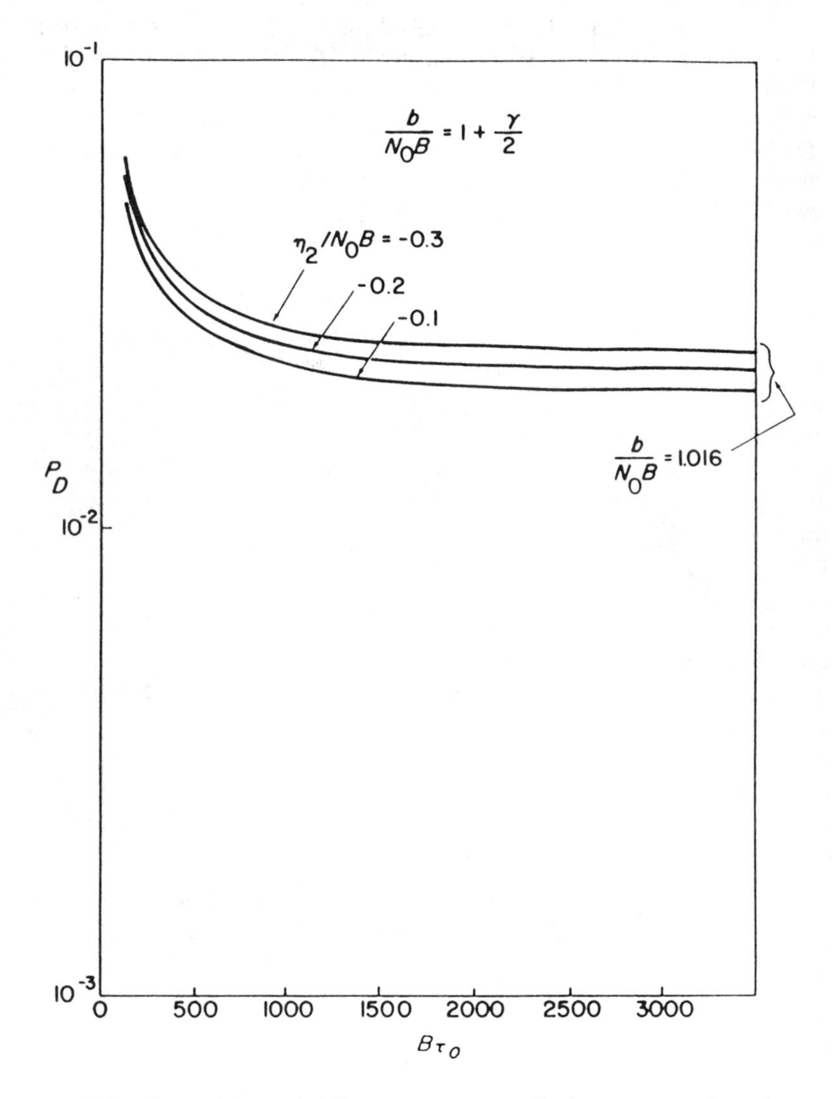

Figure 1.58. Detection probability versus normalized test truncation time with normalized lower detection threshold as a parameter.

the dwell time τ_d per test cell in the search mode should be as small as practical; however, a large τ_d is required to ensure a high probability of detecting the correct cell once it is found. In the lock mode, a very high probability of detection is required to ensure that the detector will not prematurely declare a loss of lock and reinitiate the search, thereby disrupting synchronization. However, since in the lock mode search time is no longer a strong consideration, advantage of this fact can be taken by increasing the post-detection integration (dwell) time to meet the requirement on detection probability. Unfortunately, since the probability of entering the lock mode due to a false alarm is non-zero, the time spent on a false lock while in the lock mode will be substantially increased by the longer integration time. However, if the probability of false alarm is small, then the probability of false lock (falsely entering the lock mode) will likewise be small and hence the mean acquisition time will not be significantly increased. In conclusion, it appears that a salient feature of an SLS should be that the detector parameters are changed upon entering the lock mode from the search mode and vice versa. Furthermore, within each mode, a suitable algorithm should be applied to the "hits" and "misses" (detector threshold crossings or their lack thereof) so as to circumvent the unique relation (see (1.81)) that exists among false alarm probability, detection probability, and dwell time for a single threshold decision, and thus allow the conflicting requirements on τ_d discussed above to be satisfied.

In order to understand in more detail how the above considerations affect acquisition performance, it is convenient to consider a specific SLS and choose a suitable analytical approach for evaluating its behavior. A typical SLS [9] is illustrated in state/transition form in Figure 1.59. This strategy is implicitly assumed to operate in conjunction with the single dwell time PN acquisition system of Figure 1.4. In particular, for the first time a cell is tested (state 1), a miss (failure of the decision variable Z to exceed the detection threshold) results in immediate rejection of the cell and a phase step to the next cell (see Figure 1.4). On the other hand, a hit (Z exceeds the threshold) on the first test of a cell advances the SLS to state 2, whereupon the identical cell is retested. If a second hit occurs, the SLS enters the lock mode. A miss in state 2 causes a return to state 1. Additional hits and misses produce similar transitions between states of the SLS. It is to be emphasized that for the SLS of Figure 1.59, the dwell time τ_{d1} is identical for search states 1 and 2.

Just as a single hit does not put the SLS in the lock mode, three successive misses are required to reinitiate the search mode. Any other combination of hits and misses will maintain the SLS in the lock mode once it has entered that mode. Furthermore, the dwell time τ_{d2} ($> \tau_{d1}$) is assumed to be the same for all three lock mode states.

1.8.1 Mean and Variance of the Acquisition Time

A suitable analytical approach for evaluating the behavior of the SLS is to represent it as a finite Markov chain with absorbing boundaries. Such a Markov chain model for the SLS of Figure 1.59 is illustrated in Figure 1.60. Note that Figure 1.60 is analogous to the generating function flow graph for the single dwell system (Figure 1.5) except that, for convenience, we have omitted the branch parameter z which was previously used to mark time as one proceeded through the graph. Each branch of Figure 1.60, however, is still labelled with the transition probability appropriate for going from one

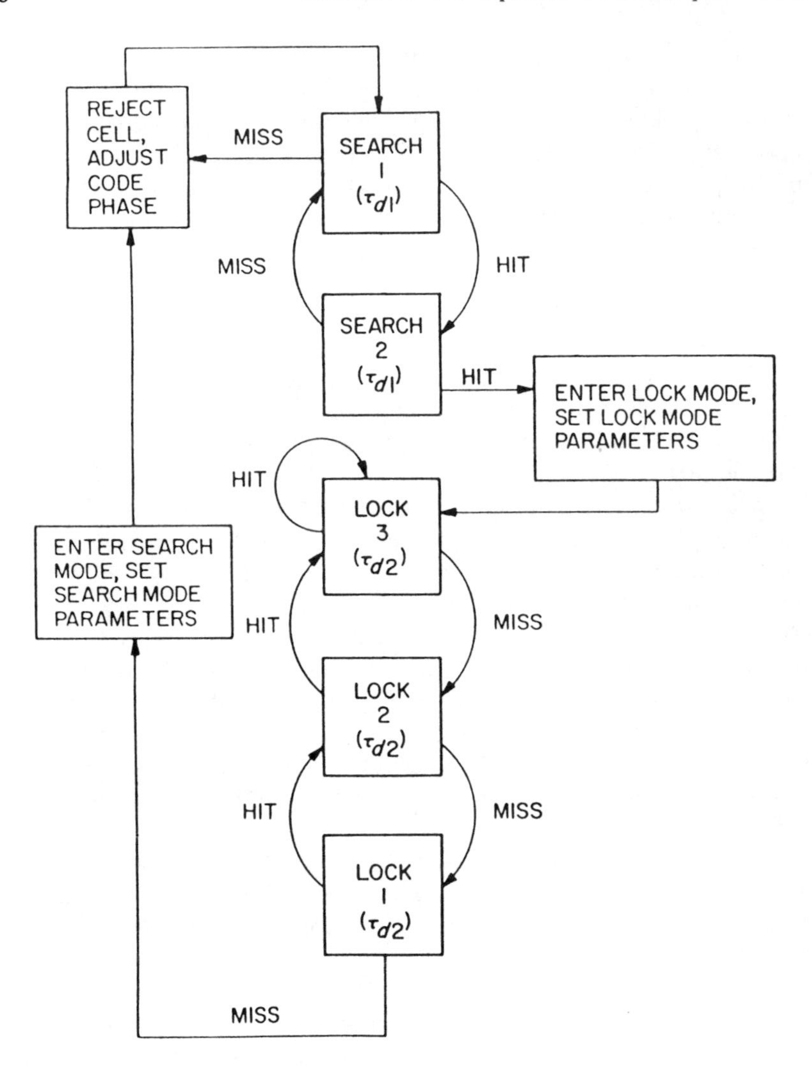

Figure 1.59. A search/lock strategy.

state to the other. Using straightforward techniques for analyzing Markov chains with absorbing boundaries, it can be shown [9] that the mean and variance of the acquisition time of the combination of the single dwell acquisition system of Figure 1.4 and the SLS of Figure 1.59 are given by

$$\bar{T}_{ACQ} = \frac{(2 - P_L) q \bar{\tau}_d}{2 P_L} \tag{1.288}$$

and

$$\sigma^2_{ACQ} = \bar{\tau}_d^2 q^2 \left(\frac{1}{12} + \frac{1}{P_L^2} - \frac{1}{P_L} \right) \tag{1.289}$$

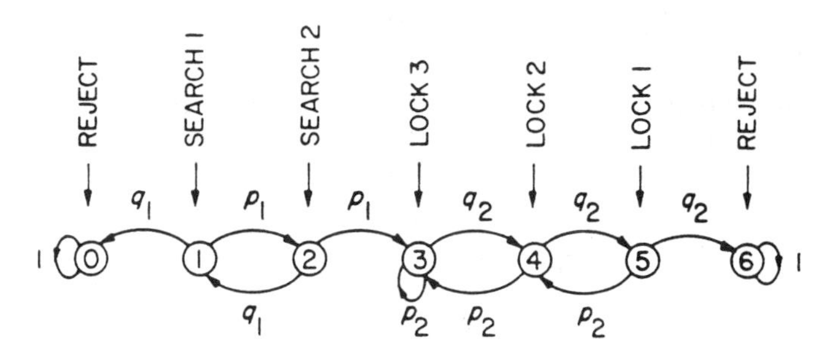

p_0 = P(HIT|SEARCH MODE) $q_0 = 1 - p_0$

p_1 = P(HIT|LOCK MODE) $q_1 = 1 - p_1$

Figure 1.60. Markov chain model of search/lock strategy.

where P_L is the probability of lock, i.e., the probability of entering the lock mode assuming the search has reached the correct cell, and $\bar{\tau}_d$ is the mean dwell time for an incorrect cell. In terms of the Markov chain model of Figure 1.60, P_L is simply the probability of going from state 1 to state 3 with $p_1 = P_{D1}$ and $q_1 = 1 - P_{D1}$ where P_{D1} is the detection probability for the search mode. Furthermore, $\bar{\tau}_d$ is the mean time to reach states 0 or 6 (the two absorbing states) from state 1 with $p_1 = P_{FA1}$, $q_1 = 1 - P_{FA1}$, $p_2 = P_{FA2}$, and $q_2 = 1 - P_{FA2}$ where P_{FA1} and P_{FA2} are, respectively, the false alarm probabilities in the search and lock modes.

Before proceeding to an evaluation of P_L and $\bar{\tau}_d$ for the SLS of Figure 1.59, we draw attention to the similarity of (1.288) and (1.4), the latter being the mean acquisition time for the single dwell acquisition acting alone (i.e., in the absence of the SLS). Clearly without any hit verification, the probability of lock would simply be equal to the detection probability of the detector in the search mode of operation, i.e.,

$$P_L = P_D. \tag{1.290}$$

Furthermore, the average dwell time for an incorrect cell without an SLS is the average of the dwell time for a miss (which occurs with probability $1 - P_{FA}$) and the dwell time for a hit (which occurs with probability P_{FA}) including the penalty of K dwell time units to discover the false alarm. Thus,

$$\begin{aligned}\bar{\tau}_d &= \tau_d(1 - P_{FA}) + (\tau_d + K\tau_d)P_{FA}\\ &= \tau_d(1 + KP_{FA}).\end{aligned} \tag{1.291}$$

Finally, substituting (1.290) and (1.291) in (1.288) results in (1.4), as it naturally should.

1.8.1.1 Evaluation of Probability of Lock

The events contributing to an entering of the lock mode starting in search state 1 are as follows:

hit-hit

hit-miss-hit-hit

hit-miss-hit-miss-hit-hit

⋮

$$\underbrace{\text{hit-miss-hit-miss} \ldots \text{hit-miss}}_{n \text{ hits, } n \text{ misses}}\text{-hit-hit.}$$

Since the above events are mutually exclusive, the probability of lock is simply the sum of the probabilities of these events, i.e.,

$$\begin{aligned} P_L &= p_1^2 + p_1 q_1 p_1^2 + (p_1 q_1)^2 p_1^2 + \cdots (p_1 q_1)^n p_1^2 + \cdots \\ &= p_1^2 \sum_{n=0}^{\infty} (p_1 q_1)^n = \frac{p_1^2}{1 - p_1 q_1} = \frac{p_1^2}{1 - p_1 + p_1^2} \end{aligned} \tag{1.292}$$

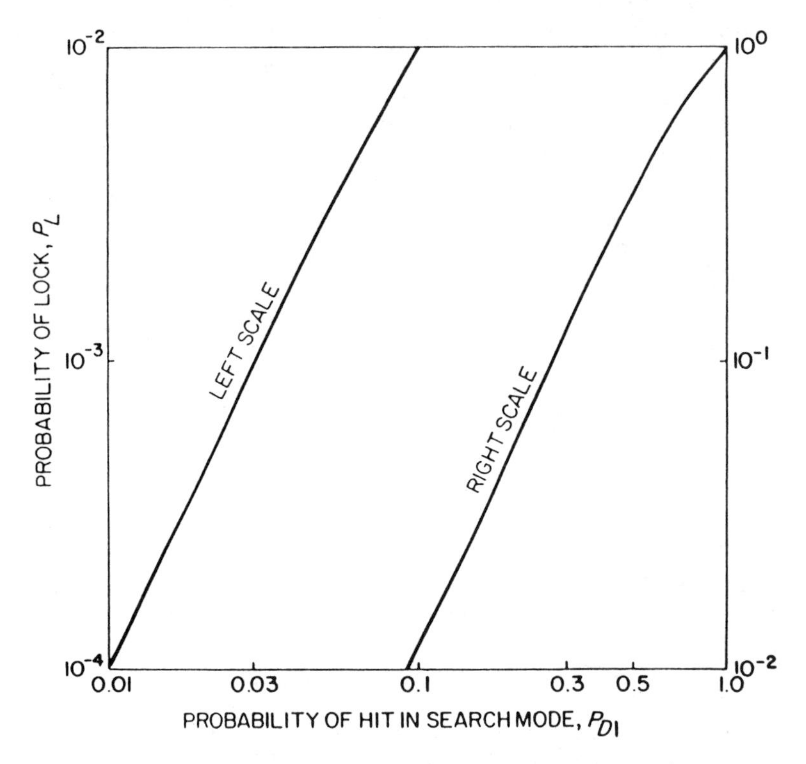

Figure 1.61. Probability of lock versus search mode detection probability (reprinted from [9]).

or in view of the previously mentioned substitution for p_1,

$$P_L = \frac{P_{D1}^2}{1 - P_{D1} + P_{D1}^2}. \tag{1.293}$$

Figure 1.61 is a plot of P_L versus P_{D1}.

1.8.1.2 Evaluation of Mean Dwell Time

The mean dwell time can also easily be computed by first identifying the events contributing to a dismissal of an incorrect cell starting in search state 1, and then assigning the appropriate dwell time and probability of occurrence to each of these events. Considering first those events which dismiss an incorrect cell *without entering the lock mode*, we have the following:

miss
hit-miss-miss
hit-miss-hit-miss-miss
⋮
$\underbrace{\text{hit-miss-hit-miss}\ldots\text{hit-miss}}_{n \text{ hits}, n \text{ misses}}\text{-miss}$

Thus, the component of the mean dwell time associated with these events is

$$\begin{aligned}\bar{\tau}_d^{(1)} &= \tau_{d1}(1 - P_{FA1}) + 3\tau_{d1}P_{FA1}(1 - P_{FA1})^2 \\ &\quad + \cdots (2n+1)\tau_{d1}P_{FA1}^n(1 - P_{FA1})^{n+1} + \cdots \\ &= \tau_{d1}(1 - P_{FA1}) \sum_{n=0}^{\infty} (2n+1)\left[P_{FA1}(1 - P_{FA1})\right]^n \end{aligned} \tag{1.294}$$

or, since

$$\sum_{n=0}^{\infty} (2n+1)x^n = \frac{1+x}{(1-x)^2}, \tag{1.295}$$

$$\bar{\tau}_d^{(1)} = \tau_{d1}(1 - P_{FA1})\frac{1 + P_{FA1}(1 - P_{FA1})}{\left[1 - P_{FA1}(1 - P_{FA1})\right]^2}. \tag{1.296}$$

Considering next the events which dismiss an incorrect cell by first *entering the lock mode*, we have the following:

hit-hit-lock mode
hit-miss-hit-hit-lock mode
⋮
$\underbrace{\text{hit-miss-hit-miss}\ldots\text{hit-miss}}_{n \text{ hits}, n \text{ misses}}\text{-hit-hit-lock mode.}$
⋮

For the moment, we do not identify, in the above, the possible paths through and out of the lock mode. We merely use the words "lock mode" to denote the collection of these paths and associate with them an average penalty time T_p. Shortly, we shall evaluate T_p in terms of the lock mode false alarm probability and dwell time for the specific SLS of Figure 1.59. Also note that previously, when we considered the single dwell acquisition system alone, T_p was chosen equal to $K\tau_d$.

For the events listed above, the contribution to the mean dwell time is given by

$$\begin{aligned}\bar{\tau}_d^{(2)} &= (2\tau_{d1} + T_p)P_{FA1}^2 + (4\tau_{d1} + T_p)P_{FA1}^3(1 - P_{FA1}) \\ &\quad + \cdots ((2n+2)\tau_{d1} + T_p)P_{FA1}^{n+2}(1 - P_{FA1})^n + \cdots \\ &= \tau_{d1}P_{FA1}^2 \sum_{n=0}^{\infty} (2n+2)[P_{FA1}(1 - P_{FA1})]^n \\ &\quad + T_p P_{FA1}^2 \sum_{n=0}^{\infty} [P_{FA1}(1 - P_{FA1})]^n \end{aligned} \quad (1.297)$$

or

$$\bar{\tau}_d^{(2)} = \frac{2\tau_{d1}P_{FA1}^2}{[1 - P_{FA1}(1 - P_{FA1})]^2} + \frac{T_p P_{FA1}^2}{1 - P_{FA1}(1 - P_{FA1})}. \quad (1.298)$$

Adding (1.296) and (1.298), the total mean dwell time is given by

$$\bar{\tau}_d = \frac{(1 + P_{FA1})\tau_{d1} + P_{FA1}^2 T_p}{1 - P_{FA1} + P_{FA1}^2}. \quad (1.299)$$

Using a procedure similar to the above, wherein the dwell time and probability associated with each possible path originating at state 3 and terminating at state 6 of Figure 1.60 is identified, it can be shown that

$$T_p = \left[\frac{3 - 4P_{FA2} + 2P_{FA2}^2}{(1 - P_{FA2})^3}\right]\tau_{d2}. \quad (1.300)$$

Substituting (1.300) in (1.299) gives the desired result for the mean dwell time.

Figure 1.62 is an illustration of the mean dwell time normalized by the search mode dwell time versus the search mode false alarm probability with the lock mode false alarm probability as a parameter. Also the lock mode dwell time is assumed to be five times the search mode dwell time as in the example considered in [9], which has practical application to the Space Shuttle program.

Finally, the mean acquisition time is obtained by substituting (1.293) and (1.299) in (1.288). As a numerical illustration of the result of these substitutions, we continue with the example considered in [9] where the following

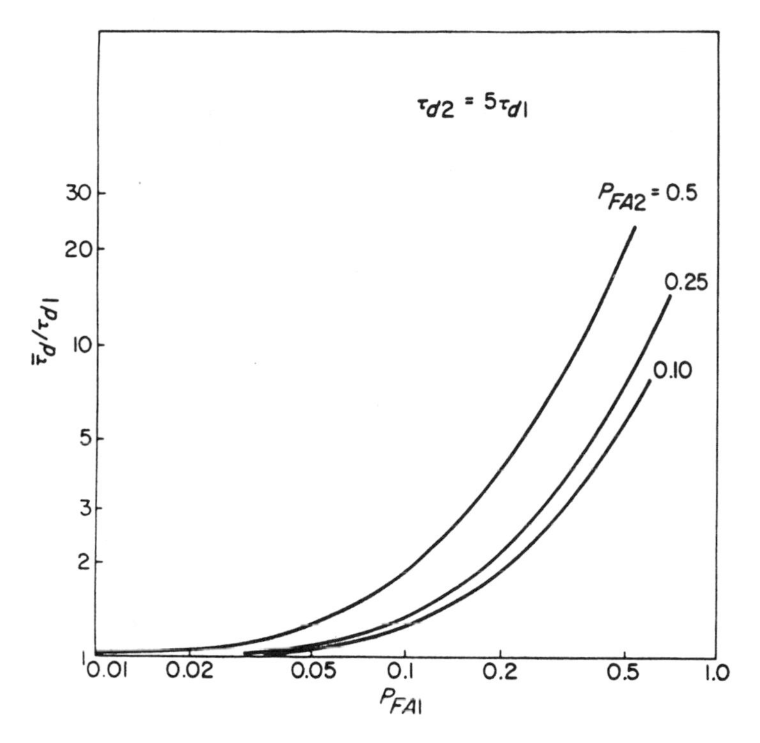

Figure 1.62. Mean dwell time versus search mode false alarm probability (reprinted from [9]).

additional parameter specifications were given:

$$\begin{aligned} \tau_{d1} &= \text{Search Mode Dwell Time} = .91 \text{ ms} \\ \tau_{d2} &= \text{Lock Mode Dwell Time} = 5\tau_{d1} = 4.55 \text{ ms} \\ q &= \text{Number of Search Cells} = 4094 \\ & \quad (\text{PN code of length 2047 chips searched in } 1/2 \text{ chips} \\ & \quad \text{increments}) \\ B &= \text{Predetection bandwidth} = 500 \text{ kHz} \\ (P/N_0)_0 &= \text{Nominal signal-to-noise spectral density} = 54.7 \text{ dB-Hz}. \end{aligned} \tag{1.301}$$

Furthermore, a worst case correlation loss $L = .5$ was assumed during the search mode, while during the lock mode L was set equal to .81 to simulate a delay error of .1 chip.

Using the above, we first compute the effective signal-to-noise ratio γ' in the pre-detection filter bandwidth as defined by (1.62) (with $A^2 = P$)

multiplied by L, i.e.,

$$\gamma' = \frac{PL}{N_0 B} = \begin{cases} \frac{P}{N_0} \times 10^{-6} \text{ (search mode)} \\ \frac{P}{N_0} \times 1.62 \times 10^{-6} \text{ (lock mode)} \end{cases}. \quad (1.302)$$

Then, using γ' of (1.302) for $A^2/N_0 B$ in (1.81), this equation can be applied to find P_{D1} when $P_{FA1} = .01$ and $B\tau_{d1} = 455$, and P_{D2} when $P_{FA2} = 0.5$ and $B\tau_{d2} = 2275$. The results of these computations are illustrated in Figure 1.63. Combining the results of Figure 1.63 for P_{D1} versus P/N_0 and those of Figure 1.61 for P_L versus P_{D1} enables one to determine P_L as a function of P/N_0. For a lock mode false alarm probability $P_{FA2} = 0.5$ and search

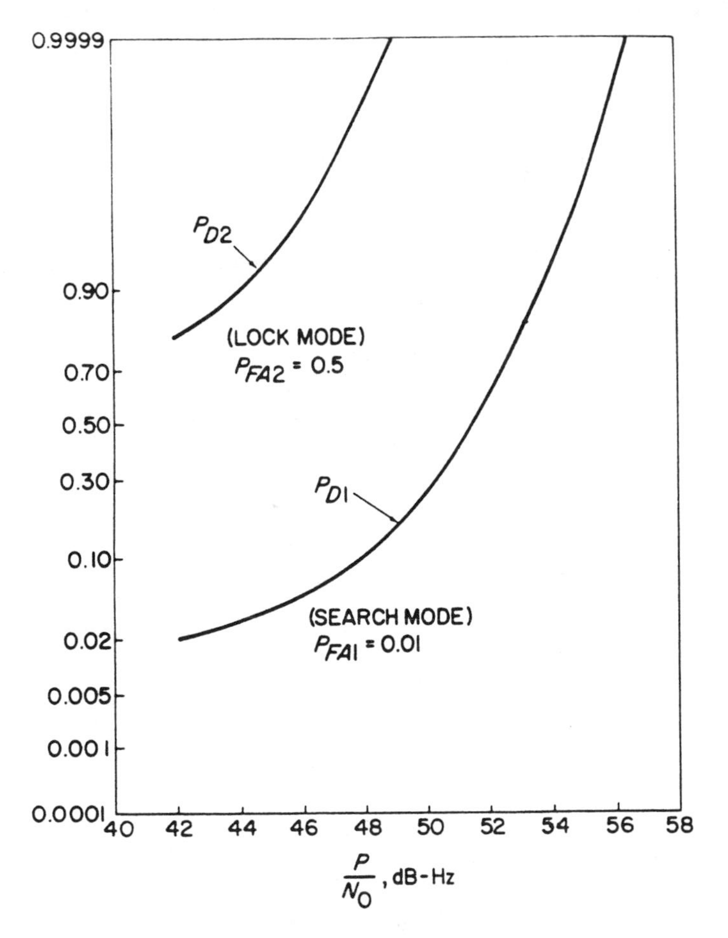

Figure 1.63. Detection performance (reprinted from [9]).

mode false alarm probabilities $P_{FA1} = .001, .01, .03$, and 0.1, we obtain from (1.300) and (1.299) the corresponding values of mean dwell time $\bar{\tau}_d = .912$, .934, 1.016, and 1.7 ms *which are independent of* P/N_0. Finally, using the above-determined functional relationship between P_L and P/N_0 together with the values of $\bar{\tau}_d$ in (1.288) gives the mean acquisition time of the system, which is illustrated versus P/N_0 in Figure 1.64. Note that, for smaller values of P_{FA1}, $\overline{T}_{ACQ}$ increases faster with decreasing P/N_0 than is the case for larger P_{FA1}. The effect is primarily due to the increased P_{D1} which results from increased P_{FA1}.

We hasten to add that all of the results of this section have assumed the absence of code Doppler or its derivatives. To include these effects, one

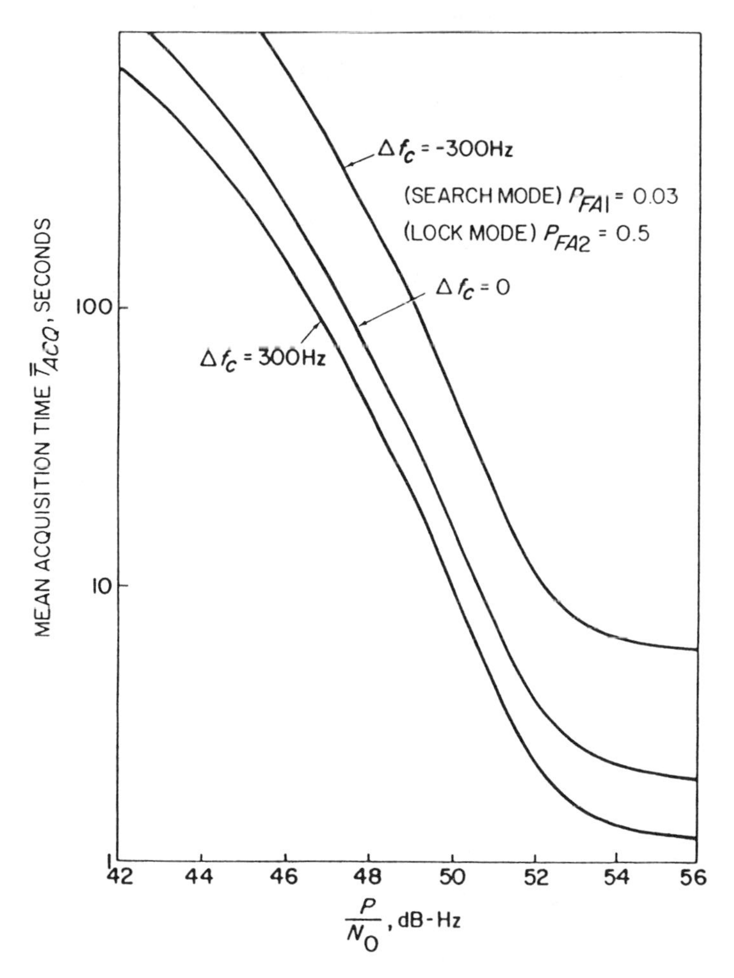

Figure 1.64. Mean acquisition time performance; ±300 Hz frequency error (reprinted from [9]).

would simply apply the modifications discussed in Sections 1.2.3 and 1.2.8 to (1.288) and (1.289). For example, the relation for mean acquisition time in the presence of code Doppler analogous to (1.48a) would now be (see (1.288))

$$\overline{T}_{ACQ} = \frac{\left(\dfrac{2 - P_L}{2P_L}\right) q'\bar{\tau}_d}{1 + \dfrac{q'}{N_u}\Delta f_c \bar{\tau}_d} = \frac{\overline{T}_{ACQ}\big|_{\text{no code Doppler}}}{1 + \dfrac{q'}{N_u}\Delta f_c \bar{\tau}_d} \tag{1.303}$$

where again N_u/q' represents the search update in the absence of Doppler, e.g., one-half of a chip, and $\Delta f_c \bar{\tau}_d$ is the code phase shift due to Doppler during the mean dwell time. As a numerical illustration of the application of (1.303), Figure 1.64 plots $\overline{T}_{ACQ}$ versus P/N_0 for the previous example with now $\Delta f_c = -300$ Hz or $\Delta f_c = +300$ Hz and $N_u/q' = 1/2$.

1.8.2 Another Search / Lock Strategy

Another approach [1] to providing an SLS incorporates a search mode which is modelled after the multiple dwell time acquisition procedure discussed in Section 1.3. In particular, the search mode again consists of two states; however, unlike Figure 1.59, the integration (dwell) times are different for the two states. Furthermore, a miss on state 2 does not return the SLS to state 1 but rather immediately dismisses the cell as being incorrect (see Figure 1.65). The basic philosophy behind the above strategy is to assign a small dwell time τ_{d1} to the first search state so as to search the code phases quickly and a larger dwell time τ_{d2} to the second search state to provide a better estimate (higher probability of detection and lower false alarm probability) of whether the correct cell has been found. In this way, some of the false alarm protection is apportioned in the first integration and the remaining (usually greater) protection is placed in the second integration. Finally, the lock mode portion of the SLS uses a third integration time τ_{d3} (in practice it could be the same as τ_{d2}) with the same algorithm as in Figure 1.59, i.e., a reinitiation of the search requires three consecutive misses.

Before proceeding with the performance analysis of the SLS in Figure 1.65, we point out its similarity with the multiple (here double) dwell time acquisition system alluded to above. In particular, the double dwell time system which incorporates the search mode of the SLS in Figure 1.65 employs *independent* (non-overlapping) integration intervals for its two dwells, whereas a two-dwell version of the multiple dwell time procedure discussed in Section 1.3 uses overlapping integration intervals.

Since the SLS of Figure 1.65 can also be modelled by a Markov chain, the mean and variance of the acquisition time are still given by (1.288) and (1.289), however, with different relationships for P_L and $\bar{\tau}_d$. Clearly, since

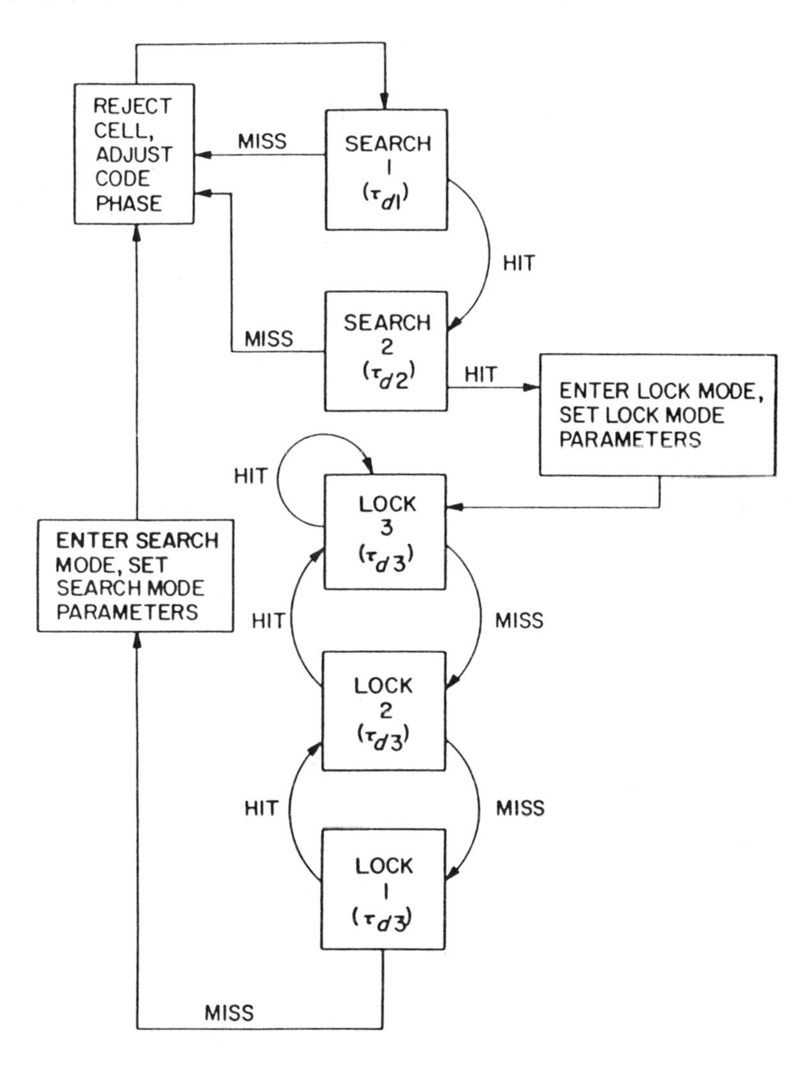

Figure 1.65. Another search/lock strategy.

the only event which causes an entering of the lock mode starting in search state 1 is hit-hit, the probability of lock is now given by

$$P_L = P_{D1} P_{D2} \tag{1.304}$$

where P_{D1} and P_{D2} are, respectively, the detection probabilities for search states 1 and 2. To compute the mean dwell time we again separate the events into those that cause a cell dismissal without entering the lock mode and those that do likewise by passing through the lock mode. In the case of the former, we observe from Figure 1.65 that there are only two appropriate events, namely, miss and hit-miss. Thus, the corresponding component of the mean dwell time is

$$\bar{\tau}_d^{(1)} = \tau_{d1}(1 - P_{FA1}) + (\tau_{d1} + \tau_{d2})P_{FA1}(1 - P_{FA2}) \tag{1.305}$$

where P_{FA1} and P_{FA2} are, respectively, the false alarm probabilities for search states 1 and 2. For the latter case, we have already observed that only two successive hits cause an entering of the lock mode, which is accompanied by a penalty of T_p sec before rejecting the cell. Thus, this corresponding component of the mean dwell time is

$$\bar{\tau}_d^{(2)} = (\tau_{d1} + \tau_{d2} + T_p)P_{FA1}P_{FA2}. \tag{1.306}$$

Finally, adding (1.305) and (1.306) gives the mean dwell time as

$$\bar{\tau}_d = \tau_{d1} + \tau_{d2}P_{FA1} + T_p P_{FA1}P_{FA2}. \tag{1.307}$$

Note that by letting $T_p = K\tau_{d2}$ and substituting (1.304) and (1.307) in (1.288) and (1.289), we obtain the results for the mean and variance of the acquisition time given in [1], which have also been modified as per our previous discussions to include the effects of code Doppler. Using the actual lock mode of the SLS in Figure 1.65, T_p would in reality be given by (1.300) with, in general, P_{FA2} replaced by P_{FA3} and τ_{d2} by τ_{d3}.

We conclude our discussion of this strategy by pointing out that measured values of acquisition time taken on an actual implementation of Figure 1.65 in the code acquisition portion of the Space Shuttle Orbiter system were accurate to within 1 dB of the theoretical results as predicted by the above equations.

1.9 FURTHER DISCUSSION

Throughout this chapter our discussion has focussed on rapid acquisition serial search techniques wherein a single code phase at a time is examined for possible alignment. A natural extension of these techniques would be to use two or more paths to simultaneously search more than one code phase at a time with the hope that by increasing complexity, the acquisition time might decrease in direct relation to the number of paths used. To this end we present here a brief discussion of the possibilities obtainable with a parallel search operation. Specifically, we consider a system where the entire q cell uncertainty region is subdivided into say $N_P(\geq 2)$ equal components each containing q/N_P cells with each of N_P paths responsible for searching one component in parallel with the remaining $N_P - 1$ paths. Furthermore, since the N_P searches progress in parallel under a common control, at any point along the way, all N_P alignment examinations must be dismissed before the search can proceed.

Referring to these joint events as "global" events, if each parallel path is characterized by a detector with false alarm probability P_{FA} and missed detection probability $\beta = 1 - P_D$, the global false alarm probability P_{FAg}

and global missed detection probability $\beta_g \triangleq 1 - P_{Dg}$ are given by

$$P_{FAg} = 1 - (1 - P_{FA})^{N_P}$$
$$\beta_g = \beta(1 - P_{FA})^{N_P - 1}. \tag{1.308}$$

For small P_{FA}, (1.308) simplifies to

$$P_{FAg} \cong N_P P_{FA}$$
$$\beta_g \cong \beta[1 - (N_P - 1)P_{FA}]. \tag{1.309}$$

As an example of the application of the above, we consider the fixed single dwell serial PN acquisition system discussed in Section 1.2 implemented now with N_P parallel search paths. For N_P and q such that q/N_P is still much greater than one, then to a good approximation (1.4) and (1.7) can be used to characterize the moments of the acquisition time of the parallel search system if q is replaced by q/N_P, P_D by P_{Dg}, and P_{FA} by P_{FAg}. For example, using the approximate relations of (1.309), the mean acquisition time would become

$$\bar{T}_{ACQ} = \frac{(1 + \beta_g)(1 + KP_{FAg})}{2(1 - \beta_g)}\left(\frac{q}{N_P}\tau_d\right)$$
$$= \frac{2 - P_D - (1 - P_D)(N_p - 1)P_{FA}}{2[P_D + (1 - P_D)(N_P - 1)P_{FA}]}\frac{(1 + KN_pP_{FA})}{N_P}(q\tau_d). \tag{1.310}$$

Clearly, for small N_P and small false alarm penalty time, the acquisition time varies approximately as an inverse linear function of the number of paths. Eventually, as N_P gets large enough where the false alarm penalty dominates, no further improvement in mean acquisition time will result.

The parallel search idea is obviously applicable to other forms of serial code search such as sequential detection where the improvement in performance would be obtained by similar replacements of q, P_D, and P_{FA} by q/N_P, P_{Dg}, and P_{FAg}, respectively, in the appropriate performance expressions.

1.10 REFERENCES

[1] J. K. Holmes and C. C. Chen, "Acquisition time performance of PN spread-spectrum systems," *IEEE Trans. Commun.*, COM-25, pp. 778–783, August 1977.

[2] W. K. Alem, "Advanced techniques for direct sequence spread spectrum acquisition," Ph.D. Dissertation, Department of Electrical Engineering, University of Southern California, February 1977.

[3] W. K. Alem and C. L. Weber, "Acquisition techniques of PN sequences," *1977 NTC Conference Record*, vol. II, pp. 35:2-1–35:2-4, December 5–7, 1977, Los Angeles, CA.
[4] R. B. Ward, "Acquisition of pseudonoise signals by sequential estimation," *IEEE Trans. Commun.*, COM-13, pp. 475–483, December 1965.
[5] R. B. Ward and K. P. Yiu, "Acquisition of pseudonoise signals by recursion aided sequential estimation," *IEEE Trans. Commun.*, COM-25, pp. 784–794, August 1977. Also see *1977 NTC Conference Record*, vol. II, pp. 35:1-1–35:1-13, December 5–7, Los Angeles, CA.
[6] D. M. DiCarlo and C. L. Weber, "Statistical performance of single dwell serial synchronization systems," *IEEE Trans. Commun.*, COM-28, No. 8, pp. 1382–1388, August 1980.
[7] D. M. DiCarlo, "Multiple dwell serial synchronization of pseudonoise signals," Ph.D. Dissertation, Department of Electrical Engineering, University of Southern California, May 1979. Also see *ICC '81 Conference Record*, pp. 34.4.1–34.4.5, June 14–18, 1981, Denver, CO.
[8] D. M. DiCarlo and C. L. Weber, "Multiple dwell serial search: Performance and application to direct sequence code acquisition," *IEEE Trans. Commun.*, COM-31, No. 5, pp. 650–659, May 1983.
[9] P. M. Hopkins, "A unified analysis of pseudonoise synchronization by envelope correlation," *IEEE Trans. Commun.*, COM-25, pp. 770–777, August 1977.
[10] A. Wald, *Sequential Analysis*, New York: John Wiley, 1947.
[11] J. V. DiFranco and W. L. Rubin, *Radar Detection*, Englewood Cliffs, NJ: Prentice-Hall, 1968, Chapter 16.
[12] C. R. Cahn, N. G. Davies, L. A. Gerhardt, G. F. Gott, and R. L. Harris, AGARD-NATO Lecture Series No. 58 on "Spread Spectrum Communications," May 28–June 6, 1973.
[13] A. Polydoros and C. L. Weber, "Rapid acquisition techniques for direct-sequence spread spectrum systems using an analog detector," *NTC '81 Conference Record*, pp. A7.1.1–A7.1.5, November 29–December 3, 1981, New Orleans, LA.
[14] A. Polydoros and C. L. Weber, "A unified approach to serial search spread-spectrum code acquisition," *IEEE Trans. Commun.*, COM-32, No. 5, pp. 542–560, May 1984.
[15] C. C. Kilgus, "Pseudonoise code acquisition using majority logic decoding," *IEEE Trans. Commun.*, COM-21, No. 6, pp. 772–774, June 1973.
[16] H. M. Pearce and M. P. Ristenblatt, "The threshold decoding estimator for synchronization with binary linear recursive sequences," *ICC '71 Conference Record*, pp. 43-25–43-30, June 12–14, 1971, Montreal, Canada.
[17] G. F. Sage, "Serial Synchronization of Pseudonoise Systems," *IEEE Trans. Commun.*, COM-12, pp. 123–127, December 1964.
[18] P. W. Baier and M. Pandit, "Non-coherent pulse detection with a large predetection bandwidth," *IEEE Trans. Commun.*, COM-26, pp. 1298–1301, August 1978.
[19] M. Pandit, "Mean acquisition time of active- and passive-correlation acquisition systems for spread spectrum communication systems," *Proc. IEEE*, vol. 128, Part F, No. 4, pp. 211–214, August 1981.

[20] J. K. Holmes and K. T. Woo, "An optimum PN code search technique for a given a priori signal location density," *NTC '78 Conference Record*, pp. 18.6.1–18.6.5, December 3–6, 1978, Birmingham, AL.
[21] W. R. Braun, "Performance analysis for the expanding search PN acquisition algorithm," *IEEE Trans. Commun.*, COM-30, pp. 424–435, March 1982.
[22] A. Weinberg, "Search strategy effects on PN acquisition performance," *NTC '81 Conference Record*, pp. F1.5.1–F1.5.5, November 29–December 3, 1981, New Orleans, LA.
[23] A. Weinberg, "Generalized analysis for the evaluation of search strategy effects on PN acquisition performance," *IEEE Trans. Commun.*, COM-31, pp. 37–49, January 1983.
[24] A. Polydoros, "Generalized serial search code acquisition: The equivalent circular state diagram approach," *MILCOM '83 Conference Record*, Washington, D.C., October 1983.
[25] W. K. Alem, G. K. Huth, J. K. Holmes, and S. Udalov, "Spread spectrum acquisition and tracking performance for shuttle communication links," *IEEE Trans. Commun.*, COM-26, pp. 1689–1702, November 1978.
[26] C. Gumacos, "Analysis of an optimum sync search procedure," *IEEE Trans. Commun.*, pp. 89–99, March 1963.
[27] J. J. Bussgang and D. Middleton, "Optimum sequential detection of signals in noise," *IEEE Trans. Inform. Theory*, IT-1, pp. 5–18, December 1955.
[28] G. E. Albert, "On the computation of the sampling characteristics of a general class of sequential decision problems," *Annals of Mathematical Statistics*, vol. 25, pp. 340–356, 1954.
[29] W. B. Kendall, "Performance of the biased square-law sequential detector in the absence of signal," *IEEE Trans. Inform. Theory*, IT-11, pp. 83–90, January 1965.
[30] R. F. Cobb and A. D. Darby, "Acquisition performance of simplified implementations of the sequential detection algorithm," *1978 NTC Conference Record*, pp. 43.4.1–43.4.7, December 4–6, 1978, Birmingham, AL.
[31] W. H. Huggins, "Signal-flow graphs and random signals," *Proc. IRE*, vol. 45, pp. 74–86, January 1957.
[32] S. J. Mason, "Feedback theory–Some properties of signal flow graphs," *Proc. IRE*, vol. 41, pp. 1144–1156, September 1953.
[33] S. J. Mason, "Feedback theory—Further properties of signal flow graphs," *Proc. IRE*, vol. 44, pp. 920–926, July 1956.
[34] M. J. Bouvier, Jr., H. E. Walls, and R. W. Boyd, "Rapid acquisition of spread spectrum signals," Army Research Office, Research Triangle Park, NC, Final Report under Contract No. DAAG29-80-C-0005, December 1980.
[35] J. I. Marcum, "A statistical theory of target detection by pulsed radar: Mathematical appendix," the RAND Corporation Report ASTIA AD101882, July 1, 1948.
[36] D. P. Morgan, J. M. Hannah, and J. H. Collins, "Spread-spectrum synchronizer using a SAW convolver and recirculation loop," *Proc. IEEE*, vol. 64, no. 5, pp. 751–753, May 1976.
[37] L. B. Milstein and P. K. Das, "Spread spectrum receiver using surface acoustic wave technology," *IEEE Trans. Commun.*, COM-25, No. 8, pp. 841–847, August 1977.

[38] A. Polydoros, "On the synchronization aspects of direct-sequence spread spectrum systems," Ph.D. Dissertation, Department of Electrical Engineering, University of Southern California, August 1982.

[39] A. Polydoros, and M. K. Simon, "Generalized serial search code acquisition: The equivalent circular state diagram approach," *IEEE Trans. Commun.*, COM-32, pp. 1260–1268, December 1984.

Chapter 2

PSEUDONOISE CODE TRACKING IN DIRECT-SEQUENCE RECEIVERS

In the previous chapter, we discussed techniques for acquiring a pseudonoise (PN) code in direct-sequence (DS) spread-spectrum (SS) receivers. Although PN acquisition is an extremely important problem, e.g., the code must customarily be acquired in as short a time as possible, the development of closed loop techniques for accurate PN tracking plays an equally important role in supporting the acquisition process once the code has been acquired. As such, the optimum design and true assessment of the performance of the PN tracking loop is an essential component of the overall receiver design.

In searching the literature, one finds that over the years there have been predominantly two PN tracking loop configurations that have been proposed and analyzed, namely, the *delay-locked loop* (DLL) [1]–[5] and the *tau-dither loop* (TDL) or *time-shared loop* [5]–[7]. Either of these configurations can be operated in a coherent or non-coherent mode depending on the system application. Furthermore, both of them fall within the class of so-called *early-late gate* type loops in that the received PN code is correlated either simultaneously or alternately with delayed and advanced versions of the receiver local code PN generator output to produce the timing error correcting characteristic. More recently, modifications of the basic TDL and DLL, namely, the *double dither loop* (DDL) [8], the *product of sum and difference DLL* ($\Sigma\Delta$ DLL) [9], and the *modified code tracking loop* (MCTL) [10], [11] have been proposed which attempt to mitigate the disadvantages of each configuration when compared with the other. Another variation, referred to as the complex sums DLL [12], has been suggested for application in environments characterized by severe dynamic range variation where reception is subject to fast fading and scintillation.

In this chapter, we focus our attention on the class of non-coherent PN tracking loops that are of interest in SS communication receivers where PN acquisition and tracking (despreading) is performed prior to carrier synchronization. Indeed, this is the more common situation in present and past SS communication systems in contrast to the other uses of PN modulation where the code is acquired and coherently tracked as a baseband modulation, e.g., ranging. Although both linear and non-linear loop analyses are possible, we shall concentrate primarily on the steady state tracking performance results obtained from the linear theory since in most situations the equivalent loop signal-to-noise ratio is sufficiently high as to justify this assumption. Following the presentation of these results, we shall discuss the acquisition (transient) behavior [4] and slip time (mean time to lose lock) performance [13] of the DLL and TDL, which, by necessity, must both be derived from consideration of the non-linear theory. Finally, the chapter concludes with a discussion of quadriphase PN tracking and a summary of other recent contributions.

2.1 THE DELAY-LOCKED LOOP

Consider the non-coherent delay-locked loop (DLL) illustrated in Figure 2.1. The input signal $x(t)$ is cross-correlated with advanced and retarded versions of the local PN code generator sequence. The results of these cross-correlation operations are then band-pass filtered, square-law envelope detected, and differenced to produce an error (discriminator) characteristic. The loop is closed by applying this differenced output to a loop filter and voltage controlled clock (VCC) that drives the PN code generator from which the PN reference sequence is obtained.

The advance (and retard) interval δ or, equivalently, the correlator spacing is restricted to a range of $\delta \leq T_c$ where T_c denotes the length (in seconds) of a PN code chip. More conveniently, we shall define δ equal to T_c/N where N is any integer larger than unity. Thus, the advanced and retarded PN signals are $2T_c/N$ apart and a loop such as this is said to have T_c/N of correlator spacing [14]. When the advance (and retard) interval is equal to one-half of a PN code chip, i.e., $N = 2$, the loop is commonly referred to as a "one-delta" loop.

2.1.1 Mathematical Loop Model and Equation of Operation

In mathematical terms, the above statements are expressed as follows. The received signal $x(t)$ is the sum of signal $s(t)$ plus additive noise $n_i(t)$ where[1]

$$s(t) = \sqrt{2S}\,c(t-\tau_t)m(t-\tau_t)\cos[\omega_0 t + \theta(t)] \tag{2.1}$$

and $n_i(t)$ has the band-pass representation

$$n_i(t) = \sqrt{2}\,\{N_c(t)\cos[\omega_0 t + \theta(t)] - N_s(t)\sin[\omega_0 t + \theta(t)]\}. \tag{2.2}$$

In (2.1) S denotes the average signal power, $c(t-\tau_t)$ is the received PN

[1]At this point, we shall only consider the case of a biphase data modulation on the carrier. Later on, we shall discuss PN spread receivers for various forms of quadriphase modulation.

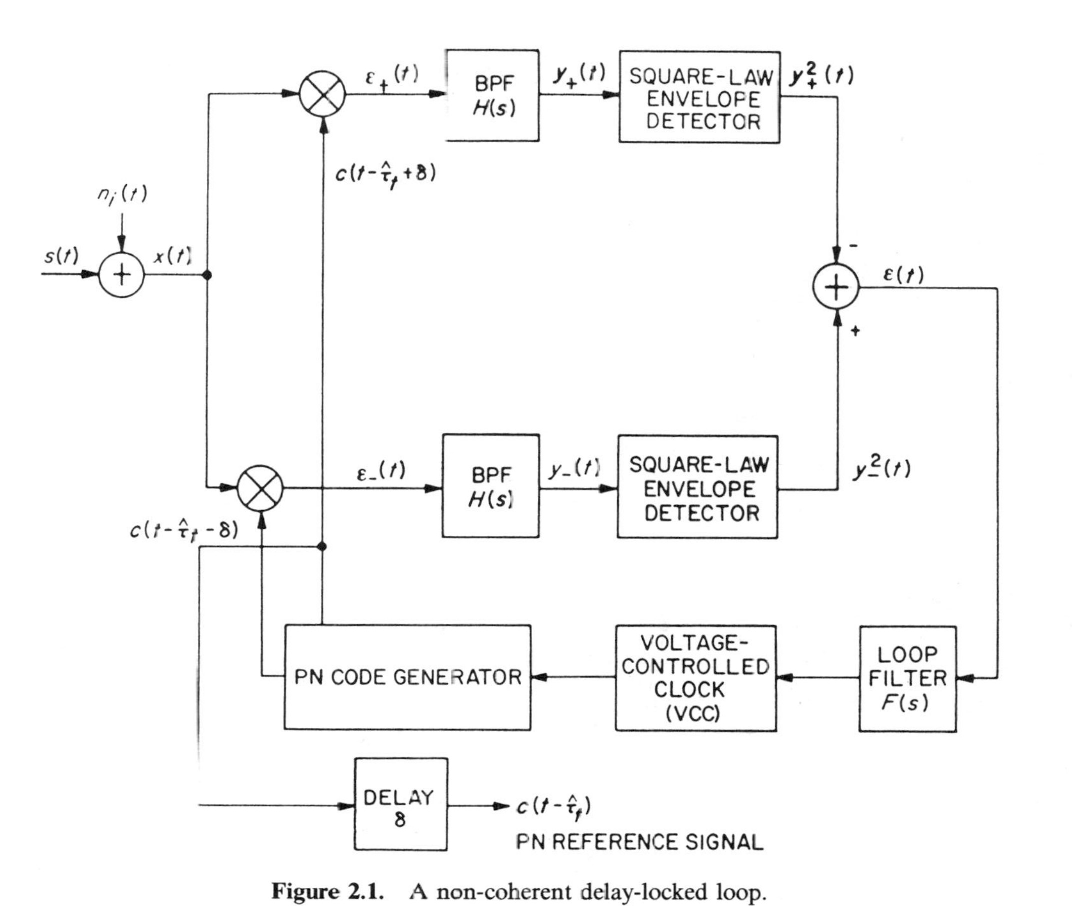

Figure 2.1. A non-coherent delay-locked loop.

signal with transmission delay τ_t, $m(t-\tau_t)$ is the data modulation in the presence of the same delay, ω_0 is the carrier radian frequency, and $\theta(t) \triangleq \theta_0 + \Omega_0 t$ is the unknown carrier phase consisting of a constant term and a term proportional to Doppler. The noise processes $N_c(t)$ and $N_s(t)$ are approximately statistically independent, stationary, low-pass white Gaussian noise processes with single-sided noise spectral density N_0 w/Hz (see [15] or [16]) and one-sided bandwidth $B_N \ll \omega_0/2\pi$.

If the advanced and retarded PN reference signals are respectively given by $c(t-\hat{\tau}_t+\delta)$ and $c(t-\hat{\tau}_t-\delta)$ where $\hat{\tau}_t$ denotes the DLL's estimate of τ_t, then the corresponding cross-correlator (phase detector) outputs become

$$\begin{aligned}\varepsilon_{\pm}(t) &= \sqrt{2S}\,K_m m(t-\tau_t)\overline{c(t-\tau_t)c(t-\hat{\tau}_t\pm\delta)}\cos[\omega_0 t+\theta(t)]\\ &\quad+\sqrt{2S}\,K_m m(t-\tau)\big[c(t-\tau_t)c(t-\hat{\tau}_t\pm\delta)\\ &\quad-\overline{c(t-\tau_t)c(t-\hat{\tau}_t\pm\delta)}\big]\cos[\omega_0 t+\theta(t)]\\ &\quad+K_m c(t-\hat{\tau}_t\pm\delta)n_i(t)\end{aligned}\tag{2.3}$$

with K_m denoting the phase detector gain assumed to be identical for both[2] and the overbar referring to statistical expectation. For large PN code period p, we have that

$$R_{PN_+}(\varepsilon_t) \triangleq \overline{c(t-\tau_t)c(t-\hat{\tau}_t+\delta)} = \begin{cases} 0; & \varepsilon_t \le -\dfrac{1}{N}-1 \\ 1+\dfrac{1}{N}+\varepsilon_t; & -1-\dfrac{1}{N} \le \varepsilon_t \le -\dfrac{1}{N} \\ 1-\dfrac{1}{N}-\varepsilon_t; & -\dfrac{1}{N} < \varepsilon_t \le 1-\dfrac{1}{N} \\ 0; & \varepsilon_t > 1-\dfrac{1}{N} \end{cases}$$

$$\begin{aligned}R_{PN_-}(\varepsilon_t) &\triangleq \overline{c(t-\tau_t)c(t-\hat{\tau}_t-\delta)} = R_{PN_+}\left(\varepsilon_t-\frac{2}{N}\right)\\ R_{PN_\pm}(\varepsilon_t) &= R_{PN_\pm}(\varepsilon_t+np);\ n=\pm1,\pm2,\pm3,\ldots.\end{aligned}\tag{2.4}$$

where $\varepsilon_t \triangleq (\tau_t-\hat{\tau}_t)/T_c$ denotes the normalized transmission delay error. Figure 2.2 illustrates these two autocorrelation functions.

Letting $H_\ell(s)$ denote the low-pass equivalent of the band-pass filter transfer function $H(s)$, and

$$\begin{aligned}s_{c_\pm}(t-\tau_t,\varepsilon_t) &\triangleq c(t-\tau_t)c(t-\hat{\tau}_t\pm\varepsilon_t)\\ &\quad-\overline{c(t-\tau_t)c(t-\hat{\tau}_t\pm\varepsilon_t)}\end{aligned}$$

[2] In practice, the two phase detectors may not have identical gains, which obviates the point that the DLL is sensitive to gain imbalance.

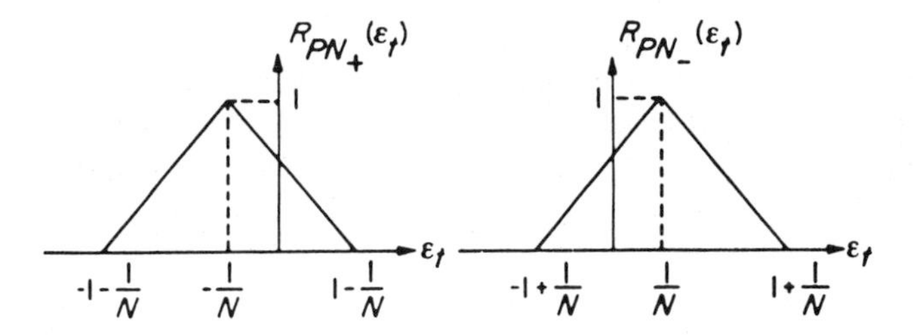

Figure 2.2. Autocorrelation functions of the advanced and retarded PN code.

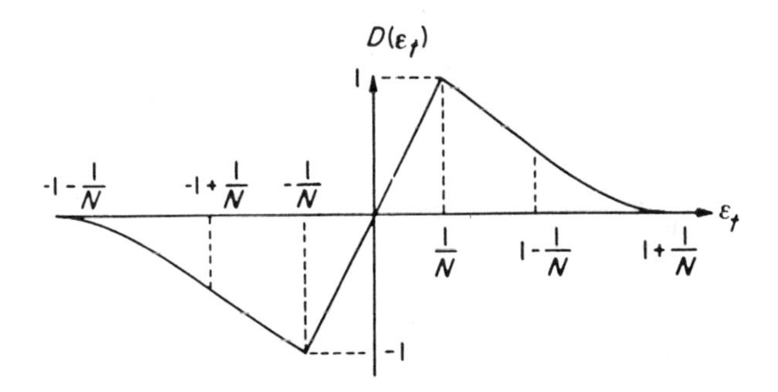

Figure 2.3. Discriminator characteristic.

denote the *PN code self-noise* proccsses, then combining (2.2) and (2.3) we get (see Figure 2.1)

$$\begin{aligned} y_{\pm}(t) &= \sqrt{2S}\, K_m \hat{m}(t-\tau_t) R_{PN_{\pm}}(\varepsilon_t)\cos[\omega_0 t + \theta(t)] \\ &\quad + \sqrt{2S}\, K_m \hat{s}_{c_{\pm}}(t-\tau_t, \varepsilon_t)\cos[\omega_0 t + \theta(t)] \\ &\quad + \sqrt{2}\, K_m \hat{N}_{c_{\pm}}(t)\cos[\omega_0 t + \theta(t)] \\ &\quad - \sqrt{2}\, K_m \hat{N}_{s_{\pm}}(t)\sin[\omega_0 t + \theta(t)] \end{aligned} \tag{2.5}$$

where[3]

$$\begin{aligned} \hat{m}(t) &= H_\ell(p) m(t) \\ \hat{s}_{c_{\pm}}(t, \varepsilon_t) &= H_\ell(p)\left[m(t) s_{c_{\pm}}(t, \varepsilon_t)\right] \\ \hat{N}_{c_{\pm}}(t) &= H_\ell(p)\left[c(t-\tau_t \pm \varepsilon_t) N_c(t)\right] \\ \hat{N}_{s_{\pm}}(t) &= H_\ell(p)\left[c(t-\tau_t \pm \varepsilon_t) N_s(t)\right]. \end{aligned} \tag{2.6}$$

[3]In what follows we shall write differential equations in compact form by introducing the Heaviside operator $p \triangleq d/dt$.

When the single-sided loop bandwidth B_L is much less than the PN code chip rate $1/T_c$ (most cases of practical interest), then, the effect of the PN code self-noise on loop performance can, to a first approximation, be neglected. Thus, ignoring the self-noise term in (2.5) and the second harmonic terms produced by the square-law envelope detectors, we find that the input to the loop filter is given by

$$e(t) \triangleq y_-^2(t) - y_+^2(t) = SK_m^2\hat{m}^2(t-\tau_t)D(\varepsilon_t) + K_m^2 n_e(t,\varepsilon_t) \tag{2.7}$$

where

$$D(\varepsilon_t) \triangleq R_{PN_-}^2(\varepsilon_t) - R_{PN_+}^2(\varepsilon_t) = \begin{cases} 0; \ \varepsilon_t \le -1 - \dfrac{1}{N} \\ -\left(1 + \dfrac{1}{N} + \varepsilon_t\right)^2; \ -1 - \dfrac{1}{N} < \varepsilon_t \le -1 + \dfrac{1}{N} \\ -\dfrac{4}{N}(1+\varepsilon_t); \ -1 + \dfrac{1}{N} < \varepsilon_t < -\dfrac{1}{N} \\ 4\varepsilon_t\left(1 - \dfrac{1}{N}\right); \ |\varepsilon_t| \le \dfrac{1}{N} \\ \dfrac{4}{N}(1-\varepsilon_t); \ \dfrac{1}{N} < \varepsilon_t \le 1 - \dfrac{1}{N} \\ \left(1 + \dfrac{1}{N} - \varepsilon_t\right)^2; \ 1 - \dfrac{1}{N} < \varepsilon_t \le 1 + \dfrac{1}{N} \\ 0; \ \varepsilon_t > 1 + \dfrac{1}{N} \end{cases}$$

$$D(\varepsilon_t) = D(\varepsilon_t + np); \ n = \pm 1, \pm 2, \pm 3, \ldots . \tag{2.8}$$

is the loop S-curve or *discriminator characteristic* (see Figure 2.3) and $n_e(t,\varepsilon_t)$ is the equivalent additive noise defined by

$$\begin{aligned} n_e(t,\varepsilon_t) &= \hat{N}_{c_-}^2(t) - \hat{N}_{c_+}^2(t) + \hat{N}_{s_-}^2(t) - \hat{N}_{s_+}^2(t) \\ &\quad + 2\sqrt{S}\,\hat{m}(t-\tau_t)\left\{R_{PN_-}(\varepsilon_t)\hat{N}_{c_-}(t) - R_{PN_+}(\varepsilon_t)\hat{N}_{c_+}(t)\right\}. \end{aligned} \tag{2.9}$$

The instantaneous (normalized) delay estimate $\hat{\tau}_t/T_c$ of the PN code generator output is related (in operator form) to $e(t)$ by

$$\frac{\hat{\tau}_t}{T_c} = \frac{K_{VCC}F(p)}{p}e(t) \tag{2.10}$$

where $F(s)$ is the loop filter transfer function and K_{VCC} is the gain of the voltage controlled clock which drives the PN code generator. Thus, combining (2.7) and (2.10) and letting $K \triangleq K_m^2 K_{VCC}$ denote the loop gain, the stochastic integro-differential equation of operation of Figure 2.1 becomes

$$\frac{\hat{\tau}_t}{T_c} = \frac{KF(p)}{p}\left[S\hat{m}^2(t-\tau_t)D(\varepsilon_t) + n_e(t,\varepsilon_t)\right] \tag{2.11}$$

or

$$\varepsilon_t = \frac{\tau_t}{T_c} - \frac{KF(p)}{p}\left[S\hat{m}^2(t-\tau_t)D(\varepsilon_t) + n_e(t,\varepsilon_t)\right]. \tag{2.12}$$

Consider now decomposing $\hat{m}^2(t-\tau_t)D(\varepsilon_t)$ into its mean value[4] plus a *modulation self-noise* term, viz.,

$$\begin{aligned}\hat{m}^2(t-\tau_t)D(\varepsilon_t) &= \langle\overline{\hat{m}^2(t-\tau_t)}\rangle D(\varepsilon_t)\\ &\quad + \left[\hat{m}^2(t-\tau_t) - \langle\overline{\hat{m}^2(t-\tau_t)}\rangle\right]D(\varepsilon_t)\end{aligned} \tag{2.13}$$

where $\langle\ \ \rangle$ denotes time average, and

$$\langle\overline{\hat{m}^2(t-\tau_t)}\rangle \triangleq M_2 = \int_{-\infty}^{\infty} S_m(f)|H_\ell(j2\pi f)|^2\, df \tag{2.14}$$

with $S_m(f)$ the power spectral density of the data modulation. It has been previously shown [15] in a similar situation that if the loop bandwidth B_L is much less than the data symbol rate $R_s = 1/T_s$ then the modulation self-noise term can be ignored with negligible error. Thus, (2.12) simplifies to

$$\dot{\varepsilon}_t = \frac{\dot{\tau}_t}{T_c} KF(p)\eta SM_2\left[D_n(\varepsilon_t) + \frac{n_e(t,\varepsilon_t)}{\eta SM_2}\right] \tag{2.15}$$

where $D_n(\varepsilon_t) \triangleq (1/\eta)D(\varepsilon_t)$ is the normalized discriminator characteristic with unit slope at the origin, the dot denotes differentiation with respect to time, and

$$\eta \triangleq \frac{4(N-1)}{N}. \tag{2.16}$$

2.1.2 Statistical Characterization of the Equivalent Additive Noise

It is of interest in what follows to determine the autocorrelation function $R_e(\tau)$ of the equivalent additive noise $n_e(t,\varepsilon_t)$. Thus, defining

$$R_e(\tau,\varepsilon_t) \triangleq \overline{n_e(t,\varepsilon_t)n_e(t+\tau,\varepsilon_t)} \tag{2.17}$$

with $n_e(t,\varepsilon_t)$ defined in (2.9), we obtain after considerable algebraic manipulation

$$R_e(\tau,\varepsilon_t) = 8R_{\hat{N}}^2(\tau) + 4SR_{\hat{m}}(\tau)R_{\hat{N}}(\tau)f(\varepsilon_t) \tag{2.18}$$

[4]Note that since $\overline{\hat{m}^2(t)}$ is a cyclostationary process, both statistical and time averages are required to determine its mean value.

where

$$R_{\hat{N}}(\tau) = \frac{N_0}{2}\int_{-\infty}^{\infty} |H_\ell(j2\pi f)|^2 e^{j2\pi f\tau}\, df$$

$$R_{\hat{m}}(\tau) = \frac{N_0}{2}\int_{-\infty}^{\infty} S_m(f)|H_\ell(j2\pi f)|^2 e^{j2\pi f\tau}\, df$$

$$f(\varepsilon_t) \triangleq R_{PN_+}^2(\varepsilon_t) + R_{PN_-}^2(\varepsilon_t) = \begin{cases} 0; \ \varepsilon_t \le -1 - \dfrac{1}{N} \\ \left(1 + \dfrac{1}{N} + \varepsilon_t\right)^2; \ -1 - \dfrac{1}{N} < \varepsilon_t \le -1 + \dfrac{1}{N} \\ 2\left[\dfrac{1}{N^2} + (1 + \varepsilon_t)^2\right]; \ -1 + \dfrac{1}{N} < \varepsilon_t < -\dfrac{1}{N} \\ 2\left[\left(1 - \dfrac{1}{N}\right)^2 + \varepsilon_t^2\right]; \ |\varepsilon_t| \le \dfrac{1}{N} \\ 2\left[\dfrac{1}{N^2} + (1 - \varepsilon_t)^2\right]; \ \dfrac{1}{N} < \varepsilon_t \le 1 - \dfrac{1}{N} \\ \left(1 + \dfrac{1}{N} - \varepsilon_t\right)^2; \ 1 - \dfrac{1}{N} < \varepsilon_t \le 1 + \dfrac{1}{N} \\ 0; \ \varepsilon_t > 1 + \dfrac{1}{N}. \end{cases} \tag{2.19}$$

Since the DLL bandwidth is ordinarily designed to be narrow with respect to the equivalent noise bandwidth of $n_e(t, \varepsilon_t)$, we can approximate $n_e(t, \varepsilon_t)$ as a delta correlated process with equivalent single-sided noise spectral density

$$N_e(\varepsilon_t) = 2\int_{-\infty}^{\infty} R_e(\tau, \varepsilon_t)\, d\tau. \tag{2.20}$$

Substituting (2.18) together with (2.19) into (2.20) and simplifying yields

$$N_e(\varepsilon_t) = 4N_0^2\int_{-\infty}^{\infty} |H_\ell(j2\pi f)|^4\, df + 4SN_0 f(\varepsilon_t)\int_{-\infty}^{\infty} S_m(f)|H_\ell(j2\pi f)|^4\, df \tag{2.21}$$

or, alternately,

$$N_e(\varepsilon_t) = 2SN_0\left[2M_4 f(\varepsilon_t) + 2\frac{K_L}{\rho_H}\right] \tag{2.22}$$

where in addition

$$K_L \triangleq \frac{\int_{-\infty}^{\infty} |H_\ell(j2\pi f)|^4\, df}{\int_{-\infty}^{\infty} |H_\ell(j2\pi f)|^2\, df}$$

$$M_4 \triangleq \int_{-\infty}^{\infty} S_m(f)|H_\ell(j2\pi f)|^4\, df \tag{2.23}$$

and B_H denotes the two-sided noise bandwidth of the equivalent low-pass filter $H_\ell(s)$, i.e.,

$$B_H = \int_{-\infty}^{\infty} |H_\ell(j2\pi f)|^2 \, df \tag{2.24}$$

or equivalently the band-pass noise bandwidth of $H(s)$. Also, in (2.22)

$$\rho_H = \frac{S}{N_0 B_H} \tag{2.25}$$

denotes the signal-to-noise ratio in this bandwidth.

2.1.3 Linear Analysis of DLL Tracking Performance

When the equivalent loop signal-to-noise ratio is large, the tracking performance of the DLL can be determined from (2.15) with $D_n(\varepsilon_t)$ replaced by simply ε_t. Under this assumption and further assuming that $\dot{\tau}_t = 0$, one can write down, by inspection of (2.15), an expression for the mean-squared tracking jitter, viz.,

$$\sigma_\varepsilon^2 = \overline{\varepsilon_t^2} = \frac{\overline{N_e(\varepsilon_t)} B_L}{(\eta S M_2)^2}. \tag{2.26}$$

Substituting (2.19) and (2.22) in (2.26) yields

$$\sigma_\varepsilon^2 = \frac{N_0 B_L}{2S} \left[\frac{M_4\left[1 + \dfrac{16}{\eta^2}\sigma_\varepsilon^2\right] + \dfrac{8K_L}{\rho_H \eta^2}}{M_2^2} \right] \tag{2.27}$$

or solving for σ_ε^2

$$\sigma_\varepsilon^2 = \frac{1}{2\rho} \left\{ \frac{M_4 + \dfrac{8K_L}{\rho_H \eta^2}}{M_2^2\left[1 - \dfrac{8}{\eta^2 \rho}\left(\dfrac{M_4}{M_2^2}\right)\right]} \right\} \tag{2.28}$$

where $\rho \triangleq S/N_0 B_L$. Since for the linear analysis case ρ is assumed to be large, then to a first approximation (2.28) can be simplified to

$$\sigma_\varepsilon^2 = \frac{1}{2\rho} \left\{ \frac{M_4 + \dfrac{8K_L}{\rho_H \eta^2}}{M_2^2} \right\} \triangleq \frac{1}{2\rho \mathscr{S}_L} \tag{2.29}$$

where $\mathscr{S}_L$ is the "squaring loss" of the DLL i.e., the ratio of signal × signal to signal × noise plus noise × noise distortions. Alternately in terms of the data symbol signal-to-noise ratio $E_s/N_0 \triangleq ST_s/N_0$ and the ratio of

Table 2.1
Evaluation of M_2 for one- and two-pole Butterworth filters.

	(Signal × Signal Distortion)$^{1/2}$, M_2; $\lvert H_\ell(j2\pi f)\rvert^2 = \dfrac{1}{1+\left(\dfrac{f}{f_c}\right)^{2n}}$
	NRZ; $S_m(f) = T_s \dfrac{\sin^2 \pi f T_s}{(\pi f T_s)^2}$
$n = 1$	$1 - \dfrac{1}{2B_H/R_s}[1 - \exp(-2B_H/R_s)]$
$n = 2$	$1 - \dfrac{1}{4B_H/R_s}\{1 - \exp(-2B_H/R_s)[\cos(2B_H/R_s) - \sin(2B_H/R_s)]\}$
	Manchester Code; $S_m(f) = T_s \dfrac{\sin^4 \pi f T_s/2}{(\pi f T_s/2)^2}$
$n = 1$	$1 - \dfrac{1}{2B_H/R_s}[3 - 4\exp(-B_H/R_s) + \exp(-2B_H/R_s)]$
$n = 2$	$1 - \dfrac{1}{4B_H/R_s}\{3 - 4\exp(-B_H/R_s)[\cos(B_H/R_s) - \sin(B_H/R_s)]$ $+\exp(-2B_H/R_s)[\cos(2B_H/R_s) - \sin(2B_H/R_s)]\}$

band-pass filter bandwidth B_H to data rate R_s, we can write

$$\mathscr{S}_L = \frac{S \times S}{S \times N + N \times N} = \frac{M_2^2}{M_4 + K_L \dfrac{B_H/R_s}{2E_s/N_0}\left(\dfrac{N}{N-1}\right)^2} \tag{2.30}$$

where we have also made use of the definition of η in (2.16). It should be noted that (2.30) is quite similar to the expression for squaring loss of a Costas loop used for carrier synchronization of a BPSK signal (see Equation (46) of [17]). Furthermore, one can conclude from (2.30) that the squaring loss of a DLL with a correlator spacing $\delta = T_c/N$ is equal to the squaring loss of a DLL with a correlator spacing of $T_c/2$ (a "one-delta" loop) and a data rate of $4[(N-1)/N]^2 R_s$. Equivalently, then, one need only plot curves of squaring loss for the "one-delta" loop whereupon all other cases can be derived from these curves by appropriately modifying the data rate R_s.

Tables 2.1 and 2.2 present closed form results for M_2 and M_4, corresponding to one- and two-pole Butterworth filters and NRZ or Manchester coded data [18]. Also for an n-pole Butterworth filter [17],

$$K_L = \frac{n-1}{n} \tag{2.31}$$

and

$$B_H = 2f_c \left[\frac{\dfrac{\pi}{2n}}{\sin \dfrac{\pi}{2n}}\right] \tag{2.32}$$

Table 2.2
Evaluation of M_4 for one- and two-pole Butterworth filters.

	Signal × Noise Distortion, M_4; $\lvert H_\ell(j2\pi f)\rvert^2 = \dfrac{1}{1+\left(\dfrac{f}{f_c}\right)^{2n}}$
	NRZ
$n=1$	$1-\dfrac{3-(3+2B_H/R_s)\exp(-2B_H/R_s)}{4B_H/R_s}$
$n=2$	$1-\dfrac{5-\{4B_H/R_s\cos(2B_H/R_s)+5[\cos(2B_H/R_s)-\sin(2B_H/R_s)]\}\exp(-2B_H/R_s)}{16B_H/R_s}$
	Manchester Code
$n=1$	$1-\dfrac{9-4(3+B_H/R_s)\exp(-B_H/R_s)+(3+2B_H/R_s)\exp(-2B_H/R_s)}{4B_H/R_s}$
$n=2$	$1-\dfrac{15-\{8B_H/R_s\cos(B_H/R_s)+20[\cos(B_H/R_s)-\sin(B_H/R_s)]\}\exp(-B_H/R_s)}{16B_H/R_s}$ $-\dfrac{\{4B_H/R_s\cos(2B_H/R_s)+5[\cos(2B_H/R_s)-\sin(2B_H/R_s)]\}\exp(-2B_H/R_s)}{16B_H/R_s}$

where f_c is the 3 dB cutoff frequency of the equivalent low-pass filter $H_\ell(j2\pi f)$.

Figures 2.4 to 2.6 plot $\mathscr{S}_L$ of (2.30) in dB versus B_H/R_s with E_s/N_0 as a parameter for $N=2$, the case of Manchester coded data and one-, two-, and infinite-pole (ideal) Butterworth filters for $H_\ell(s)$ respectively. We observe that at each value of E_s/N_0, there exists an optimum filter band-

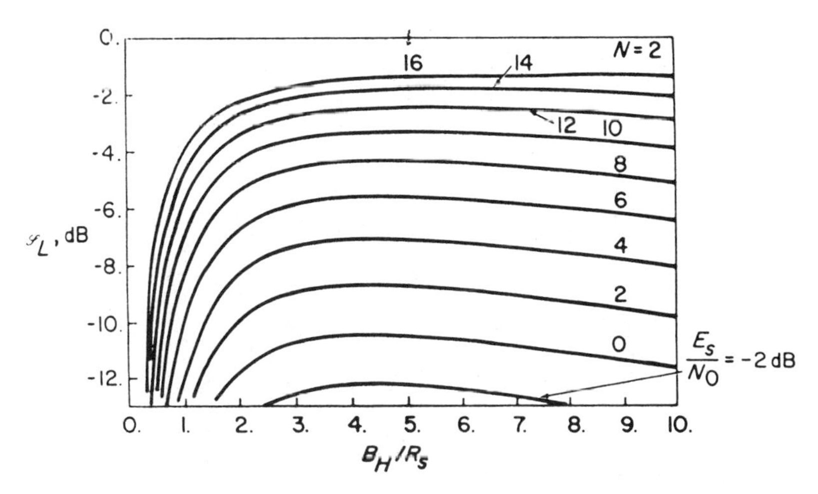

Figure 2.4. Squaring loss variations versus B_H/R_s for various values of E_s/N_0; one-pole Butterworth filter, Manchester coding.

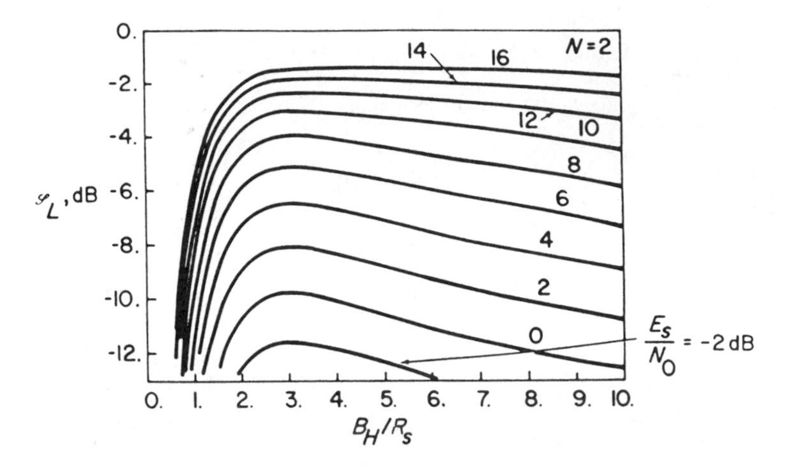

Figure 2.5. Squaring loss variations versus B_H/R_s for various values of E_s/N_0; two-pole Butterworth filter, Manchester coding.

width in the sense of minimizing the loop's squaring loss. From (2.29), such optimization of $\mathcal{S}_L$ is equivalent to minimizing the loop's tracking jitter. Similar optimization behavior of squaring loss as a function of B_H/R_s can also be observed for NRZ data.

As examples, Figures 2.7 and 2.8 illustrate $\sigma_{\varepsilon_{\min}}$ versus E_s/N_0 with $\delta_s \triangleq 1/B_L T_s$ (the ratio of data rate to loop bandwidth) as a parameter for

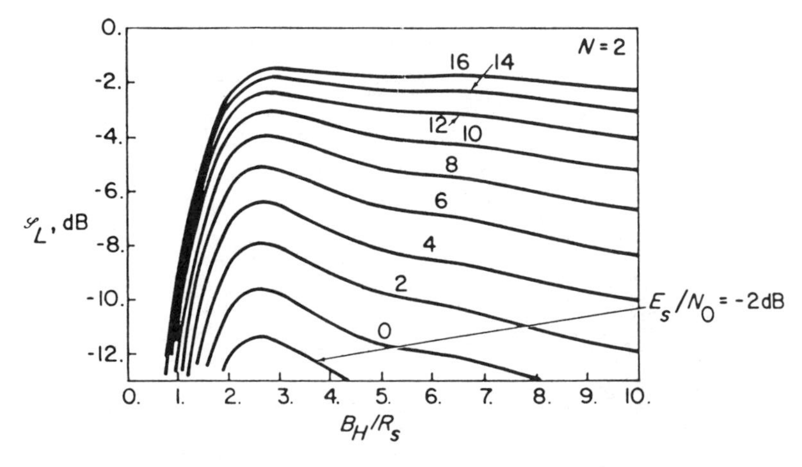

Figure 2.6. Squaring loss variations versus B_H/R_s for various values of E_s/N_0; ideal filter, Manchester coding.

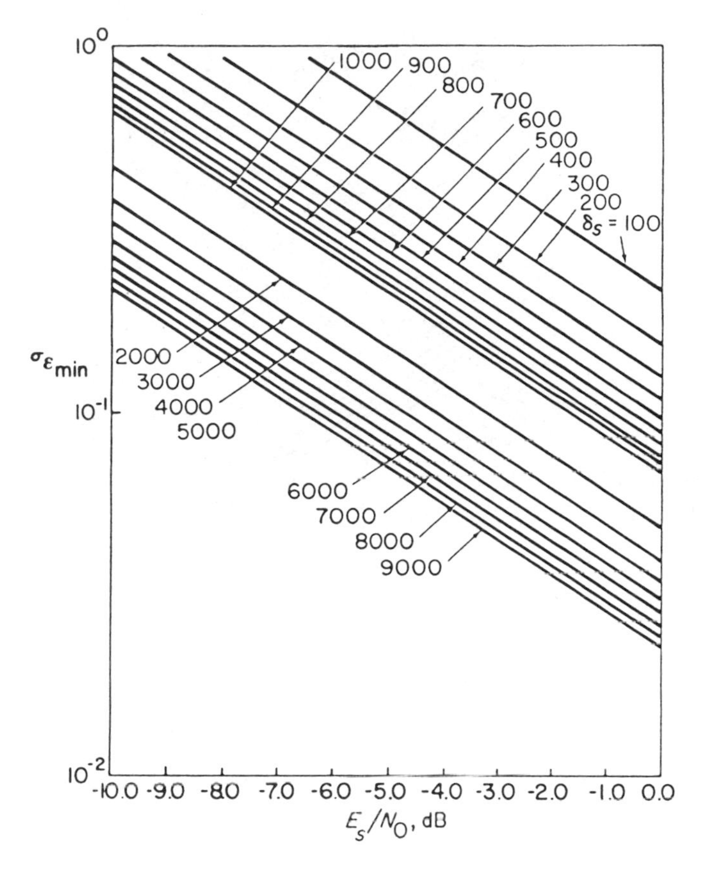

Figure 2.7. Linear tracking jitter performance of non-coherent DLL; two-pole Butterworth filter.

two-pole Butterworth and ideal filters and Manchester coded data. In arriving at these results, we have made the substitution

$$\rho \triangleq \frac{S}{N_0 B_L} = \frac{E_s}{N_0}\delta_s. \tag{2.33}$$

2.2 THE TAU-DITHER LOOP

Consider the non-coherent tau-dither loop (TDL) illustrated in Figure 2.9 whose operation is described as follows. The received signal plus noise is alternately (as opposed to simultaneously) correlated with the advanced and retarded versions of the locally generated PN code (thus the name "dither" loop) to produce an error signal, which, when band-pass filtered, envelope

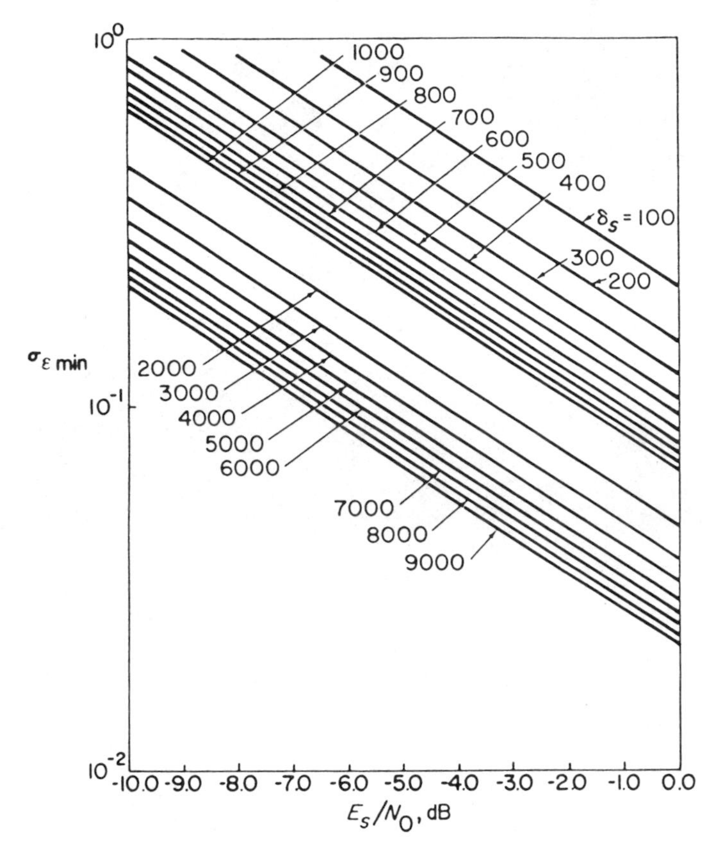

Figure 2.8. Linear tracking jitter performance of non-coherent DLL; ideal filter.

detected, and alternately inverted by the binary signal $q(t)$, drives the voltage controlled clock (VCC) through the loop filter $F(s)$. One obvious advantage of the TDL over the DLL is the fact that only a single input correlator is required, thus eliminating the problems of gain imbalance and other mismatches that are present in a two-channel loop such as the DLL.

2.2.1 Mathematical Loop Model and Equation of Operation

In deriving the loop model and discussing its performance, we shall draw heavily on the notation and results already presented for the DLL. For the purpose of analysis, one can show [6] that when the dither frequency f_d is low relative to the noise bandwidth B_H of the band-pass filter (the usual case of interest), the TDL has the equivalent loop model illustrated in Figure 2.10. Starting then with $y_+(t)$ and $y_-(t)$ as defined in (2.5), the

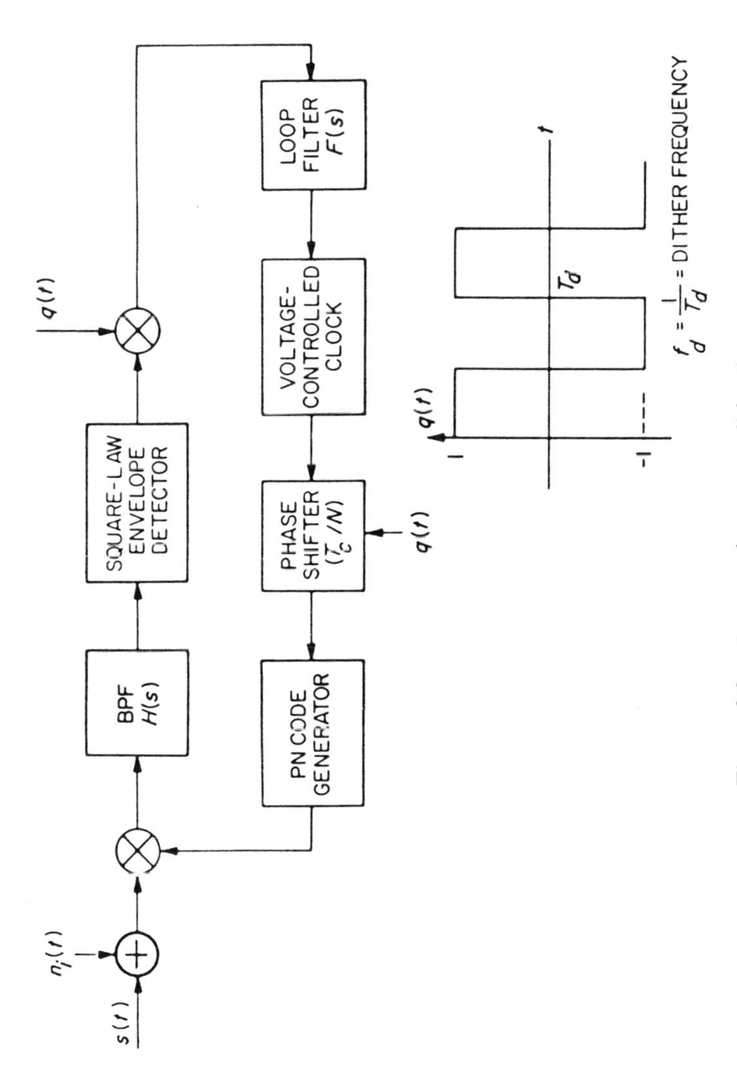

Figure 2.9. A non-coherent tau-dither loop.

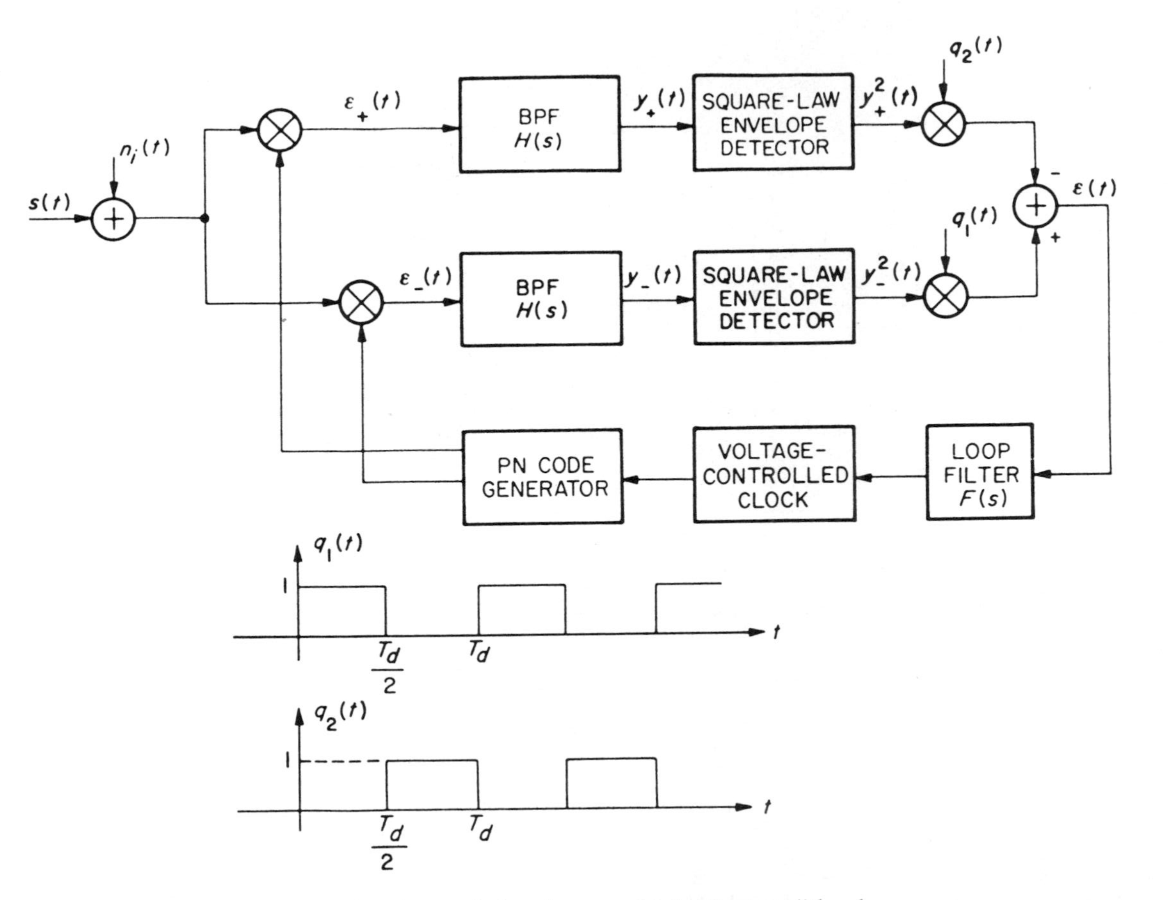

Figure 2.10. An equivalent loop model for the tau-dither loop.

input to the loop filter is now given by

$$\begin{aligned} e(t) &\triangleq y_-^2(t)q_1(t) - y_+^2(t)q_2(t) \\ &= SK_m^2\hat{m}^2(t-\tau_t)\left[q_1(t)R_{PN_-}^2(\varepsilon_t) - q_2(t)R_{PN_+}^2(\varepsilon_t)\right] \\ &\quad + K_m^2 n_e'(t,\varepsilon_t) \end{aligned} \tag{2.34}$$

where

$$\begin{aligned} n_e'(t,\varepsilon_t) &= q_1(t)\left[\hat{N}_{c_-}^2(t) + \hat{N}_{s_-}^2(t)\right] - q_2(t)\left[\hat{N}_{c_+}^2(t) + \hat{N}_{s_+}^2(t)\right] \\ &\quad + 2\sqrt{S}\,\hat{m}(t-\tau_t)\left\{q_1(t)R_{PN_-}(\varepsilon_t)\hat{N}_{c_-}(t)\right. \\ &\quad \left. - q_2(t)R_{PN_+}(\varepsilon_t)\hat{N}_{c_+}(t)\right\}. \end{aligned} \tag{2.35}$$

Recognizing that $q_1(t) - q_2(t) = q(t)$ and $q_1(t) + q_2(t) = 1$, we see that (2.34) simplifies to

$$e(t) = SK_m^2\hat{m}^2(t-\tau_t)D'(t,\varepsilon_t) + K_m^2 n_e'(t,\varepsilon_t) \tag{2.36}$$

where

$$D'(t,\varepsilon_t) \triangleq q_1(t)R_{PN_-}^2(\varepsilon_t) - q_2(t)R_{PN_+}^2(\varepsilon_t)$$

$$= \begin{cases} 0; \ \varepsilon_t \leq -1 - \dfrac{1}{N} \\ -q_2(t)\left[1 + \dfrac{1}{N} + \varepsilon_t\right]^2; \ -1 - \dfrac{1}{N} < \varepsilon_t \leq -1 + \dfrac{1}{N} \\ q(t)\left[(1+\varepsilon_t)^2 + \left(\dfrac{1}{N}\right)^2\right] - \dfrac{2}{N}(1+\varepsilon_t); \ -1 + \dfrac{1}{N} < \varepsilon_t < -\dfrac{1}{N} \\ q(t)\left[\left(1 - \dfrac{1}{N}\right)^2 + \varepsilon_t^2\right] + 2\left(1 - \dfrac{1}{N}\right)\varepsilon_t; \ |\varepsilon_t| \leq \dfrac{1}{N} \\ q(t)\left[(1-\varepsilon_t)^2 + \left(\dfrac{1}{N}\right)^2\right] + \dfrac{2}{N}(1-\varepsilon_t); \ \dfrac{1}{N} < \varepsilon_t \leq 1 - \dfrac{1}{N} \\ q_1(t)\left[1 + \dfrac{1}{N} - \varepsilon_t\right]^2; \ 1 - \dfrac{1}{N} < \varepsilon_t \leq 1 + \dfrac{1}{N} \\ 0; \ \varepsilon_t > 1 + \dfrac{1}{N} \end{cases} \tag{2.37}$$

$$D'(t,\varepsilon_t) = D'(t,\varepsilon_t + np); \qquad n = \pm 1, \pm 2, \pm 3, \ldots . \tag{2.38}$$

As in the DLL case, since the loop bandwidth is narrow with respect to the data rate and here also with respect to the dither frequency, $f_d = 1/T_d$, we can replace $\hat{m}^2(t-\tau_t)D'(t,\varepsilon_t)$ by

$$\langle\overline{\hat{m}^2(t-\tau_t)}D'(t,\varepsilon_t)\rangle = \langle\overline{\hat{m}^2(t-\tau_t)}\rangle\langle D'(t,\varepsilon_t)\rangle. \tag{2.39}$$

Thus, since $\langle q(t)\rangle = 0$ and $\langle q_1(t)\rangle = \langle q_2(t)\rangle = 1/2$, we get

$$D'(\varepsilon_t) \triangleq \langle D'(t,\varepsilon_t)\rangle = \begin{cases} 0; \ \varepsilon_t \le -1 - \dfrac{1}{N} \\ -\dfrac{1}{2}\left(1 + \dfrac{1}{N} + \varepsilon_t\right)^2; \ -1 - \dfrac{1}{N} < \varepsilon_t \le -1 + \dfrac{1}{N} \\ -\dfrac{2}{N}(1+\varepsilon_t); \ -1 + \dfrac{1}{N} < \varepsilon_t < -\dfrac{1}{N} \\ 2\varepsilon_t\left(1 - \dfrac{1}{N}\right); \ |\varepsilon_t| \le \dfrac{1}{N} \\ \dfrac{2}{N}(1-\varepsilon_t); \ \dfrac{1}{N} < \varepsilon_t \le 1 - \dfrac{1}{N} \\ \dfrac{1}{2}\left(1 + \dfrac{1}{N} - \varepsilon_t\right)^2; \ 1 - \dfrac{1}{N} < \varepsilon_t \le 1 + \dfrac{1}{N} \\ 0; \ \varepsilon_t > 1 + \dfrac{1}{N} \end{cases} \tag{2.40}$$

and (2.36) further simplifies to

$$e(t) = SK_m^2 M_2 D'(\varepsilon_t) + K_m^2 n_e'(t,\varepsilon_t) \tag{2.41}$$

where M_2 is defined in (2.14). Comparing $D'(\varepsilon_t)$ of (2.40) with $D(\varepsilon_t)$ of (2.8), we observe that the TDL suffers an effective reduction in signal power of 3 dB relative to the DLL. Using (2.10) and the assumptions leading up to (2.15), we obtain the stochastic differential equation which characterizes the TDL, viz.,

$$\dot{\varepsilon}_t = \frac{\dot{\tau}_t}{T_c} - \frac{1}{2}KF(p)\eta SM_2\left[D_n(\varepsilon_t) + \frac{n_e'(t,\varepsilon_t)}{\frac{1}{2}\eta SM_2}\right] \tag{2.42}$$

where $D_n(\varepsilon_t) \triangleq (2/\eta)D'(\varepsilon_t)$ is identical to the normalized discriminator characteristic for the DLL.

2.2.2 Statistical Characterization of the Equivalent Additive Noise

What remains is to determine the power spectral density $N_e'(\varepsilon_t)$ of the delta-correlated process $n_e'(t,\varepsilon_t)$, i.e.,

$$N_e'(\varepsilon_t) = 2\int_{-\infty}^{\infty} R_e'(\tau,\varepsilon_t)\,d\tau \tag{2.43}$$

where

$$R_e'(\tau,\varepsilon_t) \triangleq \overline{n_e'(t,\varepsilon_t)n_e'(t+\tau,\varepsilon_t)}. \tag{2.44}$$

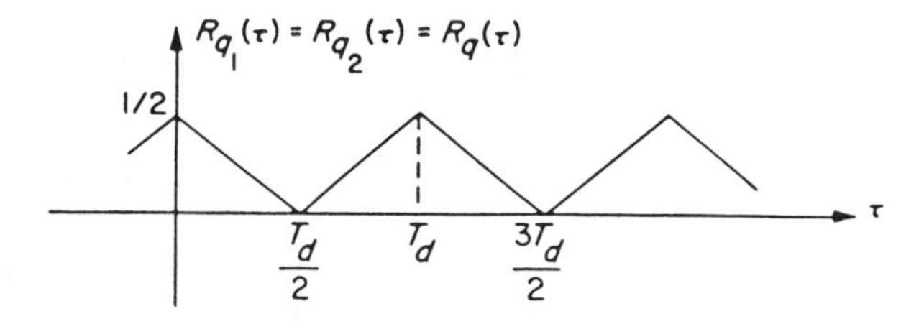

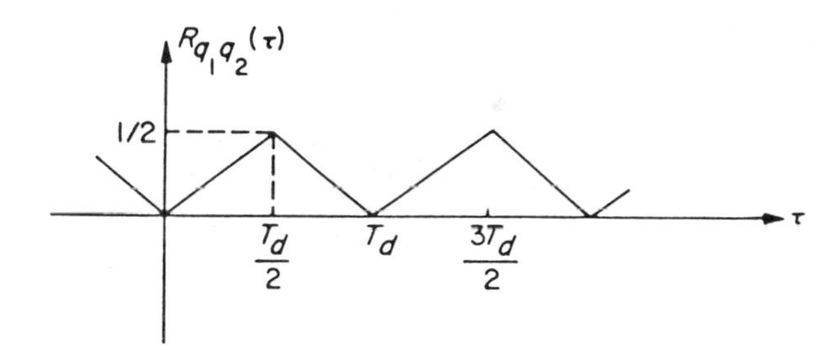

Figure 2.11. Autocorrelation functions of $q_1(t)$ and $q_2(t)$ and cross-correlation function of $q_1(t)$ and $q_2(t)$.

Denoting the autocorrelation and cross-correlation functions of the switching waveforms by

$$\begin{aligned} R_{q_1}(\tau) &\triangleq \langle q_1(t) q_1(t+\tau) \rangle \\ R_{q_2}(\tau) &\triangleq \langle q_2(t) q_2(t+\tau) \rangle \\ R_{q_1 q_2}(\tau) &\triangleq \langle q_1(t) q_2(t+\tau) \rangle \end{aligned} \tag{2.45}$$

we find that

$$R_{q_1}(\tau) = R_{q_2}(\tau) = \tfrac{1}{2} - R_{q_1 q_2}(\tau) \triangleq R_q(\tau) \tag{2.46}$$

where $R_q(\tau)$ is illustrated in Figure 2.11. Substituting (2.35) into (2.44) and making use of (2.46), we find after considerable algebraic manipulation that

$$\begin{aligned} R_e'(\tau, \varepsilon_t) = {} & 8R_{\hat{N}}^2(\tau) R_q(\tau) + 8R_{\hat{N}}^2(0)\left[2R_q(\tau) - \tfrac{1}{2}\right] \\ & + 4SR_{\hat{m}}(\tau) R_{\hat{N}}(\tau) R_q(\tau) f(\varepsilon_t) \end{aligned} \tag{2.47}$$

where $R_{\hat{N}}(\tau)$, $R_{\hat{m}}(\tau)$, and $f(\varepsilon_t)$ are all defined in (2.19). Integration of (2.47) as required in (2.43) can alternately be accomplished in the frequency domain, viz.,

$$\begin{aligned} N_e'(\varepsilon_t) = {} & 16\int_{-\infty}^{\infty} \left[S_{\hat{N}}(f) * S_{\hat{N}}(f)\right] S_q(-f)\, df \\ & + 8Sf(\varepsilon_t)\int_{-\infty}^{\infty} \left[S_{\hat{m}}(f) * S_{\hat{m}}(f)\right] S_q(-f)\, df \end{aligned} \tag{2.48}$$

where the asterisk denotes convolution, and

$$S_{\hat{N}}(f) = \mathscr{F}\{R_{\hat{N}}(\tau)\} = \frac{N_0}{2}|H_\ell(j2\pi f)|^2$$

$$S_{\hat{m}}(f) = \mathscr{F}\{R_{\hat{m}}(\tau)\} = S_m(f)|H_\ell(j2\pi f)|^2$$

$$S_q(f) = \mathscr{F}\{R_q(\tau)\} = \frac{1}{4}\delta(f) + \frac{1}{4}\sum_{\substack{n=-\infty \\ n\text{ odd}}}^{\infty}\left(\frac{2}{n\pi}\right)^2\delta\left(f - \frac{n}{T_d}\right). \tag{2.49}$$

Substituting (2.49) into (2.48), we obtain, after much simplification, an expression analogous to (2.22), i.e.,

$$N_e'(\varepsilon_t) = \frac{SN_0}{2}\left[2M_4'f(\varepsilon_t) + 2\frac{K_L'}{\rho_H}\right] \tag{2.50}$$

where

$$M_4' = M_4 + 2\sum_{n=1,3,5\ldots}^{\infty}\left(\frac{2}{n\pi}\right)^2 M_{4n}$$

$$K_L' = K_L + 2\sum_{n=1,3,5\ldots}^{\infty}\left(\frac{2}{n\pi}\right)^2 K_{L_n}$$

$$M_{4n} \triangleq \int_{-\infty}^{\infty} S_m(f)|H_\ell(j2\pi f)|^2\left|H_\ell\left[j2\pi\left(\frac{n}{T_d} - f\right)\right]\right|^2 df$$

$$K_{L_n} = \frac{\displaystyle\int_{-\infty}^{\infty}|H_\ell(j2\pi f)|^2\left|H_\ell\left[j2\pi\left(\frac{n}{T_d} - f\right)\right]\right|^2 df}{\displaystyle\int_{-\infty}^{\infty}|H_\ell(j2\pi f)|^2\, df} \tag{2.51}$$

and K_L and M_4 are defined in (2.23) and ρ_H is defined in (2.25).

2.2.3 Linear Analysis of TDL Tracking Performance

As for the DLL, we can write down, by inspection of (2.42), an expression for the mean-squared tracking jitter for the case $\dot{\tau}_t = 0$, viz.,

$$\sigma_\varepsilon'^2 = \frac{\overline{N_e'(\varepsilon_t)B_L}}{\left(\frac{1}{2}\eta SM_2\right)^2} \tag{2.52}$$

which upon substitution of (2.50) and (2.19) becomes

$$\sigma_\varepsilon'^2 = \frac{1}{2\rho}\left\{\frac{M_4' + \dfrac{8K_L'}{\rho_H\eta^2}}{M_2^2\left[1 - \dfrac{8}{\eta^2\rho}\left(\dfrac{M_4'}{M_2^2}\right)\right]}\right\} \tag{2.53}$$

or, to a first approximation

$$\sigma_{\varepsilon}'^{2} = \frac{1}{2\rho}\left\{\frac{M_4' + \dfrac{8K_L'}{\rho_H \eta^2}}{M_2^2}\right\} = \frac{1}{2\rho \mathscr{S}_L'} \tag{2.54}$$

where $\mathscr{S}_L'$ is the "squaring loss" of the TDL which is given by (2.30) with M_4 and K_L replaced by M_4' and K_L'. A comparison of the linear tracking jitter performances of the DLL and TDL depends then simply on the ratio of $\mathscr{S}_L'$ to $\mathscr{S}_L$, namely,

$$\frac{\mathscr{S}_L}{\mathscr{S}_L'} = \frac{M_4 + \dfrac{8K_L}{\rho_H \eta^2}}{M_4' + \dfrac{8K_L'}{\rho_H \eta^2}}. \tag{2.55}$$

Clearly, from the definitions of M_{4n} and K_{L_n} as given in (2.51), we see that $M_{4n} < M_4$ and $K_{L_n} < K_L$ for any n, in particular, n odd, and T_d finite. Thus, from (2.51)

$$\begin{aligned} M_4' &< M_4 + \frac{8}{\pi^2} \sum_{n=1,3,5\ldots}^{\infty} \frac{1}{n^2} M_4 = 2M_4 \\ K_L' &< K_L + \frac{8}{\pi^2} \sum_{n=1,3,5\ldots}^{\infty} \frac{1}{n^2} K_L = 2K_L. \end{aligned} \tag{2.56}$$

Substituting the bounds of (2.56) into (2.55), we find that

$$\frac{\mathscr{S}_L'}{\mathscr{S}_L} > \frac{1}{2} \tag{2.57}$$

or equivalently, *the linear theory mean-squared timing error for the TDL is less than* 3 *dB worse than that of the DLL.*

Although the integrals in (2.51) are in general difficult to evaluate in closed form, the case where $H_\ell(s)$ is an ideal filter allows some simplification. In particular,

$$K_{L_n} = \frac{\displaystyle\int_{-B_H/2+n/T_d}^{B_H/2} df}{\displaystyle\int_{-B_H/2}^{B_H/2} df} = \begin{cases} 1 - \dfrac{n}{B_H T_d}; & n \le \lfloor B_H T_d \rfloor \triangleq n_0 \\ 0; & n > n_0 \end{cases} \tag{2.58}$$

where the notation $\lfloor x \rfloor$ denotes the largest integer less than or equal to x. Thus, from (2.51),

$$K_L' = 1 + \frac{8}{\pi^2} \sum_{n=1,3,5,\ldots}^{n_0} \frac{1}{n^2} - \frac{8}{\pi^2 B_H T_d} \sum_{n=1,3,5,\ldots}^{n_0} \frac{1}{n}. \tag{2.59}$$

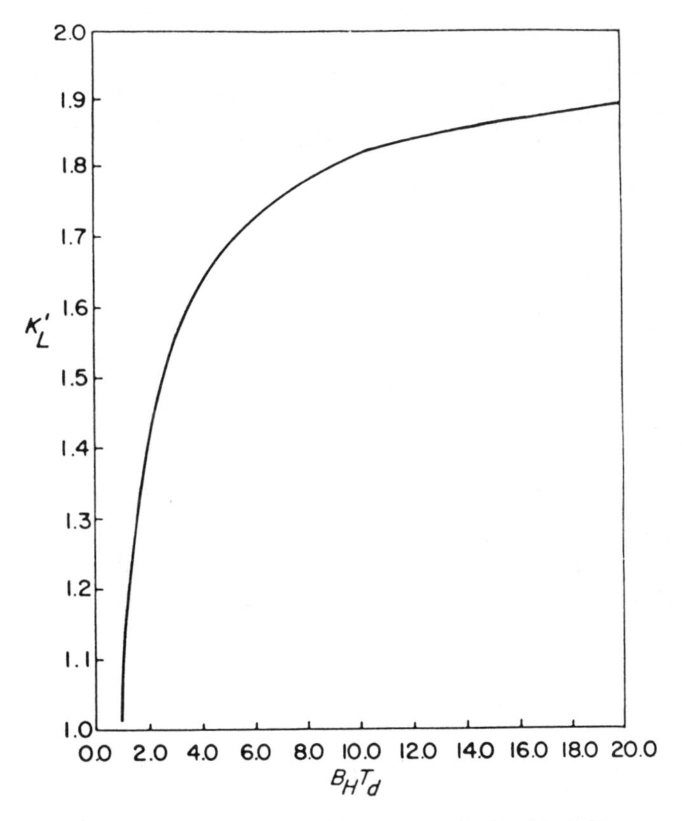

Figure 2.12. A plot of K_L' versus $B_H T_d$; ideal filter.

Figure 2.12 plots K_L' versus $B_H T_d$. Similarly, for the case of Manchester-coded data of rate $R_s = 1/T_s$,

$$M_{4n} = \int_{-B_H/2+n/T_d}^{B_H/2} \frac{\sin^4 \dfrac{\pi f T_s}{2}}{\left(\dfrac{\pi f T_s}{2}\right)^2} df = \int_{-B_H T_s/4}^{B_H T_s/4} \frac{\sin^4 \pi x}{(\pi x)^2} dx$$

$$- \int_{-B_H T_s/4}^{-B_H T_s/4 + n T_s/2T_d} \frac{\sin^4 \pi x}{(\pi x)^2} dx \tag{2.60}$$

and

$$M_4' = \left[1 + \frac{8}{\pi^2} \sum_{n=1,3,5,\ldots}^{n_0} \frac{1}{n^2}\right] \int_{-B_H T_s/4}^{B_H T_s/4} \frac{\sin^4 \pi x}{(\pi x)^2} dx - \frac{8}{\pi^2} \sum_{n=1,3,5,\ldots}^{n_0} \frac{1}{n^2}$$

$$\times \int_{(B_H T_s/4)[1-2n/B_H T_d]}^{B_H T_s/4} \frac{\sin^4 \pi x}{(\pi x)^2} dx \tag{2.61}$$

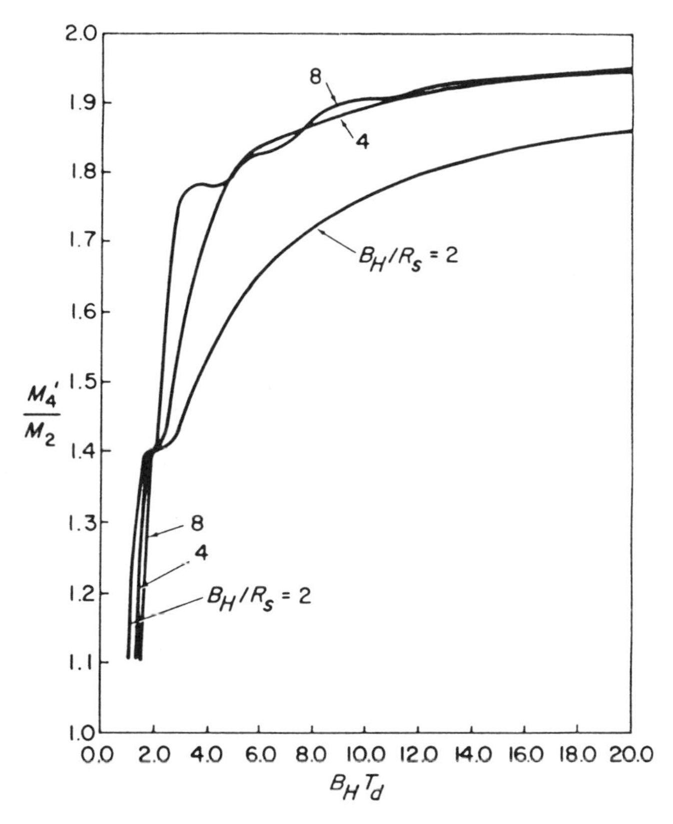

Figure 2.13. Plots of M_4'/M_2 versus $B_H T_d$ with B_H/R_s as a parameter; ideal filter, Manchester coding.

where the first integral in (2.61) is in reality $M_2 = M_4$. Figure 2.13 plots M_4' (normalized by M_2) versus $B_H T_d$ for various values of the ratio of filter bandwidth to data rate, B_H/R_s.

At this point, it is reasonable to expect that if one were to plot $\mathcal{S}_L'$ versus B_H/R_s with E_s/N_0 as a parameter, then at each value of E_s/N_0, there would exist an optimum filter bandwidth in the sense of minimizing the loop's squaring loss. Figure 2.14 illustrates the validity of this statement for the case of an ideal filter with $\mathcal{S}_L'$ as determined from (2.54) together with (2.14), (2.59), and (2.61). The corresponding minimum tracking jitter performance as described by (2.54) is illustrated in Figure 2.15. In both of these figures, the value of $B_H T_d$ was chosen equal to four. Comparing Figure 2.15 with Figure 2.8, we observe that over the entire range of parameter variations chosen, the TDL is approximately 1.06 dB poorer than the DLL.[5]

[5] The comparison here is made on the basis of equal $\sigma_{\epsilon_{\min}}$ and the signal-to-noise ratio penalty of 1.06 dB is obtained directly from the computational data rather than the curves themselves.

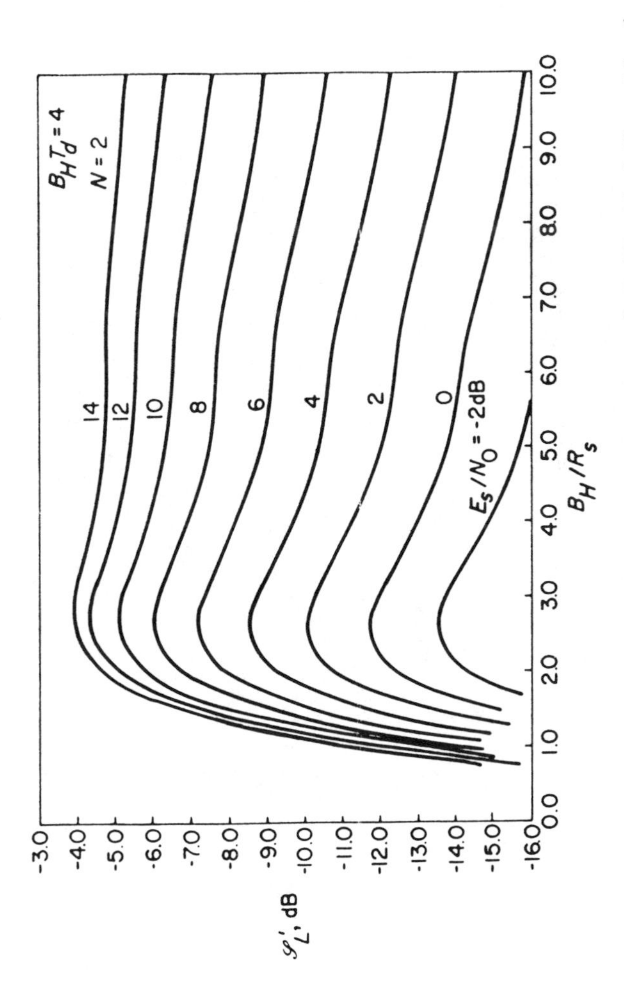

Figure 2.14. Squaring loss variations versus B_H/R_s for various values of E_s/N_0; ideal filter, Manchester coding.

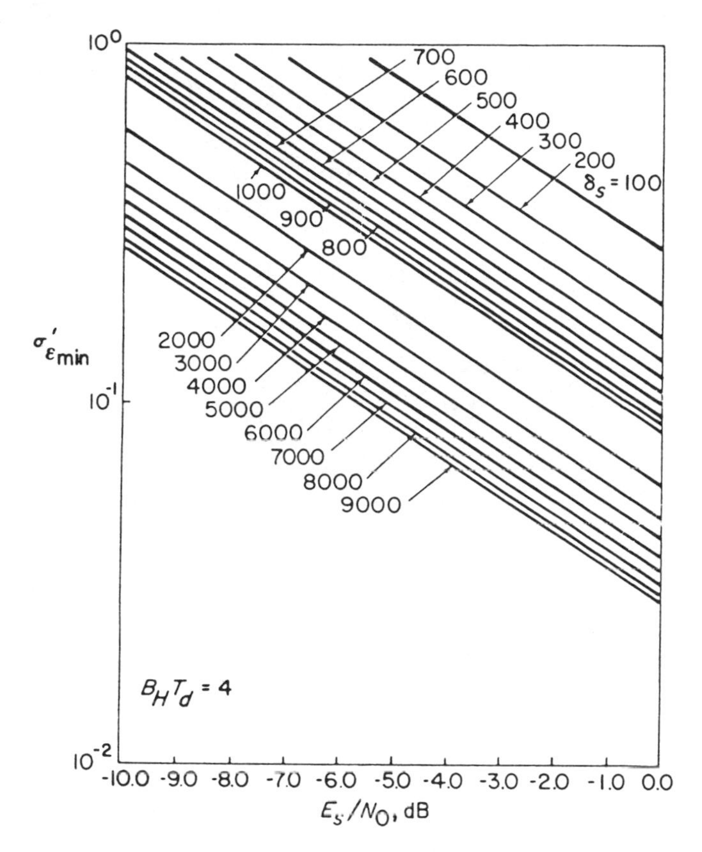

Figure 2.15. Linear tracking jitter performance of non-coherent TDL; ideal filter.

As $B_H T_d$ is increased (typically by lowering the dither frequency relative to the arm filter bandwidth), the performance penalty also increases approaching 1.5 dB in the limit as $B_H T_d$ approaches infinity. Clearly, this situation is never reached in practice, nor in theory, since the assumption made in the analysis that the dither frequency be large relative to the loop bandwidth breaks down.

It is perhaps interesting to see how the optimized performance results presented in this chapter compare with the early results of Gill [3] and Hartmann [6]. In particular, both these authors performed their analyses neglecting the band-limiting effect of the arm filters. Thus, if one sets $K_L = M_2 = M_4 = 1$ in (2.29), and substitutes $(E_s/N_0)/(B_H/R_s)$ for ρ_H one arrives at Gill's result[6] for the normalized mean-squared tracking error of

[6]Actually, Gill and Hartmann considered only the "one-delta" loop, i.e., $N = 2$.

the DLL, namely

$$\sigma_\varepsilon^2 = \frac{1}{2\rho}\left[1 + \frac{2B_H/R_s}{E_s/N_0}\right]. \tag{2.62}$$

A similar analysis to Gill's was performed by Hartmann for the TDL. His result for the normalized mean-squared tracking error (analogous to (2.54)) is

$$\sigma_\varepsilon'^2 = \frac{1}{\rho}\left[0.905 + \frac{4B_H/R_s}{E_s/N_0}\left(0.453 - \frac{0.2}{B_H T_d}\right)\right] \tag{2.63}$$

which for $B_H T_d = 4$ becomes

$$\sigma_\varepsilon'^2 = \frac{1}{\rho}\left[0.905 + \frac{1.612 B_H/R_s}{E_s/N_0}\right]. \tag{2.64}$$

Numerical comparison of (2.62) and (2.64) with the results in Figures 2.8 and 2.15 reveals that both Gill's and Hartmann's simple results are optimistic by about .9 dB [7].

One should also note that if arm filter band-limiting effects were totally ignored for the TDL, then again $K_L = M_2 = M_4 = 1$ and M_4' and K_L' would achieve their upper bounds as in (2.56), in which case, (2.54) would simplify (for $N = 2$) to

$$\sigma_\varepsilon'^2 = \frac{1}{\rho}\left[1 + \frac{2B_H/R_s}{E_s/N_0}\right]. \tag{2.65}$$

Comparing (2.65) with (2.62), we observe the often-quoted (although incorrect) result that the TDL suffers a 3 dB degradation in signal-to-noise performance relative to the DLL.

Finally, we point out that increasing N (decreasing the advance (retard) interval) decreases the mean-squared tracking jitter for both the DLL and TDL. This observation is easily concluded from (2.29) and (2.54) together with (2.16). However, increasing N also decreases the linear tracking region of the discriminator characteristic (see Figure 2.3) and thus increases the loop's tendency to lose lock. This tradeoff between decreasing mean-squared tracking jitter at the expense of increased sensitivity to loss of lock is characteristic of all early-late gate types of loops [15, Chapter 9].

2.3 ACQUISITION (TRANSIENT) BEHAVIOR OF THE DLL AND TDL

In this section, we discuss the transient response of the DLL and TDL with particular emphasis on their acquisition behavior in the presence of an initial code rate offset of the incoming PN code relative to that of the clock that generates the local PN code replica at the receiver. When discussing the transient response behavior of a DLL or TDL, or for that matter any PN code tracking loop, there are primarily two questions of interest:

1. What is the maximum relative code rate offset (due to code Doppler, clock instabilities, etc.) between the received and locally generated PN codes so that the received signal can still be acquired? Equivalently, what is the maximum search rate (velocity) to achieve acquisition?
2. How long do the transients last, i.e., how long does it take to acquire?

The answer to the first question may be obtained (in a noise-free environment) by examination of the phase-plane trajectories. These trajectories are plots of normalized code delay error rate $\dot{\varepsilon}_t$ versus normalized code delay error ε_t with normalized time as a parameter along the curve. To obtain these trajectories for the DLL, we begin by rewriting the system equation of noise-free operation, as given by (2.15), in the normalized form

$$p_0(y - x) = GF_0(p_0)D_n(x) \tag{2.66}$$

where

$$\tau \triangleq \omega_n t$$

$$p_0 \triangleq \frac{d}{d\tau} = \left(\frac{1}{\omega_n}\right)\frac{d}{dt} = \frac{p}{\omega_n}$$

$$x \triangleq \frac{\tau}{T_c}$$

$$y \triangleq \varepsilon_t$$

$$G \triangleq \eta SKM_2/\omega_n$$

$$F_0(p_0) = F_0\left(\frac{p}{\omega_n}\right) \triangleq F(p) \tag{2.67}$$

with ω_n the *radian natural frequency* of the loop.

For a second-order loop with linear closed loop transfer function [16]

$$\begin{aligned} H(s) &= \frac{1 + 2\zeta s/\omega_n}{1 + (1/G + 2\zeta)(s/\omega_n) + (s/\omega_n)^2} \\ &= \frac{\omega_n GF(s)}{s + \omega_n GF(s)} \end{aligned} \tag{2.68}$$

the product of the loop gain G and the filter transfer function $F(s)$ becomes

$$GF(s) = \frac{1 + 2\zeta s/\omega_n}{1/G + s/\omega_n} \tag{2.69}$$

or

$$GF_0(p_0) = \frac{1 + 2\zeta p_0}{1/G + p_0} \tag{2.70}$$

where ζ is the loop's *damping factor*. For a critically damped loop ($\zeta =$

$1/\sqrt{2}$), (2.70) simplifies to

$$GF_0(p_0) = \frac{1 + \sqrt{2}\, p_0}{1/G + p_0}, \tag{2.71}$$

which, upon substitution into (2.66), yields

$$\dot{y}/G + \ddot{y} = \dot{x}/G + \ddot{x} + D_n(x) + \sqrt{2}\, D_n'(x)\dot{x}. \tag{2.72}$$

The dot now denotes the derivative with respect to normalized time (τ) and the prime denotes the derivative with respect to the normalized transmission delay (x). The solution of the second-order partial differential equation in (2.66) for the phase-plane trajectories is facilitated by defining $\gamma \triangleq \ddot{x}/\dot{x} = d\dot{x}/dx$, which results in

$$\gamma = -\frac{D_n(x) + \left[\sqrt{2}\, D_n'(x) + 1/G\right]\dot{x} - \dot{y}/G - \ddot{y}}{\dot{x}}. \tag{2.73}$$

For a constant search velocity, $\ddot{y} = 0$ and the above equation simplifies to

$$\gamma = \frac{D_n(x) + \left[\sqrt{2}\, D_n'(x) + 1/G\right]\dot{x} - \dot{y}/G}{\dot{x}}. \tag{2.74}$$

Statistical methods (e.g., Newton's method [19]) of solving differential equations can now be applied to (2.74) to compute the trajectories in the $(\dot{x}, x)$ plane for given initial conditions. One then looks for the maximum $\dot{y}$ for which the phase-plane trajectories will eventually reach the $(0, \dot{y}/G)$ point, i.e., the DLL will phase and frequency lock.

The acquisition trajectories for $G = 10$, $\zeta = 1/\sqrt{2}$, $N = 2$ and $N = 4$ are shown in Figures 2.16 and 2.17, respectively [4], [14].[7] It is found that the maximum normalized search rate for $N = 2$ is $\dot{y} = 1.0$, while for $N = 4$, the maximum normalized search rate is $\dot{y} = 0.5$. Furthermore, the open loop gain has little effect on the trajectories for $G > 10$ [14].

The second question raised above can be dealt with by using the definition of γ as a starting point and computing the acquisition transients as a function of time and then finding the acquisition time. Figure 2.18 shows the transient response of the DLL for $G = 100$, $\zeta = 1/\sqrt{2}$, $N = 2$ and $N = 4$. The search rate is chosen to be $\dot{y} = 0.9$ for the first case and $\dot{y} = 0.45$ for the second case, respectively. The graphs show that the acquisition time (time required for the transient to subside within $|x| = 0.1$) for $N = 2$ is shorter than that for $N = 4$. The actual acquisition time can be computed from the definition of the normalized time given in (2.67) and the relation between the single-sided loop bandwidth B_L and the loop radian

[7] Historically acquisition trajectories were first found in [1] and [3] but were later shown to be in error [4].

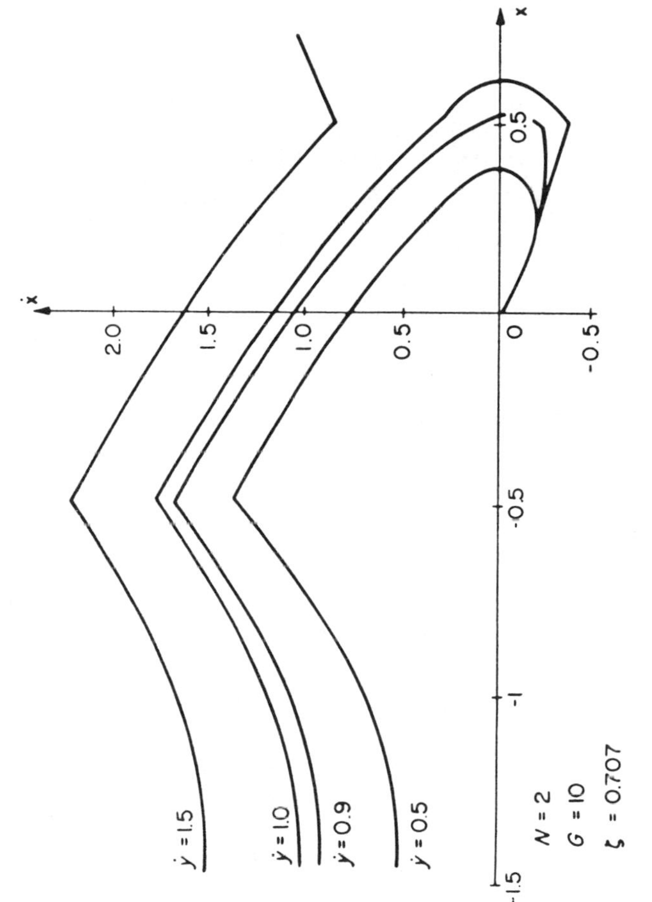

Figure 2.16. Acquisition trajectories for $N = 2$ (reprinted from [14]).

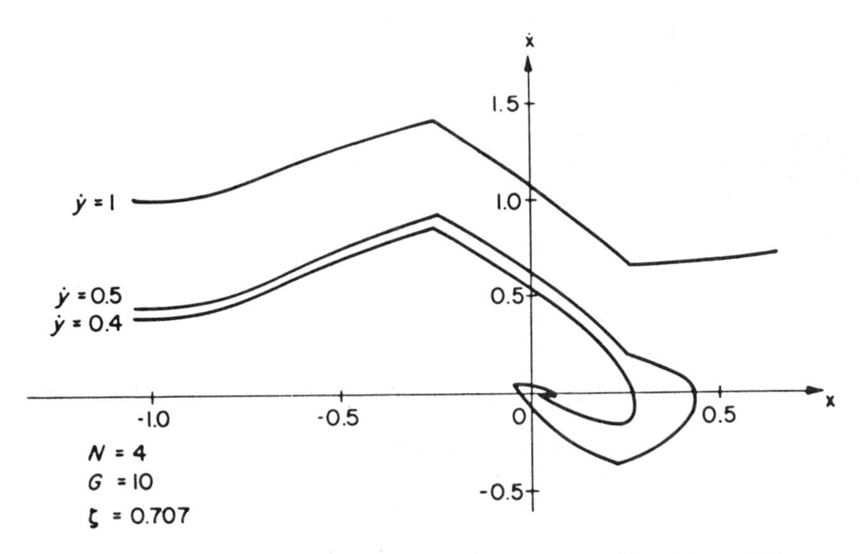

Figure 2.17. Acquisition trajectories for $N = 4$ (reprinted from [14]).

natural frequency ω_n. Since from [16]

$$\omega_n = \left(\frac{8\zeta}{4\zeta^2 + 1}\right) B_L \tag{2.75}$$

then for critically damped loops $\omega_n = B_L/.5303$ and

$$t_{\text{ACQ}} = \frac{.5303\tau_{ACQ}}{B_L}. \tag{2.76}$$

Table 2.3 summarizes the results for several different values of loop bandwidth.

Finally, the actual maximum search velocity in chips/sec (which can be interpreted as the maximum allowable drift in the code) can be found from the definition of the normalized search velocity $\dot{y}$. As a function of the single-sided loop noise bandwidth B_L, the search velocity (v_s) is

$$v_s = \left(\frac{8\zeta}{4\zeta^2 + 1}\right) \dot{y} B_L \text{ chips/sec} \tag{2.77}$$

which for critically damped loops becomes

$$v_s = 1.8857 \dot{y} B_L \text{ chips/sec.} \tag{2.78}$$

Although all our attention has focussed on the DLL, a comparison of (2.15) and (2.42) in the absence of noise reveals that except for a factor of two in the equivalent gain G, the TDL and DLL have identical acquisition performance.

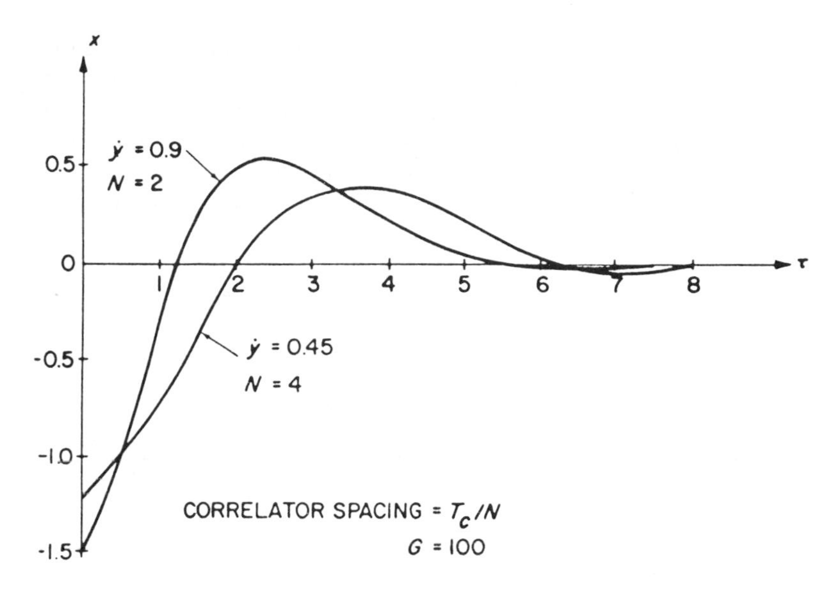

Figure 2.18. Transient response of delay lock loop (reprinted from [14]).

Table 2.3
Acquisition time (sec).

B_L (Hz)	100	200	300	400	
$N = 2$	0.0244	0.0122	0.0081	0.0061	$\dot{y} = 0.9$
$N = 4$	0.0292	0.0146	0.0097	0.0073	$\dot{y} = 0.45$

2.4 MEAN TIME TO LOSS-OF-LOCK FOR THE DLL AND TDL

The ability of the code tracking loop to maintain lock is an important consideration in assessing the overall performance of a DS/SS receiver. One measure of this ability, which is undoubtedly the most informative, is the probability of remaining in lock for a given interval of time. Unfortunately, analytical evaluation of this measure is difficult, and thus an alternate but still informative measure often used is the mean time to lose lock. Although for a carrier tracking loop such as a phase-locked loop (PLL) this performance measure is well defined [16], its definition for a PN code tracking loop requires some clarification. For our purpose, we shall define out-of-lock to occur when the loop error signal goes beyond its uncorrelated value, or equivalently, the delay error exceeds the range of the discriminator characteristic around the lock point, i.e., $\pm T_c(N+1)/N$.

The mean time to loss-of-lock is a special case of the more general problem of finding the n-th moment of the first passage time of the error process in a synchronous control system (SCS). The solutions to problems of this nature are typically obtained by assuming that the noise process driving the system is wideband compared to the system bandwidth, in which case the error process can be assumed to be Markovian and its probability density function is a solution to the Fokker-Planck equation. Without belaboring the details, one can show that by applying the appropriate boundary conditions to the time-dependent solution of the one-dimensional Fokker-Planck equation, the first moment of the first passage time (mean time to lose lock) of the error process $x(t)$ in a first-order SCS with symmetrical boundaries $\pm b$ and symmetrical restoring force $h(x)$ [i.e., $h(x) = h(-x)$] is given by [16]

$$\overline{T} = \frac{1}{K_2}\int_0^b \int_0^b \exp[U(y) - U(x)]\, dy\, dx \tag{2.79}$$

where $U(x)$ is the system potential function which is related to the restoring force by

$$U(x) \triangleq -\int^x h(y)\, dy \tag{2.80}$$

and K_2 is the second-order intensity coefficient in the Fokker-Planck equation.

For the DLL, the error process x is the normalized delay error ε_t and $h(x)$ is linearly related to the normalized discriminator characteristic by

$$h(x) = -\rho_L D_n(x);\ \rho_L \triangleq 2\rho\mathscr{S}_L = \sigma_\varepsilon^{-2} \tag{2.81}$$

Thus,

$$U(x) = \rho_L \int^x D_n(y)\, dy \triangleq \rho_L \mathscr{D}_n(x) \tag{2.82}$$

Furthermore, $b = (N+1)/N$ and K_2 evaluates to

$$K_2 = \frac{2\eta^2 B_L}{\rho_L}. \tag{2.83}$$

Finally, then substituting (2.82) and (2.83) in (2.79) gives the desired result for the mean time to loss-of-lock (normalized by the loop bandwidth) of the DLL, namely,

$$B_L\overline{T} = \frac{\rho_L}{2\eta^2}\int_0^{(N+1)/N}\int_0^{(N+1)/N} \exp\{\rho_L[\mathscr{D}(y) - \mathscr{D}(x)]\}\, dy\, dx. \tag{2.84}$$

Comparing (2.15) with (2.42), it is easily seen that (2.84) also applies to a first-order TDL if ρ_L is replaced by

$$\rho_L' \triangleq 2\rho\mathscr{S}_L'. \tag{2.85}$$

Figure 2.19 illustrates $10\log_{10}(B_L\overline{T})$ as computed from (2.84) versus $\sigma_L = 1/\sqrt{\rho_L}$ for $N = 2$, 4, and 8. Clearly, the mean time to lose lock decreases with increasing N in agreement with our previous observation concerning the width of the linear tracking region.

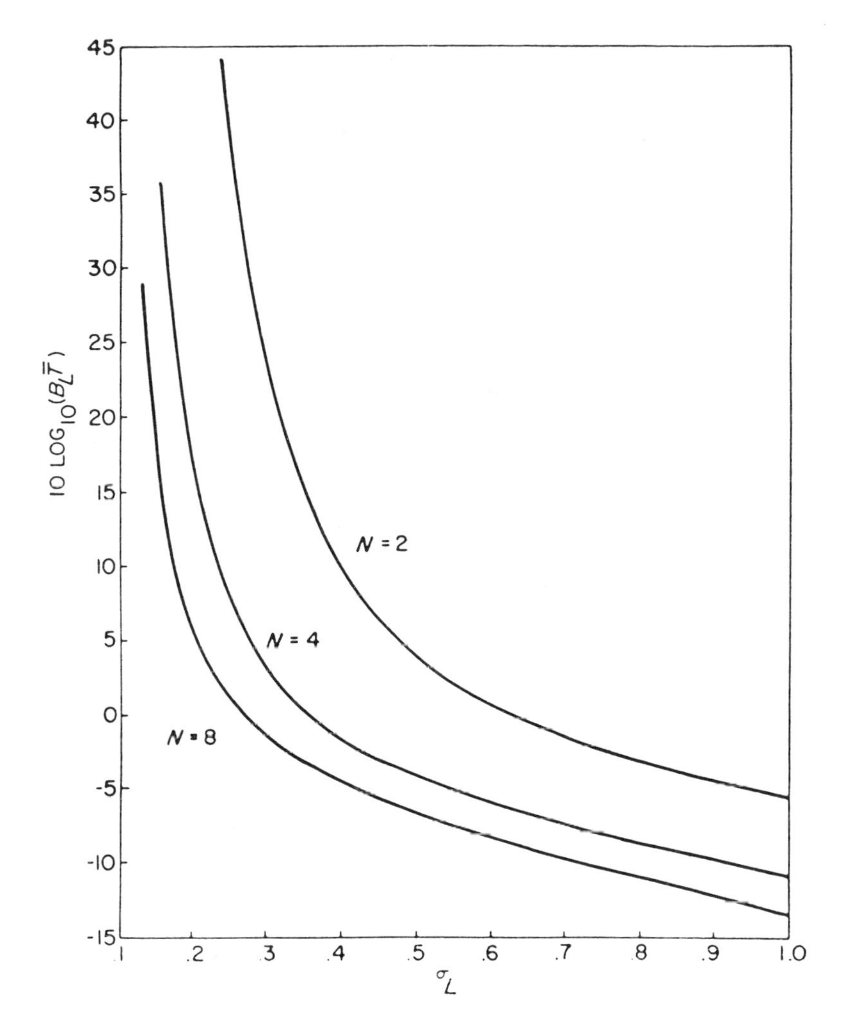

Figure 2.19. Mean time to loss-of-lock performance of delay-locked loop.

2.5 THE DOUBLE DITHER LOOP

The double dither loop (DDL) [8] is a PN code tracking loop that combines the desirable features of the DLL and TDL, i.e., the effects of detector imbalance are eliminated at no significant cost in noise performance. To understand better how this is accomplished, it is convenient to first redraw Figure 2.9 in its conceptually equivalent form illustrated in Figure 2.20. Here a single pair of time-synchronous dither switches is used to accomplish the alternation between early and late codes at the input phase detector and the post-detection multiplication by the square wave $q(t)$. The salient feature of the DDL is that it employs two sets of time synchronous dither

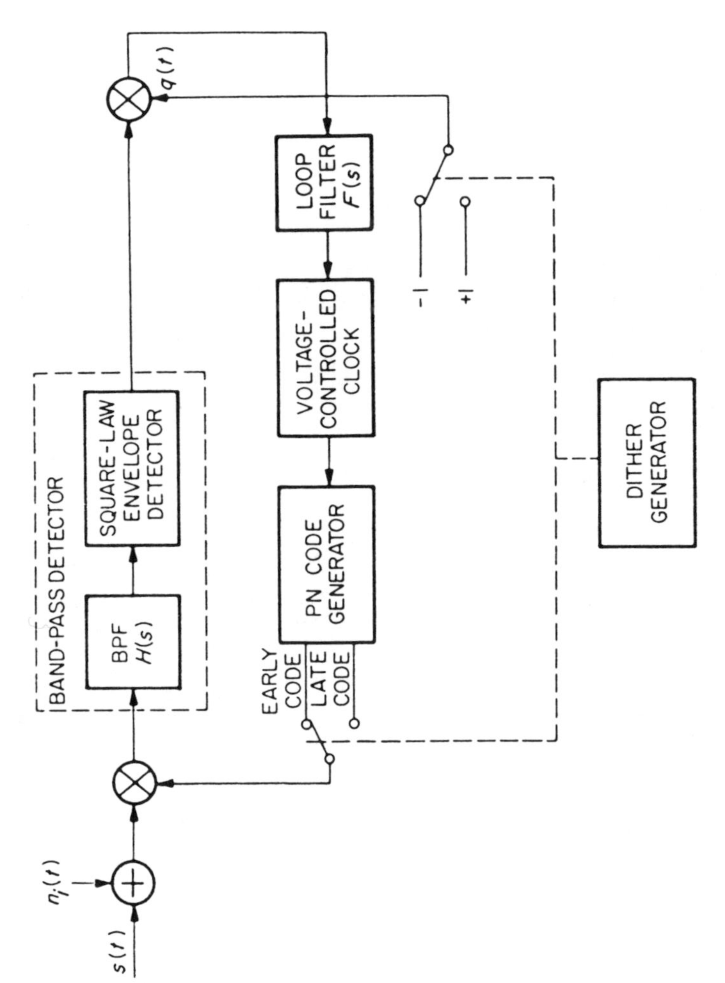

Figure 2.20. A conceptually equivalent version of Figure 2.9.

switches that time share two square-law envelope detectors alternately between the two correlators (see Figure 2.21). From an implementation point of view, the two switched post-multipliers and summer can be replaced by a single switched differencer as in Figure 2.22.

An equivalent loop model for Figure 2.21, which is valid for analysis purposes, is (analogous to Figure 2.10) illustrated in Figure 2.23. The input to the loop filter is given by

$$\begin{aligned} e(t) &= \left(y_{-1}^2(t) - y_{+2}^2(t)\right)q_1(t) + \left(y_{-2}^2(t) - y_{+1}^2(t)\right)q_2(t) \\ &= y_{-1}^2(t)q_1(t) - y_{+1}^2(t)q_2(t) \\ &\quad - \left(y_{+2}^2(t)q_1(t) - y_{-2}^2(t)q_2(t)\right). \end{aligned} \tag{2.86}$$

If both band-pass detectors of the DDL are identical, then in Figure 2.23, $y_{+1}(t) = y_{+2}(t) = y_+(t)$ and $y_{-1}(t) = y_{-2}(t) = y_-(t)$ in which case (2.86) simplifies to

$$e(t) = y_{-1}^2(t) - y_+^2(t) \tag{2.87}$$

since again $q_1(t) + q_2(t) = 1$. Note that (2.87) is identical to (2.7) and thus *under ideal balanced conditions, the DDL has the same performance as the DLL*. This conclusion can also be obtained by interpreting Figure 2.21 in the following manner. Note that while the TDL of Figure 2.9 *time shares* the early and late PN codes over a single channel (thus the loop error signal contains only the correlation of the input PN code with *either* the early or late local PN code), the DDL, by using two channels, allows *both* the early and late codes to be present for correlation in each half dither interval. Thus, in effect, the DDL error signal can be thought of as being generated by alternately switching between two DLLs which differ only in that the band-pass detectors in the two channels of one loop are in the reversed position in the other loop. Clearly, if both channels of each loop contain identical band-pass detectors, then the reversal produces no change and the effective alternate switching between the two error signals has no effect. On the other hand, if the band-pass detectors of the DDL are not identical (perhaps different gains and dc offsets), then the effective switching between the two hypothetical DLLs causes the dc offsets to cancel in the resulting time-averaged error signal. Also this error signal will have a gain proportional to the average of the two channel gains in the DDL.

2.6 THE PRODUCT OF SUM AND DIFFERENCE DLL

The product of sum and difference DLL ($\Sigma\Delta$ DLL) [9] is another configuration that purports to combat the gain imbalance problem of the DLL without sacrificing its tracking performance. The vehicle by which this is accomplished is the replacement of the "difference of squares" operation of the DLL with a "sum and difference product." In particular, the DLL

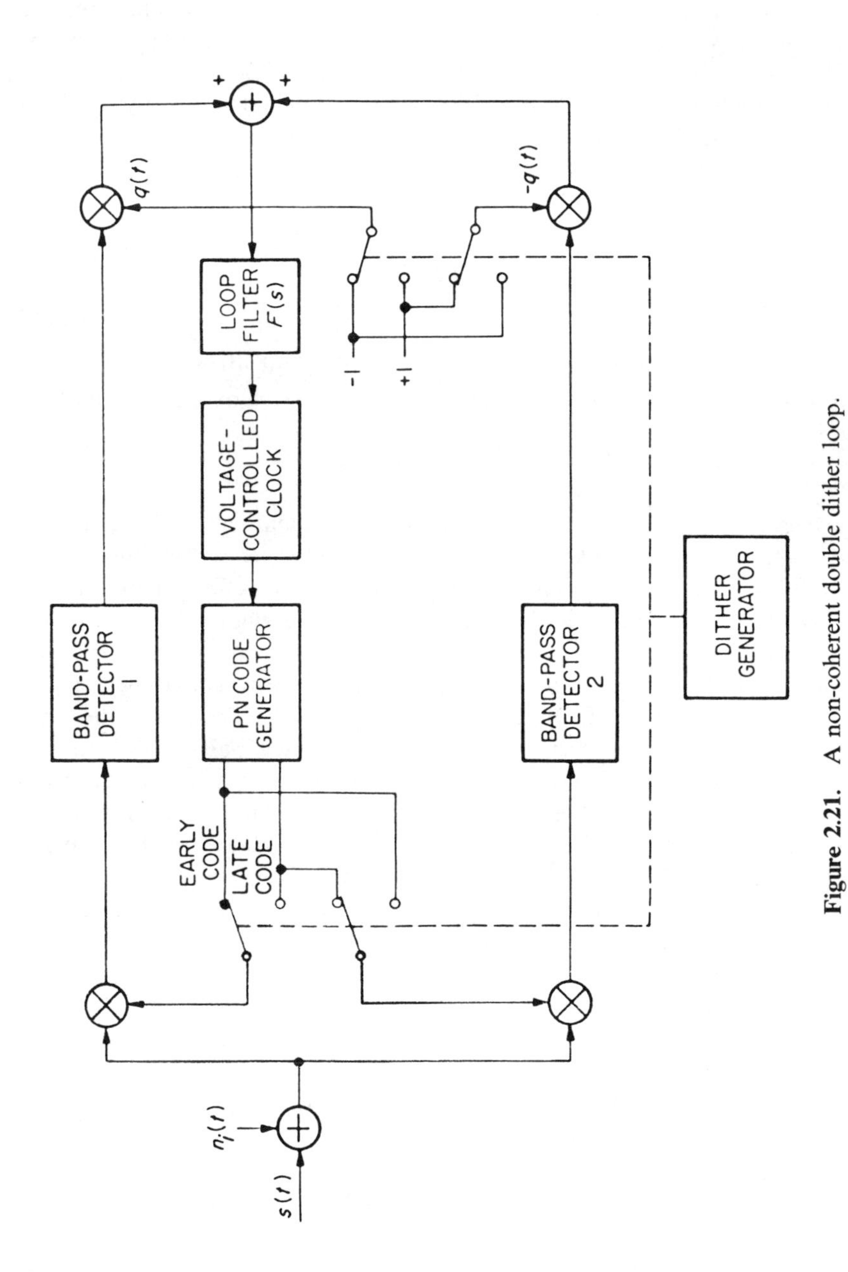

Figure 2.21. A non-coherent double dither loop.

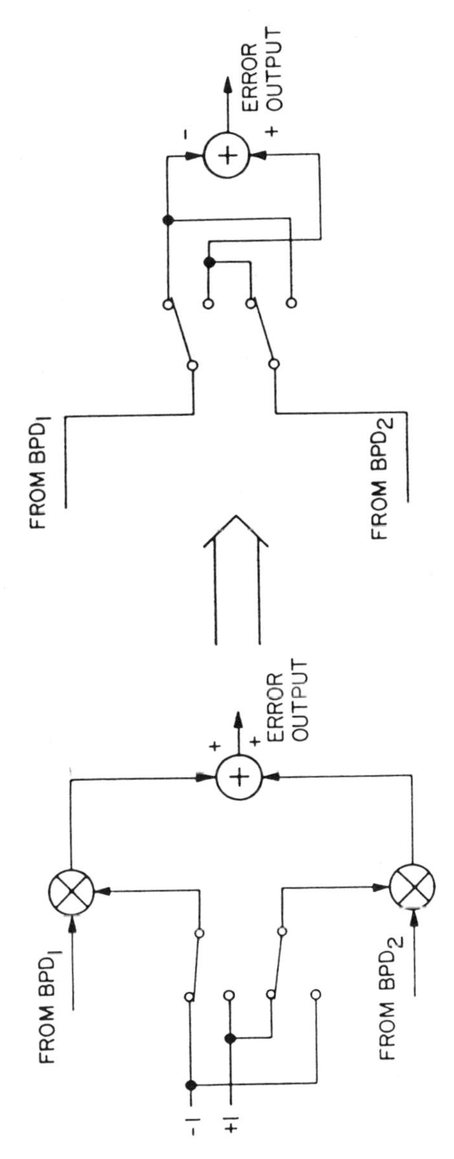

Figure 2.22. A simplification of the implementation in Figure 2.21.

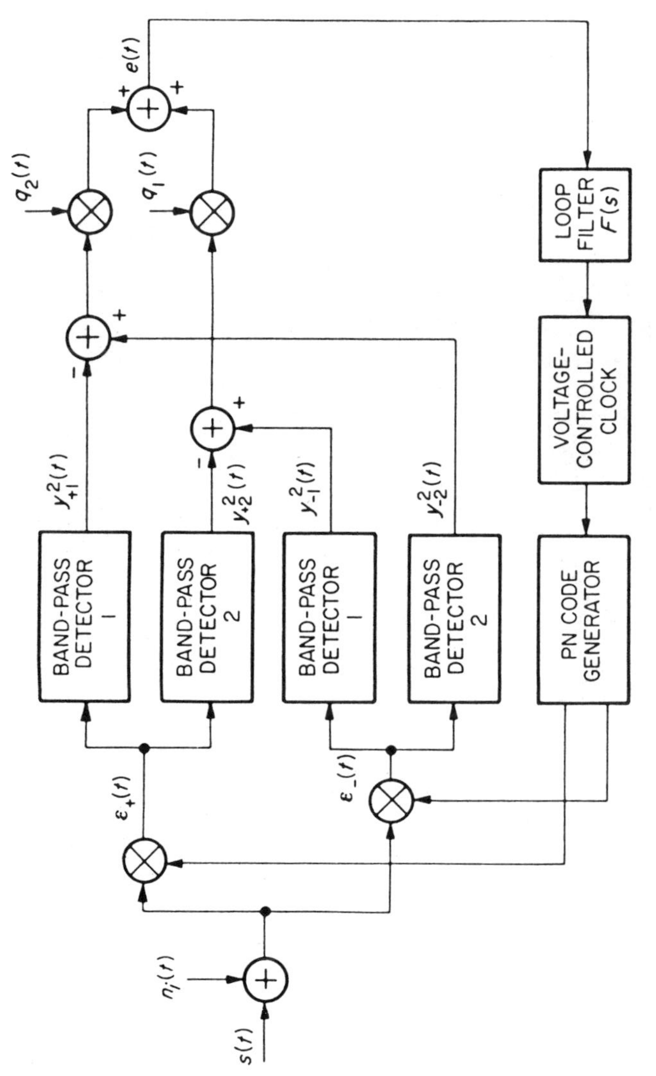

Figure 2.23. An equivalent loop model for the double dither loop.

computes as its error signal[8]

$$\begin{aligned} e(t) &= \left[K_{m_-} H(p)\varepsilon'_-(t)\right]^2 - \left[K_{m_+} H(p)\varepsilon'_+(t)\right]^2 \\ &= K_{m_-}^2 y'^2_-(t) - K_{m_+}^2 y'^2_+(t) \end{aligned} \tag{2.88}$$

where $\varepsilon'_\pm(t)$ and $y'_\pm(t)$ are normalized versions of their counterpart definitions in (2.3) and (2.5), respectively, e.g.,

$$\varepsilon'_\pm(t) \triangleq x(t)c(t - \hat{\tau}_t \pm \delta) = \varepsilon_\pm(t)/K_m \tag{2.89}$$

and similarly for $y'_\pm(t)$. On the other hand, the ΣΔ DLL (Figure 2.24) computes as its error signal

$$\begin{aligned} e(t) &= \left[K_{m_+} H(p)\left(\varepsilon'_-(t) + \varepsilon'_+(t)\right)\right]\left[K_{m_-} H(p)\left(\varepsilon'_-(t) - \varepsilon'_+(t)\right)\right] \\ &= K_{m_+} K_{m_-}\left(y'_-(t) + y'_+(t)\right)\left(y'_-(t) - y'_+(t)\right) \\ &= K_{m_+} K_{m_-}\left(y'^2_-(t) - y'^2_+(t)\right). \end{aligned} \tag{2.90}$$

Clearly, from (2.88), any unbalance in the arm gains, i.e., $K_{m_-} \neq K_{m_+}$, will produce an undesirable loop dc offset, whereas (2.90) is insensitive to this effect. Certainly, if $K_{m_-} = K_{m_+}$ the two loops will have identical theoretical performance. Any further merits of the ΣΔ DLL over the conventional DLL are a matter of practical implementation and a detailed discussion of these considerations is beyond the scope of our presentation here. The interested reader is referred to [9].

2.7 THE MODIFIED CODE TRACKING LOOP

Still another PN code tracking loop configuration that attempts to combat the gain imbalance problem of the DLL without sacrificing tracking performance, but now with hardware simplicity rivalling the TDL, is the modified code tracking loop (MCTL) [10], [11] illustrated in Figure 2.25. The principal idea of this configuration is to replace the sum channel signal of the ΣΔ DLL with a reference signal derived from the on-time PN code, the primary advantage being the elimination of an entire processing channel. The secondary advantage is that since the on-time channel experiences less noise power than the sum channel of Figure 2.24 does, it should serve as a better demodulation reference for the difference channel signal. In fact, in view of this, the mean-squared tracking jitter of Figure 2.25 should ideally be smaller than that of the traditional DLL of Figure 2.1 or the ΣΔ DLL of Figure 2.24.

[8] Here we allow the two phase detectors to have different gains, which we shall further assume represent all the contributors to gain in the two DLL arms.

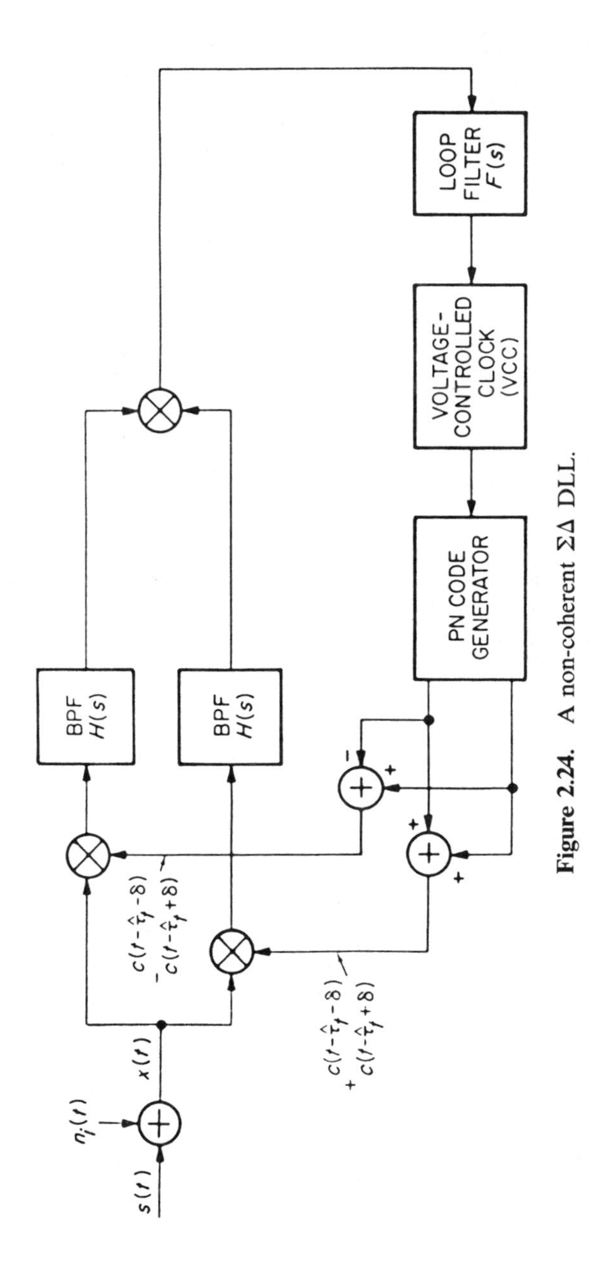

Figure 2.24. A non-coherent ΣΔ DLL.

Indeed the above turns out to be the case, as will be quantitatively demonstrated shortly. Before doing so, however, and also before discussing other behavioral characteristics of the MCTL and its shortcomings, we point out that the implementation of Figure 2.25 can be reconfigured to more closely resemble that of Figure 2.24 and thereby achieve a further reduction in hardware required. In particular, the difference channel signal can be generated as per the dashed lines in Figure 2.25, thus eliminating one mixer. Note, however, that in this alternate mechanization, the reference signal formed from the difference of the early and late PN codes is not a constant envelope waveform which therefore places strict linearity requirements on the single remaining mixer. This constraint also applies to the $\Sigma\Delta$ DLL of Figure 2.24, which conceptually could also be implemented, analogous to Figure 2.25, by forming the sum and difference signals after the input mixers.

Having derived the loop model and discussed the performance of the DLL in great detail, we shall be extremely brief in the analogous presentation for the MCTL, merely presenting the key results in summary form. In fact, to highlight the similarities between the two code tracking loops and allow easy comparison of their differences, we shall use the same equation numbers as in Section 2.1 (with a prime superscript) where appropriate.

Again assuming an input as in (2.1) and (2.2), and making similar assumptions to those leading up to (2.7), the input to the loop filter of the MCTL can be shown [11] to be given by[9]

$$e(t) = y_o(t)y_\Delta(t) = SK_m^2\hat{m}^2(t-\tau_t)\tilde{D}(\varepsilon_t) + K_m^2\tilde{n}_e(t,\varepsilon_t) \tag{2.7'}$$

where

$$\tilde{D}(\varepsilon_t) \triangleq R_{PN}(\varepsilon_t)\{R_{PN_-}(\varepsilon_t) - R_{PN_+}(\varepsilon_t)\}$$

$$= \begin{cases} 0; & \varepsilon_t \le -1 \\ -\frac{3}{2} - \frac{5}{2}\varepsilon_t - \varepsilon_t^2; & -1 < \varepsilon_t \le -\frac{1}{2} \\ 2\varepsilon_t - 2\varepsilon_t^2; & -\frac{1}{2} < \varepsilon_t \le \frac{1}{2} \\ \frac{3}{2} - \frac{5}{2}\varepsilon_t + \varepsilon_t^2; & \frac{1}{2} < \varepsilon_t \le 1 \\ 0; & \varepsilon_t > 1 \end{cases}$$

$$\tilde{D}(\varepsilon_t) = \tilde{D}(\varepsilon_t + np); \qquad n = \pm 1, \pm 2, \pm 3, \ldots \tag{2.8'}$$

is the loop discriminator characteristic and $\tilde{n}_e(t,\varepsilon_t)$ is the equivalent

[9] For simplicity of presentation, we shall pursue only the "one-delta" loop wherein $N = 2$.

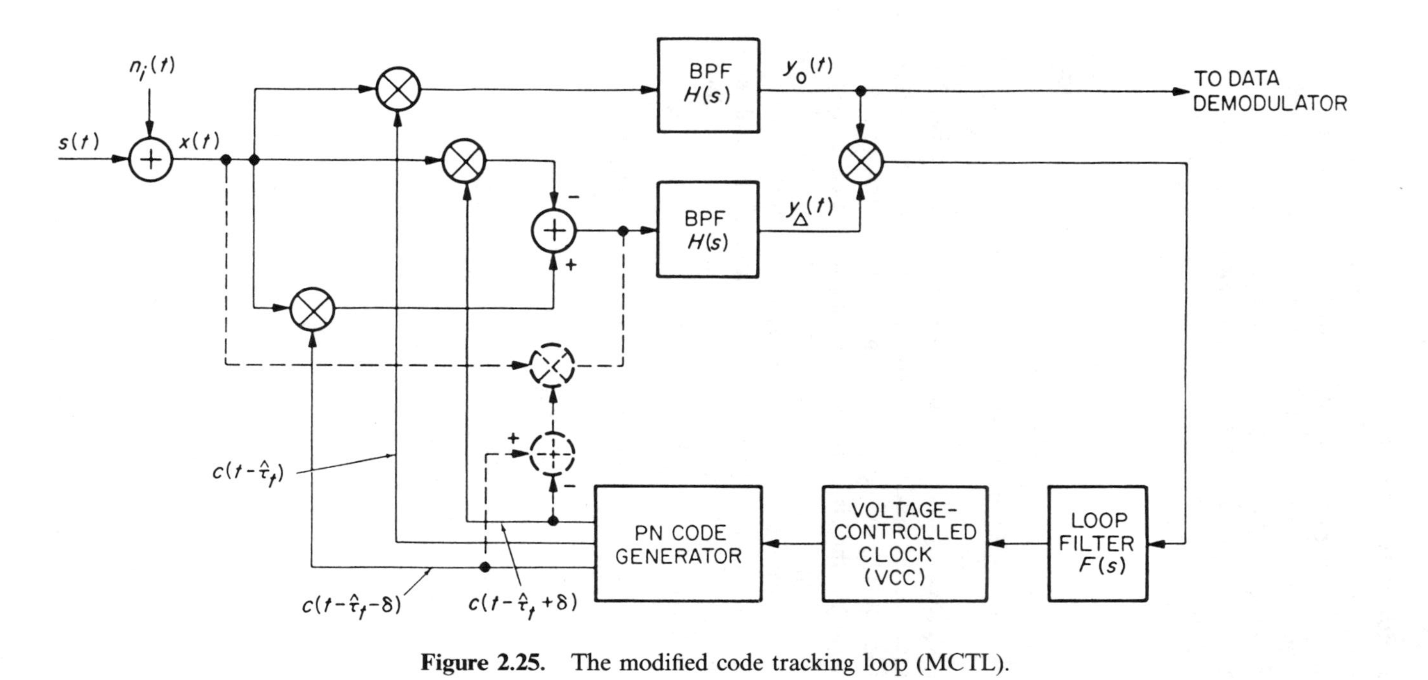

Figure 2.25. The modified code tracking loop (MCTL).

additive noise defined by

$$\begin{aligned}\tilde{n}_e(t,\varepsilon_t) &= \hat{N}_{co}(t)\hat{N}_{c\Delta}(t) + \hat{N}_{so}(t)\hat{N}_{s\Delta}(t) \\ &\quad + \sqrt{S}\,\hat{m}(t-\tau_t) \\ &\quad \times\Big\{R_{PN}(\varepsilon_t)\hat{N}_{c\Delta}(t) + \big[R_{PN_-}(\varepsilon_t) \\ &\quad - R_{PN_+}(\varepsilon_t)\big]\hat{N}_{co}(t)\Big\}\end{aligned} \tag{2.9$'$}$$

with

$$\begin{aligned}\hat{N}_{co}(t) &= H_\ell(p)[c(t-\hat{\tau}_t)N_c(t)] \\ \hat{N}_{so}(t) &= H_\ell(p)[c(t-\hat{\tau}_t)N_s(t)] \\ \hat{N}_{c\Delta}(t) &= H_\ell(p)[\{c(t-\hat{\tau}_t+\delta) - c(t-\hat{\tau}_t-\delta)\}N_c(t)] \\ \hat{N}_{s\Delta}(t) &= H_\ell(p)[\{c(t-\hat{\tau}_t+\delta) - c(t-\hat{\tau}_t-\delta)\}N_s(t)].\end{aligned} \tag{2.6$'$}$$

Figure 2.26 is a comparative illustration of the discriminator characteristics of the DLL and the MCTL. We immediately observe that the non-zero region of the MCTL characteristic is only 2/3 that of the DLL and thus the modified loop has a 1/3 less pull-in capability. Furthermore, although the two discriminator characteristics have identical slopes at $\varepsilon_t = 0$, the DLL always creates a larger error voltage for any value of timing error.

Despite these disadvantages, when compared with the DLL, the MCTL does have an improved noise performance as previously mentioned. Specifi-

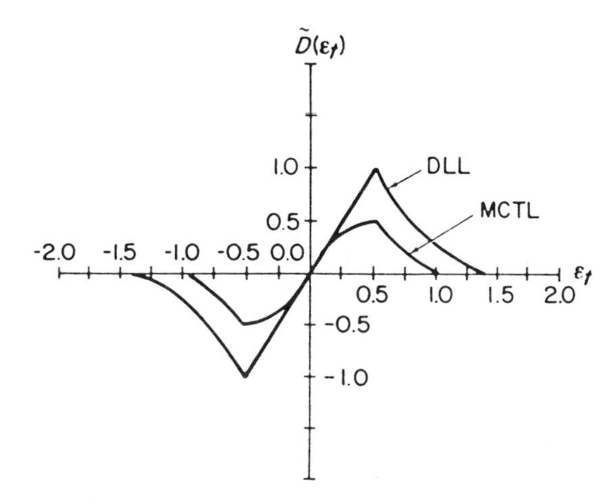

Figure 2.26. One-delta loop discriminator characteristics for the DLL and MCTL (reprinted from [11]).

cally, the equivalent noise spectral density $\tilde{N}_e(\varepsilon_t)$ of $\tilde{n}_e(t, \varepsilon_t)$ is given by [11]:

$$\tilde{N}_e(\varepsilon_t) = 2SN_0\left[M_4\left\{R_{PN}^2(\varepsilon_t) + \tfrac{1}{2}\left[R_{PN_+}(\varepsilon_t) - R_{PN_-}(\varepsilon_t)\right]^2\right\} + \frac{K_L}{\rho_H}\right] \tag{2.22'}$$

with K_L and M_4 defined in (2.23) and ρ_H in (2.25). Following steps similar to those leading up to (2.29), we find that the normalized mean-squared timing error for the MCTL is given by

$$\tilde{\sigma}_\varepsilon^2 = \frac{1}{2\rho\tilde{\mathscr{S}}_L} \tag{2.29'}$$

where the squaring loss $\tilde{\mathscr{S}}_L$ is now

$$\tilde{\mathscr{S}}_L = \frac{M_2^2}{M_4 + K_L\dfrac{B_H/R_s}{E_s/N_0}}. \tag{2.30'}$$

Comparing (2.30′) with (2.30) for $N = 2$, we observe that the $N \times N$ power of the MCTL is one-half that of the DLL, thus producing an associated reduction in mean-squared tracking jitter. To demonstrate the magnitude of

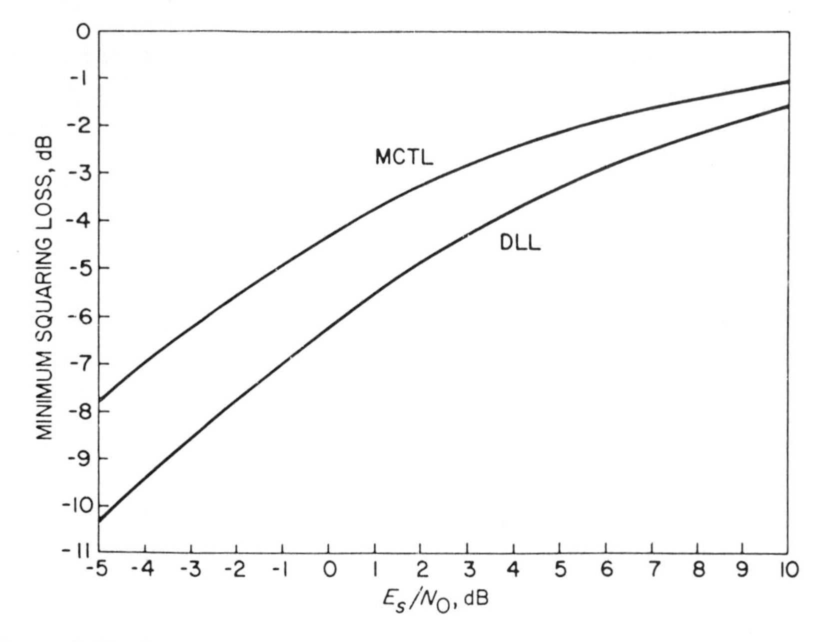

Figure 2.27. Minimum squaring loss comparison for NRZ data modulation (reprinted from [11]).

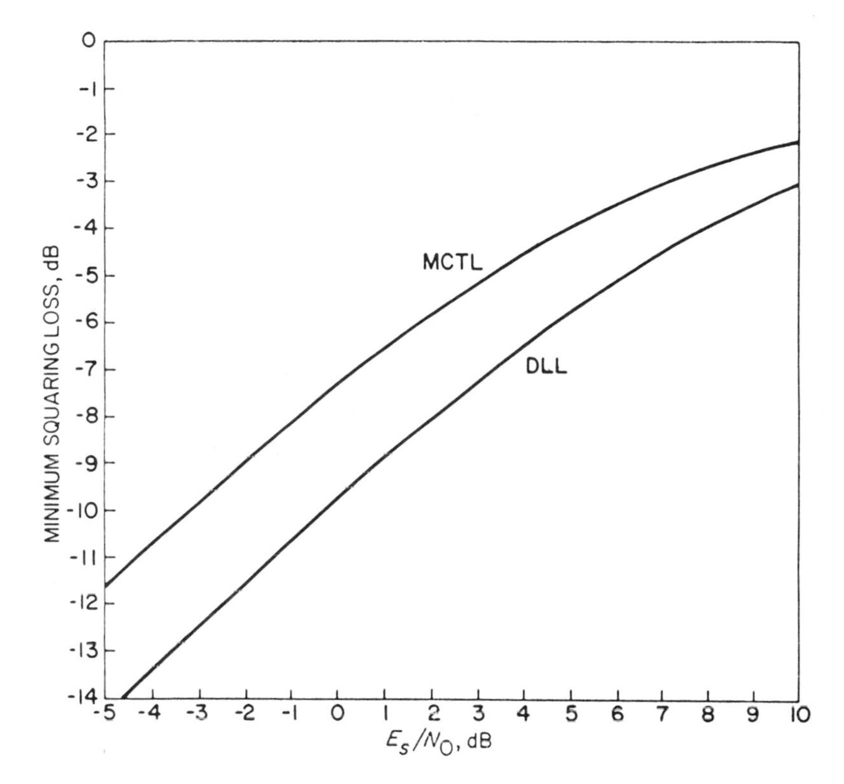

Figure 2.28. Minimum squaring loss comparison for Manchester data modulation (reprinted from [11]).

this reduction, it is sufficient to numerically compare the minimum squaring loss of (2.30) with that of (2.30′) as is done in Figures 2.27 and 2.28 for the case of NRZ or Manchester data and two-pole Butterworth band-pass filters. The appropriate expressions for K_L, M_2, and M_4 are obtained from Tables 2.1 and 2.2.

With regard to the acquisition behavior of the MCTL, it has been shown [11] that for equal rms tracking jitters, i.e., $\sigma_{\text{MCTL}} = \sigma_{\text{DLL}}$, the maximum normalized search rate is given by

$$\dot{y} = .6\frac{\mathscr{S}_L|_{\text{MCTL}}}{\mathscr{S}_L|_{\text{DLL}}} = .6\frac{M_4 + K_L\dfrac{2B_H/R_s}{E_s/N_0}}{M_4 + K_L\dfrac{B_H/R_s}{E_s/N_0}} \tag{2.91}$$

as compared with the previously found $\dot{y} = 1$ for the "one-delta" DLL. Figure 2.29 illustrates $\dot{y}$ as a function of E_s/N_0 for NRZ and Manchester data types, and two-pole Butterworth band-pass filters. Also shown is the

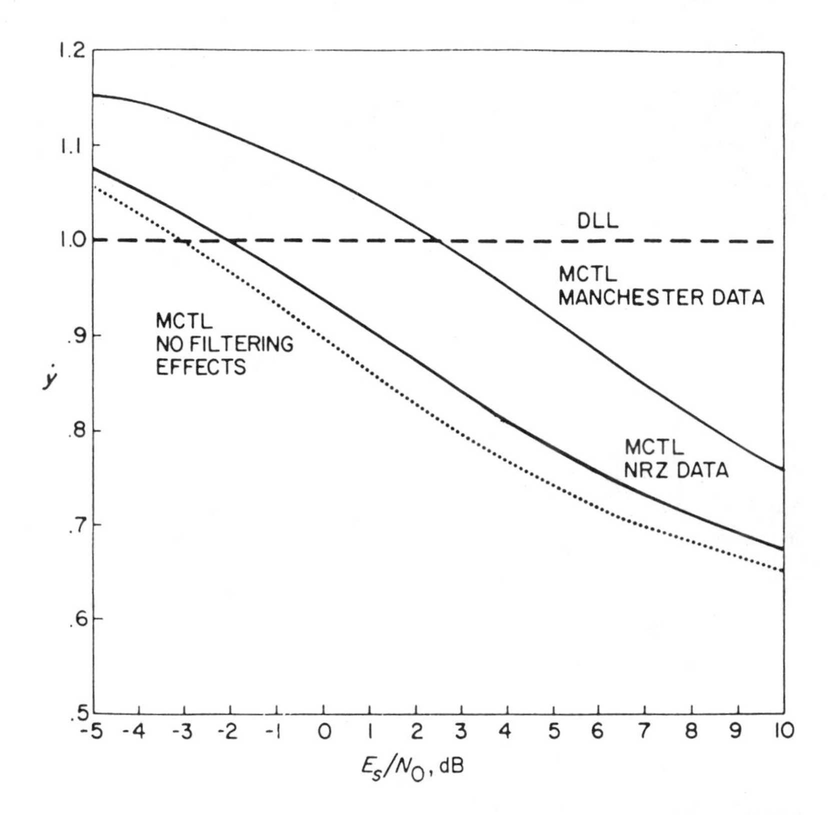

Figure 2.29. Normalized search rate comparison (reprinted from [11]).

curve corresponding to ignoring the arm filter band-limiting effects, i.e., $M_2 = M_4 = K_L = 1$ and $B_H = R_s$. We observe that for small values of E_s/N_0, the MCTL indeed has a higher search rate capability than the DLL, whereas for large values of E_s/N_0, it asymptotically approaches a maximum decrease of 40% in search rate capability.

Finally, when compared with the $\Sigma\Delta$ DLL, the MCTL has the advantage of being significantly less sensitive to gain imbalances at low values of pre-detection signal-to-noise ratio ρ_H resulting in lower tracking bias errors. At high ρ_H's, the gain imbalance sensitivities of the two configurations are nearly equivalent, both being of course much less sensitive than the traditional DLL.

2.8 THE COMPLEX SUMS LOOP (A PHASE-SENSING DLL)

The complex sums loop [12] is by far the least conventional of all the loops discussed thus far in that its operation requires a spread-spectrum signal format wherein the PN code is *phase* modulated on the transmitted carrier rather than the usual amplitude modulation case. In this sense, the complex sums loop may be regarded as the phase modulation analog of the amplitude-sensing ΣΔ DLL discussed previously. Indeed, the input signal plus noise is correlated with the sum and difference of quadrature carriers, *phase* modulated respectively by the advanced and retarded versions of the locally generated PN code (see Figure 2.30). The resultant correlations are first band-pass filtered and then band-pass limited (BPL) to remove the amplitude modulation. The relative phase between the two BPL outputs then represents a measure of the PN code delay error.

Since in virtually all DS/SS systems in use today the PN code is amplitude modulated on the transmitted carrier, particularly when the data modulation is also amplitude modulated on the carrier, we shall discontinue any further discussion of this loop, having included its mention merely for the sake of completeness. This is not to say that the complex sums loop is not capable of performance comparable with the DLL; indeed, it has been theoretically shown [12] to offer a factor of 4 improvement in rms tracking error and a factor of 2.67 improvement in maximum search velocity when compared with amplitude sensing correlation receivers such as the DLL. Rather, its lack of widespread acceptance in the design of current DS/SS receivers precludes our giving it extensive coverage.

2.9 QUADRIPHASE PN TRACKING

Until now we have assumed that the PN spreading code is superimposed on a suppressed carrier binary data modulation. It is our intent in this section to investigate the applicability of the previous PN tracking techniques to various forms of quadriphase PN modulation (QPN).

The simplest form of QPN is obtained by spreading a quadriphase-shift-keyed (QPSK) modulation with a single PN code. In this case, the transmission-delayed signal analogous to (2.1) becomes

$$\begin{aligned} s(t) = \sqrt{S}\,c(t-\tau_t)\{ & m_1(t-\tau_t)\sin[\omega_0 t + \theta(t)] \\ & + m_2(t-\tau_t)\cos[\omega_0 t + \theta(t)]\} \end{aligned} \tag{2.92}$$

where $m_1(t)$ and $m_2(t)$ are unit power statistically independent binary data modulations of the same data rate and the remaining nomenclature is as previously provided. If one uses the DLL of Figure 2.1 to PN track the sum of $s(t)$ of (2.92) and $n_i(t)$ of (2.2), then, without belaboring the details, it can be shown that, analogous to (2.7), the error signal $e(t)$ becomes

$$e(t) = \tfrac{1}{2}SK_m^2\left[\hat{m}_1^2(t-\tau_t) + \hat{m}_2^2(t-\tau_t)\right] + K_m^2 n_e(t,\varepsilon_t) \tag{2.93}$$

where the equivalent noise $n_e(t,\varepsilon_t)$ is now given by

$$\begin{aligned} n_e(t,\varepsilon_t) = {} & \hat{N}_{c_-}^2(t) - \hat{N}_{c_+}^2(t) + \hat{N}_{s_-}^2(t) - \hat{N}_{s_+}^2(t) \\ & + \sqrt{2S}\,\hat{m}_2(t-\tau_t)\{R_{PN_-}(\varepsilon_t)\hat{N}_{c_-}(t) - R_{PN_+}(\varepsilon_t)\hat{N}_{c_+}(t)\} \\ & - \sqrt{2S}\,\hat{m}_1(t-\tau_t)\{R_{PN_-}(\varepsilon_t)\hat{N}_{s_-}(t) - R_{PN_+}(\varepsilon_t)\hat{N}_{s_+}(t)\}. \end{aligned} \tag{2.94}$$

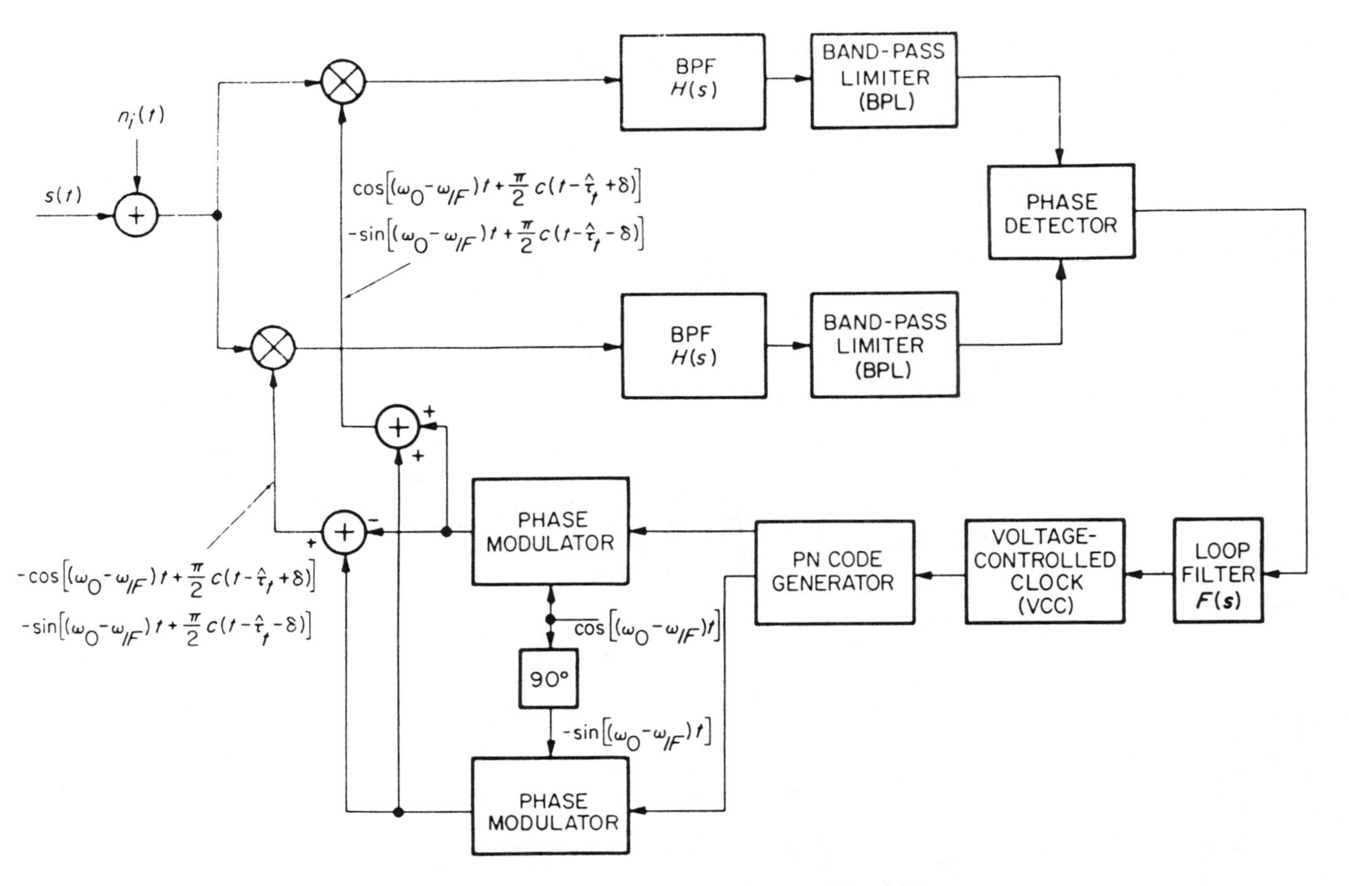

Figure 2.30. The complex sums PN tracking loop.

Now, since

$$\overline{\langle \hat{m}_1^2(t-\tau_t)\rangle} = \overline{\langle \hat{m}_2^2(t-\tau_t)\rangle} = M_2 \tag{2.95}$$

with M_2 defined in (2.14) and, because $m_1(t)$ and $m_2(t)$ are independent, the auto-correlation function of (2.94) is again given by (2.18). Thus, we observe that the equation of operation remains unchanged from (2.15). In conclusion, *the tracking and acquisition performance of the DLL with a QPN input as in* (2.92) *is identical to that with the biphase PN input of* (2.1).

Another form of QPN is obtained by spreading inphase and quadrature biphase modulated carriers with *independent* PN codes. Such a situation is typical of applications where separate addressing of each channel is required, as for example, in a multiple-access type system. Here the received signal (in the absence of noise) has the form

$$\begin{aligned} s(t) = {} & \sqrt{S}\,c_1(t-\tau_t)m_1(t-\tau_t)\sin[\omega_0 t+\theta(t)] \\ & +\sqrt{S}\,c_2(t-\tau_t-\tau_\Delta)m_2(t-\tau_t)\cos[\omega_0 t+\theta(t)]. \end{aligned} \tag{2.96}$$

If the two codes have identical chip rates, they are often staggered relative to one another by half a chip, i.e., $\tau_\Delta = T_c/2$. This form of QPN is referred to as staggered quadriphase PN (SQPN) and is particularly used on non-linear satellite channels to reduce regeneration of sidelobes removed by transmitter filtering prior to transmission over the channel. Furthermore, from a practical implementation standpoint, $c_2(t)$ is often generated as a time-shifted version of $c_1(t)$ where the time shift corresponds to a large number of code chips, often as many as half the code period.

Consider once again using the DLL of Figure 2.1 to PN track the sum of $s(t)$ of (2.96) and $n_i(t)$ of (2.2). If the PN generator of the DLL is arbitrarily selected to match $c_1(t)$, then, since, by the assumption of code independence,

$$\overline{c_2(t-\tau_t-\tau_\Delta)c_1(t-\hat{\tau}_t\pm\delta)} = 0 \tag{2.97}$$

and the fact that the inphase and quadrature self-noise processes can be neglected, we obtain a loop error signal identical to (2.7) except that S is replaced by $S/2$ in both its signal and noise components. Stated another way, the DLL tracks the channel corresponding to $c_1(t-\tau_t)$ (which contains half the total power) as if the other channel were absent. As such, a 3 dB signal-to-noise ratio penalty is paid relative to that for a PN spread binary data modulation as in (2.1). This 3 dB penalty in signal-to-noise ratio does not, however, directly translate into a 3 dB increase in mean-squared tracking jitter due to the non-linear dependence of the loop squaring loss on S/N_0 (see (2.29) and (2.30)). Once having obtained proper code alignment for $c_1(t-\tau_t)$, the despreading code for $c_2(t-\tau_t-\tau_\Delta)$ can be derived by an appropriate shift of the local PN generator provided that the two codes were generated as suggested above. If indeed the two codes are totally unrelated, i.e., they were generated by separate PN generators with, in general, completely different tap connections and code periods, then two separate DLLs must be employed in the receiver, each having a local PN generator matched to one of the two codes. Again, the performance of each DLL would behave as per the above discussion.

Finally, if the two codes have different chip rates in addition to different code structure, one must again employ separate DLLs for each code where now, in addition to having different local PN generators, the two loops would also have different voltage-controlled clocks, each matched to the appropriate chip rate of the code being tracked.

Before concluding this section, we also point out that quadriphase PN is not limited only to balanced QPSK but indeed can also be applied to unbalanced QPSK data modulation by a simple generalization of (2.96), namely,

$$s(t) = \sqrt{2S_1}\, c_1(t - \tau_t) m_1(t - \tau_t) \sin[\omega_0 t + \theta(t)] + \sqrt{2S_2}\, c_2(t - \tau_t - \tau_\Delta) m_2(t - \tau_t) \cos[\omega_0 t + \theta(t)] \quad (2.98)$$

Here, S_1, the power in channel 1, is, in general, unequal to S_2, the power in channel 2, and the data rates $1/T_1, 1/T_2$ of $m_1(t)$ and $m_2(t)$, respectively, are no longer restricted to be equal. Examples of such PN spread signals are typical of many of the transmission modes of the Tracking and Data Relay Satellite System (TDRSS) [20]. Once again, depending on the relation between the two PN codes, either one or two DLLs are required to provide the necessary PN tracking as per the discussion for balanced QPSK.

2.10 FURTHER DISCUSSION

To conclude this chapter, we briefly summarize some of the most recent contributions to the subject of PN tracking. The primary intent here is to acquaint the reader with the current status of effort in the area without going into the level of detail characteristic of the previous sections of this chapter. It is not intended that the reader come away with the idea that the contributions discussed here are therefore of lesser importance; rather, they should be looked upon as evidence of continued interest in the subject and a springboard for future endeavors.

One idea for improvement in PN tracking loop performance is offered by Wakabayashi, Nakagawa, and Tsunogae [21], who suggest an improved delay-locked loop (IDLL) with an effective increased number of correlators, thus allowing one to shape the loop discriminator characteristic in such a way as to expand the loop's correlation range without affecting its lock range. Although the specific results in [21] are described for a coherent DLL, the concept is readily applicable to a non-coherent DLL. As an example, consider the non-coherent IDLL illustrated in Figure 2.31, which for $N = 2$ represents a slight modification of the loop in Figure 2.1. The

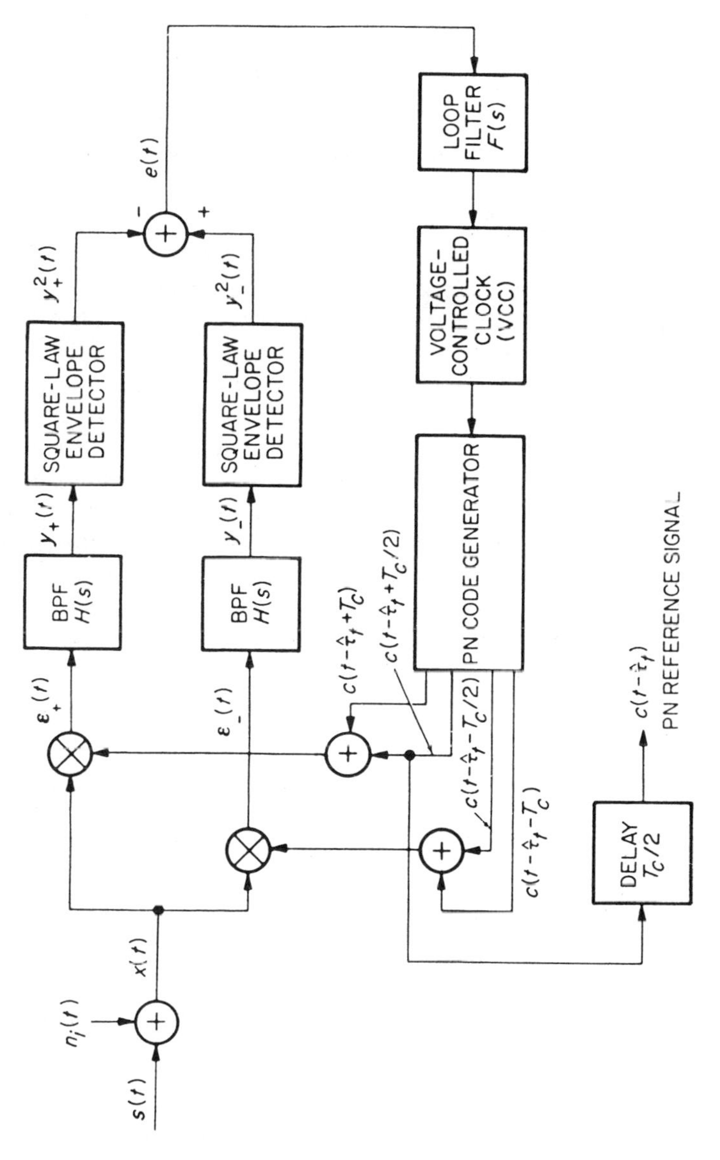

Figure 2.31. A non-coherent improved delay-locked loop (IDLL).

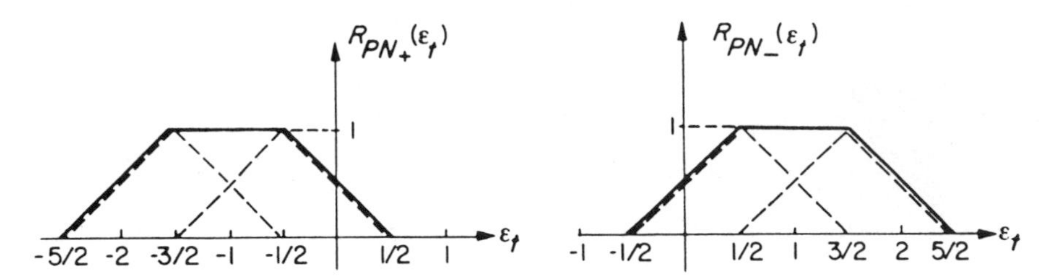

Figure 2.32. Autocorrelation functions of the advanced and retarded correlator outputs for a non-coherent IDLL.

particular modification that distinguishes Figure 2.31 from Figure 2.1 is the effective addition of two correlations of the input signal with two new phase-shifted PN reference signals which are advanced and retarded, respectively, by a full chip relative to the on-time PN reference signal. Although conceptually four correlations are now being formed, the two advanced and two delayed reference signals are first summed so that for implementation only two correlators are needed. Figure 2.32 illustrates the component and resultant advanced and delayed correlation functions analogous to Figure 2.2. Figure 2.33 shows the corresponding discriminator characteristic analogous to Figure 2.3. Note that, as previously mentioned, the lock range of the loop ($\pm T_c/2$) and its gain (positive slope of the discriminator characteristic) are unaffected by the modification, whereas the correlation range has been extended from $\pm 3T_c/2$ to $\pm 5T_c/2$. Clearly, the addition of additional correlations with more phase-shifted PN reference signals can increase the correlation region even further.

All of our discussions of PN tracking thus far have assumed a transmission channel devoid of propagation disturbances. Bogusch, Guigliano, Knepp, and Michelet [22] consider the effects of frequency-selective scintil-

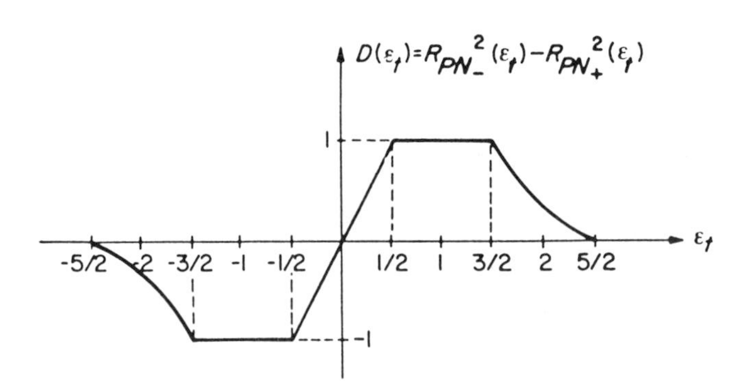

Figure 2.33. Discriminator characteristic.

lation (fading), such as that produced by an ionospheric channel whose coherence bandwidth is less than the signalling bandwidth, on the PN code correlation and tracking functions in a DS/SS system. Consideration was given to both coherent and non-coherent DLLs or TDLs. Also, since the results were obtained using a simulation model of the receiver, several other different loop configurations were programmed in as design options in addition to allowing such parameters as bandwidth and order of the tracking loop to be varied at will. For example, the possibility of having the PN tracking loop Doppler-aided from the carrier tracking loop [23] was included. This type of accommodation of channel dynamics involves using the Doppler estimate formed in the carrier tracking loop, e.g., a composite AFC/Costas loop [24], appropriately scaled by the ratio of PN code chip rate to carrier frequency, to rate-aid the PN tracking loop. Another variation included in the simulation was the option of *time sharing* the single code loop for PN receivers that are required to simultaneously track signals from several satellites.

The objective of the investigation was to identify and evaluate those design configurations out of the above class that would provide robust performance in a frequency-selective scintillation environment. In this regard, the following qualitative conclusions were reached:

1. A non-coherent code loop is less susceptible to losing lock than the equivalent coherent one since the former does not depend on carrier phase lock which is difficult to maintain in scintillation conditions.
2. A dedicated (non-time-shared) loop is more robust than a time-shared loop simply because the former samples the code correlator output more frequently and thus does not suffer a loss of effective signal level produced by the reduced measurement rate of a time-shared loop.

Last, but by no means least, is the work of Meyr [25]–[27], who applies the theory of renewal (regenerative) Markov processes to the non-linear analysis of correlative tracking systems. The method, which is applicable to systems with periodic non-linearities (such as the PLL) as well as those with non-periodic non-linearities (such as the DLL), allows a proper characterization of the cycle-slipping phenomenon of the former and the loss-of-lock phenomenon of the latter. The "periodic extension solution" [16] that has traditionally been applied in such situations is shown to be identical to the "renewal process solution" only for a first-order loop. Most significantly, the "intrinsic" or "self" noise of the DLL, which is always (even in the absence of the additive Gaussian noise) present in the loop, and which depends on the loop tracking error, is accounted for in the renewal process approach. In many applications, this intrinsic noise is dominant and cannot be neglected. We hasten to add that Meyr's work was originally motivated by the necessity of performing precise velocity and distance measurements for modern mass transportation systems [28], [29] and as such his discussions are primarily concerned with the coherent DLL as originally discussed in [1]. More recently, this work was extended to the non-coherent DLL by Polydoros [30].

2.11 REFERENCES

[1] J. J. Spilker, Jr., "Delay-lock tracking of binary signals," *IEEE Trans. Space Electr. and Telem.*, vol. SET-9, No. 1, pp. 1–8, March 1963.

[2] J. J. Spilker, Jr., and D. T. Magill, "The delay-lock discriminator—an optimum tracking device," *Proc. IRE*, vol. 49, No. 9, pp. 1403–1416, September 1961.

[3] W. J. Gill, "A comparison of binary delay-lock loop implementations," *IEEE Trans. Aerosp. and Electr. Syst.*, vol. AES-2, pp. 415–424, July 1966.

[4] P. T. Nielsen, "On the acquisition behavior of binary delay-lock loops," *IEEE Trans. Aerosp. and Electr. Syst.*, vol. AES-11, pp. 415–418, May 1975.

[5] M. K. Simon, "Noncoherent pseudonoise code tracking performance of spread spectrum receivers," *IEEE Trans. Commun.*, COM-25, No. 3, pp. 327–345, March 1977.

[6] H. P. Hartmann, "Analysis of a dithering loop for PN code tracking," *IEEE Trans. Aerosp. and Electr. Syst.*, vol. AES-10, No. 1, pp. 2–9, January 1974.

[7] T. C. Huang and J. K. Holmes, "Performance of noncoherent time-shared PN code tracking loops," *1976 NTC Record*, pp. 45.4-1–45.4-5, November 29–December 1, 1976, Dallas, TX.

[8] P. M. Hopkins, "Double dither loop for pseudonoise code tracking," *IEEE Trans. Aerosp. and Electr. Syst.*, vol. AES-13, No. 6, pp. 644–650, November 1977.

[9] D. T. LaFlame, "A delay-lock loop implementation which is insensitive to arm gain imbalance," *IEEE Trans. Commun.*, COM-27, No. 10, pp. 1632–1633, October 1979.

[10] R. A. Yost and R. W. Boyd, "A modified PN code tracking loop: Its performance and implementation sensitivities," *1980 NTC Record*, 1980, pp. 61.5.1–61.5.5, Houston, TX.

[11] R. A. Yost and R. W. Boyd, "A modified PN code tracking loop: Its performance analysis and comparative evaluation," *IEEE Trans. Commun.*, COM-30, No. 5, pp. 1027–1036, May 1982.

[12] E. F. Osborne and T. A. Schonhoff, "Delay-locked receivers with phase sensing of the correlation (error) function," *1973 NTC Conference Record*, vol. II, pp. 26B-1–26B-6, November 26–28, 1973, Atlanta, GA.

[13] J. K. Holmes and L. Biederman, "Delay-lock-loop mean time to lose lock," *IEEE Trans. Commun.*, COM-26, No. 11 (Part 1), pp. 1549–1557, November, 1978. Also see *1977 NTC Conference Record*, vol. II, pp. 34:2-1–34:2-6, December 5–7, 1977, Los Angeles, CA.

[14] W. K. Alem, G. K. Huth, and S. Udalov, *Integrated Source and Channel Encoded Digital Communication System Design Study*, Final Report, Contract No. NAS 9-13467, Exhibit E, April 13, 1977, Appendices B, C, D, Axiomatix Corp., Marina del Rey, CA.

[15] W. C. Lindsey and M. K. Simon, *Telecommunication Systems Engineering*, Englewood Cliffs, NJ: Prentice-Hall, 1973.

[16] W. C. Lindsey, *Synchronization Systems in Communication and Control*, Englewood Cliffs, NJ: Prentice-Hall, 1972.

[17] M. K. Simon and W. C. Lindsey, "Optimum performance of suppressed carrier receivers with Costas loop tracking," *IEEE Trans. Commun.*, COM-25, No. 2, pp. 215–227, February 1977.

[18] M. K. Simon, "On the calculation of squaring loss in Costas loops with arbitrary arm filters," *IEEE Trans. Commun.*, COM-26, No. 1, pp. 179–184, January 1978.

[19] I. S. Sokolnikoff and R. M. Redheffer, *Mathematics of Physics and Modern Engineering*, New York: McGraw-Hill, 1958.

[20] "Performance specification for services via the tracking and data relay satellite system," S-805-1, Goddard Space Flight Center, Greenbelt, MD, November 1976.

[21] K. Wakabayashi, M. Nakagawa, and T. Tsunogae, "Tracking performance of improved delay-locked loop," *1980 NTC Record*, pp. 24.3.1–24.3.5, 1980, Houston, TX.

[22] R. L. Bogusch, F. W. Guigliano, D. L. Knepp, and A. H. Michelet, "Frequency selective propagation effects on spread-spectrum receiver tracking," *Proc. IEEE*, vol. 69, No. 7, pp. 787–796, July 1981.

[23] C. R. Cahn, D. K. Leimer, C. L. Marsh, F. J. Huntowski, and G. D. La Rue, "Software implementation of a PN spread spectrum receiver to accommodate dynamics," *IEEE Trans. Commun.*, COM-25, No. 8, pp. 832–840, August 1977.

[24] C. R. Cahn, "Improved frequency acquisition of a Costas loop," *IEEE Trans. Commun.*, COM-25, No. 12, pp. 1453–1459, December 1977.

[25] H. Meyr, "Nonlinear analysis of correlative tracking systems using renewal process theory," *IEEE Trans. Commun.*, COM-23, No. 2, pp. 192–203, February 1975.

[26] H. Meyr, "Delay-lock tracking of stochastic signals," *IEEE Trans. Commun.*, COM-24, No. 3, pp. 331–339, March 1976.

[27] W. C. Lindsey and H. Meyr, "Complete statistical description of the phase-error process generated by correlative tracking systems," *IEEE Trans. Inform. Theory*, IT-23, No. 2, pp. 194–202, March 1977.

[28] F. Mesch et al., "Geschwindigkeitsmessung mit Korrelationsverfahren," *Messtechnik*, vol. 7, pp. 152–157, 1971; also vol. 8, pp. 163–168, 1971.

[29] H. Meyr, "Untersuchung Korrelativer Trackingsysteme mit Hilfe der Fokker-Planck Methode," Ph.D. Dissertation, Swiss Federal Institute of Technology, Zurich, Switzerland, 1973.

[30] A. Polydoros, "On the synchronization aspects of direct-sequence spread spectrum systems," Ph.D. Dissertation, Department of Electrical Engineering, University of Southern California, August 1982.

Chapter 3

TIME AND FREQUENCY SYNCHRONIZATION OF FREQUENCY-HOPPED RECEIVERS

Until now, all our discussions of FH/MFSK communication systems have assumed "ideal" synchronization conditions in the sense that the dehopper in the receiver was assumed to have perfect knowledge of the set of received hop frequencies and the instants in time at which the hop modulation changed state. In practice, such ideal conditions are almost never met. This is the lack of perfect knowledge of the phase and Doppler shift produced by the transmission channel; as such, the receiver must provide suitable means for obtaining and maintaining bona fide estimates of these synchronization state parameters. The accuracy with which this can be accomplished ultimately affects the overall error probability performance of the system.

Not unlike the synchronization problem in direct-sequence (DS) spread-spectrum (SS) systems discussed in the previous two chapters, the process of synchronizing the local hop generator with the received sequence of hop tones is ordinarily accomplished in two stages, namely, FH acquisition (coarse synchronization) and FH tracking (fine synchronization). We begin this chapter with a discussion of FH acquisition techniques, the most common of which, as we shall see shortly, have a direct resemblance to similar techniques previously discussed for PN code acquisition.

Once having explained how to coarsely align the local and received hop sequences, we offer next a discussion of a fine synchronization technique for estimation of FH timing [1]. By "fine synchronization," we mean relative timing errors between transmitter and receiver hop generators of less than a hop duration. In presenting the details and mathematical analysis of the time synchronization estimation technique, we shall first make the idealistic assumption that the transmitter and receiver hop generators are perfectly synchronized in frequency. Following this, we consider the behavior and performance of a similar estimation technique for fine frequency synchronization [2], i.e., relative frequency errors between transmitter and receiver hop generators of less than one-half the frequency spacing of the MFSK tones. Here, in calculating the degrading effect on overall system error probability performance because of the residual frequency error produced by the fine frequency estimation technique, the additional degradation due to imperfect fine time synchronization is taken into account. Finally, when both fine time and fine frequency estimators are assumed to augment each other, we are able to obtain the overall performance degradation due to the combination of both residual synchronization errors.

The interference environment in which the time and frequency estimators are assumed to operate is that of the noise (partial- or full-band) jammer. Thus, the overall performance degradation referred to above will be a function of the partial-band fraction, the noise jamming level, and the number of hops used in forming the FH timing and frequency estimates. The performance of these estimators in other narrowband interference environments such as partial-band multitone jamming can be obtained in a straightforward manner using the analytical approach in Chapter 2, Volume II.

3.1 FH ACQUISITION TECHNIQUES

Coarse frequency synchronization is the process by which the local generated hop sequence is aligned with the received hop sequence to within a fraction of a hop interval. This acquisition process is normally thought of as being accomplished in two steps. First, the degree of alignment is determined, typically, by obtaining a measure of correlation (active or passive) between the two hop sequences. Second, the correlation measure is processed by a suitable detector and decision/search algorithm to decide whether or not to continue the search. If, at any point, the search terminates, then coarse frequency acquisition is assumed to have occurred.

3.1.1 Serial Search Techniques with Active Correlation

Although our primary interest in this chapter is with slow or fast FH/MFSK, it is perhaps more instructive to first discuss the most basic non-coherent FH acquisition configuration, which, although best suited to analog information transmitted as an amplitude modulation, or no information modulation at all, nevertheless represents the simplest illustration of the abovementioned acquisition process dichotomy. As such, consider the single (fixed) dwell time serial search acquisition system illustrated in Figure 3.1. In this scheme, the received FH signal plus noise is correlated in a wideband mixer with the local hop sequence produced by an FH synthesizer driven by a PN generator whose epoch is controlled in accordance with the decision to continue the search. The result of this correlation is passed through an IF

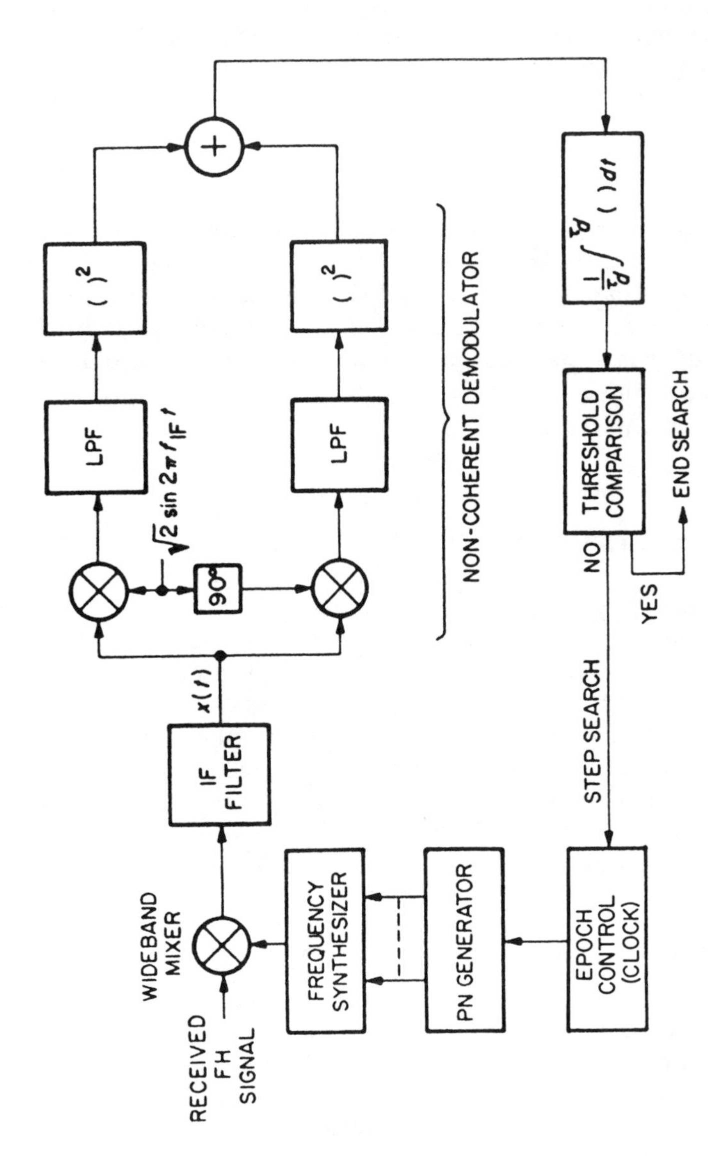

Figure 3.1. A single dwell time serial search FH acquisition system.

filter followed by an energy detector implemented here as a baseband non-coherent demodulator.[1] (The bandwidths of the IF filter and demodulator low-pass filters are chosen based upon considerations to be discussed shortly). Post-detection integration of the energy detector output produces a signal whose mean value is nominally zero when the two hop sequences are misaligned and non-zero when they are either partially or fully aligned. Thus, comparing this signal with a preset threshold allows a decision to be made as to whether or not FH acquisition has been achieved, or equivalently whether or not to step the PN code epoch and continue the search.

A similar serial search technique for acquiring PN sequences was discussed in great detail in Chapter 1. Thus, our discussion here will be, by comparison, brief and merely serve to highlight the essential differences between the two systems.

To begin, first suppose that the received FH signal and the locally generated hop signal out of the mixer will appear as in Figure 3.2a.[2] Now, if the bandwidth of the IF filter is chosen to be less than twice the hop frequency spacing, then all of the frequency components of the mixer difference signal will be outside this bandwidth, resulting in a zero correlation voltage at the demodulator input. Now suppose that the received sequence and synthesizer sequence are partially aligned, i.e., misaligned by less than a single hop interval. Then, the mixer difference signal, as illustrated in Figure 3.2b, will contain frequency components within the IF bandwidth (assuming a composite frequency error δf less than the hop spacing) which are effective for correlation detection. These "bursts" of sinusoids at a frequency $f_{IF} \quad \delta f$ have random phases relative to one another resulting in an IF filter output $x(t)$ which does not have a discrete spectral component at this frequency. In fact, for a given timing offset τ with magnitude less than a hop interval T_h, we can write $x(t)$ as

$$x(t) = \sqrt{2S}\sum_i \mathrm{rect}_\tau(t - iT_h)\cos[2\pi(f_{IF} - \delta f)t + \psi_i]$$

$$\mathrm{rect}_\tau(t) = \begin{cases} 0; & 0 \le t \le \tau \quad (\tau > 0) \\ & T_h - |\tau| \le t \le T_h \quad (\tau < 0) \\ 1; & \tau \le t \le T_h \quad (\tau > 0) \\ & 0 \le t \le T_h - |\tau| \quad (\tau < 0) \end{cases} \tag{3.1}$$

[1]Alternately, the baseband non-coherent demodulator could be replaced by a band-pass square-law envelope detector, as in our previous discussions of serial search acquisition of PN sequences in Chapter 1.

[2]For simplicity of this discussion, we shall for the time being ignore the information modulation and the additive noise.

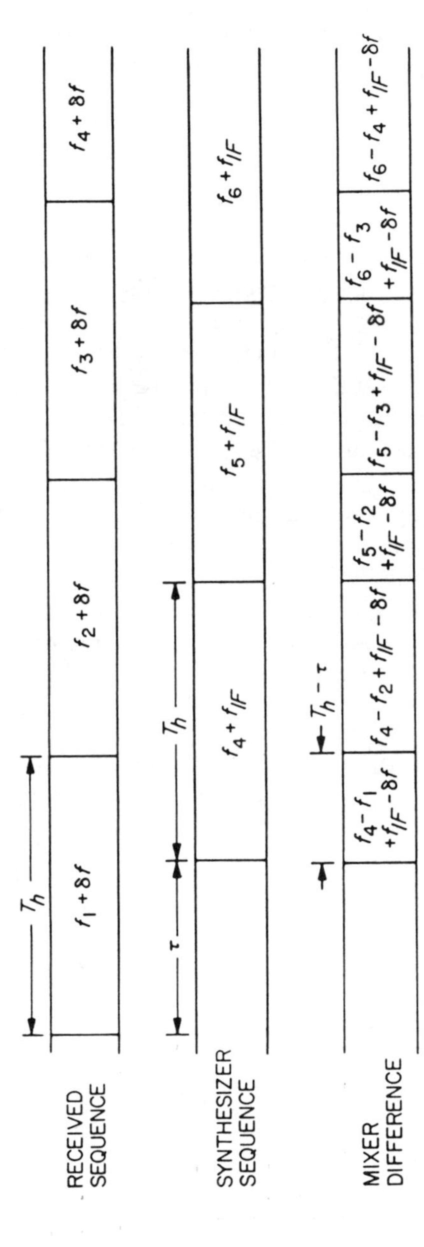

Figure 3.2a. Received FH signal and local hop signal misaligned by more than a single hop interval.

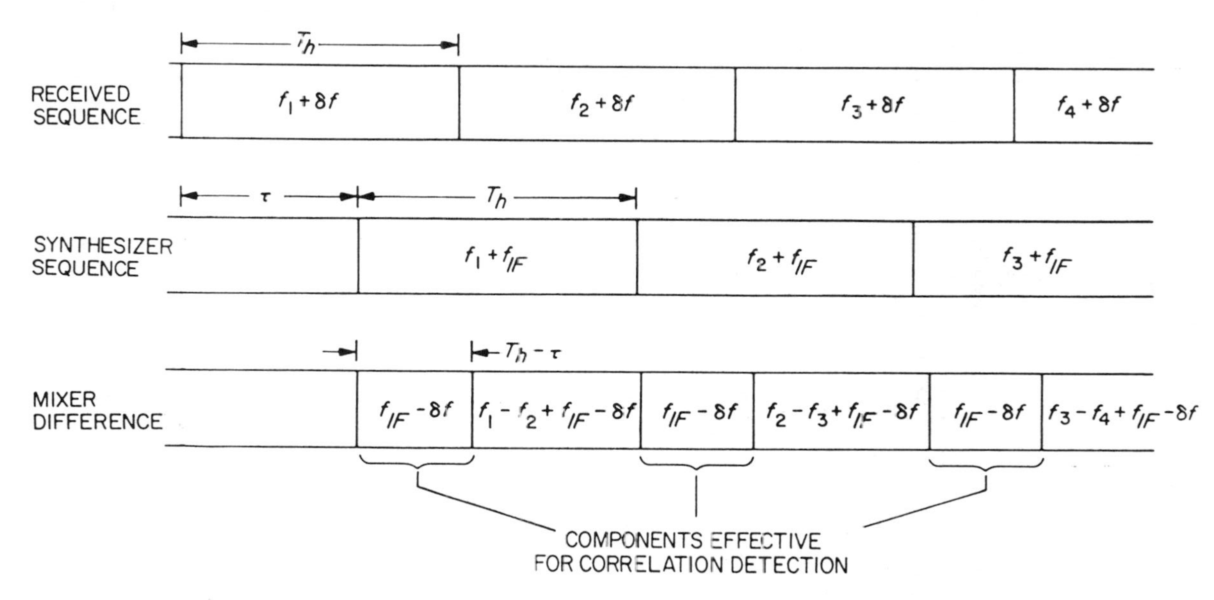

Figure 3.2b. Received FH signal and local hop signal misaligned by less than a single hop interval.

which has the power spectral density

$$S_x(f;\tau) = \frac{1}{T_h}|\mathscr{F}\{x(t)\}|^2$$

$$= \frac{S(T_h - |\tau|)^2}{T_h}\left[\frac{\sin\{\pi[f-(f_{IF}-\delta f)](T_h - |\tau|)\}}{\pi[f-(f_{IF}-\delta f)](T_h-|\tau|)}\right]^2. \quad (3.2)$$

The non-coherent demodulator forms a filtered measure of the average power in $x(t)$ by demodulating it with quadrature reference signals $\sqrt{2}\cos 2\pi f_{IF}t$ and $\sqrt{2}\sin 2\pi f_{IF}t$ and summing the squares of the resultant filtered low-pass signals. Thus, if $|H(j2\pi f)|^2$ denotes the squared magnitude of the low-pass filter transfer function, then the non-coherent demodulator output has an average value

$$R(\tau) = \int_{-\infty}^{\infty} S_x(f + f_{IF};\tau)|H(j2\pi f)|^2\,df$$

$$= \frac{S(T_h - |\tau|)^2}{T_h}\int_{-\infty}^{\infty}\left[\frac{\sin\{\pi(f+\delta f)(T_h-|\tau|)\}}{\pi(f+\delta f)(T_h-|\tau|)}\right]^2|H(j2\pi f)|^2\,df. \quad (3.3)$$

Assuming first that the bandwidth of the demodulator low-pass filters is much larger than the hop rate $1/T_h$, and, in addition, the frequency error is small (relative to this bandwidth), then (3.3) simplifies to

$$R(\tau) = \frac{S(T_h - |\tau|)^2}{T_h}\int_{-\infty}^{\infty}\left[\frac{\sin\pi f'(T_h-|\tau|)}{\pi f'(T_h-|\tau|)}\right]^2 df'$$

$$= S\left(1 - \frac{|\tau|}{T_h}\right) \quad (3.4)$$

i.e., a triangular correlation curve of width $2T_h$. In general, the non-coherent demodulator low-pass filter bandwidth must be chosen large enough to accommodate the information modulation bandwidth, the maximum system frequency error, and the hop frequency modulating spectrum. Thus, for slow frequency hopping (SFH), wherein the information symbol rate dominates this choice, the above assumption of a large low-pass filter bandwidth relative to the hop rate is valid and hence no significant filtering of the correlation curve occurs in accordance with (3.4). For fast frequency hopping (FFH) where the low-pass filter bandwidth is chosen on the order of the hop rate, significant filtering occurs and the correlation curve must be computed from (3.3). As an example of the filtering distortion of the triangular correlation function, consider the case of single-pole low-pass filters with single-sided noise bandwidth B. Then evaluation of (3.3) with

$\delta f = 0$ yields

$$R(\tau) = S\left(1 - \frac{|\tau|}{T_h}\right)\left[1 - \frac{1 - \exp\left\{-4BT_h\left(1 - \frac{|\tau|}{T_h}\right)\right\}}{4BT_h\left(1 - \frac{|\tau|}{T_h}\right)}\right] \tag{3.5}$$

which is plotted against τ/T_h in Figure 3.3 with BT_h as a parameter. We observe from this figure that in the neighborhood of $\tau = 0$, the predominant effect of the filtering is a reduction of the correlation peak by an amount approximately given by $1/4BT_h$ and a corresponding broadening of the triangular shape.

When additive noise and possibly interference signals are present, the design of the demodulator low-pass filters will be governed by considerations additional to minimum correlation function degradation, which, as we noted above, requires their bandwidth to be large. In particular, minimization of the demodulator square-law noise output requires that these same bandwidths be chosen small. Thus, as is characteristic of square-law demodulation systems, a tradeoff exists between signal × signal and signal × noise plus noise × noise degradations.

In summary, then, for SFH of an information-bearing carrier, the low-pass filter bandwidths must be commensurate with the information modulation bandwidth and therefore the demodulator output signal-to-noise ratio will be set by this bandwidth. For FFH of the same information-modulated carrier, the low-pass filter bandwidths must be large enough to accommo-

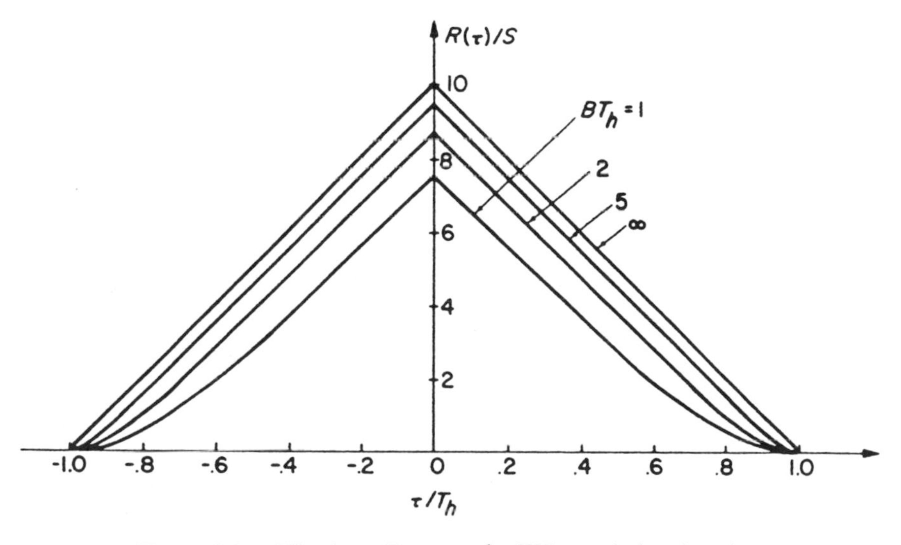

Figure 3.3. Filtering effects on the FH correlation function.

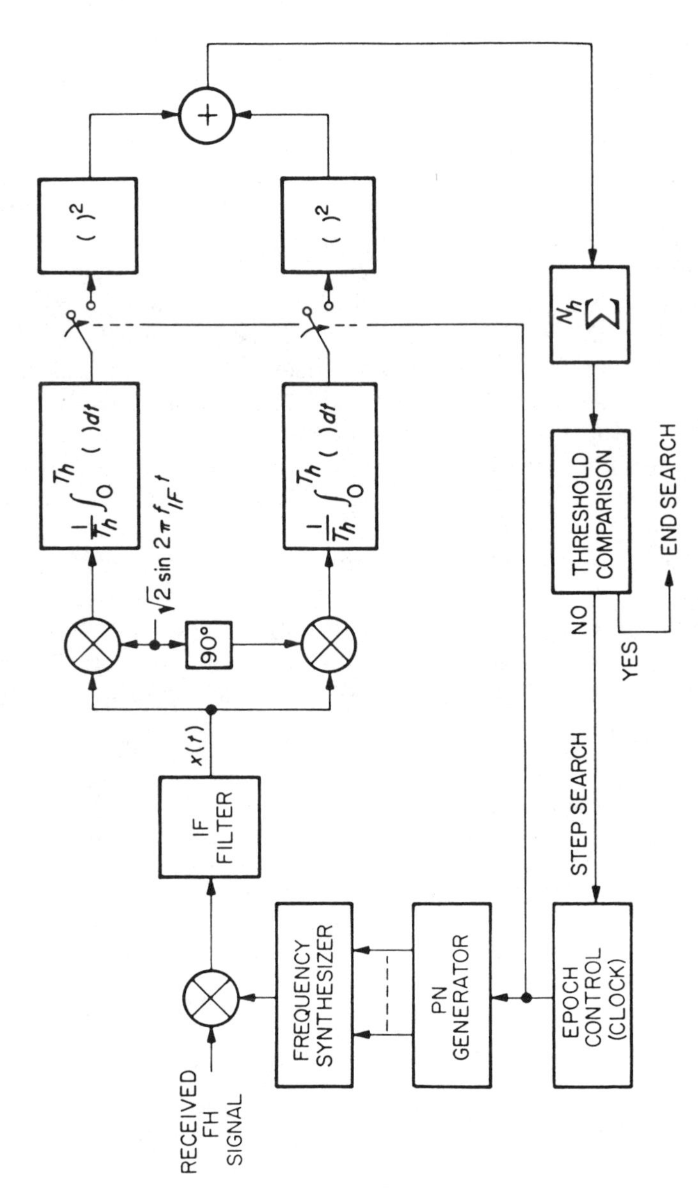

Figure 3.4. A serial search FH acquisition system with integrate-and-dump-type demodulator.

date the hop rate (which is larger than the modulation bandwidth) and can therefore be set to maximize the demodulator output signal-to-noise ratio.

One way of avoiding the degradation of the correlation curve peak in the FFH case is to replace the low-pass filters in the non-coherent demodulator with integrate-and-dump circuits as in Figure 3.4. Since for the rectangular bursts of signal correlation appearing at the demodulator input, the integrate-and-dumps act as matched filters, then the demodulator output samples have an average value

$$R(\tau) = S\frac{\sin^2 \pi\delta f(T_h - |\tau|)}{(\pi\delta f T_h)^2} \tag{3.6}$$

or for $\delta f = 0$,

$$R(\tau) = S\left(1 - \frac{|\tau|}{T_h}\right)^2. \tag{3.7}$$

It is interesting at this point to note that this very same function of time and frequency offset as expressed by (3.6) will again be significant later on in the chapter when we study the effects of time and frequency errors on fine synchronization performance.

With the previous discussion as background, we now return our attention to the case of primary interest in this chapter, namely, coarse acquisition of fast or slow FH/MFSK. A basic serial search acquisition configuration for FFH/MFSK is illustrated in Figure 3.5. For the case when the received and local hop signals are misaligned by less than a single hop interval, the bottom line of Figure 3.6 is the sequence of frequencies characterizing the mixer difference signal. If, as before, the IF filter bandwidth is chosen narrow enough to eliminate the difference of two adjacent hop frequencies, but wide enough now to pass the entire MFSK signalling frequency band, then only the frequency components corresponding to the non-crosshatched areas in Figure 3.6 will pass through this filter and be available for correlation detection. Thus, we observe that in each symbol interval T_s, which is synchronous with the local FH synthesizer, the signal component of the IF filter output will consist of $m = T_s/T_h$ bursts of sinusoid of duration $T_h - |\tau|$. These m bursts are all at the same frequency (corresponding to the particular MFSK tone transmitted in that symbol interval) but have random phases which are independent of one another. A measure of the lack of coarse time synchronization can therefore be obtained by separately combining the energies detected in each hop interval at each of the M possible MFSK frequencies $\{f_{si}; i = 1, 2, \ldots, M\}$ and then choosing the largest of these m-fold diversity combinations. Since this selection is made only once per symbol interval, post-detection accumulation (over say N_{FFH} symbols) is required, the result of which is compared with a preset threshold to determine whether or not to continue the search.

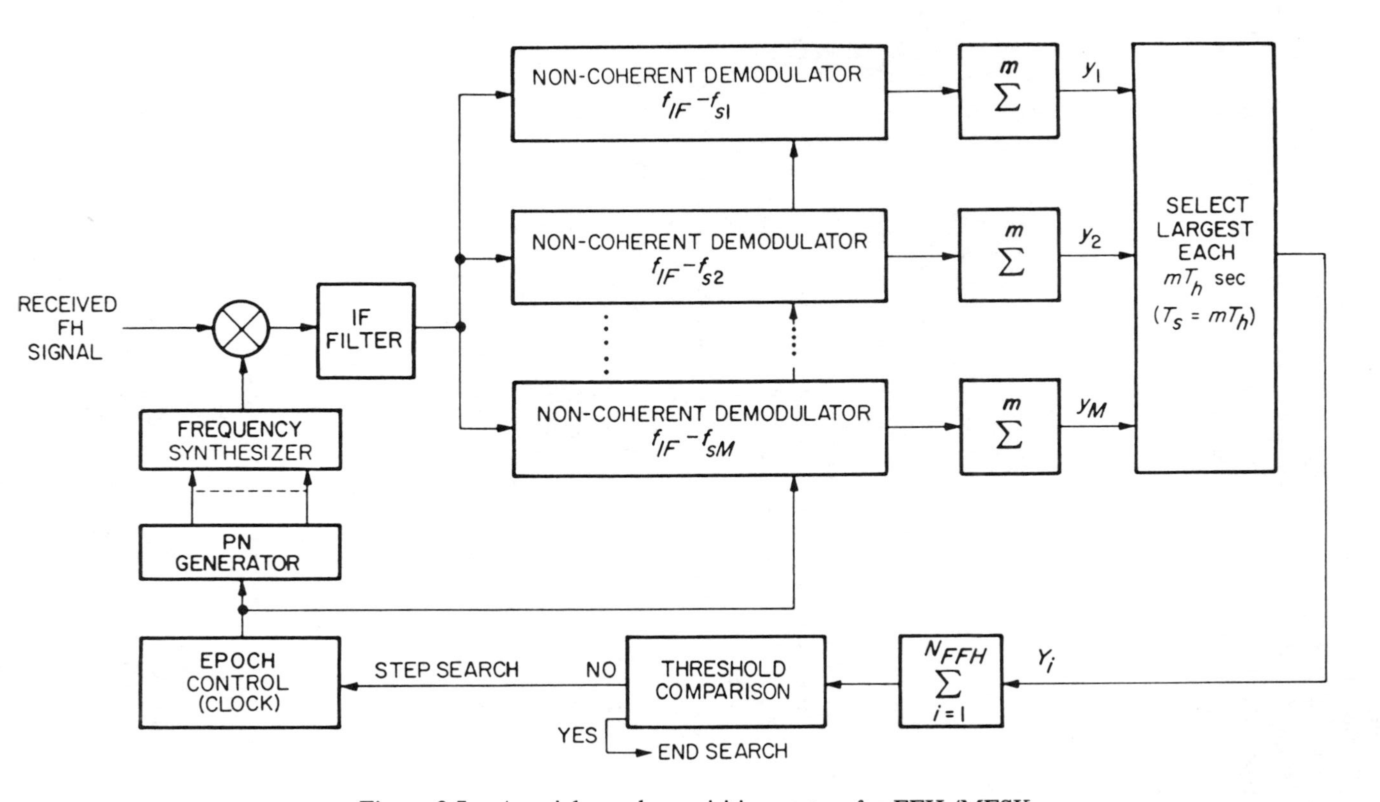

Figure 3.5. A serial search acquisition system for FFH/MFSK.

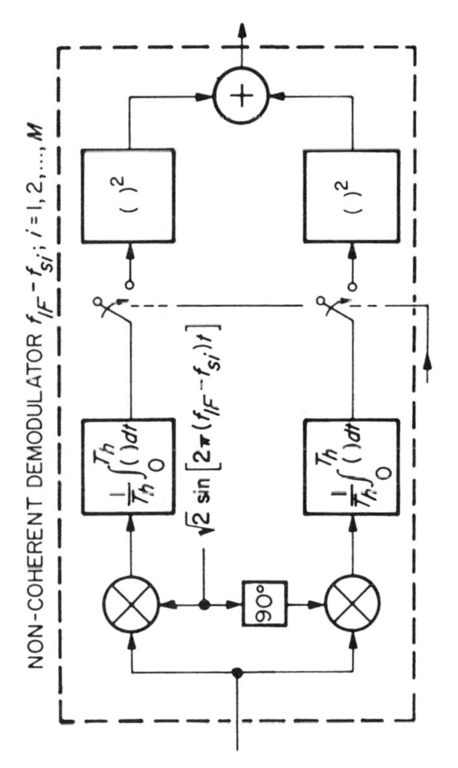

Figure 3.5 (continued)

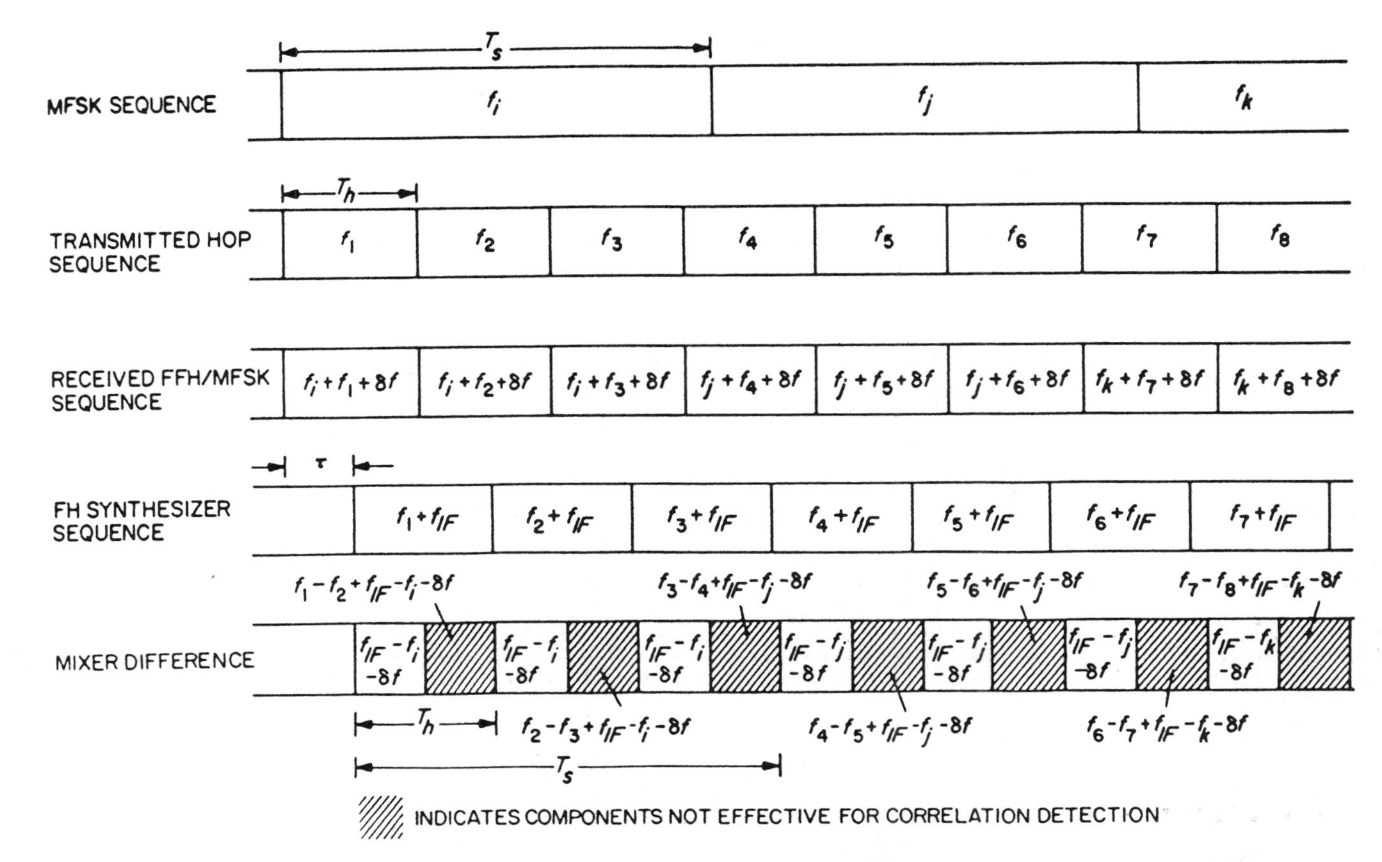

Figure 3.6. Received FFH/MFSK signal and local hop signal misaligned by less than a single hop interval.

In the absence of noise, for the symbol interval during which f_i was the frequency of the transmitted MFSK tone, the m-fold accumulated output samples of the M non-coherent demodulators are given by

$$R_k(\tau) = mS \frac{\sin^2\{\pi[\delta f - (f_{sk} - f_i)](T_h - |\tau|)\}}{\{\pi[\delta f - (f_{sk} - f_i)]T_h\}^2};$$

$$k = 1, 2, \ldots, M. \tag{3.8}$$

Thus if δf is small compared with the spacing between adjacent MFSK tones, then the largest $R_k(\tau)$ will occur for the value of k for which $f_i = f_{sk}$. Since this occurrence will be true independent of which symbol we examine, the input to the post-detection accumulator will be given by $R(\tau)$ of (3.6) multiplied by m.

For ordinary (without diversity) SFH/MFSK, the appropriate serial search acquisition system analogous to Figure 3.5 is illustrated in Figure 3.7 with a corresponding time-frequency diagram in Figure 3.8. Since in each hop interval, the mixer difference signal contains sinusoidal bursts at different frequencies corresponding to the MFSK tones transmitted in that hop, then in contrast with Figure 3.5, no non-coherent combining occurs at the outputs of the M non-coherent demodulators. Rather, the largest of these M outputs is selected each symbol interval. Post-detection accumulation (over say N_{SFH} symbols) of these selections and comparison with a preset threshold again determines whether or not to continue the search.

Another characteristic of the acquisition system in Figure 3.7 is that the set of M non-coherent demodulator outputs does not necessarily remain unchanged as one passes from symbol to symbol within a given hop. For example, if the timing error τ is less than a symbol interval T_s (as is the case illustrated in Figure 3.8), then for all symbols except the last in a given hop interval, the sets of M outputs will be identical, although not necessarily ordered the same way within a given set. Since a maximum is sought in each symbol interval, the ordering is unimportant and thus in each case a decision is made among M energy detections corresponding to an input of $T_s - \tau$ sec of a given MFSK tone and τ sec of the adjacent transmitted tone. For the last symbol of that hop, however, only $T_s - \tau$ sec of the corresponding MFSK tone is available for energy detection, the remaining τ sec corresponding to noise only. As τ increases beyond T_s sec, fewer and fewer symbol decisions will be based upon a full T_s sec of input signal. Finally, when $\tau = T_h$, the entire mixer difference signal will contain noise only.

For SFH/MFSK with diversity m, the appropriate serial search acquisition system reverts back to one resembling Figure 3.5, where the outputs of the M non-coherent demodulators are now individually summed over the m chips (one per hop) corresponding to a given symbol. As such, the integrate-and-dumps in each non-coherent demodulator operate over a chip interval

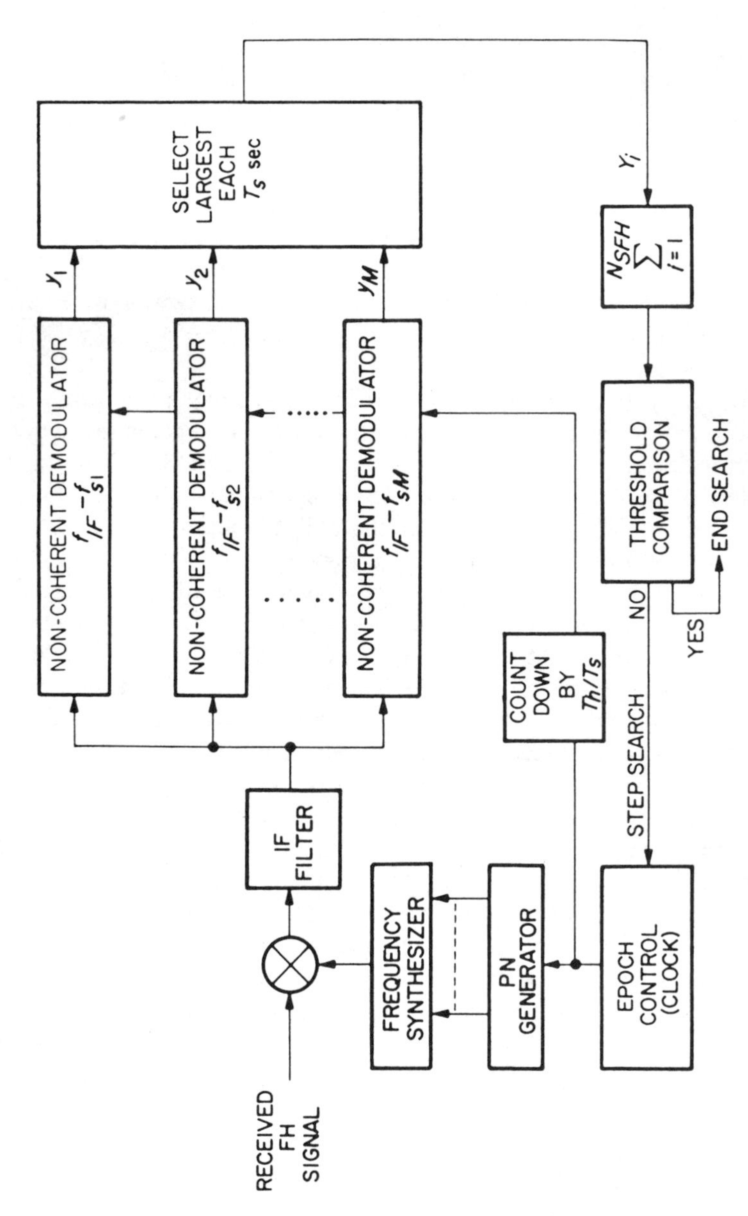

Figure 3.7. A serial search acquisition system for SFH/MFSK.

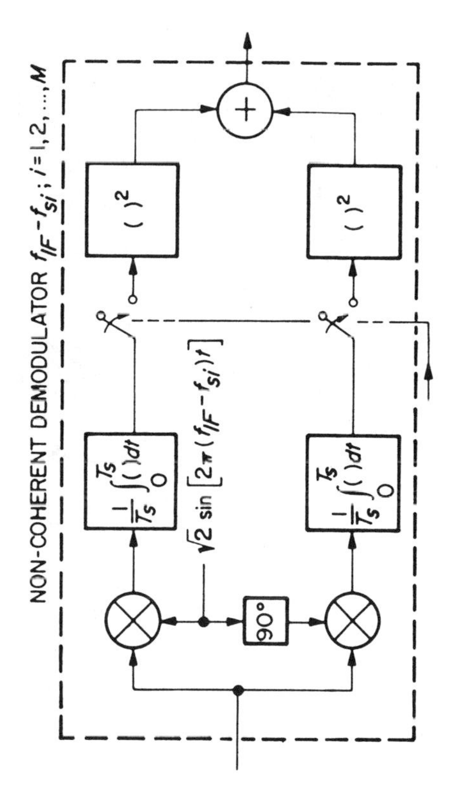

Figure 3.7 (continued)

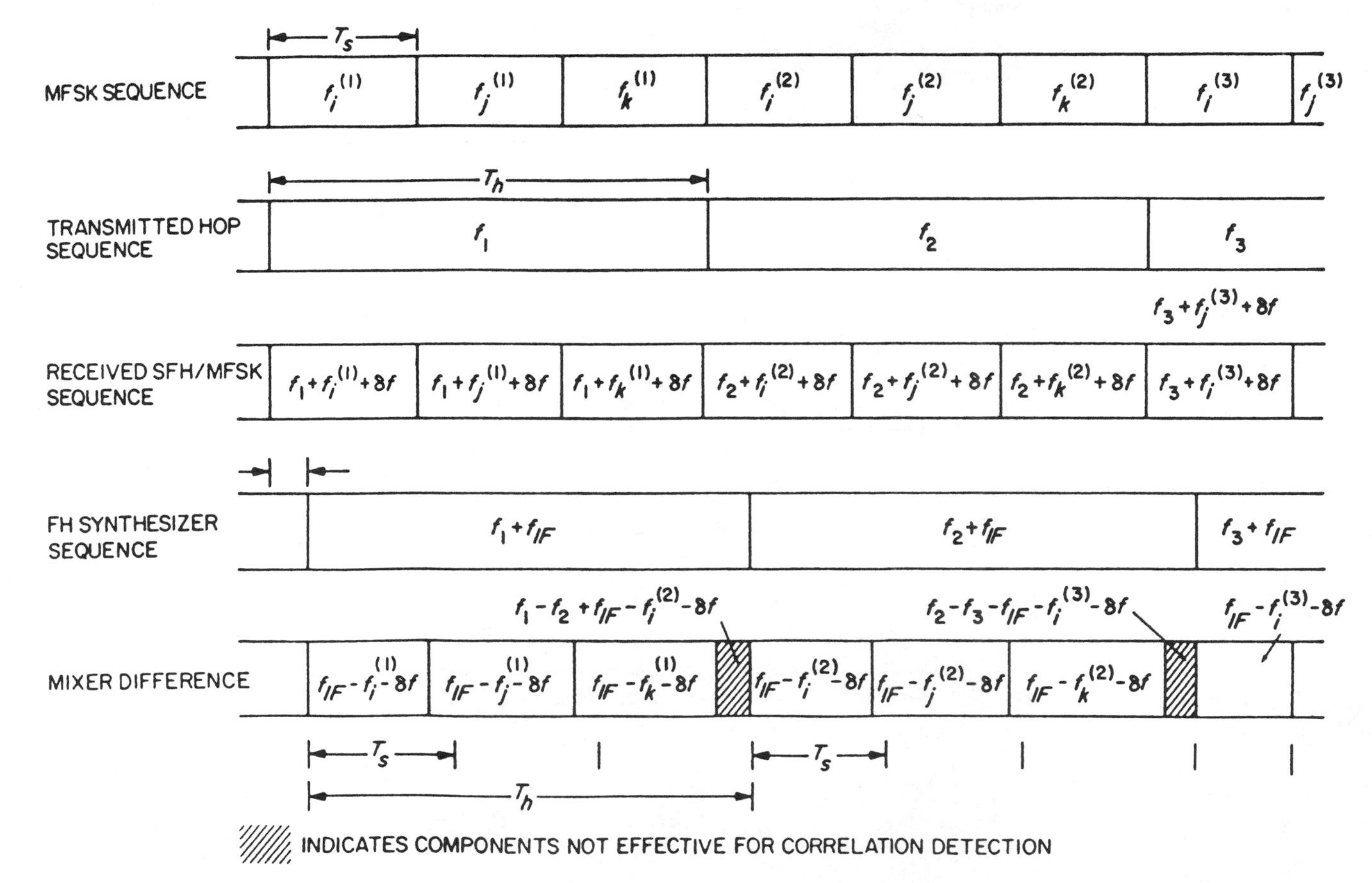

Figure 3.8. Received SFH/MFSK signal and local hop signal misaligned by less than a single hop interval.

corresponding to T_s/m and the demodulator outputs must be delayed by intervals of T_h sec before accumulation.

To evaluate the performance of the various serial search FH/MFSK acquisition systems in the presence of noise, we must determine their operating characteristic, i.e., the relation among false alarm probability P_{FA}, detection probability P_D, and dwell time τ_d. To determine this relation, we shall assume that the post-detection accumulation size N_h (actually N_{FFH} or N_{SFH}) is large so that the statistics at the input to the threshold comparison in Figure 3.5 and 3.7 may be assumed Gaussian. A similar assumption was made in Chapter 1 in connection with our discussion of serial search PN code acquisition. Because of this simplifying assumption, it is sufficient to find only the mean and variance of the signal at the post-detection accumulator input in both the in-sync and out-of-sync conditions.

To illustrate the procedure, we consider first the case of no diversity and equal symbol and hop rates. Thus, with $m = 1$ and $T_s = T_h$, Figures 3.5 and 3.7 are identical. Assuming first the out-of-sync condition ($\tau \geq T_h$), then the mixer output is noise only and the M non-coherent demodulator (normalized) outputs all have the same probability density function (pdf) given by (see (1.73) of Chapter 1)

$$p_N(y_k^*) = \begin{cases} e^{-y_k^*}; & y_k^* \geq 0 \\ 0; & \text{otherwise} \end{cases} \qquad k = 1, 2, \ldots, M. \tag{3.9}$$

On the other hand, for the "ideal" in-sync condition ($\tau = \delta f = 0$) and orthogonal MFSK tone spacing (i.e., an integer multiple of the symbol rate), then $M - 1$ of the demodulator outputs will be characterized by (3.9), while the remaining output corresponding to the transmitted tone (say f_{sl}) has the pdf (see (1.72) of Chapter 1)

$$p_{S+N}(y_l^*) = \begin{cases} e^{-(y_l^* + \gamma_h)} I_0\left(2\sqrt{\gamma_h y_l^*}\right); & y_l^* \geq 0 \\ 0; & \text{otherwise} \end{cases} \tag{3.10}$$

where $\gamma_h \triangleq ST_h/N_0$ is the hop signal-to-noise ratio, or, in this case, also the symbol signal-to-noise ratio.

Letting $Y_i{}^*$ denote the random variable corresponding to the largest of the M non-coherent demodulator normalized outputs at the i-th sampling (once per hop) instant, then the probability density function of $Y_i{}^*$ is given by

$$q_N(Y_i{}^*) = \frac{d}{dY_i{}^*}\left[P_N(Y_i{}^*)\right]^M = Mp_N(Y_i{}^*)\left[P_N(Y_i{}^*)\right]^{M-1} \tag{3.11}$$

for the out-of-sync condition and

$$q_{S+N}(Y_i^*) = \frac{d}{dY_i^*}\{P_{S+N}(Y_i^*)[P_N(Y_i^*)]^{M-1}\}$$

$$= p_{S+N}(Y_i^*)[P_N(Y_i^*)]^{M-1}$$

$$+(M-1)p_N(Y_i^*)P_{S+N}(Y_i^*)[P_N(Y_i^*)]^{M-2} \quad (3.12)$$

for the in-sync condition where $P_N(Y^*)$ and $P_{S+N}(Y^*)$ are, respectively, the probability *distribution* functions corresponding to the pdf's $p_N(y^*)$ and $p_{S+N}(y^*)$ of (3.9) and (3.10), i.e.,

$$P_N(Y^*) = \int_{-\infty}^{Y^*} p_N(y^*)\,dy^*$$

$$P_{S+N}(Y^*) = \int_{-\infty}^{Y^*} p_{S+N}(y^*)\,dy^*. \quad (3.13)$$

Substituting (3.9) and (3.10) into (3.13) and the results of these integral evaluations into (3.12) gives for the in-sync condition

$$q_{S+N}(Y_i^*) = \begin{cases} \exp[-(Y_i^* + \gamma_h)]\,I_0\left(2\sqrt{\gamma_h Y_i^*}\right)[1-\exp(-Y_i^*)]^{M-1} \\ \quad +(M-1)\exp(-Y_i^*)[1-\exp(-Y_i^*)]^{M-2} \\ \quad \times \int_0^{Y_i^*} \exp[-(Y+\gamma_h)]\,I_0\left(2\sqrt{\gamma_h Y}\right)dY;\ Y \geq 0 \\ 0;\ \text{otherwise.} \end{cases}$$

$$(3.14)$$

The corresponding result for the out-of-sync condition is obtained by letting $\gamma_h = 0$ in (3.14), i.e.,

$$q_N(Y_i^*) = \begin{cases} M\exp(-Y_i^*)[1-\exp(-Y_i^*)]^{M-1};\ Y_i^* \geq 0 \\ 0;\ \text{otherwise.} \end{cases} \quad (3.15)$$

As previously mentioned, we need to determine the first two central moments of Y_i^* in order to evaluate the operating characteristic of the acquisition system. From (3.14), we can determine the mean of Y_i^* for the perfectly in-sync condition as

$$\mu_{S+N} \triangleq \int_{-\infty}^{\infty} Y_i^* q_{S+N}(Y_i^*)\,dY_i^*$$

$$= 1 + \gamma_h + (M-1)\sum_{k=0}^{M-2} \frac{(-1)^k}{(k+2)(k+1)^2}\binom{M-2}{k}\exp\left[-\left(\frac{k+1}{k+2}\right)\gamma_h\right]$$

$$(3.16)$$

and for the out-of-sync condition,

$$\mu_N = 1 + (M-1)\sum_{k=0}^{M-2} \frac{(-1)^k}{(k+2)(k+1)^2}\binom{M-2}{k}. \tag{3.17}$$

Note that the leading terms of (3.16) and (3.17) correspond to the means of y^* as determined from $p_{S+N}(y^*)$ and $p_N(y^*)$ in (3.10) and (3.9), respectively (see (1.75) and (1.76) of Chapter 1). Similarly, the mean-squared value of Y_i^* under the two sync conditions is determined as

$$\overline{(Y_i^*)^2_{S+N}} = 2 + 4\gamma_h + \gamma_h^2 + 2(M-1)\sum_{k=0}^{M-2} \frac{(-1)^k}{(k+2)(k+1)^2}\binom{M-2}{k} \times\left[\left(\frac{1}{k+2}\right)\left(\frac{\gamma_h}{k+2}+1\right)+\frac{1}{k+1}\right]\exp\left[-\left(\frac{k+1}{k+2}\right)\gamma_h\right] \tag{3.18}$$

and

$$\overline{(Y_i^*)^2_N} = 2 + 2(M-1)\sum_{k-0}^{M-2} \frac{(-1)^k}{(k+2)(k+1)^2}\binom{M-2}{k}\left[\frac{1}{k+2}+\frac{1}{k+1}\right]. \tag{3.19}$$

Thus, the in-sync and out-of-sync variances of Y_i^* are given by

$$\sigma_{S+N}^2 = \overline{(Y_i^*)^2_{S+N}} - \mu_{S+N}^2$$
$$\sigma_N^2 = \overline{(Y_i^*)^2_N} - \mu_N^2 \tag{3.20}$$

where once again the leading terms will correspond to the variances of y^* (see (1.75) and (1.76) of Chapter 1).

Post-detection accumulation of Y_i^* produces the approximately Gaussian (N_h large) random variable

$$Z^* = \sum_{i=1}^{N_h} Y_i^* \tag{3.21}$$

which when compared with the normalized threshold η^* gives rise to a false alarm probability (exceeding the threshold when in the out-of-sync condition)

$$P_{FA} = \int_{\eta^*}^{\infty} \frac{1}{\sqrt{2\pi N_h \sigma_N^2}} \exp\left[-\frac{(Z^* - N_h\mu_N)^2}{2N_h\sigma_N^2}\right] dZ^*$$
$$= Q\left(\frac{\eta^* - N_h\mu_N}{\sqrt{N_h\sigma_N^2}}\right) \triangleq Q(\beta) \tag{3.22}$$

and a detection probability (exceeding the threshold when in the in-sync condition)

$$P_D = Q\left(\frac{\eta^* - N_h\mu_{S+N}}{\sqrt{N_h\sigma_{S+N}^2}}\right) = Q\left(\frac{\eta^* - N_h\mu_N - N_h(\mu_{S+N} - \mu_N)}{\sqrt{N_h\sigma_N^2}\,(\sigma_{S+N}/\sigma_N)}\right)$$

$$= Q\left(\frac{\beta - \sqrt{\dfrac{N_h}{\sigma_N^2}}\,(\mu_{S+N} - \mu_N)}{\sigma_{S+N}/\sigma_N}\right) \tag{3.23}$$

where, as in previous chapters, $Q(x)$ is the Gaussian probability integral. Eliminating β between (3.22) and (3.23) produces the desired system operating characteristic

$$P_D = Q\left(\frac{Q^{-1}(P_{FA}) - (\mu_{S+N} - \mu_N)\sqrt{\dfrac{N_h}{\sigma_N^2}}}{\sigma_{S+N}/\sigma_N}\right) \tag{3.24}$$

where μ_{S+N}, μ_N, σ_{S+N}^2, and σ_N^2 are determined from (3.16)–(3.20) and are all functions of the signalling alphabet size M and hop signal-to-noise ratio γ_h. Alternately, since the dwell time τ_d of the system is related to the accumulation size N_h by

$$N_h = \frac{\tau_d}{T_h}, \tag{3.25}$$

then (3.24) can be expressed in terms of the dwell time-hop rate product, which produces a relation analogous to (1.81) of Chapter 1. Figures 3.9 and 3.10 are plots of false alarm probability P_{FA} versus normalized dwell time τ_d/T_h with detection probability P_D as a parameter for $\gamma_h = -20$ dB and either 2-ary or 8-ary FSK, respectively. Clearly, as the number of signalling levels M increases, the required post-detection accumulation increases proportionally.

When m-diversity is employed, then the appropriate pdf's analogous to (3.9) and (3.10) become

$$p_N(y_k^*) = \begin{cases} \dfrac{(y_k^*)^{m-1}}{(m-1)!}\exp(-y_k^*);\ y_k^* \geq 0 \\ 0;\ \text{otherwise} \end{cases} \tag{3.26}$$

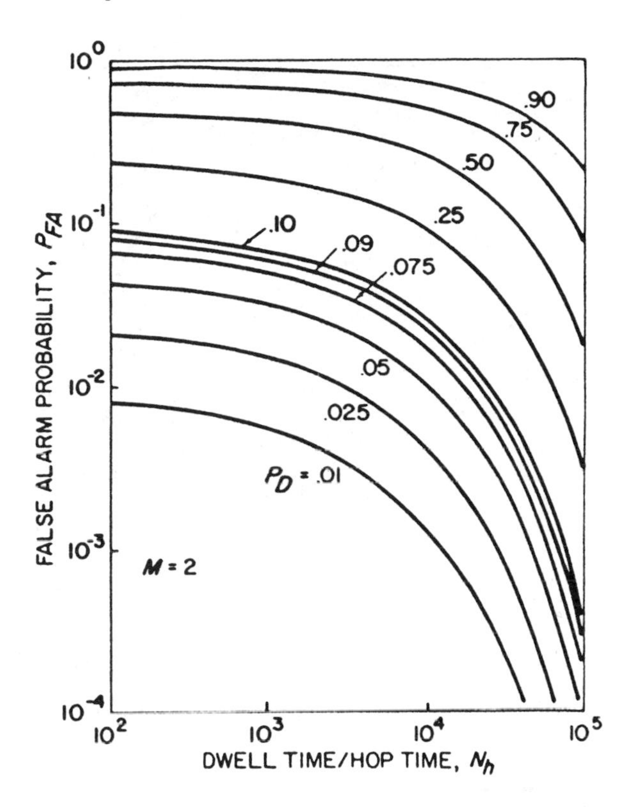

Figure 3.9. False alarm and detection probability performance of serial search FH/MFSK acquisition system; $\gamma_h = -20$ dB.

and

$$p_{S+N}\left(y_k^*\right) = \begin{cases} \left(\dfrac{y_k^*}{m\gamma_h}\right)^{(m-1)/2} \exp\left[-\left(y_k^* + m\gamma_h\right)\right] I_{m-1}\left(\sqrt{4m\gamma_h y_k^*}\right); \; y_k^* > 0 \\ 0; \text{ otherwise.} \end{cases} \tag{3.27}$$

Similarly the out-of-sync and in-sync pdf's for the largest of the M noncoherently combined normalized demodulator outputs are given respectively by

$$q_N\left(Y_i^*\right) = \begin{cases} \dfrac{M\left(Y_i^*\right)^{m-1}}{(m-1)!} \exp\left(-Y_i^*\right)\left[1 - \sum_{k=0}^{m-1} \dfrac{\left(Y_i^*\right)^k}{k!} \exp\left(-Y_i^*\right)\right]^{M-1}; \\ 0; \text{ otherwise} \end{cases}$$

$$Y_i^* \geq 0 \tag{3.28}$$

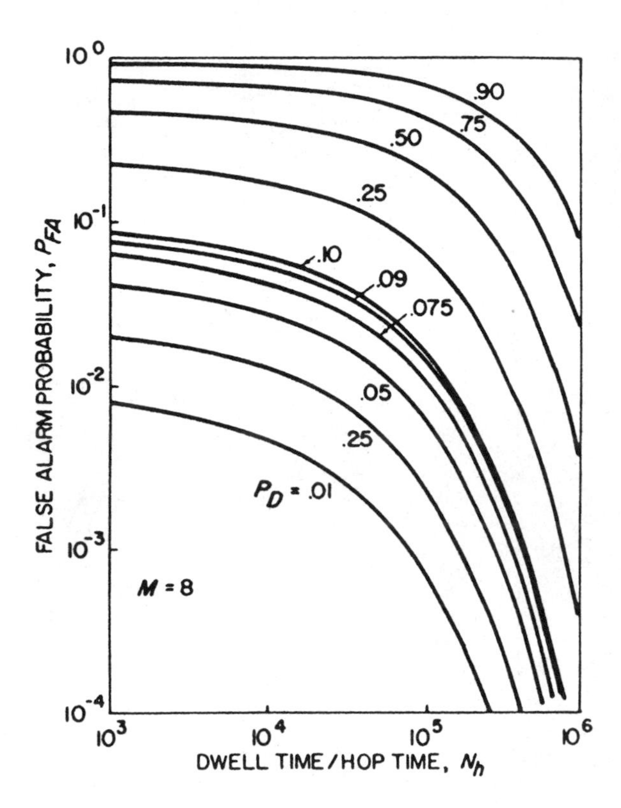

Figure 3.10. False alarm and detection probability performance of serial search FH/MFSK acquisition system; $\gamma_h = -20$ dB.

and

$$q_{S+N}(Y_i^*) = \begin{cases} \left(\dfrac{Y_i^*}{m\gamma_h}\right)^{(m-1)/2} \exp\left[-(Y_i^* + m\gamma_h)\right] I_{m-1}\left(\sqrt{4m\gamma_h Y_i^*}\right) \\ \times\left[1 - \displaystyle\sum_{k=0}^{m-1} \frac{(Y_i^*)^k}{k!} \exp(-Y_i^*)\right]^{M-1} \\ +(M-1)\dfrac{(Y_i^*)^{m-1}}{(m-1)!}\exp(-Y_i^*) \\ \times\left[1 - \displaystyle\sum_{k=0}^{m-1} \frac{(Y_i^*)^k}{k!} \exp(-Y_i^*)\right]^{M-2} \displaystyle\int_0^{Y_i^*} \left(\frac{Y}{m\gamma_h}\right)^{(m-1)/2} \\ \times \exp\left[-(Y + m\gamma_h)\right] I_{m-1}\left(\sqrt{4m\gamma_h Y}\right) dY;\ Y_i^* \geq 0 \\ 0;\ \text{otherwise} \end{cases} \tag{3.29}$$

with first two moments

$$
\begin{aligned}
\overline{(Y_i^*)^n_{S+N}} &= [m(1+\gamma_h)]^n + (n-1)m(1+2\gamma_h) \\
&\quad + (M-1)\sum_{k=0}^{M-2}\binom{M-2}{k}(-1)^k \exp\left[-\left(\frac{k+1}{k+2}\right)m\gamma_h\right] \\
&\quad \times \frac{1}{(k+1)^n(k+2)^m}\left\{\sum_{j=0}^{k(m-1)} C_{kj}\frac{(m+j+n-1)!}{(m-1)!(k+1)^{m+j}}\right. \\
&\quad \times \sum_{l=0}^{m+j+n-1}\left(\frac{k+1}{k+2}\right)^l L_l^{(m-1)}\left(-\frac{m\gamma_h}{k+2}\right) \\
&\quad \left. - \sum_{j=0}^{(k+1)(m-1)} C_{k+1,j}\frac{(j+n)!}{(k+2)^{j+n}} L_{j+n}^{(m-1)}\left(-\frac{m\gamma_h}{k+2}\right)\right\} \\
\overline{(Y_i^*)^n_N} &= \overline{(Y_i^*)^n_{S+N}}\Big|_{\gamma_h=0};\ n = 1,2
\end{aligned}
\tag{3.30}
$$

where $L_k^{(m-1)}(x)$ is the k-th generalized Laguerre polynomial of order $m-1$ [3] and C_{kj} are multinomial coefficients which satisfy the recursion relationship

$$
C_{kj} = \begin{cases} 1; & j = 0 \\ \dfrac{1}{j}\displaystyle\sum_{l=1}^{\min(j,m-1)} \frac{kl+l-j}{l!} C_{k,j-l} & j = 1,2,\ldots,k(m-1). \end{cases}
\tag{3.31}
$$

Thus, recognizing that μ_{S+N} and μ_N correspond to (3.30) with $n = 1$, and further obtaining σ_{S+N} and σ_N from (3.20) using (3.30) evaluated for $n = 2$, one uses (3.24) to obtain the system operating characteristic for the m-diversity case.

We mention in passing that for acquisition in noise, but in the absence of information modulation (see Figure 3.4 for the appropriate system), one merely sets $M = 1$ in (3.16)–(3.20), which, when substituted into (3.24), gives the simple result

$$
P_D = Q\left[\frac{Q^{-1}(P_{FA}) - \sqrt{N_h}\,\gamma_h}{\sqrt{1+2\gamma_h}}\right].
\tag{3.32}
$$

Note that if the acquisition system of Figure 3.1 were used in place of that in Figure 3.4, then (1.32) would still be appropriate with γ_h replaced by $S/2N_0B$ where B is again the single-sided low-pass filter noise bandwidth. Under these conditions, (3.32) becomes analogous to (1.81) of Chapter 1. In fact, the same substitution is appropriate to all of the previous results for acquisition with MFSK modulation if the integrate-and-dumps in Figures 3.5 and 3.7 are replaced by low-pass filters with noise bandwidth B.

To modify the previous results to allow for a non-ideal in-sync condition, we proceed as follows. Assuming that the MFSK tones are orthogonally spaced, e.g., for FFH we could have $f_{sj} - f_{s,j-1} = k/T_h$ since $1/T_h$ is the minimum tone separation for orthogonality, then in the absence of frequency error ($\delta f = 0$), the m-fold accumulated output samples of the M non-coherent demodulators would in the absence of noise be given by (see (3.8))

$$R_i(\tau) = mS\left(1 - \frac{|\tau|}{T_h}\right)^2 \triangleq mS(1 - |\varepsilon|)^2$$

$$R_l(\tau) = 0; l = 1, 2, \ldots, M; l \neq i \tag{3.33}$$

where f_i is the transmitted tone. Thus, multiplying γ_h by the loss factor $L \triangleq (1 - |\varepsilon|)^2$ in (3.30) is sufficient to account for this degrading effect. A similar result was obtained in connection with our previous discussion of PN code acquisition (see (1.86) of Chapter 1).

When, in addition, frequency error is present, then, even for the above orthogonal tone spacing, the m-fold accumulated output samples of the M non-coherent demodulations will in the absence of noise *all* contain non-zero signal components. Further, this set of output signal components will depend on which MFSK tone was indeed transmitted; i.e.,

$$R_i(\tau) = mS\frac{\sin^2[\pi\delta f(T_h - |\tau|)]}{(\pi\delta f T_h)^2} = mS\frac{\sin^2[\pi\delta f T_h(1 - |\varepsilon|)]}{(\pi\delta f T_h)^2}$$

$$R_l(\tau) = mS\frac{\sin^2\{[\pi\delta f T_h - (l - i)k](1 - |\varepsilon|)\}}{[\pi\delta f T_h - (l - i)k]^2}; \quad l = 1, 2, \cdots, M; l \neq i. \tag{3.34}$$

As a result, all of the normalized output samples y_k^* have pdf's of the form in (3.27) with $m\gamma_h$ replaced by $mR_l(\tau)T_h/N_0$; $l = 1, 2, \ldots, M$. Although formally the procedure is straightforward, the computation of acquisition performance for this case is tedious and is not presented here. However, a similar problem will be considered in detail later on in the chapter relative to the computation of error probability performance in the presence of residual time and frequency tracking errors.

It should be obvious by now that once the system operating characteristic is determined as in (3.24), the specification of acquisition performance in terms of such measures as mean and variance of the acquisition time or probability of acquisition follows directly from the results given in Chapter 1 for serial search PN acquisition. For example, the mean acquisition time $\bar{T}_{ACQ}$ of the serial search FFH/MFSK system of Figure 3.5 is given by (1.34) of Chapter 1 with P_D and P_{FA} related as in (3.24) using μ_{S+N}, μ_N, σ_{S+N}^2, and σ_N^2 of (3.16)–(3.20). This parallelism between serial search PN and FH acquisition systems follows from the fact that the basic Markov behavior of the search stepping procedure is the same in both cases. Further parallels between serial search PN and FH acquisition systems along the lines of sequential-type detectors, multiple dwell time detectors, optimum search procedures, etc., can also be drawn, with the details omitted here for the sake of brevity.

3.1.2 Serial Search Techniques with Passive Correlation

Analogous to the matched filter techniques discussed in Chapter 1 for pseudonoise acquisition in DS/SS receivers, the rapid search capability provided by a serial search scheme with passive correlation can also be realized in FH receivers. For the simplest case of rapid acquisition of an FH sequence in the absence of any information modulation, Figure 3.11 illustrates the appropriate structure. A sequence of M consecutive frequencies $f_1, f_2, \ldots, f_M$ within the overall hop sequence is chosen as the sync pattern to which the receiver attempts to match itself. To accomplish this, the received FH signal is simultaneously mixed with these M frequencies (shifted to IF) and the result of each mixture is passed through a non-coherent demodulator (band-pass filter and square-law envelope detector). The demodulator outputs are appropriately delayed so that the sum of these outputs corresponding to the energy in M successive hop interval correlations can be formed and tested against a threshold. Clearly, when the input sequence $f_1, f_2, \ldots, f_M$ has just passed through the receiver matched filter, the above sum will have its maximum value. One hop later, each of the M correlations will have zero contribution to the sum since the corresponding mixer outputs do not pass through the band-pass filters.

A discrete time version of the matched filter receiver of Figure 3.11 can be had by replacing each of the M band-pass non-coherent demodulators by their equivalent low-pass version using integrate-and-dump filters as in Figure 3.4. Here, a threshold decision is made at discrete time instants separated by a hop time and thus the search proceeds at the hop rate.

The performance of the discrete time matched filter FH acquisition system follows directly from the detailed discussions given in Chapter 1 for the analogous PN acquisition system. Thus, other than to point out the obvious parallel between PN code chip time there and hop time here, we shall leave it to the reader to make the remaining necessary associations between the parameters of the two systems.

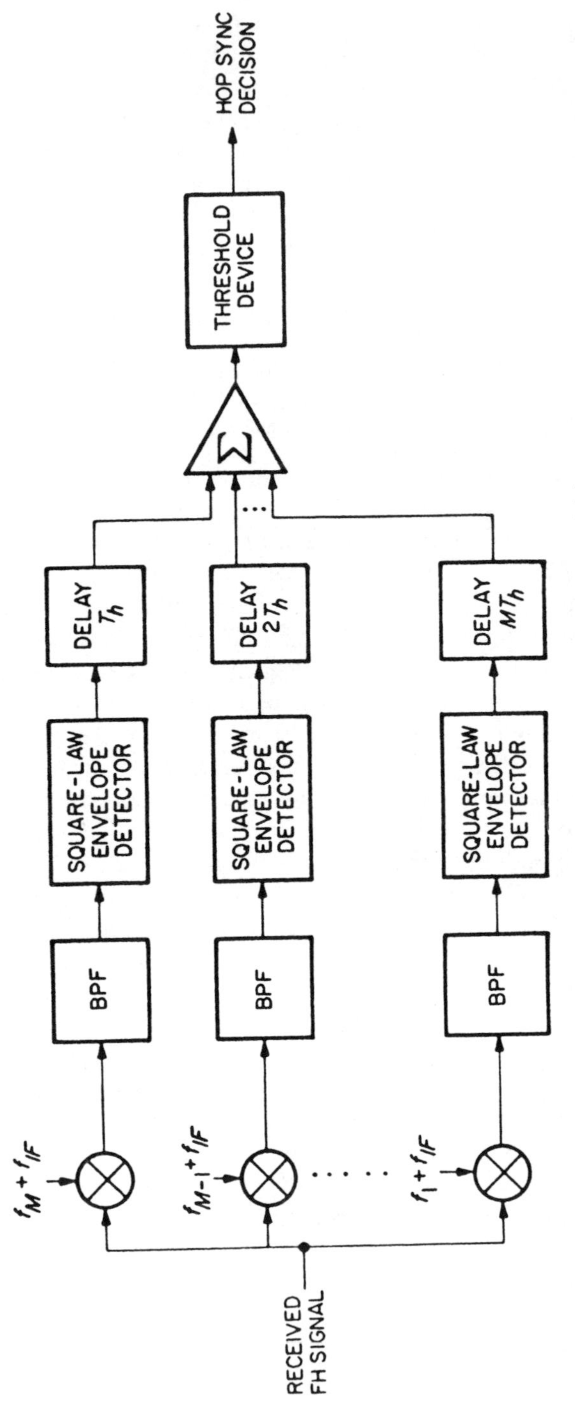

Figure 3.11. A matched filter type of FH acquisition system.

3.1.3 Other FH Acquisition Techniques

A scheme that combines the rapid search capability of passive correlation with the decision reliability of active correlation (over long time intervals) was suggested in [3] and later compared with the more conventional FH acquisition techniques in [4]. The application for which such a two-level acquisition scheme was proposed was a ground mobile radio environment where the users operate in a "push-to-talk" mode and thus the communication among them is intermittent and characterized by frequent and possibly long periods of silence. At the onset of a transmission, prior to message communication, the user sends a leader consisting of several repetitions of the hopped carrier patterns. It is on this leader sequence that the two-level synchronization scheme must acquire and, hence, the length of the leader represents the maximum time (in hops) that the receiver has for FH acquisition. The way in which the acquisition is accomplished is as follows. Each of the hop patterns begins with a specific short segment (say m hops long) referred to as a *sync prefix*. A passive correlator (m-stage matched filter) is used to detect this short m-hop sync prefix and generate a code start signal for those intervals in which its detection threshold is exceeded (see Figure 3.12). The code start signals as they occur each engage any (one) active correlator from the total bank of correlators provided and cause it to cycle through the remaining (say $k \gg m$) hops in the pattern. Non-coherent detection and post-detection integration over these k hop intervals produces an output which is compared against a second threshold. If this threshold is exceeded the test terminates and sync acquisition is declared. Otherwise, the active correlator is again made available to the common bank. If all active correlators are engaged (none are idle) when a code start signal occurs, then this signal is ignored.

Since typically the size (say C) of the bank of active correlators shared among arriving code start signals can be chosen much less than k, then a significant reduction in hardware is potentially possible compared to a full $(m + k)$ parallel correlator structure. Clearly depending on the relative choices of m, k, and bank size C, and the number (say n) of repetitions of the hopped carrier pattern in the leader, a variety of performance tradeoffs are possible between the two extremes of the traditional single-level active and single-level passive correlation schemes.

The notion of estimating from the received signal the state of the linear feedback shift register (LFSR) that generates the local PN code in DS/SS systems (see the discussion of rapid acquisition by sequential estimation in Chapter 1) can also be applied in FH/SS systems. Recall that in the DS/SS system the estimation of the PN sequence that biphase modulates the carrier is accomplished by low-pass filtering the received signal with a filter whose cutoff frequency equals the clock rate of the LFSR followed by hard-limiting. Furthermore, the recursion relation for the PN sequence can be used to improve the accuracy of the initial state estimate (resulting in recursion-aided

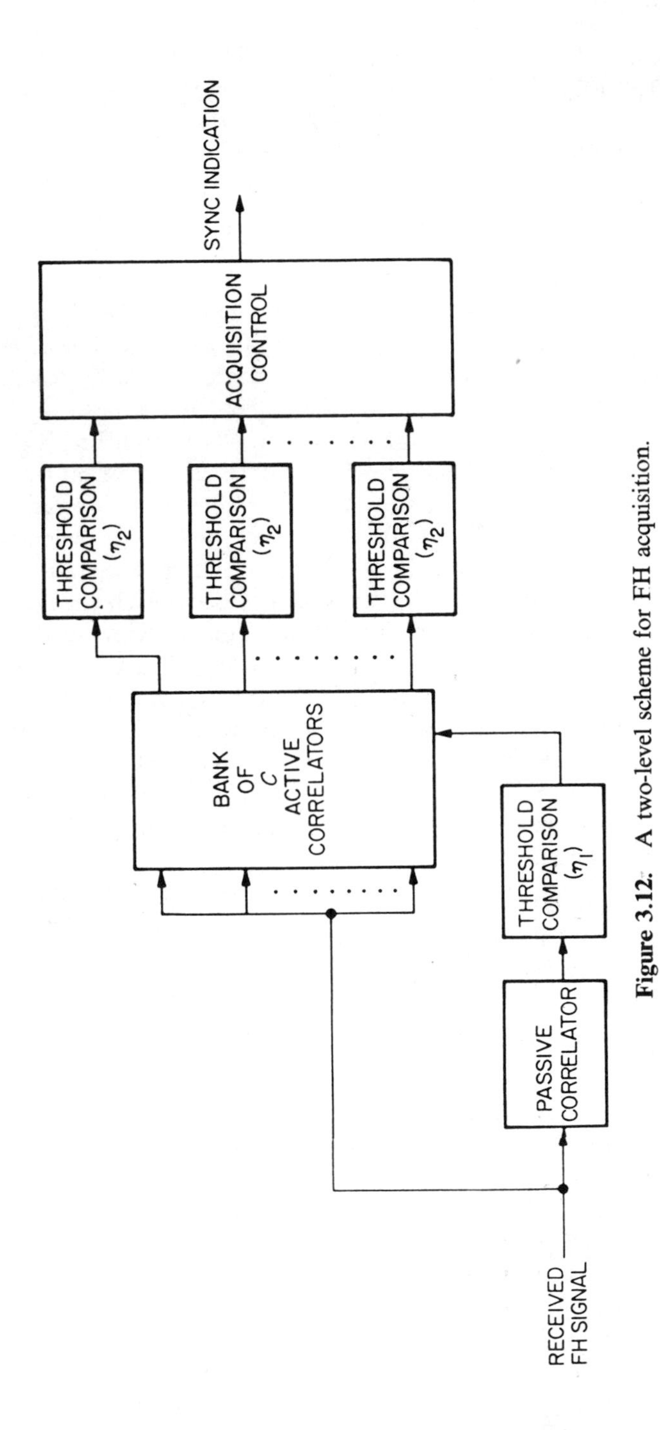

Figure 3.12. A two-level scheme for FH acquisition.

rapid acquisition by sequential estimation) and/or to determine whether the estimate is likely to be error free, thereby reducing acquisition time. In the FH/SS application, the above approach translates to estimating the received frequency over say n_1 successive hop intervals, thus requiring a form of sequential *spectral* estimation. Note that whereas in DS/SS systems an estimate based on observation of the received signal over a single chip interval provides information about only one stage of the LFSR (i.e., we need n successive chip interval estimates to load the contents of an n-stage LFSR), in FH/SS systems an estimate of the frequency in a single hop interval provides information about the entire state of the LFSR. Thus, depending on the order of the model used for the received signal, one can use either the frequency estimate in each hop interval to identify only the most significant bit (MSB) of the corresponding PN codeword, in which case we would have $n_1 = n$, or several significant bits of the LFSR ($n_1 < n$), thus further reducing the acquisition time.

Based on the above discussion, Figure 3.13 illustrates an autoregressive spectral estimation acquisition technique (ASEAT) [5, 6] that is directly analogous to the RASE technique for the DS/SS system (see Figure 3.4 of Chapter 1). The word "autoregressive" refers to the fact that the sampled received signal plus noise (after down conversion) is modelled as an autoregressive (AR) process, thus allowing identification of the instantaneous frequency of this signal by an algorithm developed by El-Ghouroury and Gupta [7].[3] This algorithm, which is incorporated in the frequency identification processor of Figure 3.13, inputs the received signal samples to a linear adaptive filter whose coefficients are updated each sample by a stochastic gradient technique [10] in accordance with the changing statistics of the input signal. The remainder of the frequency identification processor is the frequency identification algorithm [7] which determines the frequency estimate from the signal spectrum, which in turn is related to the filter coefficients through an all-pole model [10].

Note, unlike its PN counterpart (the RASE technique), the ASEAT seeks to achieve acquisition times on the order of the number of stages (n_1) of the LFSR as opposed to the length of the code ($2^{n_1} - 1$) which is characteristic of active correlation serial search techniques. The ability to accomplish this depends quite heavily on the input signal-to-noise ratio, which in turn depends on the nature of the noise interference. Typically, the ASEAT works well in a broadband Gaussian noise environment even for signal-to-noise ratios down to -15 dB [6]; but, like the RASE technique, it is highly vulnerable to narrowband interference. Here the worst case offender is a

[3]In [8], an ASEAT is proposed where the frequency identification processor employs a modification of the spectral estimation algorithms of [9] which uses partial-correlation coefficients to identify the received signal frequency in each hop interval.

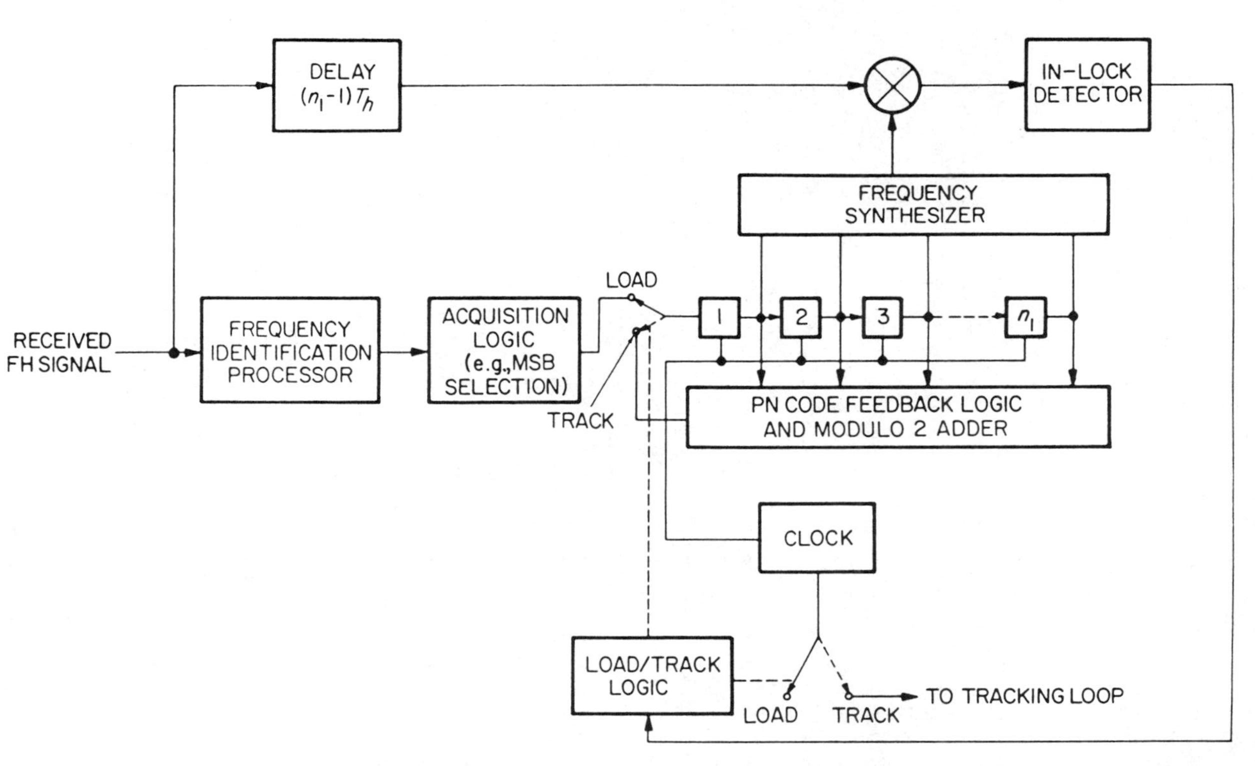

Figure 3.13. An autoregressive spectral estimation acquisition technique (ASEAT).

multitone jammer whose presence in only one of a sequence of n_1 hops might be sufficient to cause the failure of that specific acquisition trial. (Each time this occurs the process must repeat the acquisition trial until a clean record of n_1 successive hops is received without a single jammed tone.) The reason for this vulnerability again stems from the fact that the spectral estimation process is performed on a hop-by-hop basis, thus making no use of the interference rejection capability associated with the FH despreading process. Finally, we point out that the ASEAT is also applicable to hybrid SS systems such as FH/TH and FH/DS [6].

3.2 TIME SYNCHRONIZATION OF NON-COHERENT FH / MFSK SYSTEMS

Time synchronization of a conventional (non-spread) non-coherent MFSK receiver, with additive white Gaussian noise (AWGN) as the only source of disturbance, is typically achieved by transmitting a known synchronization sequence (say frequency f_1 followed by f_2) which is repeated as often as necessary until the desired degree of time synchronization accuracy is obtained. In the presence of this sequence, spectral estimates are formed from discrete (fast) Fourier transforms of the received signal plus noise over one data symbol interval and evaluated at the two frequencies, f_1 and f_2. The ratio of the difference of these two spectral estimates to twice their sum is then the maximum-likelihood estimator of the time of transition from f_1 to f_2 relative to the receiver's present time origin [11], [12]. It is emphasized that it is the *transitions* in the data from f_1 to f_2, and vice versa, that allow the determination of time synchronization by the above approach.

In a non-coherent FH/MFSK receiver, it is sufficient to transmit a *single* frequency tone corresponding to a specific data symbol and allow the frequency hopping to cause the necessary frequency transitions for estimation of time synchronization. As such, the timing estimate is once again obtained in the absence of and prior to true data transmission and, thus, the synchronization process is of a gated nature, being interleaved within the data sequence often enough to provide the desired degree of timing accuracy. The specific manner in which the FH timing estimate is formed may be understood by considering the simplified fine time synchronization of an FH/MFSK system such as that illustrated in Figure 3.14. The transmitted FH signal is successively advanced and delayed *in time* relative to its nominal synchronization position. The received FH signal plus jamming noise is cross-correlated with the local frequency hop generator. Alternately, the local frequency hop generator could be advanced and then delayed in time while the transmitter hop generator remains fixed in its nominal synchronization position. Since the *relative* timing offset between transmitter and receiver hop generators is all that is effectual in producing the timing estimate, either implementation will conceptually produce the same

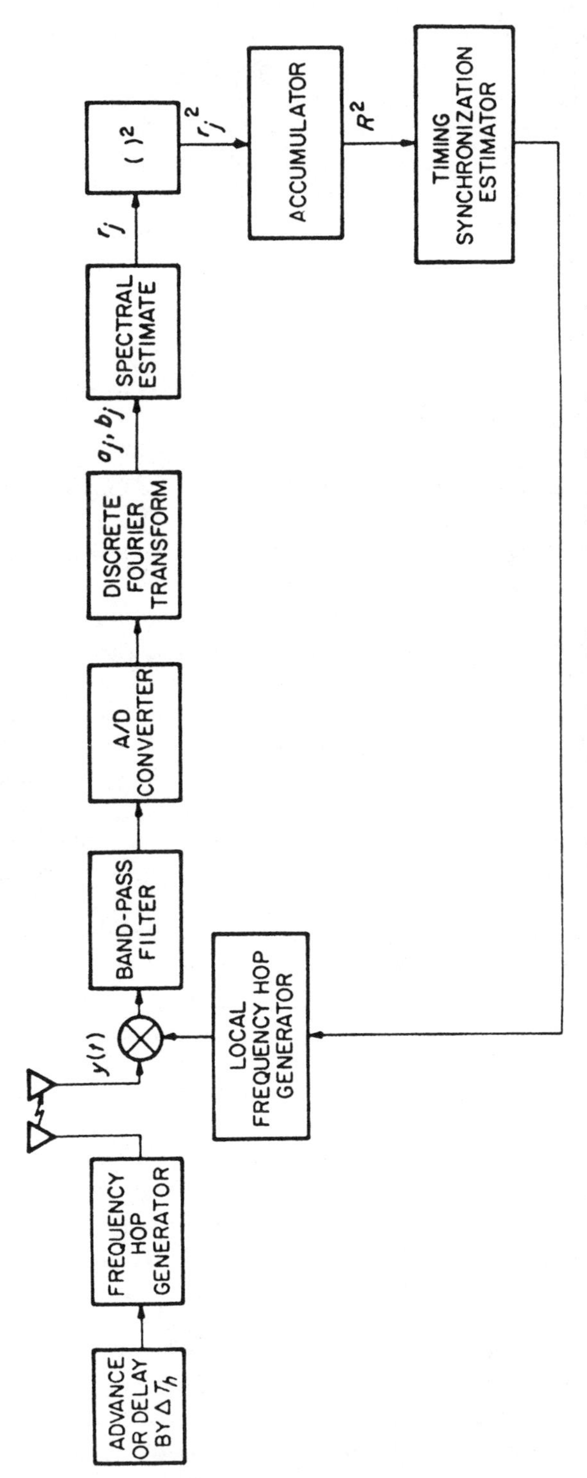

Figure 3.14. Simplified time synchronization of an FH system with on-board processing.

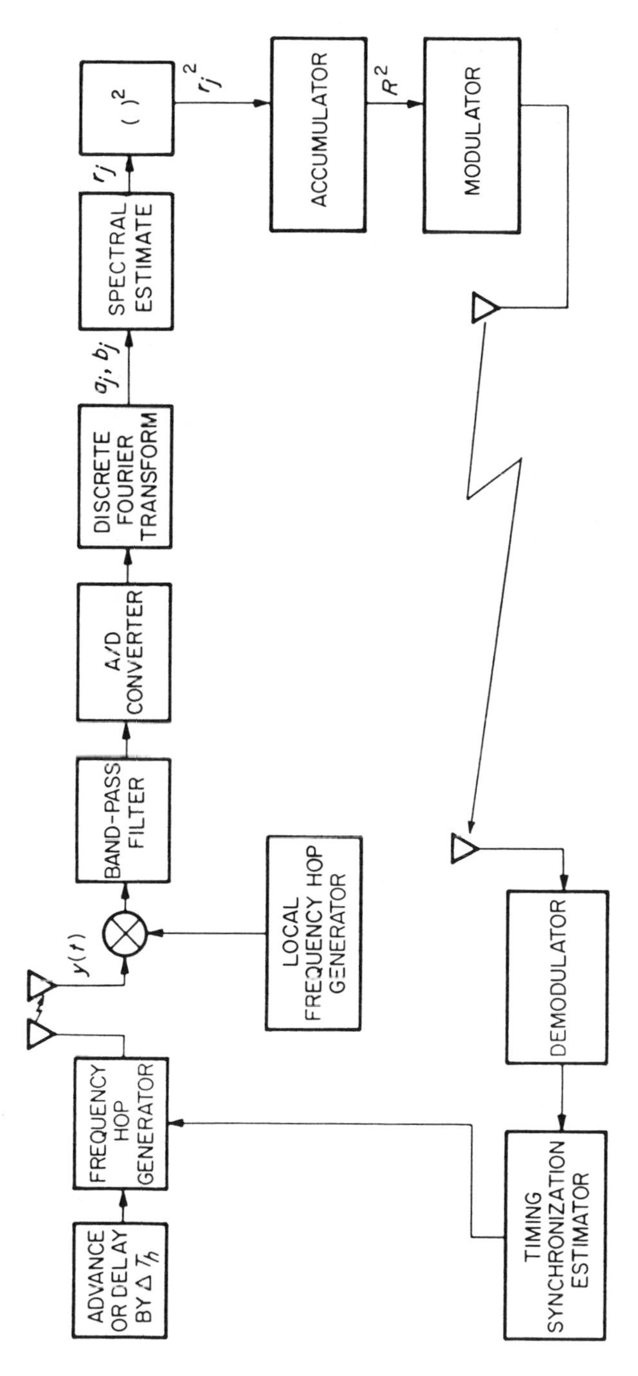

Figure 3.15. Simplified time synchronization of an FH system with a passive processor.

performance with the choice governed by the particular system application. Typically, the former implementation is preferable from the standpoint of reducing receiver complexity.

Assuming that the spacing between successive frequency hops is far outside the bandwidth of the band-pass filter, then in the absence of perfect time synchronization, only a fraction of the total signal energy available in a single hop interval will pass through this filter since the remaining fraction of the hop interval will contain noise only. The output of the band-pass filter is passed through an A/D converter and the resultant signal samples are discrete Fourier transformed to produce spectral estimates corresponding to the advanced and delayed transmitted frequency hop. The squares of these estimates are then accumulated over many hop intervals and the square roots of these accumulated values are then used in much the same fashion as described for the conventional MFSK receiver to form a time synchronization estimate [11], [12]. Finally, this estimate, which is formed in the receiver, is directly used to update the current timing position of the local hop generator. Alternately, in the case of a passive processor such as a satellite, the accumulated estimates could be transmitted back to the originating terminal, where the timing estimate would be formed and used to correct the transmitted hop timing (see Figure 3.15). Once again the specific details and mathematical analysis of the above time synchronization estimation technique are essentially immune to the activity or passivity of the processor. Hence, in the sections that follow we shall pursue the simplified system of Figure 3.14 with the understanding that the results apply to either implementation.

3.2.1 The Case of Full-Band Noise Jamming

3.2.1.1 Signal Model and Spectral Computations

The transmitted signal $s^{(j)}(t)$ in the j-th hop interval is of the form

$$s^{(j)}(t) = \sqrt{2S}\sin 2\pi\left(f_s + f_j\right)t;\ (j-1)T_h \leq t \leq jT_h \tag{3.35}$$

where S is the average power, f_s is the frequency corresponding to the transmitted data symbol, and f_j is the j-th hop frequency. Assuming first that the additive Gaussian distributed jamming noise $J(t)$ is spread across the entire hop frequency band, then in the same hop interval, the received signal is given by

$$y(t) = \sqrt{2S}\sin\left[2\pi\left(f_s + f_j\right)t - \phi_j\right] + J(t);\ (j-1)T_h \leq t \leq jT_h \tag{3.36}$$

where ϕ_j is the unknown received signal phase in this interval, assumed to be uniformly distributed on $(0, 2\pi)$, and $J(t)$ is assumed to have a flat spectral density N_J and band-pass expansion about the sum of f_s and the

j-th hop frequency given by

$$J(t) \triangleq \sqrt{2}\, J_{c1}(t)\cos 2\pi(f_s + f_j)t - \sqrt{2}\, J_{s1}(t)\sin 2\pi(f_s + f_j)t. \tag{3.37}$$

Letting τ denote the time synchronization error between the received signal and the local frequency hop generator, then in its normal (not delayed or advanced) synchronization position, the output of this generator can be expressed as

$$r(t) = 2\sin\left[2\pi(f_s + f_j + f_{IF})t\right]; \quad (j-1)T_h - \tau \le t \le jT_h - \tau \tag{3.38}$$

where f_{IF} is the IF center frequency of the band-pass filter. Cross-correlating $y(t)$ with $r(t)$ and assuming, as previously mentioned, that the hop frequency difference is outside the bandwidth of the IF filter, then the output $x(t)$ of this filter is given by

$$x(t) \triangleq y(t)r(t)$$

$$= \begin{cases} J'(t); & \text{or} \begin{array}{l} (j-1)T_h - \tau \le t \le (j-1)T_h \quad (\tau \ge 0) \\ jT_h \le t \le jT_h - \tau \quad (\tau < 0) \end{array} \\ \sqrt{2S}\cos(2\pi f_{IF}t - \phi_j) + J'(t); & \text{or} \begin{array}{l} (j-1)T_h \le t \le jT_h - \tau \quad (\tau \ge 0) \\ (j-1)T_h - \tau \le t \le jT_h(\tau < 0) \end{array} \end{cases} \tag{3.39}$$

where

$$J'(t) \triangleq \sqrt{2}\, J_{c2}(t)\cos[2\pi f_{IF}t] - \sqrt{2}\, J_{s2}(t)\sin[2\pi f_{IF}t]. \tag{3.40}$$

If the band-pass filter output is now sampled at the Nyquist rate, then there will be $N_s = 2B_{IF}T_h$ samples in each hop interval where B_{IF} denotes the IF noise bandwidth of the band-pass filter. Letting $x_{ij} = x(iT_h/N_s + (j-1)T_h)$ denote the i-th sample ($i = 0, 1, \ldots, N_s - 1$), in the j-th hop interval, then these samples are statistically independent Gaussian random variables with variance $\sigma_x^2 = N_J B_{IF} = N_J(N_s/2T_h)$.

Taking the sine and cosine discrete Fourier transforms of these samples and evaluating them at $f = f_{IF}$, one has, in the j-th hop interval,

$$a_j \triangleq \sum_{i=0}^{N_s-1} x_{ij}\cos\left(2\pi f_{IF}\frac{i}{N_s}T_h\right)$$

$$b_j \triangleq \sum_{i=0}^{N_s-1} x_{ij}\sin\left(2\pi f_{IF}\frac{i}{N_s}T_h\right) \tag{3.41}$$

from which the spectral estimate

$$r_j \triangleq \sqrt{a_j^2 + b_j^2} \tag{3.42}$$

is obtained. Letting $t = iT_h/N_s + (j-1)T_h$ in (3.39) and substituting in (3.41), we arrive at the following results (for large N_s) for the first two statistical moments of a_j and b_j, i.e.,

$$\overline{a_j} \triangleq E\{a_j\} = \begin{cases} \dfrac{\sqrt{2S}\,N_s(1-|\varepsilon|)}{2}\cos\varphi_j; & |\varepsilon| \le 1 \\ 0; & |\varepsilon| > 1 \end{cases}$$

$$\overline{b_j} \triangleq E\{b_j\} = \begin{cases} \dfrac{\sqrt{2S}\,N_s(1-|\varepsilon|)}{2}\sin\varphi_j; & |\varepsilon| \le 1 \\ 0; & |\varepsilon| > 1 \end{cases}$$

$$\sigma_a^2 \triangleq E\left\{\left(a_j - \overline{a_j}\right)^2\right\} \triangleq \sigma^2 = \frac{N_J}{4T_h}N_s^2$$

$$\sigma_b^2 \triangleq E\left\{\left(b_j - \overline{b_j}\right)^2\right\} \triangleq \sigma^2 = \frac{N_J}{4T_h}N_s^2 \tag{3.43}$$

where $\varepsilon \triangleq \tau/T_h$ is the time synchronization error normalized to the hop interval and $\varphi_j = \phi_j - 2\pi(j-1)f_{IF}T_h$. Also, a_j and b_j are Gaussian random variables with conditional pdf's (for $|\varepsilon| \le 1$)

$$p(a_j|\phi_j) = \frac{1}{\sqrt{2\pi\sigma^2}}\exp\left\{-\frac{1}{2\sigma^2}\left[a_j - \xi(1-|\varepsilon|)\cos\phi_j\right]^2\right\}$$

$$p(b_j|\phi_j) = \frac{1}{\sqrt{2\pi\sigma^2}}\exp\left\{-\frac{1}{2\sigma^2}\left[b_j - \xi(1-|\varepsilon|)\sin\phi_j\right]^2\right\} \tag{3.44}$$

where we have introduced the notation

$$\xi \triangleq \frac{\sqrt{2S}\,N_s}{2}. \tag{3.45}$$

Further, letting γ_h denote the ratio of signal energy per hop-to-jamming noise spectral density, i.e.,

$$\gamma_h \triangleq \frac{ST_h}{N_J} = \frac{\xi^2}{2\sigma^2} \tag{3.46}$$

then r_j is a Rician-distributed random variable with pdf (conditioned on ε with $|\varepsilon| \le 1$)

$$p(r_j|\varepsilon) = \begin{cases} \dfrac{r_j}{\sigma^2}\exp\left\{-\left[\dfrac{r_j^2}{2\sigma^2} + \gamma_h(1-|\varepsilon|)^2\right]\right\} I_0\left[\sqrt{2\gamma_h}\,\dfrac{r_j}{\sigma}(1-|\varepsilon|)\right]; & 0 \le r_j \le \infty \\ 0; \text{ elsewhere.} \end{cases} \tag{3.47}$$

If the transmitter hop frequency generator is now advanced and delayed by $\Delta T_h (0 \leq \Delta \leq 1/2)$ from its nominal synchronization position and the corresponding spectral estimates denoted by r_{j+} and r_{j-}, then an appropriate estimator of time synchronization is

$$\hat{\varepsilon} = \frac{r_{j+} - r_{j-}}{K_\Delta (r_{j+} + r_{j-})}, \tag{3.48}$$

where K_Δ is a constant whose value is chosen relative to that of the normalized advance-delay fraction Δ. In the absence of jammer noise, we have that

$$\hat{\varepsilon} = \begin{cases} \dfrac{2\varepsilon}{K_\Delta (2 - 2\Delta)}; & |\varepsilon| \leq \Delta \\ \dfrac{2\Delta}{K_\Delta (2 - 2|\varepsilon|)}; & \Delta \leq |\varepsilon| \leq 1/2. \end{cases} \tag{3.49}$$

Thus, the maximum region over which $\hat{\varepsilon}$ is a linear function of ε would occur for $\Delta = 1/2$ in which case K_Δ would be chosen equal to 2, so that over this interval $\hat{\varepsilon} = \varepsilon$. In what follows, we shall assume these values for Δ and K_Δ, or equivalently from (3.48),

$$\hat{\varepsilon} = \frac{r_{j+} - r_{j-}}{2(r_{j+} + r_{j-})}. \tag{3.50}$$

Furthermore, since the advance and delay of the transmitter hop generator does not affect the variance of the discrete Fourier transform components, then from (3.43) and (3.47), we have for $|\varepsilon| \leq \Delta = 1/2$,

$$p(r_{j\pm}|\varepsilon) = \begin{cases} \dfrac{r_{j\pm}}{\sigma^2} \exp\left\{ -\left[\dfrac{r_{j\pm}^2}{2\sigma^2} + \gamma_h \left(\dfrac{1}{2} \pm \varepsilon \right)^2 \right] \right\} I_0 \left[\sqrt{2\gamma_h} \dfrac{r_{j\pm}}{\sigma} \left(\dfrac{1}{2} \pm \varepsilon \right) \right]; \\ 0; \text{ elsewhere } \quad 0 \leq r_{j\pm} \leq \infty. \end{cases} \tag{3.51}$$

If it wasn't for the presence of the additive jamming noise, (3.50) would be a perfect estimator of time synchronization. However, in the presence of noise, $\hat{\varepsilon}$ of (3.50), which is computed on the basis of spectral estimates from a *single* hop interval, would possess a large variance. Thus, to produce an estimator with small variance, we must first accumulate the spectral estimates over many hop intervals, say N_h, before forming our estimate of ε in the manner of (3.50). In particular, letting

$$R_{\pm} = \sqrt{\frac{1}{N_h} \sum_{j=1}^{N_h} r_{j+}^2}, \tag{3.52}$$

then we define our estimator of time synchronization by

$$\hat{\varepsilon} = \frac{R_+ - R_-}{2(R_+ + R_-)}. \tag{3.53}$$

In order to calculate the variance of the estimator $\hat{\varepsilon}$, we must first compute its pdf (conditioned on ε). From (3.51) and (3.52), one can show that

$$p(R_\pm|\varepsilon) = \begin{cases} \dfrac{N_h R_\pm}{\sigma^2}\left(\dfrac{R_\pm^2}{2\sigma^2\gamma_h\left(\dfrac{1}{2} \pm \varepsilon\right)^2}\right)^{(N_h-1)/2} \\ \times \exp\left\{-N_h\left[\dfrac{R_\pm^2}{2\sigma^2} + \gamma_h\left(\dfrac{1}{2} \pm \varepsilon\right)^2\right]\right\} \\ \times I_{N_h-1}\left[\sqrt{2\gamma_h}\,N_h\left(\dfrac{1}{2} \pm \varepsilon\right)\dfrac{R_\pm}{\sigma}\right]; \; R_\pm \geq 0, |\varepsilon| \leq \dfrac{1}{2} \\ 0; \text{ elsewhere.} \end{cases} \tag{3.54}$$

Then, by a straightforward transformation of variables and the fact that R_+ and R_- are statistically independent (conditioned on ε), we obtain the desired result, namely,

$$p(\hat{\varepsilon}|\varepsilon) = \begin{cases} N_h^2\left(\dfrac{1}{4} - \hat{\varepsilon}^2\right)\exp\left[-N_h\gamma_h\left(\dfrac{1}{2} + 2\varepsilon^2\right)\right] \\ \times \displaystyle\int_0^\infty y^3\left[\dfrac{y^2\left(\dfrac{1}{4} - \hat{\varepsilon}^2\right)}{2\gamma_h\left(\dfrac{1}{4} - \varepsilon^2\right)}\right]^{N_h-1} \exp\left\{-\dfrac{N_h y^2}{2}\left(\dfrac{1}{2} + 2\hat{\varepsilon}^2\right)\right\} \\ \times I_{N_h-1}\left[\sqrt{2\gamma_h}N_h\left(\dfrac{1}{2} + \varepsilon\right)\left(\dfrac{1}{2} + \hat{\varepsilon}\right)y\right] \\ \times I_{N_h-1}\left[\sqrt{2\gamma_h}N_h\left(\dfrac{1}{2} - \varepsilon\right)\left(\dfrac{1}{2} - \hat{\varepsilon}\right)y\right] dy; \; |\hat{\varepsilon}| \leq \dfrac{1}{2}, \\ 0; \text{ elsewhere} \end{cases} \tag{3.55}$$

from which the conditional variance of the estimator $\hat{\varepsilon}$ is given by

$$\sigma_{\hat{\varepsilon}|\varepsilon}^2 = \int_{-1/2}^{1/2}(\hat{\varepsilon} - \mu_{\hat{\varepsilon}|\varepsilon})^2 p(\hat{\varepsilon}|\varepsilon)\, d\hat{\varepsilon}, \tag{3.56}$$

where

$$\mu_{\hat{\varepsilon}|\varepsilon} \triangleq E\{\hat{\varepsilon}|\varepsilon\} = \int_{-1/2}^{1/2}\hat{\varepsilon}p(\hat{\varepsilon}|\varepsilon)\, d\hat{\varepsilon}. \tag{3.57}$$

3.2.1.2 *Results for Large N_h*

The general result of (3.55) can also be simplified when N_h, the number of hop intervals over which the spectral estimates are accumulated, is large. More specifically, for large N_h, we can apply the central limit theorem to (3.52) from which $Z_{\pm} \triangleq R_{\pm}^2$ are Gaussian random variables with

$$\mu_{\pm}(\varepsilon) \triangleq E\{Z_{\pm}|\varepsilon\} = 2\sigma^2\left[1 + \gamma_h\left(\frac{1}{2} \pm \varepsilon\right)^2\right]$$

$$\sigma_{\pm}^2(\varepsilon) \triangleq E\left\{(Z_{\pm} - \mu_{\pm})^2|\varepsilon\right\} = \frac{(2\sigma^2)^2}{N_h}\left[1 + 2\gamma_h\left(\frac{1}{2} \pm \varepsilon\right)^2\right]. \quad (3.58)$$

Thus, the conditional pdf's of R_+ and R_- are

$$p(R_{\pm}|\varepsilon) = \begin{cases} \dfrac{2R_{\pm}}{\sqrt{2\pi\sigma_{\pm}^2(\varepsilon)}}\exp\left\{-\dfrac{\left(R_{\pm}^2 - \mu_{\pm}(\varepsilon)\right)^2}{2\sigma_{\pm}^2(\varepsilon)}\right\}; \; R_{\pm} \geq 0 \\ 0; \text{ elsewhere.} \end{cases} \quad (3.59)$$

Using methods similar to those employed in arriving at (3.55), we obtain,

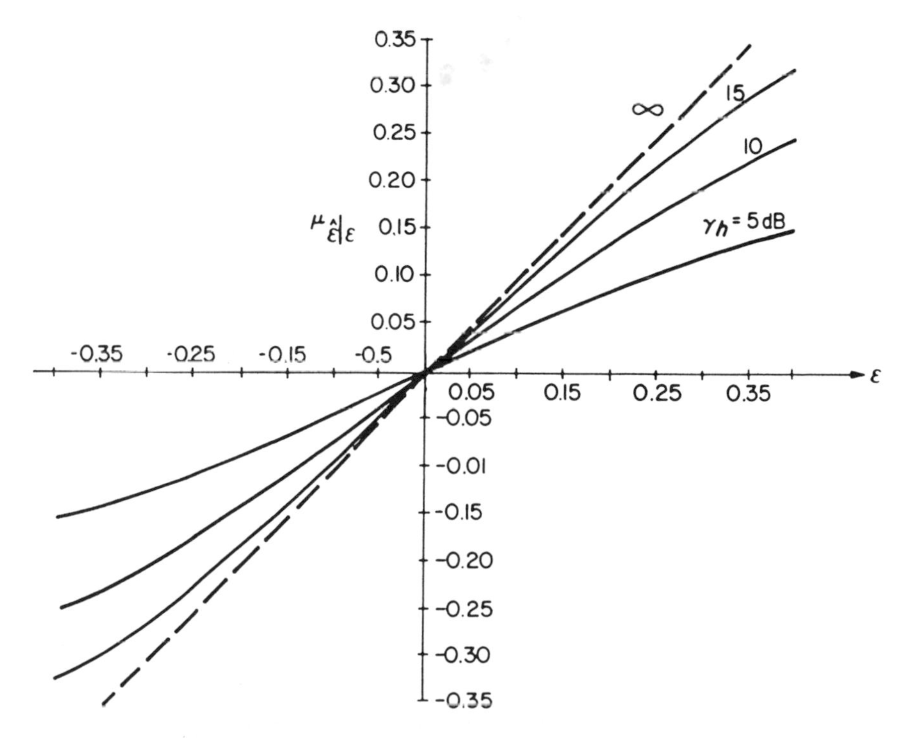

Figure 3.16. Conditional mean $\mu_{\hat{\varepsilon}|\varepsilon}$ versus ε with γ_h as a parameter; $N_h = 10$.

after much simplification,

$$p(\hat{\varepsilon}|\varepsilon) = \begin{cases} \dfrac{N_h\left(\dfrac{1}{4} - \hat{\varepsilon}^2\right)\sigma_T^2}{\pi\sqrt{\left[1 + 2\gamma_h\left(\dfrac{1}{2} + \varepsilon\right)^2\right]\left[1 + 2\gamma_h\left(\dfrac{1}{2} - \varepsilon\right)^2\right]}} \\ \times\left\{\exp\left\{-\dfrac{\bar{x}_1^2}{2\sigma_1^2} - \dfrac{\bar{x}_2^2}{2\sigma_2^2}\right\} + \sqrt{2\pi}\,\sigma_T\left(\dfrac{\bar{x}_1}{\sigma_1^2} + \dfrac{\bar{x}_2}{\sigma_2^2}\right)\exp\left\{-\dfrac{(\bar{x}_1 - \bar{x}_2)^2}{2(\sigma_1^2 + \sigma_2^2)}\right\}\right. \\ \left.\times\left[1 - Q\left(\sigma_T\left(\dfrac{\bar{x}_1}{\sigma_1^2} + \dfrac{\bar{x}_2}{\sigma_2^2}\right)\right)\right]\right\};\ |\hat{\varepsilon}| \le \dfrac{1}{2} \\ 0;\ \text{elsewhere} \end{cases} \tag{3.60}$$

where

$$\bar{x}_1 = \frac{\mu_+}{\left(\dfrac{1}{2} + \hat{\varepsilon}\right)^2 2\sigma^2} = \frac{1 + \gamma_h\left(\dfrac{1}{2} + \varepsilon\right)^2}{\left(\dfrac{1}{2} + \hat{\varepsilon}\right)^2}\sigma_1^2 = \frac{\sigma_+^2}{\left[2\sigma^2\left(\dfrac{1}{2} + \hat{\varepsilon}\right)^2\right]^2}$$

$$= \frac{1 + 2\gamma_h\left(\dfrac{1}{2} + \varepsilon\right)^2}{N_h\left(\dfrac{1}{2} + \hat{\varepsilon}\right)^4}$$

$$\bar{x}_2 = \frac{\mu_-}{\left(\dfrac{1}{2} - \hat{\varepsilon}\right)^2 2\sigma^2} = \frac{1 + \gamma_h\left(\dfrac{1}{2} - \varepsilon\right)^2}{\left(\dfrac{1}{2} - \hat{\varepsilon}\right)^2}\sigma_2^2 = \frac{\sigma_-^2}{\left[2\sigma^2\left(\dfrac{1}{2} - \hat{\varepsilon}\right)^2\right]^2}$$

$$= \frac{1 + 2\gamma_h\left(\dfrac{1}{2} - \varepsilon\right)^2}{N_h\left(\dfrac{1}{2} - \hat{\varepsilon}\right)^4} \tag{3.61}$$

and

$$\sigma_T^2 \triangleq \frac{\sigma_1^2\sigma_2^2}{\sigma_1^2 + \sigma_2^2}. \tag{3.62}$$

The conditional mean and variance of $\hat{\varepsilon}$ are still determined from (3.57) and (3.56) with $p(\hat{\varepsilon}|\varepsilon)$ as given in (3.60). Figure 3.16 is a plot of this conditional

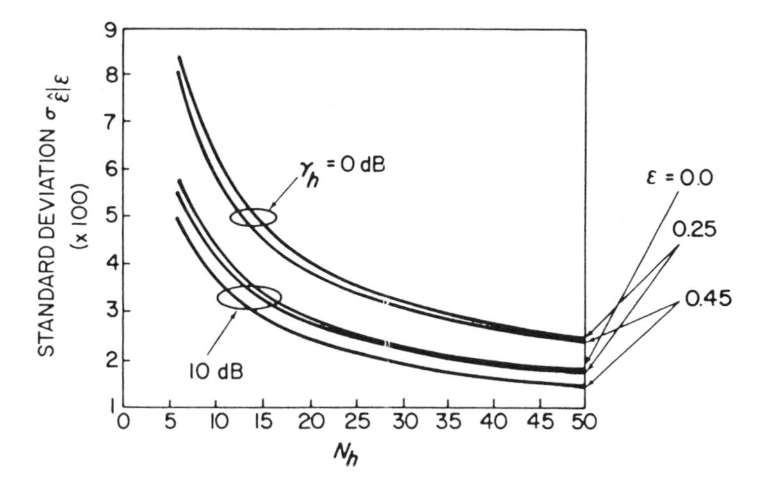

Figure 3.17. Conditional standard deviation $\sigma_{\hat{\varepsilon}|\varepsilon}$ versus N_h with γ_h and ε as parameters.

mean versus ε with $N_h = 10$ and γ_h as a parameter. Figure 3.17 is the corresponding plot of the conditional standard deviation of $\hat{\varepsilon}$ versus N_h with ε and γ_h as parameters.

3.2.2 The Case of Partial-Band Noise Jamming

When the additive jamming noise is not spread over the total hop frequency band, then the previous results can be modified to account for this fact as follows. Let N_h still be the total number of hop intervals per time synchronization estimate, of which ρN_h are now contaminated by jamming noise of power spectral density N_J/ρ and $(1-\rho)N_h$ are noise free.[4] As in our previous discussions of partial-band noise jamming, ρ denotes the fraction of the total hop frequency band that is jammed. Then analogous to (3.52), we have that

$$R_{\pm} = \sqrt{\frac{1}{N_h}\sum_{j=1}^{\rho N_h} r_{j\pm}^2 + (1-\rho)\xi^2\left(\tfrac{1}{2} \pm \varepsilon\right)^2} \tag{3.63}$$

[4] For values of ρ such that ρN_h and $(1-\rho)N_h$ are not integer, we take the nearest integers, respectively, to these quantities.

with pdf's

$$p(R_{\pm}|\varepsilon) = \begin{cases} \dfrac{\rho N_h R_{\pm}}{\sigma^2}\left(\dfrac{R_{\pm}^2 - (1-\rho)\xi^2\left(\frac{1}{2}\pm\varepsilon\right)^2}{2\sigma^2\rho\gamma_h\left(\frac{1}{2}\pm\varepsilon\right)^2}\right)^{(\rho N_h - 1)/2} \\ \times\exp\left\{-\rho N_h\left[\dfrac{R_{\pm}^2-(1-\rho)\xi^2\left(\frac{1}{2}\pm\varepsilon\right)^2}{2\sigma^2} + \rho\gamma_h\left(\frac{1}{2}\pm\varepsilon\right)^2\right]\right\} \\ \times I_{\rho N_h - 1}\left[\rho N_h\sqrt{2\rho\gamma_h}\left(\frac{1}{2}\pm\varepsilon\right)\sqrt{\dfrac{R_{\pm}^2-(1-\rho)\xi^2\left(\frac{1}{2}\pm\varepsilon\right)^2}{\sigma^2}}\right]; \\ R_{\pm}\geq 0 \\ 0;\ \text{elsewhere.} \end{cases} \tag{3.64}$$

Then, analogous to (3.55), we have that

$$p(\hat{\varepsilon}|\varepsilon) = \begin{cases} (\rho N_h)^2\left(\frac{1}{4}-\hat{\varepsilon}^2\right)\exp\left[-\rho^2 N_h\gamma_h\left(\frac{1}{2}+2\varepsilon^2\right)\right] \\ \times\displaystyle\int_0^\infty y^3\left[\dfrac{y_+y_-\left(\frac{1}{4}-\hat{\varepsilon}^2\right)}{2\rho\gamma_h\left(\frac{1}{4}-\varepsilon^2\right)}\right]^{\rho N_h - 1} \\ \times\exp\left\{-\dfrac{\rho N_h}{2}\left[y_+^2\left(\frac{1}{2}+\hat{\varepsilon}\right)^2 + y_-^2\left(\frac{1}{2}-\hat{\varepsilon}\right)^2\right]\right\} \\ \times I_{\rho N_h - 1}\left[\rho N_h\sqrt{2\rho\gamma_h}\left(\frac{1}{2}+\varepsilon\right)\left(\frac{1}{2}+\hat{\varepsilon}\right)y_+\right] \\ \times I_{\rho N_h - 1}\left[\rho N_h\sqrt{2\rho\gamma_h}\left(\frac{1}{2}-\varepsilon\right)\left(\frac{1}{2}-\hat{\varepsilon}\right)y_-\right]dy; \\ |\hat{\varepsilon}|\leq\frac{1}{2} \\ 0;\ \text{elsewhere} \end{cases} \tag{3.65}$$

where

$$y_{\pm}^2 \triangleq y^2 - 2(1-\rho)\gamma_h\frac{\left(\frac{1}{2}\pm\varepsilon\right)^2}{\left(\frac{1}{2}\pm\hat{\varepsilon}\right)^2}. \tag{3.66}$$

Note that when $\rho = 1$, i.e., jamming over the total hop frequency band, then $y_+ = y_- = y$, and (3.65) reduces to (3.55) as it should.

3.2.2.1 Results for Large ρN_h

As was true for (3.55), the general result of (3.65) can be simplified now when ρN_h is large. Once again, $Z_{\pm} \triangleq R_{\pm}^2$, with $R_{\pm}$ now defined in (3.63), becomes a Gaussian random variable with

$$\mu_{\pm}(\varepsilon) \triangleq E\{Z_{\pm}|\varepsilon\} = 2\frac{\sigma^2}{\rho}\left\{(1-\rho)\rho\gamma_h\left(\tfrac{1}{2}\pm\varepsilon\right)^2 + \rho\left[1+\rho\gamma_h\left(\tfrac{1}{2}\pm\varepsilon\right)^2\right]\right\}$$

$$= 2\sigma^2\left[1+\gamma_h\left(\tfrac{1}{2}\pm\varepsilon\right)^2\right]$$

$$\sigma_{\pm}^2(\varepsilon) \triangleq E\left\{(Z_{\pm}-\mu_{\pm})^2|\varepsilon\right\} = \frac{\rho^2\left(2\dfrac{\sigma^2}{\rho}\right)^2}{\rho N_h}\left[1+2\rho\gamma_h\left(\tfrac{1}{2}\pm\varepsilon\right)^2\right]$$

$$= \frac{(2\sigma^2)^2}{\rho N_h}\left[1+2\rho\gamma_h\left(\tfrac{1}{2}\pm\varepsilon\right)^2\right]. \tag{3.67}$$

Note that $\mu_{+}(\varepsilon)$ are independent of ρ but $\sigma_{\pm}^2(\varepsilon)$ are not. Thus, the conditional pdf's of R_+ and R_- are still given by (3.59) with $\mu_+(\varepsilon)$, $\sigma_+^2(\varepsilon)$, $\mu_-(\varepsilon)$, and $\sigma_-^2(\varepsilon)$, now defined by (3.67), and similarly $p(\hat{\varepsilon}|\varepsilon)$ is given by (3.60) with γ_h and N_h replaced by $\rho\gamma_h$ and ρN_h, respectively, $\bar{x}_1$ and $\bar{x}_2$ given by (3.61), and

$$\sigma_1^2 = \frac{\left[1+2\rho\gamma_h\left(\tfrac{1}{2}+\varepsilon\right)^2\right]}{\rho N_h\left(\tfrac{1}{2}+\hat{\varepsilon}\right)^4};\ \sigma_2^2 = \frac{\left[1+2\rho\gamma_h\left(\tfrac{1}{2}-\varepsilon\right)^2\right]}{\rho N_h\left(\tfrac{1}{2}-\hat{\varepsilon}\right)^4} \tag{3.68}$$

with σ_T^2 still defined in (3.62) using now σ_1^2 and σ_2^2 of (3.68).

3.2.3 The Effects of Time Synchronization Error on FH/MFSK Error Probability Performance

The presence of a time synchronization error in an FH/MFSK receiver causes a degradation in system error probability performance that is attributable to the following two factors. First, the signal component of the receiver correlator corresponding to the true transmitted frequency is attenuated. Second, a spillover of transmitted signal energy occurs in each of the adjacent $M-1$ correlator outputs where, ordinarily (perfect time sync), only noise appears. This second contribution to the performance degradation, namely, the presence of signal components in the incorrect frequency correlator outputs, is referred to as a loss of orthogonality [13]. Clearly, then, the first step in assessing the impact of a time synchronization error ε on the performance of the FH/MFSK receiver is to evaluate the *signal attenuation* and *loss of orthogonality* degradations in terms of the synchronization error and then use these results to arrive at an expression for the ε-conditional error probability of the system.

To illustrate the procedure we shall first discuss the case of FH/MFSK with no diversity, i.e., one data symbol per hop. Following this we shall extend these results to the case of FH/MFSK with m chips per symbol diversity and non-coherent combining at the receiver. The performances of these SS techniques have previously been discussed in Chapter 2, Volume II, for a perfectly synchronized system and thus our purpose here is to show how they are modified to account for a time synchronization error.

3.2.3.1 Conditional Error Probability Performance—No Diversity

Based on the spectral computations performed in Section 3.2.1.1, it is clear that the spectral estimate r_j corresponding to the actual transmitted frequency in the j-th hop interval is characterized by (3.42) and has the ε-conditional pdf $p(r_j|\varepsilon)$ given by (3.47). Thus, from (3.47), the signal energy attenuation caused by the lack of perfect time synchronization is represented by the factor

$$D_j(\varepsilon) = (1 - |\varepsilon|)^2. \tag{3.69}$$

Assuming now that the MFSK tones are orthogonally spaced by k/T_h ($1/T_h$ is the minimum tone separation for orthogonality), then the spectral estimate r_{jn} for an incorrect correlator spaced in frequency by nk/T_h from the correct one is obtained by evaluating the discrete Fourier transform operations of (3.41) at the frequency $f = f_{IF} + nk/T_h$ rather than $f = f_{IF}$. If a_{jn} and b_{jn}, respectively, denote the results of these operations, then it can be shown that the loss of orthogonality degradation $D_{jn}(\varepsilon)$ is given by

$$D_{jn}(\varepsilon) \triangleq \frac{\bar{a}_{jn}^2 + \bar{b}_{jn}^2}{\xi^2} = \frac{\sin^2[\pi nk(1 - |\varepsilon|)]}{N_s^2 \sin^2 \dfrac{\pi nk}{N_s}} \tag{3.70}$$

where ξ is defined in (3.45). For large N_s, (3.70) simplifies to

$$D_{jn}(\varepsilon) = (1 - |\varepsilon|)^2 \left[\frac{\sin \pi nk(1 - |\varepsilon|)}{\pi nk(1 - |\varepsilon|)}\right]^2. \tag{3.71}$$

Note that for $\varepsilon = 0$ and $n \neq 0$, $D_{jn} = 0$, i.e., in the perfectly synchronized system, the incorrect correlator outputs consist of noise alone.

Now, since

$$r_{jn} = \sqrt{a_{jn}^2 + b_{jn}^2} \tag{3.72}$$

then, analogous to (3.47), the ε-conditional pdf of r_{jn} is given by

$$p(r_{jn}|\varepsilon) = \begin{cases} \dfrac{r_{jn}}{\sigma^2} \exp\left\{-\left[\dfrac{r_{jn}^2}{2\sigma^2} + \gamma_h D_{jn}(\varepsilon)\right]\right\} I_0\left[\sqrt{2\gamma_h D_{jn}(\varepsilon)}\, \dfrac{r_{jn}}{\sigma}\right]; & 0 \le r_{jn} \le \infty \\ 0; \text{ otherwise.} \end{cases} \tag{3.73}$$

To compute the ε-conditional error probability, it is convenient to order the spectral estimates as $r^{(1)}, r^{(2)}, \ldots, r^{(M)}$ where $r^{(1)}$ corresponds to the lowest frequency MFSK tone and $r^{(M)}$ corresponds to the highest frequency

MFSK tone. Then, if, in the j-th hop interval, the l-th tone in the set is transmitted, the conditional probability of symbol error for that transmission, denoted by $P_s(l|\varepsilon)$ is described by the probability

$$\begin{aligned} P_s(l|\varepsilon) &= 1 - \text{Prob}\{r^{(l)} = \max r^{(i)};\ i = 1,2,\dots,M\} \\ &= 1 - \int_0^\infty p(r^{(l)}|\varepsilon) \int_0^{r^{(l)}} \cdots \int_0^{r(l)} \prod_{\substack{i=1 \\ i \neq l}}^{M} p(r^{(i)}|\varepsilon)\, dr^{(i)}. \end{aligned} \tag{3.74}$$

Since $p(r^{(l)}|\varepsilon)$ is given by (3.47) and $p(r^{(l+n)}|\varepsilon)$ equals $p(r_{jn}|\varepsilon)$ of (3.73), then after some simplification (3.74) becomes

$$\begin{aligned} P_s(l|\varepsilon) = 1 - \int_0^\infty y \exp\left\{ -\left[\frac{y^2}{2} + \gamma_h D_j(\varepsilon) \right] \right\} I_0\left[\sqrt{2\gamma_h D_j(\varepsilon)}\, y \right] \\ \times \prod_{\substack{n=1-l \\ n \neq 0}}^{M-l} \left[1 - Q\left(\sqrt{2\gamma_h D_{jn}(\varepsilon)}\,, y \right) \right] dy \end{aligned} \tag{3.75}$$

where $Q(\alpha, \beta)$ is Marcum's Q-function [14] and as such

$$1 - Q(\alpha, \beta) = \int_0^\beta x \exp\left(-\frac{x^2 + \alpha^2}{2} \right) I_0(\alpha x)\, dx. \tag{3.76}$$

Finally, the average ε-conditional symbol error probability is given by

$$P_s(\varepsilon) = \frac{1}{M} \sum_{l=1}^{M} P_s(l|\varepsilon) \tag{3.77}$$

and the corresponding ε-conditional bit error probability $P_b(\varepsilon)$ is related to (3.77) by

$$P_b(\varepsilon) = \frac{M}{2(M-1)} P_s(\varepsilon). \tag{3.78}$$

Also, since for no diversity the hop signal-to-noise ratio γ_h is equal to the MFSK symbol energy-to-jammer-noise spectral density ratio E_s/N_J, then the bit energy-to-jammer noise spectral density ratio E_b/N_J is simply given by

$$\frac{E_b}{N_J} = \frac{\gamma_h}{\log_2 M}. \tag{3.79}$$

Using (3.77)–(3.79) together with (3.71) and (3.75), Figure 3.18 is an illustration of $P_b(\varepsilon)$ versus E_b/N_J in dB with ε as a parameter for 4-ary FSK and the minimum orthogonal tone spacing, i.e., $M = 4$ and $k = 1$. The performance degradation, namely, the additional E_b/N_J required at a given value of ε relative to that required at $\varepsilon = 0$, is plotted in Figure 3.19 versus timing error for $P_b(\varepsilon) = 10^{-2}$. Also shown is the composition of the performance degradation in terms of its signal attenuation and loss of orthogonality components. We note that for small timing errors signal

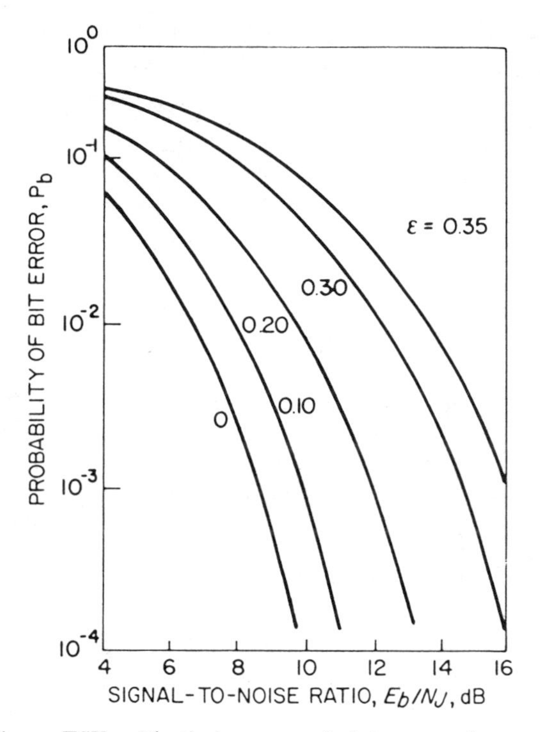

Figure 3.18. 4-ary FSK with timing error (minimum orthogonal tone spacing) (reprinted from [13]).

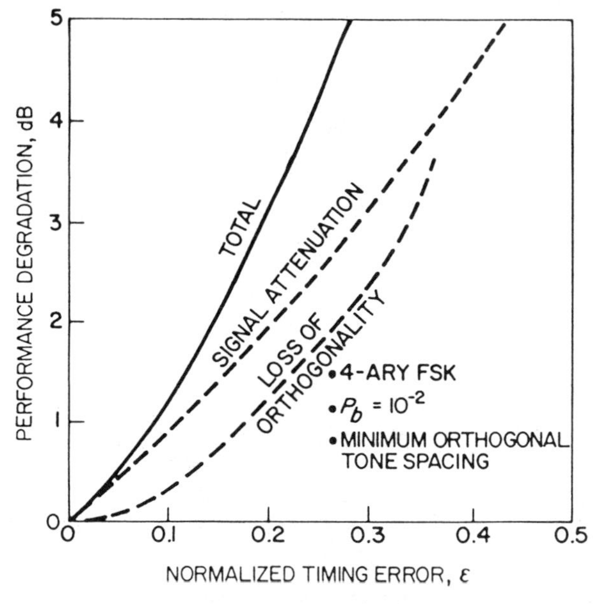

Figure 3.19. Performance degradation due to timing error (reprinted from [13]).

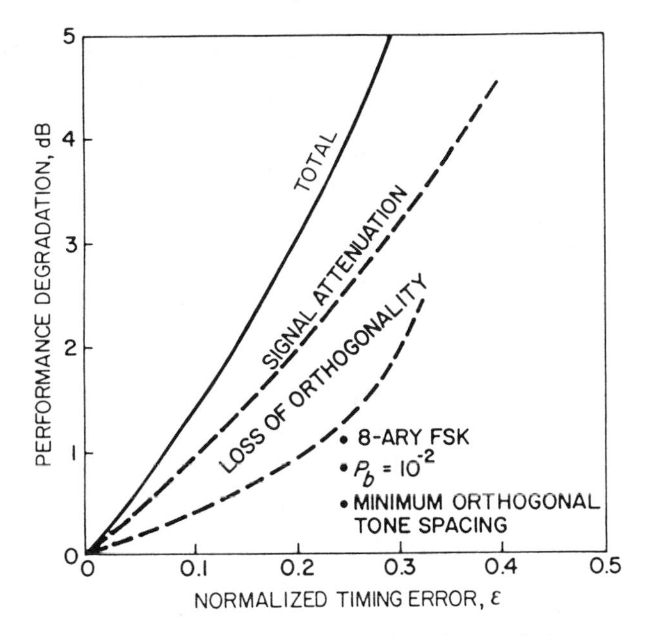

Figure 3.20. 8-ary FSK performance degradation due to timing error (reprinted from [13]).

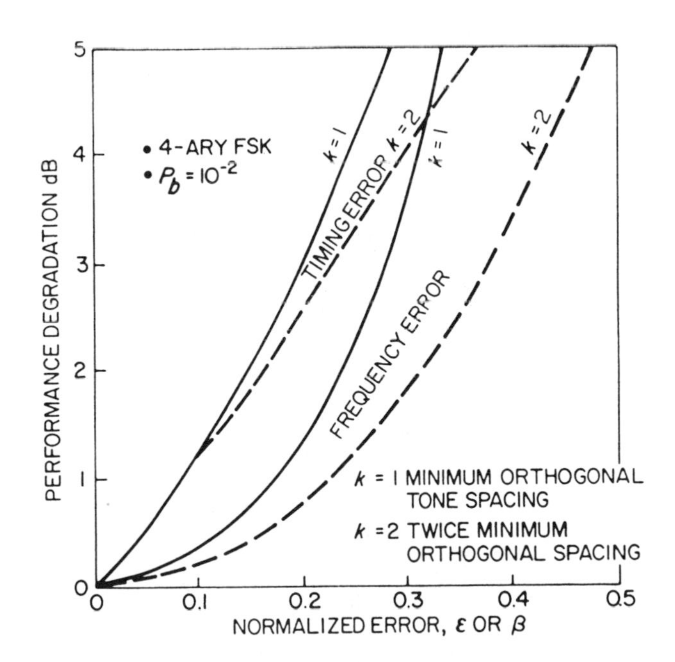

Figure 3.21. Performance degradation due to synchronization errors for different tone spacings (reprinted from [13]).

attenuation is the dominant cause of degradation, whereas for large timing errors the loss of the orthogonality component plays an equally, if not more, important role. Figure 3.20 illustrates similar performance degradation results for 8-ary FSK. These results, when compared with the corresponding 4-ary FSK performance results of Figure 3.19, indicate that increasing the number of tones M decreases the performance degradation due to the timing synchronization error. Finally, Figure 3.21 demonstrates the effect of increasing the MFSK tone spacing to twice its minimum orthogonal value. The additional results shown there for frequency error will be explained later on in the chapter when we discuss that subject.

3.2.3.2 Conditional Error Probability Performance—m-Diversity with Non-Coherent Combining

When the same MFSK symbol is transmitted on m different hops, and the symbol decision is based on the non-coherent combining of the m corresponding detector outputs for that tone, then, assuming all m chips are jammed, the conditional pdf for the spectral estimates formed in the receiver is given by

$$p(r|\varepsilon) = \begin{cases} \dfrac{r}{\sigma^2}\left(\dfrac{r^2}{2\sigma^2 m\gamma_h'}\right)^{(m-1)/2} \exp\left[-\left(\dfrac{r^2}{2\sigma^2} + m\gamma_h'\right)\right] I_{m-1}\left(\sqrt{2m\gamma_h'}\,\dfrac{r}{\sigma}\right); & r \geq 0 \\ 0; \text{ otherwise} \end{cases} \tag{3.80}$$

where for the correct tone, r corresponds to r_j, and

$$\gamma_h' = \gamma_h D_j(\varepsilon) \tag{3.81}$$

with $D_j(\varepsilon)$ defined in (3.69). For the $M-1$ incorrect tones, r corresponds to r_{jn}, and

$$\gamma_h' = \gamma_h D_{jn}(\varepsilon) \tag{3.82}$$

with $D_{jn}(\varepsilon)$ defined in (3.70) or (3.71). Thus, following the steps leading to the evaluation of (3.75), we can immediately write down the corresponding result for FH/MFSK with m-diversity and non-coherent combining, namely,

$$\begin{aligned} P_s(l|\varepsilon) = 1 - \int_0^\infty y\left(\frac{y^2}{2m\gamma_h D_j(\varepsilon)}\right)^{(m-1)/2} &\exp\left\{-\left[\frac{y^2}{2} + m\gamma_h D_j(\varepsilon)\right]\right\} \\ \times I_{m-1}\left[\sqrt{2m\gamma_h D_j(\varepsilon)}\,y\right] & \\ \times \prod_{\substack{n=1-l \\ n\neq 0}}^{M-l} \left[1 - Q_m\left(\sqrt{2m\gamma_h D_{jn}(\varepsilon)}\,,\, y\right)\right] dy & \end{aligned} \tag{3.83}$$

where $Q_M(\alpha, \beta)$ is the generalized Q-function and as such

$$1 - Q_M(\alpha, \beta) = \int_0^{\beta} x\left(\frac{x}{\alpha}\right)^{M-1} \exp\left(-\frac{x^2 + \alpha^2}{2}\right) I_{M-1}(\alpha x)\, dx. \quad (3.84)$$

The E_b/N_J performance degradation at $P_b = 10^{-2}$ as a function of timing error is illustrated in Figure 3.22 for 4-ary FSK with minimum orthogonal tone spacing and three values of m. Increasing m clearly reduces the degradation since non-coherent combining reduces the effect of loss of orthogonality. Non-coherent combining, however, does not affect the signal attenuation loss component and thus this loss, as shown in the figure, represents a lower bound on the total degradation as m increases.

Thus far in this section we have implicitly assumed a full-band jammer. For the worst case partial-band noise jammer of a perfectly synchronized FH/MFSK system as discussed in Chapter 2, Volume II, $P_s(l|\varepsilon)$ of (3.75) would become

$$\begin{aligned} P_s(l|\varepsilon) = \frac{K_\rho}{E_b/N_J} \Bigg\{ 1 - \int_0^{\infty} y \exp\left\{ -\left[\frac{y^2}{2} + K_\rho(\log_2 M) D_j(\varepsilon) \right] \right\} \\ \times I_0\left[\sqrt{2K_\rho(\log_2 M) D_j(\varepsilon)}\, y \right] \\ \times \prod_{\substack{n=1-l \\ n \neq 0}}^{M-l} \left[1 - Q\left(\sqrt{2K_\rho(\log_2 M) D_{jn}(\varepsilon)}, y \right) \right] dy \Bigg\} \\ - \frac{K_\rho f(\varepsilon; K_\rho)}{E_b/N_j} \end{aligned} \quad (3.85)$$

where, for a given M, K_ρ is determined by the worst case partial-band fraction

$$\rho_{\mathrm{wc}} = \begin{cases} \dfrac{K_\rho}{E_b/N_J}; & E_b/N_J > K_\rho \\ 1; & E_b/N_J \leq K_\rho \end{cases} \quad (3.86)$$

and is tabulated as γ (in dB) in Table 2.1 of Chapter 2, Volume II, for various values of $K = \log_2 M$. Note that $f(\varepsilon; K_\rho)$ is not a function of E_b/N_J and thus for a given ε, the degradation in error probability performance is constant. Also, using (3.78),

$$P_b(l|\varepsilon) = \frac{MK_\rho f(\varepsilon; K_\rho)}{2(M-1)E_b/N_J} \quad (3.87)$$

and for $\varepsilon = 0$,

$$\begin{aligned} P_b(l|0) &= \frac{MK_\rho f(0; K_\rho)}{2(M-1)E_b/N_J} \\ &= \frac{A}{E_b/N_J} \end{aligned} \quad (3.88)$$

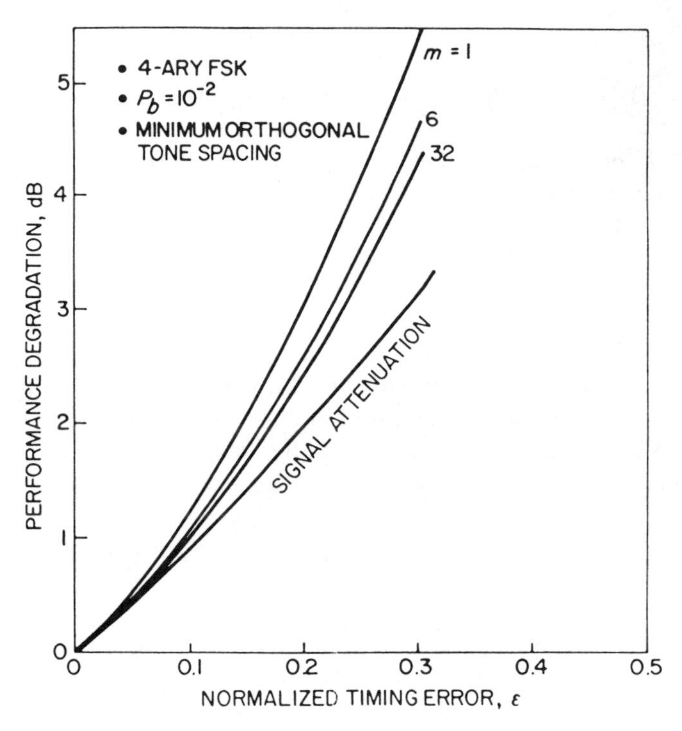

Figure 3.22. Performing degradation due to timing error with chip combining (reprinted from [13]).

where A is tabulated as β in Table 2.1 of Chapter 2, Volume II, for various values of $K = \log_2 M$.

For the worst case partial-band noise jammer of an m-diversity FH/MFSK system with non-coherent combining at the receiver, the conditional symbol error probability $P_s(l|\varepsilon)$ of (3.83) is modified to become

$$P_s(l|\varepsilon) = \rho_{\text{wc}}\left\{1 - \int_0^\infty y\left(\frac{y^2}{2m^*\rho_{\text{wc}}\gamma_h D_j(\varepsilon)}\right)^{(m^*-1)/2} \times \exp\left\{-\left[\frac{y^2}{2} + m^*\rho_{\text{wc}}\gamma_h D_j(\varepsilon)\right]\right\} \times I_{m^*-1}\left[\sqrt{2m^*\rho_{\text{wc}}\gamma_h D_j(\varepsilon)}\, y\right] \times \prod_{\substack{n=1-l \\ n\neq 0}}^{M-l}\left[1 - Q_m\left(\sqrt{2m^*\rho_{\text{wc}}\gamma_h D_{jn}(\varepsilon)}\,, y\right)\right] dy\right\} \quad (3.89)$$

where

$$\rho_{\mathrm{wc}} = \tfrac{3}{4};\; m^* = \left(\frac{\log_2 M}{4}\right)\frac{E_b}{N_J} \tag{3.90a}$$

are the worst case partial-band fraction and optimum diversity for the perfectly synchronized system (see Chapter 2, Volume II), and analogous to (3.78), γ_h is related to E_b/N_J by

$$\frac{E_b}{N_J} = \frac{m^*\gamma_h}{\log_2 M}. \tag{3.90b}$$

Actually, the quantities in (3.90a) are derived from a minimax solution of a Chernoff bound on the error probability. Nevertheless, it is convenient to use them in the exact expression for error probability of (3.89).

3.2.3.3 Average Error Probability Performance in the Presence of Time Synchronization Error Estimation

If the estimator $\hat{\varepsilon}$ of (3.53) is used for FH time synchronization of the non-coherent receiver, then a residual time offset $\eta(\varepsilon) \triangleq \varepsilon - \hat{\varepsilon}$ arises which affects system performance in the same manner as just discussed for an uncompensated time error ε. In particular, it is clear that in the presence of the residual offset, a signal attenuation degradation occurs that is given by

$$D_j(\eta) = (1 - |\varepsilon - \hat{\varepsilon}|)^2 = (1 - |\eta(\varepsilon)|)^2;\; \eta(\varepsilon) \triangleq \varepsilon - \hat{\varepsilon}. \tag{3.91}$$

Likewise, a loss of orthogonality degradation analogous to (3.71) occurs that is given by

$$D_{jn}(\eta) = (1 - |\eta(\varepsilon)|)^2\left[\frac{\sin \pi nk(1 - |\eta(\varepsilon)|)}{\pi nk(1 - |\eta(\varepsilon)|)}\right]^2. \tag{3.92}$$

Thus, if $p_{\eta|\varepsilon}(\eta|\varepsilon)$ denotes the ε-conditional probability density function of the residual offset $\eta(\varepsilon)$, and is given by

$$p_{\eta|\varepsilon}(\eta|\varepsilon) = p_{\hat{\varepsilon}|\varepsilon}(\varepsilon - \eta|\varepsilon) \tag{3.93}$$

where the right-hand side of (3.93) is given by either (3.55), (3.60), or (3.65), it then follows that the average bit error probability P_b is

$$P_b = 2\int_0^{1/2} d\varepsilon \int_{\varepsilon-1/2}^{\varepsilon+1/2} P_b(\eta)\, p_{\hat{\varepsilon}|\varepsilon}(\varepsilon - \eta|\varepsilon)\, d\eta. \tag{3.94}$$

In (3.94), $P_b(\eta)$ is the η-conditional bit error probability obtained from (3.78) together with (3.77) and (3.75) or (3.83) with ε replaced by η.

Substitution of (3.78) and (3.93) in (3.94) requires evaluation of a double integral to obtain numerical results for P_b. To somewhat simplify matters, we observe from Figure 3.17 that, for the range of values of interest, $\sigma_{\hat{\varepsilon}|\varepsilon}$ is comparatively small so that $\hat{\varepsilon}$ is very close to its conditional mean $\mu_{\hat{\varepsilon}|\varepsilon}$ with high probability. Equivalently, $p_{\eta|\varepsilon}(\eta|\varepsilon)$ may be approximated by a delta function located at $\varepsilon - \mu_{\hat{\varepsilon}|\varepsilon}$ or from (3.93)

$$p_{\hat{\varepsilon}|\varepsilon}(\varepsilon - \eta|\varepsilon) = \delta\left(\eta - (\varepsilon - \mu_{\hat{\varepsilon}|\varepsilon})\right). \tag{3.95}$$

Substituting (3.95) into (3.94) gives the much simplified result

$$P_b = 2\int_0^{1/2} P_b(\varepsilon - \mu_{\hat{\varepsilon}|\varepsilon})\, d\varepsilon. \tag{3.96}$$

To evaluate (3.96) (assuming large N_h), we first compute $\mu_{\hat{\varepsilon}|\varepsilon}$ from (3.57) using $p(\hat{\varepsilon}|\varepsilon)$ from (3.60) with γ_h replaced by $(\log_2 M)E_b/N_J$ as in (3.79).

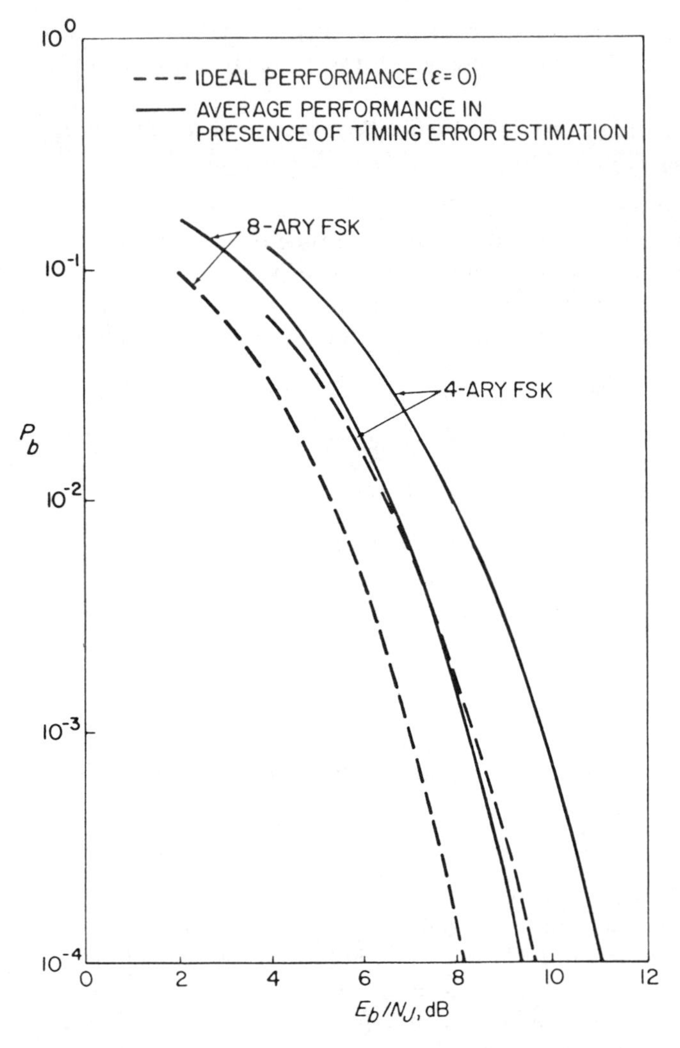

Figure 3.23. Average bit error probability performance in the presence of timing error estimation; $N_h = 10$.

Figure 3.23 is an illustration of the average bit error probability performance of (3.62) for 4-ary and 8-ary FSK with $N_h = 10$. In computing these results, (3.78) together with (3.75) and (3.77) were used for the conditional bit error probability.

3.3 FREQUENCY SYNCHRONIZATION OF NON-COHERENT FH / MFSK SYSTEMS

Frequency synchronization of a conventional (non-spread) non-coherent MFSK receiver has been typically achieved by transmitting a single known MFSK frequency, which is repeated as often as necessary within the true data stream, until the desired degree of frequency synchronization accuracy is obtained. Spectral estimates in the form of discrete Fourier transforms of the receiver signal are formed with those adjacent to the transmitted MFSK frequency used to form the frequency error estimator. For example, Chadwick and Springett [12] used the ratio of the difference of these two adjacent spectral estimates to twice the spectral estimate of the transmitted frequency as an approximation to the maximum likelihood estimator of frequency error. The advantage of this estimator, or, for that matter, any estimator formed from spectral estimates of the standard MFSK tones, is that frequency error estimation could be used during the true data transmission for frequency tracking. Unfortunately, however, using the standard MFSK frequencies forms a very poor estimator since it can be shown (see Appendix 3A) that, for any function of the standard MFSK frequencies, the slope of the conditional mean of the estimator is zero for zero frequency error.

A more suitable approach, which, we shall see shortly, also applies in the SS application, is to transmit a single known frequency chosen halfway between two standard MFSK frequencies. By using the spectral estimates evaluated at these two standard MFSK frequencies, a frequency error estimator can now be formed which, in the absence of noise, will be a linear function of frequency error.

To see how the above approach can be applied to an FH/MFSK communication system, consider the simplified frequency synchronization system illustrated in Figure 3.24. Letting $f_o \pm m/2T_h$; $m = 1, 2, \ldots, M/2$ denote the standard MFSK frequencies used for data transmission, then during fine frequency synchronization, we generate the single data symbol frequency equal to f_o, which is halfway between the two center (innermost) standard frequencies. This data frequency is frequency-hopped over the SS bandwidth. As in the case of the time synchronization system, the received signal plus jamming noise is first cross-correlated with the local hop generator, which has a *frequency* error relative to the transmitted signal equal to λ Hz. Also, we assume here that only coarse time synchronization has been obtained, and thus the local hop generator is also in *time* error

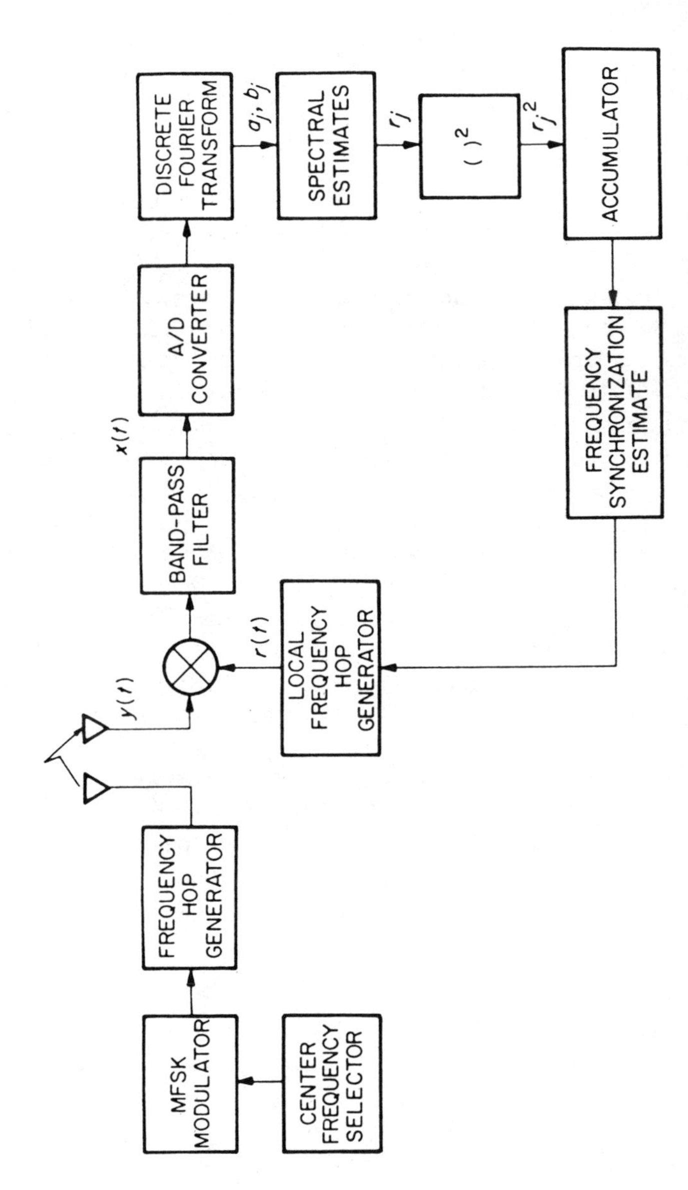

Figure 3.24. Simplified frequency synchronization of a frequency-hopped system with on-board processing.

relative to the transmitted signal by an amount equal to τ seconds, where, as before, τ is less than a hop duration. The cross-correlation is band-pass filtered and the output of this filter is passed through an A/D converter. The resultant signal samples are discrete Fourier transformed to produce spectral estimates corresponding to the MFSK frequencies for each frequency hop. The squares of these estimates are then accumulated over many hop intervals and the square roots of these accumulated values are then used to form the frequency synchronization estimate. Finally, this estimate, which is formed in the receiver, is directly used to update the current frequency position of the local hop generator. Alternately, as for the time synchronization only case, the system in Figure 3.24 can be modified in the same manner that the system in Figure 3.14 was changed to Figure 3.15 to allow for a system whose receiver is a passive processor.

3.3.1 The Case of Full-Band Noise Jamming

3.3.1.1 Signal Model and Spectral Computations

The transmitted signal in the j-th hop interval is still characterized by (3.35) with, however, f_s replaced by f_o. Using similar replacements in (3.36) and (3.37), the received signal $y(t)$ and jammer noise $J(t)$ are still, respectively, given by these equations. The output of the local FH generator in the presence of a timing error τ and frequency error λ can be expressed as

$$r(t) = 2\sin\left[2\pi(f_o + f_j + \lambda + f_{IF})t\right]; \quad (j-1)T_h - \tau \le t \le jT_h - \tau. \tag{3.97}$$

Cross-correlating $y(t)$ with $r(t)$, the output $x(t)$ of the band-pass filter gives

$$x(t) \triangleq \begin{cases} J'(t) & (j-1)T_h - \tau \le t \le (j-1)T_h \quad (\tau \ge 0) \\ & \text{or} \\ & jT_h \le t \le jT_h - \tau \quad (\tau < 0) \\ \sqrt{2S}\cos\left[2\pi(f_{IF} + \lambda)t - \phi_j\right] + J'(t) & \\ & (j-1)T_h \le t \le jT_h - \tau \quad (\tau \ge 0) \\ & \text{or} \\ & (j-1)T_h - \tau \le t \le jT_h \quad (\tau < 0) \end{cases} \tag{3.98}$$

where $J'(t)$ is still given by (3.40). Sampling $x(t)$ at the Nyquist rate and taking the sine and cosine discrete Fourier transforms of these samples evaluated at the two center standard MFSK frequencies $f = f_{IF} \pm 1/2T_h$, one has, in the j-th hop interval,

$$a_{j\pm} \triangleq \sum_{i=0}^{N_s-1} x_{ij} \cos\left[2\pi\left(f_{IF} \pm \frac{1}{2T_h}\right)\frac{i}{N_s}T_h\right]$$
$$b_{j\pm} \triangleq \sum_{i=0}^{N_s-1} x_{ij} \sin\left[2\pi\left(f_{IF} \pm \frac{1}{2T_h}\right)\frac{i}{N_s}T_h\right] \qquad (3.99)$$

from which the spectral estimates

$$r_{j\pm} \triangleq \sqrt{a_{j\pm}^2 + b_{j\pm}^2} \qquad (3.100)$$

are obtained. Letting $t = iT_h/N_s + (j-1)T_h$ in (3.98) and substituting into (3.99), we arrive at the following results (for large N_s) for the first two statistical moments of $a_{j\pm}$ and $b_{j\pm}$, that is,

$$\bar{a}_{j\pm} \triangleq E\{a_{j\pm}\} = \begin{cases} \dfrac{\sqrt{2S}\,N_s}{2}\operatorname{sinc}[\pi(1/2 \mp \beta), (1-|\varepsilon|)]\cos\varphi_{j\pm}; & |\varepsilon| \le 1 \\ 0; & |\varepsilon| > 1 \end{cases}$$

$$\bar{b}_{j\pm} \triangleq E\{b_{j\pm}\} = \begin{cases} \dfrac{\sqrt{2S}\,N_s}{2}\operatorname{sinc}[\pi(1/2 \mp \beta), (1-|\varepsilon|)]\sin\varphi_{j\pm}; & |\varepsilon| \le 1 \\ 0; & |\varepsilon| > 1 \end{cases}$$

$$\sigma_a^2 \triangleq E\left\{(a_{j\pm} - \bar{a}_{j\pm})^2\right\} = \sigma^2 = \frac{N_J}{4T_h}N_s^2$$
$$\sigma_b^2 \triangleq E\left\{(b_{j\pm} - \bar{b}_{j\pm})^2\right\} = \sigma^2 = \frac{N_J}{4T_h}N_s^2 \qquad (3.101)$$

where

$$\varphi_{j\pm} \triangleq \pi(\pm 1/2 - \beta)(1-|\varepsilon|) + \phi_j - 2\pi(j-1)f_{IF}T_h, \qquad (3.102)$$
$$\operatorname{sinc}[x, y] \triangleq \sin(xy)/x, \qquad (3.103)$$

and $\beta \triangleq \lambda T_h$ is the frequency synchronization error normalized by the hop rate (also, the MFSK frequency spacing). Noting again that $a_{j\pm}$ and $b_{j\pm}$ are conditionally Gaussian random variables, then the random variables $r_{j\pm}$ are Rician-distributed with pdf's (conditioned on ε and β with $|\varepsilon| \le 1$ and $|\beta| \le 1/2$)

$$p(r_{j\pm}|\varepsilon,\beta) = \begin{cases} \dfrac{r_{j\pm}}{\sigma^2}\exp\left\{-\left[\dfrac{r_{j\pm}^2}{2\sigma^2} + \gamma_\pm\right]\right\} \\ \times I_0\left[\sqrt{2\gamma_\pm}\,\dfrac{r_{j\pm}}{\sigma}\right]; & 0 \le r_{j\pm} \le \infty \\ 0; \text{ elsewhere} \end{cases} \qquad (3.104)$$

where

$$\gamma_{\pm} \triangleq \gamma_h(\mathrm{sinc}[\pi(1/2 \mp \beta), (1 - |\varepsilon|)])^2 \tag{3.105}$$

and γ_h is as defined in (3.46).

To produce an estimator with small variance, the spectral estimates must again be accumulated over many hop intervals, say, N_h, before forming the estimate $\hat{\beta}$. In particular, letting $R_{\pm}$ be defined identical to (3.52) using, however, $r_{j\pm}$ of (3.100), then, analogous to (3.53), the estimator of frequency synchronization is given by

$$\hat{\beta} = \frac{R_+ - R_-}{2(R_+ - R_-)} \tag{3.106}$$

whose first two statistical moments are

$$\mu_{\hat{\beta}|\beta} \triangleq E\{\hat{\beta}|\beta\} = \int_{-1/2}^{1/2} \hat{\beta} p(\hat{\beta}|\beta)\, d\hat{\beta} \tag{3.107}$$

$$\sigma^2_{\hat{\beta}|\beta} = \int_{-1/2}^{1/2} (\hat{\beta} - E\{\hat{\beta}|\beta\})^2 p(\hat{\beta}|\beta)\, d\hat{\beta} \tag{3.108}$$

where $p(\hat{\beta}|\beta)$ is the β-conditional pdf of $\hat{\beta}$. Proceeding directly to the results for large N_h, we again apply the central-limit theorem to (3.52) from which $z_{\pm} = R^2_{\pm}$ are Gaussian random variables whose first two statistical moments are given by

$$\mu_{\pm}(\beta) \triangleq E\{z_{\pm}|\beta\} = 2\sigma^2[1 + \gamma_{\pm}]$$

$$\sigma^2_{\pm}(\beta) \triangleq E\{(z_{\pm} - \mu_{\pm})^2|\beta\} = \frac{(2\sigma^2)^2}{N_h}[1 + 2\gamma_{\pm}]. \tag{3.109}$$

Using the Gaussian conditional pdf's for R_+ and R_- together with (3.106), the pdf of $\hat{\beta}$ conditioned on β is given by

$$p(\hat{\beta}|\beta) = \begin{cases} \dfrac{N_h(\frac{1}{4} - \hat{\beta}^2)\sigma_T^2}{\pi\sqrt{(1 + 2\gamma_+)(1 + 2\gamma_-)}}\left\{\exp\left\{-\dfrac{\bar{x}_1^2}{2\sigma_1^2} - \dfrac{\bar{x}_2^2}{2\sigma_2^2}\right\}\right. \\ \quad + \sqrt{2\pi}\,\sigma_T\left(\dfrac{\bar{x}_1}{\sigma_1^2} + \dfrac{\bar{x}_2}{\sigma_2^2}\right)\exp\left\{-\dfrac{(\bar{x}_1 - \bar{x}_2)^2}{2(\sigma_1^2 + \sigma_2^2)}\right\} \\ \quad \left.\times\left[1 - Q\left(\sigma_T\left(\dfrac{\bar{x}_1}{\sigma_1^2} + \dfrac{\bar{x}_2}{\sigma_2^2}\right)\right)\right]\right\}; \quad |\hat{\beta}| \le \dfrac{1}{2} \\ 0; \quad \text{elsewhere} \end{cases} \tag{3.110}$$

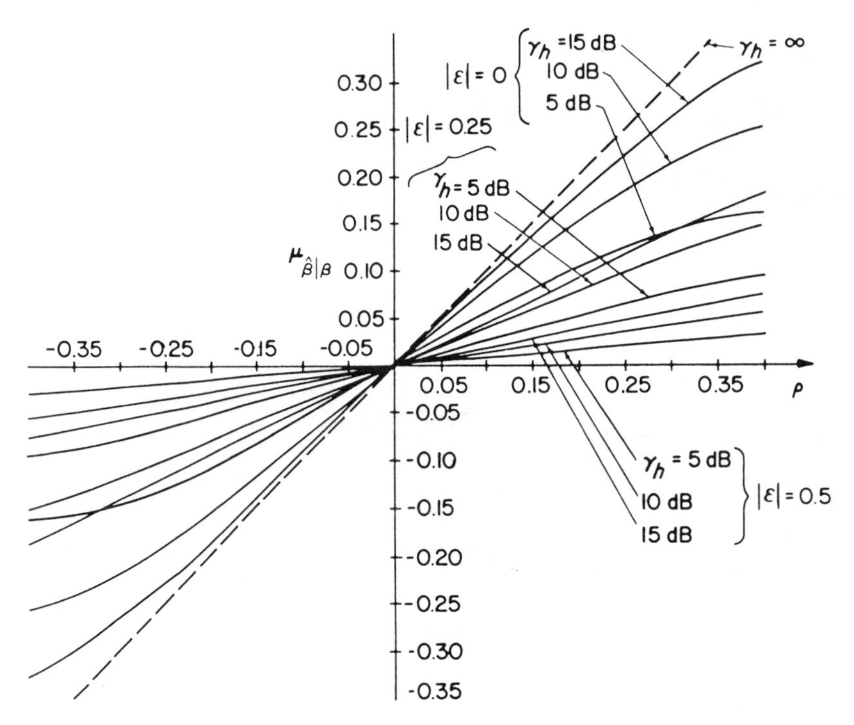

Figure 3.25. Conditional mean $\mu_{\hat{\beta}|\beta}$ versus β with γ_h and ε as parameters; $N_h = 10$.

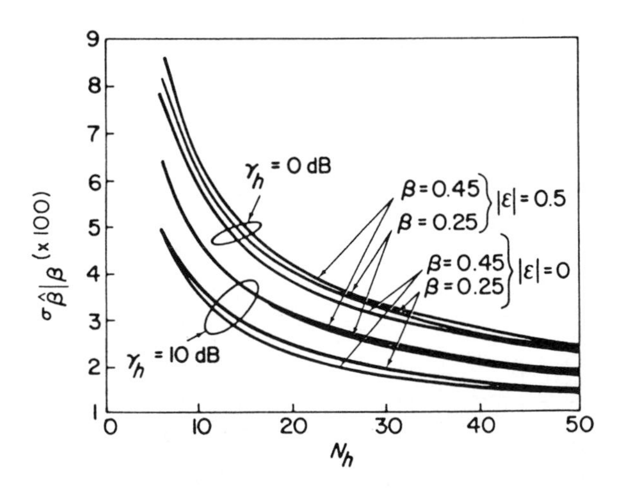

Figure 3.26. Conditional standard deviation $\sigma_{\hat{\beta}|\beta}$ versus N_h with γ_h, β and ε as parameters.

where

$$\bar{x}_1 = \frac{\mu_+}{\left(\frac{1}{2} + \hat{\beta}\right)^2 2\sigma^2}; \; \bar{x}_2 = \frac{\mu_-}{\left(\frac{1}{2} - \hat{\beta}\right)^2 2\sigma^2}$$

$$\sigma_1^2 = \frac{\sigma_+^2}{\left[2\sigma^2\left(\frac{1}{2} + \hat{\beta}\right)^2\right]^2}; \; \sigma_2^2 = \frac{\sigma_-^2}{\left[2\sigma^2\left(\frac{1}{2} - \hat{\beta}\right)^2\right]^2};$$

$$\sigma_T^2 = \frac{\sigma_1^2 \sigma_2^2}{\sigma_1^2 + \sigma_2^2}. \tag{3.111}$$

The conditional mean $\mu_{\hat{\beta}|\beta}$ from (3.107) and the conditional standard deviation $\sigma_{\hat{\beta}|\beta}$ from (3.108) are presented in Figures 3.25 and 3.26, respectively. It is seen from Figure 3.25 that the slope of $\mu_{\hat{\beta}|\beta}$ is non-zero at the origin but decreases significantly as the absolute value of the normalized time synchronization error $|\varepsilon|$ is increased. Figure 3.26 shows that, for the range of parameter values of interest, $\sigma_{\hat{\beta}|\beta}$ is comparatively small so that the random variable $\hat{\beta}$ is very close to the mean $\mu_{\hat{\beta}|\beta}$ with high probability.

3.3.2 The Case of Partial-Band Noise Jamming

Analogous to (3.63), the square root of the accumulated spectral estimates is now

$$R_{\pm} = \sqrt{\frac{1}{N_h} \sum_{j=1}^{\rho N_h} r_{j\pm}^2 + (1-\rho)\xi^2 \left(\operatorname{sinc}[\pi(1/2 \mp \beta), (1-|\varepsilon|)]\right)^2}. \tag{3.112}$$

For large ρN_h, the central-limit theorem can be applied to (3.112). Once again, $z_{\pm} = R_{\pm}^2$ are Gaussian random variables with the first two statistical moments given by

$$\mu_{\pm}(\beta) \triangleq E\{z_{\pm}|\beta\} = 2\sigma^2[1 + \gamma_{\pm}]$$

$$\sigma_{\pm}^2(\beta) \triangleq E\left\{(z_{\pm} - \mu_{\pm})^2|\beta\right\} = \frac{(2\sigma^2)^2}{\rho N_h}[1 + 2\rho\gamma_{\pm}] \tag{3.113}$$

and, hence, $p(\hat{\beta}|\beta)$ is given by (3.110) with N_h replaced by ρN_h, $\gamma_{\pm}$ of (3.105) with γ_h replaced by $\rho\gamma_h$, and $\bar{x}_1$, $\bar{x}_2$, σ_1^2, and σ_2^2 as defined in (3.111) but evaluated using $\mu_{\pm}$ and $\sigma_{\pm}^2$ of (3.113).

3.3.3 The Effects of Frequency Synchronization Error on FH / MFSK Error Probability Performance

The presence of a frequency synchronization error in an FH/MFSK receiver causes a degradation in system error probability performance due to factors not unlike those produced by a timing synchronization error. In fact, both signal attenuation and loss of orthogonality degradations once again exist; however, the functional dependence of these degradation components on the frequency error is quite different from the corresponding relationships for a timing error. Nevertheless, once these differences are identified, the remaining task of relating the above degradations to their impact on system error probability performance is straightforward in view of our previous detailed discussion for the effects of time synchronization errors. Thus, our discussion here will be brief and, wherever possible, draw heavily upon the results given in Section 3.2.3.

Starting first with the simple case of FH/MFSK with no diversity and orthogonal tones spaced by k/T_h, then if, for example, the transmitted MFSK symbol in the j-th hop interval is given by

$$s^{(j)}(t) = \sqrt{2S}\,\sin\left[2\pi\left(f_o + f_j + \frac{1}{2T_h}\right)t\right]; \quad (j-1)T_h \le t \le jT_h \tag{3.114}$$

then following the development in (3.97)–(3.103), and taking the sine and cosine Fourier transforms at $f = f_{IF} + 1/2T_h$, the spectral estimate r_j corresponding to the transmitted MFSK symbol has the conditional pdf

$$p(r_j|\varepsilon,\beta) = \begin{cases} \dfrac{r_j}{\sigma^2}\exp\left\{-\left[\dfrac{r_j^2}{2\sigma^2} + \gamma_h D_j(\varepsilon,\beta)\right]\right\} I_0\left[\sqrt{2\gamma_h D_j(\varepsilon,\beta)}\,\dfrac{r_j}{\sigma}\right]; & 0 \le r_j \le \infty \\ 0; \text{ otherwise} \end{cases} \tag{3.115}$$

where

$$D_j(\varepsilon,\beta) = \text{sinc}^2[\pi\beta, 1 - |\varepsilon|]. \tag{3.116}$$

Similarly, the spectral estimate r_{jn} for an incorrect correlator spaced in frequency by nk/T_h from the correct one has the pdf of (3.115) with $D_j(\varepsilon,\beta)$ replaced by

$$D_{jn}(\varepsilon,\beta) = \text{sinc}^2[\pi(nk+\beta), 1 - |\varepsilon|]. \tag{3.117}$$

Note that for $\beta = 0$, $D_j(\varepsilon,\beta)$ of (3.116) and $D_{jn}(\varepsilon,\beta)$ of (3.117) reduce, respectively, to $D_j(\varepsilon)$ of (3.69) and $D_{jn}(\varepsilon)$ of (3.71).

Comparing (3.115) with (3.73), it is clear that the bit error probability performance conditioned on fixed frequency and time synchronization errors is given by (3.78) together with (3.75) and (3.77) where $D_j(\varepsilon,\beta)$ and $D_{jn}(\varepsilon,\beta)$ are used in place of $D_j(\varepsilon)$ and $D_{jn}(\varepsilon)$ in (3.75).

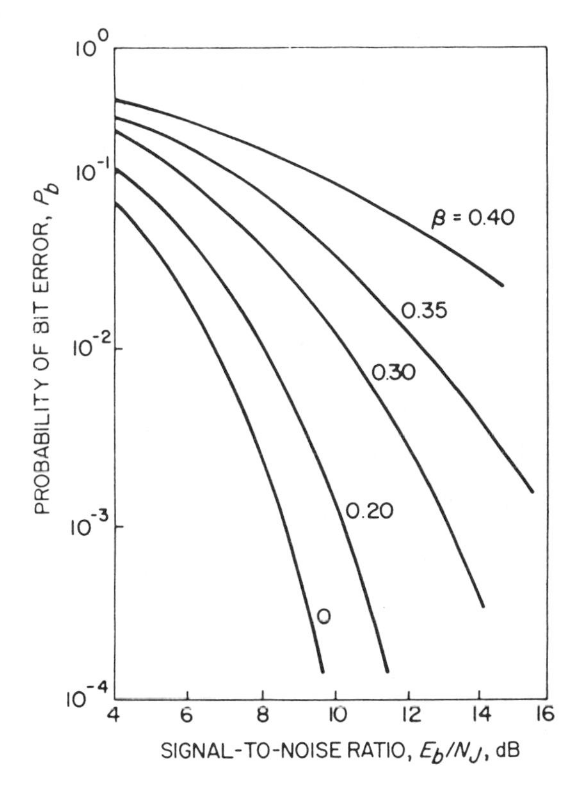

Figure 3.27. 4-ary FSK with frequency error (minimum orthogonal tone spacing) (reprinted from [13]).

Figures 3.27, 3.28, and 3.29 are the analogous results for performance in the presence of frequency error alone to those in Figures 3.18, 3.19, and 3.20, which depict performance in the presence of timing error alone. Comparing Figure 3.28 with Figure 3.19, for example, we observe that in the case of frequency error, the loss of orthogonality is the dominant degradation component for all β, whereas, as previously mentioned, for time synchronization error, loss of orthogonality dominates only for large error values.

Returning to Figure 3.21, we observe that increasing the MFSK tone spacing to twice its minimum orthogonal value has a more pronounced effect on the performance improvement achieved in the presence of frequency error alone than that when timing error alone is present, particularly when the synchronization errors are large. When both time and frequency errors exist simultaneously, Figure 3.30 illustrates a set of curves that represent contours of constant E_b/N_J degradation for a fixed bit error probability. Both 4-ary and 8-ary FSK results are provided.

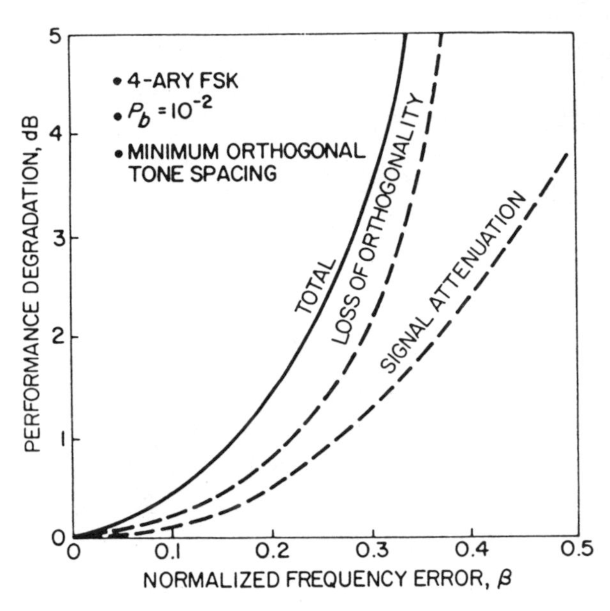

Figure 3.28. Performance degradation due to frequency error (reprinted from [13]).

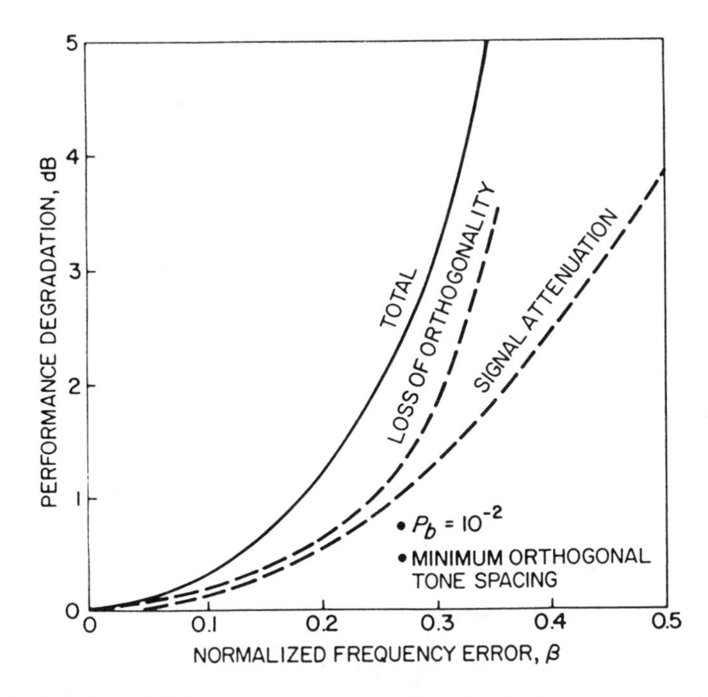

Figure 3.29. 8-ary FSK performance degradation due to frequency error (reprinted from [13]).

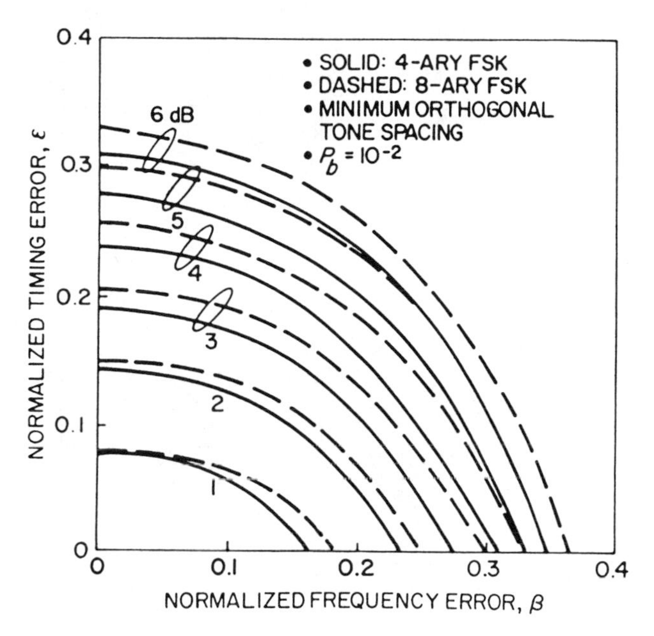

Figure 3.30. Performance degradation due to time and frequency synchronization errors (reprinted from [13]).

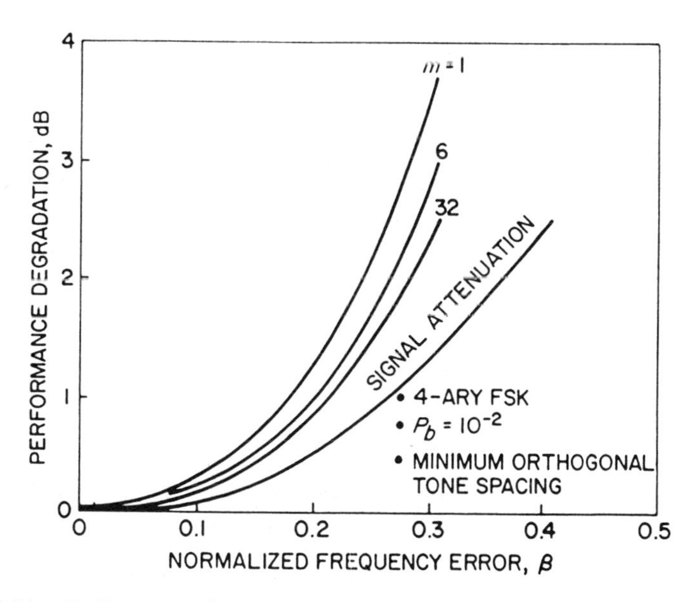

Figure 3.31. Performance degradation due to frequency error with chip combining (reprinted from [13]).

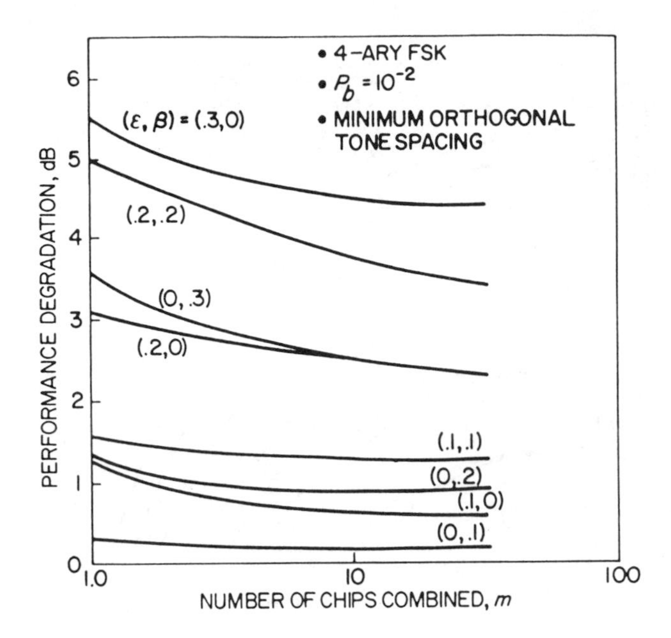

Figure 3.32. Effect of chip combining on degradation due to synchronization errors (reprinted from [13]).

Finally, when m-diversity and non-coherent combining are superimposed on the basic FH/MFSK system of above, then again all of the results of Section 3.2.3.2 apply after making the same replacements of $D_j(\varepsilon, \beta)$ and $D_{jn}(\varepsilon, \beta)$ for $D_j(\varepsilon)$ and $D_{jn}(\varepsilon)$. In this regard, Figure 3.31 provides, for frequency error alone, the analogous results to Figure 3.22. Again we observe that increasing m improves performance; however, a comparison of the two figures reveals that the reduction of loss of orthogonality by non-coherent combining plays a more prominent role with frequency errors than with timing errors. When both time and frequency errors are present and fixed, Figure 3.32 illustrates the performance degradation as a function of m, the number of chips combined.

3.3.3.1 Average Error Probability Performance in the Presence of Frequency Synchronization Error Estimation

If the estimator $\hat{\beta}$ of (3.106) is used for FH frequency synchronization and ε is the fixed normalized time synchronization error, then a residual frequency offset $\nu(\beta) \triangleq \beta - \hat{\beta}$ arises, which, as in our previous discussions, affects system performance by reducing the signal energy available for the non-coherent detection of the transmitted MFSK symbol and spreading signal energy into adjacent MFSK frequency detectors. In particular, it is clear that in the presence of the residual offset, a signal attenuation degradation occurs that is given by

$$\begin{aligned} D_j(\varepsilon, \nu) &= \mathrm{sinc}^2[\pi(\beta - \hat{\beta}), 1 - |\varepsilon|] \\ &= \mathrm{sinc}^2[\pi\nu(\beta), 1 - |\varepsilon|] \end{aligned} \tag{3.118}$$

and a loss of orthogonality also occurs that is given by

$$D_{jn}(\varepsilon, \nu) = \mathrm{sinc}^2[\pi(nk + \nu(\beta)), 1 - |\varepsilon|]. \tag{3.119}$$

Thus, if $p_{\nu|\beta}(\nu|\beta)$ denotes the β-conditional pdf of the residual error $\nu(\beta)$, then analogous to (3.93)

$$p_{\nu|\beta}(\nu|\beta) = p_{\hat{\beta}|\beta}(\beta - \nu|\beta). \tag{3.120}$$

It then follows that conditioned on ε, the average bit error probability $P_b(\varepsilon)$ is

$$P_b(\varepsilon) = 2\int_0^{1/2} d\beta \int_{\beta-1/2}^{\beta+1/2} P_b(\varepsilon, \nu)\, p_{\hat{\beta}|\beta}(\beta - \nu|\beta)\, d\nu \tag{3.121}$$

where $P_b(\varepsilon, \nu)$ is obtained from (3.78) together with (3.77) and (3.75) with $D_j(\varepsilon, \nu)$ and $D_{jn}(\varepsilon, \nu)$ used in place of $D_j(\varepsilon)$ and $D_{jn}(\varepsilon)$.

Since, as previously noted, $\sigma_{\hat{\beta}|\beta}$ is comparatively small, we may make a simplifying assumption analogous to (3.95), namely,

$$p_{\hat{\beta}|\beta}(\beta - \nu|\beta) = \delta(\nu - (\beta - \mu_{\hat{\beta}|\beta})) \tag{3.122}$$

in which case (3.121) simplifies to

$$P_b(\varepsilon) = 2\int_0^{1/2} P_b(\varepsilon, \beta - \mu_{\hat{\beta}|\beta})\, d\beta. \tag{3.123}$$

Analogous to Figure 3.23, Figure 3.33 is an illustration of the average bit error probability performance of (3.123) for 4-ary and 8-ary FSK with no timing error ($\varepsilon = 0$) and $N_h = 10$. Comparing these two figures, we observe that the average bit error probability is considerably less degraded by a residual frequency error than by a residual timing error.

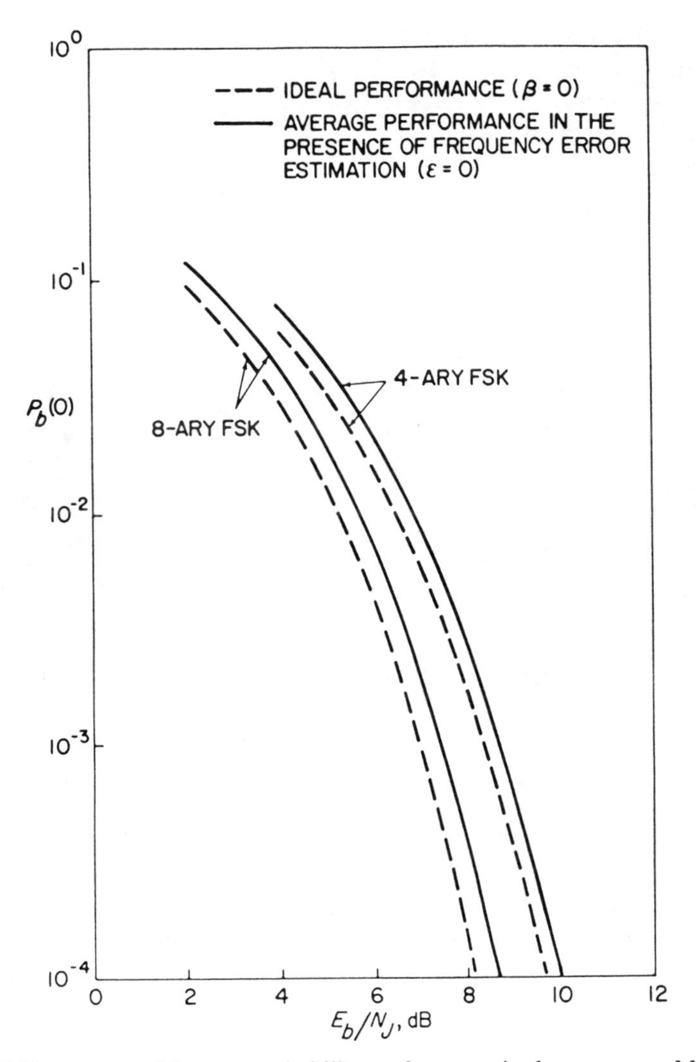

Figure 3.33. Average bit error probability performance in the presence of frequency error estimation; $\varepsilon = 0$, $N_h = 10$.

Finally, if both the fine time and fine frequency estimators of (3.53) and (3.106), respectively, are employed, then the overall error probability performance in the presence of the combination of the two residual synchronization errors can be computed from

$$P_b = 4\int_0^{1/2} d\varepsilon \int_0^{1/2} d\beta \int_{\varepsilon-1/2}^{\varepsilon+1/2} \int_{\beta-1/2}^{\beta+1/2} P_b(\varepsilon, \nu)\, p_{\hat{\beta}|\beta}(\beta - \nu|\beta) \times p_{\hat{\varepsilon}|\varepsilon}(\varepsilon - \eta|\varepsilon)\, d\nu\, d\eta \tag{3.124}$$

or from the approximate simplified expression

$$P_b = 4\int_0^{1/2}\int_0^{1/2} P_b(\varepsilon - \mu_{\hat{\varepsilon}|\varepsilon}, \rho - \mu_{\hat{\beta}|\beta})\, d\beta\, d\varepsilon. \tag{3.125}$$

3.4 REFERENCES

[1] M. K. Simon, A. Polydoros, and G. K. Huth, "Time synchronization of a frequency-hopped MFSK communication system," *ICC'81 Conference Record*, June 1981, pp. 76.1.1–76.1.5, Denver, CO.

[2] G. K. Huth, A. Polydoros, and M. K. Simon, "Frequency synchronization of a frequency-hopped MFSK communication system," *ICC'81 Conference Record*, June 1981, pp. 34.1.1–34.1.5, Denver, CO.

[3] S. S. Rappaport and D. L. Schilling, "A two level coarse code acquisition scheme for spread spectrum radio," *NTC'79 Conference Record*, November 1979, pp. 54.6.1–54.6.6, Birmingham, AL.

[4] C. A. Putnam, S. S. Rappaport, and D. L. Schilling, "A comparison of schemes for coarse acquisition of frequency hopped spread spectrum signals," *NTC'81 Conference Record*, December 1981, pp. 34.2.1–34.2.5, New Orleans, LA. Also see *IEEE Trans. Commun.*, COM-31, No. 2, pp. 183–189, February 1983.

[5] G. S. Takhar, A. K. Elhakeem, and S. C. Gupta, "Frequency hopping acquisition by autoregressive spectral estimation," *ICC'78 Conference Record*, June 1978, pp. 16.4.1–16.4.5, Toronto, Canada.

[6] A. K. Elhakeem, G. S. Takhar, and S. C. Gupta, "New code acquisition techniques in spread spectrum communication," *IEEE Trans. Commun.*, COM-28, no. 2, pp. 249–257, February 1980.

[7] H. S. El-Ghouroury and S. C. Gupta, "Algorithmic measurement of digital instantaneous frequency," *IEEE Trans. Commun.*, COM-24, no. 10, pp. 1115–1122, October 1976.

[8] J. A. Ponnusamy and M. D. Srinath, "Acquisition of pseudonoise codes in FH systems," *IEEE Trans. Aerospace and Electronic Systems*, AES-17, no. 3, pp. 335–341, May 1981.

[9] M. D. Srinath and M. M. Viswanathan, "Sequential algorithm for identification of parameters of an autoregressive process," *IEEE Trans. Automatic Control*," AC-20, pp. 542–546, August 1975.

[10] L. J. Griffiths, "Rapid measurements of digital instantaneous frequency," *IEEE Trans. Acoustics, Speech, and Signal Processing*, ASSP-25, pp. 510–519, December 1977.

[11] W. C. Lindsey and M. K. Simon, *Telecommunication Systems Engineering*, Englewood Cliffs, NJ: Prentice-Hall, 1973, Chapter 10.

[12] H. D. Chadwick and J. C. Springett, "The design of a low data rate MFSK communication system," *IEEE Trans. Commun. Tech.*, COM-18, no. 6, pp. 740–750, December 1970.

[13] F. S. Nakamoto, R. W. Middlestead, and C. R. Wolfson, "Impact of time and frequency errors on processing satellites with MFSK modulation," *ICC'81 Conference Record*, June 14-18, 1981, pp. 37.3.1–37.3.5, Denver, CO.

[14] J. I. Marcum, *Table of Q Functions*, ASTIA Document No. AD116551, January 1, 1950, RAND Corporation, Santa Monica, CA.

APPENDIX 3A: TO PROVE THAT A FREQUENCY ESTIMATOR BASED UPON ADJACENT SPECTRAL ESTIMATES TAKEN AT INTEGER MULTIPLES OF 1/T CANNOT BE UNBIASED

Let k/T denote the observed frequency and j/T the nominal signal frequency. Then $i/T \triangleq (k-j)/T$ represents the frequency spacing of the observed frequency relative to the nominal signal frequency. In the presence of a normalized frequency error $\beta = \lambda T$, the pdf of the spectral estimates r_i is given by

$$p(r_i) = \begin{cases} \dfrac{r_i}{\sigma^2}\exp\left\{-\dfrac{1}{2\sigma^2}\left[r_i^2 + \xi^2\operatorname{sinc}^2\pi(i-\beta)\right]\right\} I_0\left[\dfrac{r_i\xi|\operatorname{sinc}\pi(i-\beta)|}{\beta}\right]; \\ \qquad\qquad\qquad\qquad\qquad\qquad 0 \le r_i \le \infty \\ 0; \text{ otherwise} \end{cases} \tag{3A.1a}$$

where

$$\frac{\xi^2}{2\sigma^2} = \gamma; \quad \operatorname{sinc} x \triangleq \frac{\sin x}{x}. \tag{3A.1b}$$

Suppose we consider constructing an estimator $\hat{\beta}$ of β which is only a function of the spectral estimates at the nominal signal frequency and the two adjacent ones, i.e., r_0, r_{+1}, and r_{-1}. Thus, we propose that

$$\hat{\beta} = g\left[r_0(\beta), r_{+1}(\beta), r_{-1}(\beta)\right] \tag{3A.2}$$

where g is an arbitrary function and we have shown the dependence of the spectral estimates on the normalized frequency error β. We wish to prove that $\partial E\{\hat{\beta}|\beta\}/\partial\beta|_{\beta=0} \neq \beta$, i.e., $\hat{\beta}$ as given by (3A.2) is biased. We do this by proving something stronger, namely that

$$\left.\frac{\partial E\{\hat{\beta}|\beta\}}{\partial\beta}\right|_{\beta=0} = 0 \tag{3A.3}$$

where

$$E\{\hat{\beta}|\beta\} \triangleq \int_{-1/2}^{1/2} p(\hat{\beta}|\beta)\hat{\beta}\, d\hat{\beta}. \tag{3A.4}$$

To prove (3A.3) we must first find the conditional pdf $p(\hat{\beta}|\beta)$. If $\hat{\beta}$ is given by (3A.3), then there exists some other function f such that

$$r_0(\beta) = f\left[\hat{\beta}, r_{+1}(\beta), r_{-1}(\beta)\right]. \tag{3A.5}$$

Define

$$r_{+1}(\beta) = u$$

$$r_{-1}(\beta) = v$$

$$r_0(\beta) = f(\hat{\beta}, u, v). \qquad (3A.6)$$

Then, the Jacobian of the transformation is given by

$$J\left(\frac{r_{-i}, r_0, r_{+1}}{\hat{\beta}, u, v}\right) = \frac{\partial f(\hat{\beta}, u, v)}{\partial \hat{\beta}}. \qquad (3A.7)$$

Now

$$p(\hat{\beta}|\beta) = \int_0^\infty \int_0^\infty p(\hat{\beta}, u, v|\beta)\, du\, dv$$

$$= \int_0^\infty \int_0^\infty \left| J\left(\frac{r_{-1}, r_0, r_{+1}}{\hat{\beta}, u, v}\right)\right| p(r_{-1}, r_0, r_{+1})\, du\, dv. \qquad (3A.8)$$

Since r_{+1}, r_{-1} and r_0 are independent random variables, then from (3A.8) we get

$$p(\hat{\beta}|\beta) = \int_0^\infty \int_0^\infty \left| \frac{\partial f(\hat{\beta}, u, v)}{\partial \hat{\beta}} \right| p(u)p(v)p(f(\hat{\beta}, u, v))\, du\, dv. \qquad (3A.9)$$

Substituting (3A.1) into (3A.9) and making use of (3A.4) and (3A.6) gives

$$\begin{aligned}
E\{\hat{\beta}|\beta\} = \int_0^\infty \int_0^\infty & u'v' \exp\{-\tfrac{1}{2}(u'^2 + v'^2)\} \\
& \times \int_{-1/2}^{1/2} \hat{\beta} f(\hat{\beta}, u', v') \left| \frac{\partial f(\hat{\beta}, u', v')}{\partial \hat{\beta}} \right| \\
& \times \exp\{-\tfrac{1}{2} f^2(\hat{\beta}, u', v')\} \exp\left\{-\gamma \sum_{i=-1}^{1} \operatorname{sinc}^2 \pi(i - \beta)\right\} \\
& \times I_0\left(\sqrt{2\gamma}\, u' |\operatorname{sinc} \pi(1 - \beta)|\right) \\
& \times I_0\left(\sqrt{2\gamma}\, v' |\operatorname{sinc} \pi(1 + \beta)|\right) \\
& \times I_0\left(\sqrt{2\gamma}\, f(\hat{\beta}, u', v') |\operatorname{sinc} \pi\beta|\right) d\hat{\beta}\, du'\, dv'
\end{aligned} \qquad (3A.10)$$

where

$$u' = u/\sigma$$
$$v' = v/\sigma \tag{3A.11}$$

and γ has previously been defined in (3A.1b).

Taking the partial derivative of (3A.10) with respect to β and evaluating at $\beta = 0$ gives

$$\begin{aligned}\left.\frac{\partial E\{\hat{\beta}|\beta\}}{\partial\beta}\right|_{\beta=0} &= \int_0^\infty\int_0^\infty u'v' \exp\{-\tfrac{1}{2}(u'^2+v'^2)\}\\ &\times\int_{-1/2}^{1/2}\hat{\beta}f(\hat{\beta},u',v')\left|\frac{\partial f(\hat{\beta},u',v')}{\partial\hat{\beta}}\right|\exp\{-\tfrac{1}{2}f^2(\hat{\beta},u',v')\}\\ &\times\Bigg[\exp(-\gamma)\frac{\partial}{\partial\beta}\{I_0(\sqrt{2\gamma}\,u'|\text{sinc}\,\pi(1-\beta)|)\\ &\times I_0(\sqrt{2\gamma}\,v'|\text{sinc}\,\pi(1+\beta)|)\,I_0\left(\sqrt{2\gamma}\,f(\hat{\beta},u',v')|\text{sinc}\,\pi\beta|\right)\}\big|_{\beta=0}\\ &+\exp(-\gamma)\left[-\gamma\frac{\partial}{\partial\beta}\left\{\sum_{i=-1}^{1}\text{sinc}^2\pi(i-\beta)\right\}\Bigg|_{\beta=0}\right]\\ &\times I_0(\sqrt{2\gamma}\,f(\hat{\beta},u',v'))\Bigg]\,d\hat{\beta}\,du'\,dv'.\end{aligned} \tag{3A.12}$$

Now

$$\frac{\partial}{\partial\beta}\text{sinc}^2\pi(i-\beta) = 2\,\text{sinc}\,\pi(i-\beta)\left[\frac{\partial}{\partial\beta}\text{sinc}\,\pi(i-\beta)\right]. \tag{3A.13}$$

At $\beta = 0$,

$$\text{sinc}\,\pi(i-\beta) = 0 \text{ for } i = \pm 1$$
$$\frac{\partial}{\partial\beta}\text{sinc}\,\pi(i-\beta) = 0 \text{ for } i = 0. \tag{3A.14}$$

Thus

$$\left.\frac{\partial}{\partial\beta}\text{sinc}^2\pi(i-\beta)\right|_{\beta=0} = 0 \text{ for } i = -1, 0, +1 \tag{3A.15}$$

or

$$\left.\frac{\partial}{\partial\beta}\left[\sum_{i=-1}^{1}\text{sinc}^2\pi(i-\beta)\right]\right|_{\beta=0} = 0. \tag{3A.16}$$

This takes care of the second partial derivative in (3A.12). For the first partial derivative, we observe that

$$
\begin{aligned}
&\frac{\partial}{\partial\beta}\Big\{ I_0\big(\sqrt{2\gamma}\,u'|\operatorname{sinc}\pi(1-\beta)|\big) I_0\big(\sqrt{2\gamma}\,v'|\operatorname{sinc}\pi(1+\beta)|\big) \\
&\qquad \times I_0\big(\sqrt{2\gamma}\,f(\hat{\beta},u',v')\,|\operatorname{sinc}\pi\beta|\big)\Big|_{\beta=0} \\
&\qquad = I_1\big(\sqrt{2\gamma}\,f(\hat{\beta},u',v')\big)\left|\cancelto{0}{\frac{\partial|\operatorname{sinc}\pi\beta|}{\partial\beta}}\right|_{\beta=0} \\
&\qquad\quad + I_0\big(\sqrt{2\gamma}\,f(\hat{\beta},u',v')\big)\left\{\left|\frac{\partial I_0\big(\sqrt{2\gamma}\,u'|\operatorname{sinc}\pi(1-\beta)|\big)}{\partial\beta}\right|_{\beta=0}\right. \\
&\qquad\quad \left. + \left|\frac{\partial I_0\big(\sqrt{2\gamma}\,v'|\operatorname{sinc}\pi(1+\beta)|\big)}{\partial\beta}\right|_{\beta=0}\right\} \\
&\qquad = I_0\big(\sqrt{2\gamma}\,f(\hat{\beta},u',v')\big)\left\{ I_1\big(\sqrt{2\gamma}\,u'|\operatorname{sinc}\pi(1-\beta)|\big)\big(\sqrt{2\gamma}\,u'\big)\right. \\
&\qquad\quad \times\left|\cancelto{0}{\frac{\partial|\operatorname{sinc}\pi(1-\beta)|}{\partial\beta}}\right|_{\beta=0} \\
&\qquad\quad + I_1\big(\sqrt{2\gamma}\,v'|\operatorname{sinc}\pi(1+\beta)|\big) \\
&\qquad\quad \left.\times\big(\sqrt{2\gamma}\,v'\big)\left|\cancelto{0}{\frac{\partial|\operatorname{sinc}\pi(1+\beta)|}{\partial\beta}}\right|_{\beta=0}\right\} \\
&\qquad = 0.
\end{aligned}
\tag{3A.17}
$$

Substituting (3A.16) and (3A.17) into (3A.12) gives the desired result, i.e.

$$
\left.\frac{\partial E\{\hat{\beta}|\beta\}}{\partial\beta}\right|_{\beta=0} = 0. \tag{3A.18}
$$

Part 5

SPECIAL TOPICS

Chapter 4

LOW PROBABILITY OF INTERCEPT COMMUNICATIONS

The design of a communication link to have low probability of intercept (LPI) capability is predicated on the requirement for it to operate in a hostile environment wherein the enemy tries to detect the presence of the communicator's transmission. A typical scenario might consist of an underwater or surface vehicle (the communicator) attempting to correspond with a satellite (the receiver) via transmission of a short message, and an enemy search aircraft (the interceptor) whose mission it is to detect the presence of RF energy corresponding to this communicated message. The key words in the last sentence are *detect* and *energy* since typically the interceptor's performance is judged by his ability to determine (detect) that the communicator has initiated a transmission (energy) and not by what might occur following this accomplishment, e.g., location of the communicator, decoding of the message, etc. To further emphasize this point, the interceptor is ordinarily acquainted only with such communicator information as his frequency band, modulation format, and those spread-spectrum (SS) modulation characteristics such as bandwidth and code (hop) rate, which are insufficient by themselves to allow for decoding of the message. Thus, in the absence of information related to the time of message initiation and the secure codes used to generate the SS modulation, the interceptor's detection strategy is limited to employing some form of energy detector.

A large part of this chapter shall be devoted to discussing and comparing the merits of several different interceptor detector topologies which are important either because of their simplicity of implementation or because of their theoretically optimum performance capability. Such ability to employ a reasonably sophisticated signal feature detector, as opposed to, say, a simple wideband radiometer, is a technique the interceptor is assumed to have at his disposal for improving his detectability. This is not to say that the enemy will necessarily employ this option since, in many cases, little or nothing is gained both from a performance and cost standpoint by using other than the simplest energy detector. In fact, in those situations, it may be sufficient for the interceptor to jam the link between communicator and receiver so as to force the communicator to increase his transmitted power above the level normally required for reliable reception, thereby raising his chance of being detected. The subject of enemy jamming of a communicator's transmission, with emphasis on the various system design tradeoffs possible between the two adversaries, has been adequately treated in many of the chapters in Volumes I and II. Thus, we shall not repeat such discussions here in this chapter except in summary form in the final section.

As is true for any scenario posed for a communication system design, the extent to which the interceptor can employ any or all of the above methods for improving his detectability is determined by factors involving both cost and complexity. Some mention of these factors will be included in our discussion later on.

Having briefly mentioned the various options available to the interceptor, we complete our introductory picture by discussing the conditions and associated technologies which, when utilized by the communicator, greatly enhance his LPI position. For convenience of discussion we shall use as our model scenario the underwater or surface vehicle to satellite communication link. However, much of what follows is directly applicable to other scenarios such as communication between an airborne command post and a satellite or surface ships communicating to airborne relays.

First and foremost, the communicator must maintain as low a visual profile as possible, even when not communicating, to the extreme of completely concealing his location. Second, when transmitting, the communicator should reduce his radio detectability by minimizing his radiated power. The techniques available for accomplishing such include (1) specially designed low sidelobe antennas, (2) maximum use of channel coding to minimize the transmitter power necessary for proper message detection, (3) an optimum performance receiving system and, (4) low message bit rates and the shortest possible message lengths. Each of these are attainable to various degrees and the extent to which any of them may be employed depends upon the available implementation technologies and costs. Finally, the communicator should employ SS modulation techniques to provide anti-jam (AJ) protection against the interceptor. At this juncture, it is also worth pointing out that the communication receiver may itself attempt to jam the interceptor's receivers or otherwise confuse the interceptor by various decoy methods. Thus, the interceptor must be aware of this possibility and, if possible, guard against its occurrence.

While all of the above factors individually contribute to a maximum LPI state for the communicator, it is possible that all may not be realizable simultaneously. The reason for this is that some factors are both time and spatial dependent and the communicator may have little control over these when it becomes necessary to transmit. Variables of this nature might include (1) the transmitting antenna elevation angle when pointed to the communication receiver (which depends upon the relative transmitter and receiver positions at the time), (2) whether the satellite is receiving by means of a spot (high gain) antenna or an earth-coverage (moderate gain) antenna, and (3) the weather conditions along the surface to satellite line-of-sight communication path, which might be different for the link between the communicator and receiver than that between the communicator and interceptor. A high elevation angle generally means lower sidelobe radiation into the altitudes that the search aircraft fly as well as obviating main beam intercept at far range, while the use of the satellite spot antenna and clear weather conditions are synonymous with minimum radiated power.

The remainder of this chapter deals with the issues and answers pertaining to the tradeoffs among the various modulation, coding, and synchronization techniques used by the communicator and the sophistication of the detection technique employed by the interceptor in carrying out their respective missions. In keeping with the philosophy adopted in previous chapters, we shall intentionally omit discussion of all issues related to antenna design. This is not to say by any means that such issues are neither performance nor cost effective. In fact, one of the viable options available to the interceptor to improve its detectability is to employ multiple narrow-coverage antenna/receiver combinations that accrue gain by individually covering fractional portions of the total search area. Nevertheless, we shall focus our attention only on those issues that have a direct bearing on the previously mentioned system design considerations.

4.1 SIGNAL MODULATION FORMS

The various signal modulation forms that might be used by the communicator are no different from those already discussed in great detail in previous chapters. Thus, in this chapter we shall merely review their intrinsic form with emphasis on the LPI application.

The underlying modulation technique for data communication in many LPI systems reported upon thus far is MFSK. For such a modulation, the form of the transmitted signal in the i-th transmission interval $iT_s \leq t \leq (i+1)T_s$ is

$$s(t) = \sqrt{2S}\sin\left[2\pi(f_0 + d_i\Delta f)t + \phi_i\right] \tag{4.1}$$

where S is the transmitted power, f_0 is the carrier frequency, ϕ_i is the random phase associated with the i-th transmitted tone, $\Delta f = kT_s$ (k integer) is the frequency spacing between tones in the M-ary set, and d_i is the value of the i-th data symbol chosen from the set of integers $\{1, 2, \ldots, M\}$. To reduce the chance of the interceptor detecting his message and also to combat jamming, the communicator will employ an SS modulation which typically takes on the form of frequency hopping (FH) or a combination (hybrid) of FH with time hopping (TH) and/or direct-sequence pseudonoise (PN). Thus, the four basic SS modulations employed in most LPI systems transmitting MFSK data modulation are FH, FH/PN, FH/TH, and FH/PN/TH. The intrinsic forms of the transmitted signals corresponding to the first two of these SS modulations are[1]

FH

$$s(t) = \sqrt{2S}\sin\left[2\pi\left(f_0 + \frac{n_i + \frac{1}{2}}{T_h}\right)t + \phi_i\right]; \qquad \begin{array}{c} iT_h \leq t \leq (i+1)T_h \\ n_i \,\varepsilon\{0,1,2,\ldots,N_T - 1\} \end{array}$$

T_h = hop time interval

N_T = total number of hops in SS bandwidth (4.2)

FH/PN

$$s(t) = \sqrt{2S}\,c(t)\sin\left[2\pi\left(f_0 + \frac{n_i + \frac{1}{2}}{T_c}\right)t + \phi_i\right] \qquad \begin{array}{c} iT_h \leq t \leq (i+1)T_h \\ n_i \,\varepsilon\{0,1,2,\ldots,N_T - 1\} \end{array}$$

$c(t)$ = PN modulation

T_c = PN chip time interval. (4.3)

(Note that here the hop frequency spacing is $1/T_c$, a factor of T_h/T_c larger than for pure FH, to accommodate the bandwidth of the PN modulation.) Although the time-hopped SS modulation types are of interest, we shall focus our attention on the two more commonly found in LPI applications, namely, FH and FH/PN, occasionally making reference to the hybrid TH forms whenever appropriate.

4.2 INTERCEPTION DETECTORS

A great amount of effort has been expended over the past decade on the subject of the properties, configurations, performance, and implementation of intercept detectors and many reports and papers are available which delineate basic detector topology and optimum configurations and methods for performance analysis [1]–[6]. The results produced lay the necessary foundations and provide bounding criteria for detectability as a function of the principal parameters: detection SNR (S/N_0), total message time (T_M) or hop time (T_h), and spread-spectrum bandwidth (W_{ss}) or hop frequency spacing (W_h). (The reason for the choice between T_M or T_h and W_{ss} or W_h is tied to the choice between the two basic approaches to detecting hopped signals, as will become apparent shortly.) Section 4.2.1 presents the most

[1]For simplicity, we have not included the MFSK data modulation in (4.2) or (4.3) since it does not affect the basic form of these expressions or alter their spectral properties.

pertinent aspects of these endeavors and weighs the merits of the basic detector configurations against some practical considerations.

In Section 4.2.2, the suboptimum performance of the detector types is evaluated against the substantial problems of time and frequency synchronization. The results show how little real advantage is likely to be gained by sophisticated channelized detectors over the wideband radiometer type detector.

Finally, Section 4.2.3 begins with a discussion of some implementation considerations associated with wideband single-channel detectors and concludes with a presentation of some potential alternative detection methods, along with an assessment of conditions required for their probable use.

4.2.1 Ideal and Realizable Detectors

In the following subsections, perfect frequency and time synchronization to the received signal structure is assumed. However, no presumption is made with respect to knowledge about the pseudorandomness of the signal's SS states.

4.2.1.1 Detectability Criteria

The interceptor's task is to detect the presence of the communicator's transmission and attempt to identify the communicator's location within a specified geographic area. Since the communicator's message or transmission is not time-continuous and occupies only a brief interval, the interceptor desires a reasonably high probability that such a short message will, in fact, be detected if he is anywhere within detectable range. Thus, the detection probability, P_D, should be close to unity.

On the other hand, the interceptor does not want his equipment to indicate a state of signal detection when no actual signal is present. Such a state of false alarm caused by system noise should have a very low probability P_{FA} of occurrence, perhaps on the order of one false alarm per sortie or per day. Typical values of P_D and P_{FA} might be $P_D = 0.9$ and $P_{FA} = 10^{-6}$.

4.2.1.2 Maximum or Bounding Performance of Fundamental Detector Types

Extensive literature exists on the subject of interceptor detection techniques and performance. All of the various methods for detecting hopped signals fall into two basic types of approach: employing a wideband radiometer matched in bandwidth to the transmission (i.e., W_{ss}) and integrating energy over the entire transmission (i.e., T_M) or using multiple narrowband radiometers whose filter bandwidths and detector integration times are matched, to the bandwidth (W_h) and duration (T_h) of the hop pulse. The second of these two approaches implies, in its generic form, a requirement for a filter at each of the possible hop frequencies. Structures which ease this requirement have also been considered. The basic difference between the various structures realizable under the second approach centers on the decision procedure used to convert the hop pulse detection data into decisions about the presence of a transmission. The following is a summary of the applicable detector types and their relative practical value:

	Detector Type	*Relative Practical Value*
(1)	Wideband Energy Detector (Wideband Radiometer)	Very functional and in general use
(2)	Optimum Multichannel FH Pulse-Matched Detector	Academic—provides an optimum performance bound
(3)	Maximum Channel Filter Bank Combiner (FBC)	Suboptimum version of (2)
(4)	Optimum Partial-Band FH Pulse-Matched Detector	Realizable but complex subconfiguration of (2) [not discussed in this chapter]
(5)	Partial-Band FBC (PB-FBC)	Realizable subconfiguration of (3)

As will be seen from the following discussions, detector types (1) and (5) are those of most utilitarian value to the interceptor. The analyses in the following subsections consider only pure FH signals. In Section 4.2.1.3, the merits of other SS signal forms in terms of detector performance are discussed.

(1) Wideband Energy Detector (Radiometer)

By far the most elementary and easy to implement detector is the wideband energy detector or *radiometer*,[2] shown functionally in Figure 4.1. The wideband detector consists of a bandpass filter (BPF) of center frequency f_0 and bandwidth W (equal to the total FH spread-spectrum bandwidth W_{ss}), a square-law operation followed by a T-second integrator (reset at the end of each successive T-second period), and a comparator that weighs the integrator output against a threshold value in order to decide if a signal is received for each T-second segment. The size of T is generally dictated by the communicator's message duration T_M. When T_M is short and discontinuous, usually T is set equal to T_M for highest performance.

[2] The generic term "radiometer" refers to a square-law measurement device covering an RF band of interest. Techniques for receivers employing such devices evolved primarily to satisfy the need to measure the extremely weak, broadband non-coherent RF energy radiated by astronomical objects.

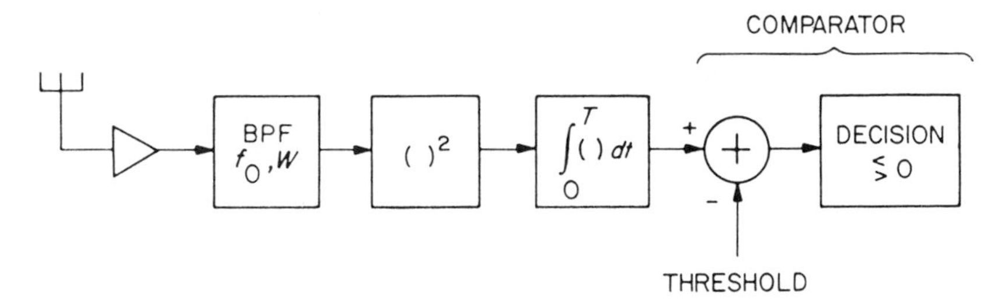

Figure 4.1. Functional wideband energy detector (radiometer).

For large $TW = T_M W_{ss}$ products (large being greater than 1,000 for the typical values of P_D and P_{FA} previously given), the wideband radiometer performance may be calculated using the equations

$$S/N_0 = d\sqrt{W_{ss}/T_M} = W_{ss} d\sqrt{1/W_{ss}T_M} \tag{4.4}$$

and

$$d = Q^{-1}(P_{FA}) - Q^{-1}(P_D) \tag{4.5}$$

where $Q^{-1}(\cdot)$ is the inverse of the Gaussian probability integral. Recognizing the similarity between Figure 4.1 and the detection portions of the single dwell serial search PN and FH acquisition schemes discussed in Chapters 1 and 3, respectively, then (4.4) together with (4.5) is identical[3] to (1.81) with the appropriate substitutions of notation, i.e., $A^2 \to S$, $\tau_d \to T_M$, and $B \to W_{ss}$. Figure 4.2 is a plot of P_D versus d in dB with P_{FA} as a parameter. For the sample typical values of $P_D = .9$ and $P_{FA} = 10^{-6}$, we obtain $d = 6$ (7.8 dB), which for given values of SS bandwidth and total message time enables computation, from (4.4), of the minimum value of S/N_0 above which the communicator is detectable.

Before leaving this subsection, we point out that using a continuous integrator (over a T-sec interval) rather than an I & D as indicated in Figure 4.1, in general, yields significantly better performance since it ensures alignment in time with the signal. However, calculations based on I & D detection and the assumption of perfect alignment of sampling times with signal occurrences will provide close estimates of the detection performance of continuous integration [5]. Thus, we have justified the ease of analysis afforded by the assumption of I & D detection with perfect message alignment. More will be said later on regarding the degradation due to imperfect alignment.

[3] One other simplifying assumption is made in arriving at (4.4) and (4.5) from (1.81), namely that $S/N_0W \ll 1$ and thus $\sqrt{1 + 2S/N_0W} \cong 1$. This is equivalent to assuming equal variances for the integrator output under signal-plus-noise and noise-only conditions.

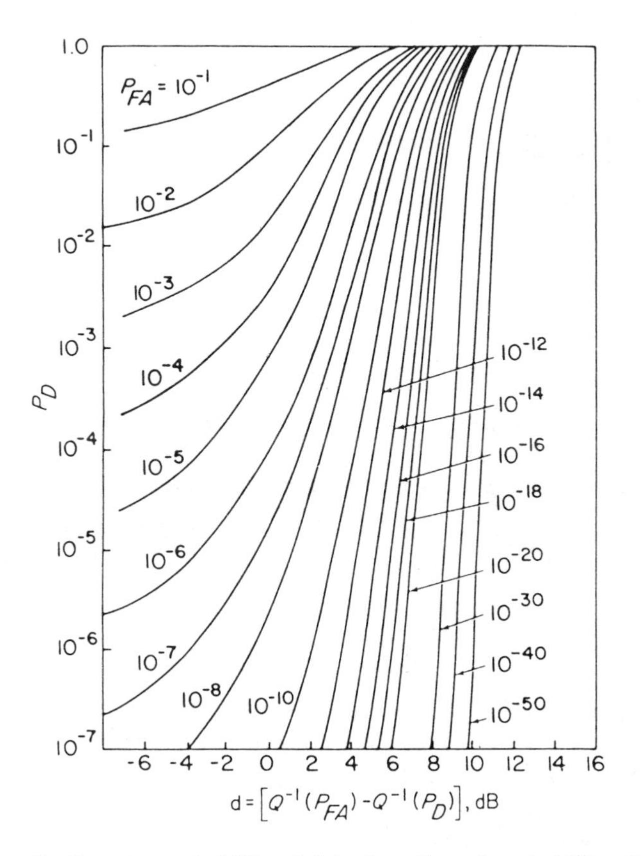

Figure 4.2. Radiometer probability of detection P_D and probability of false alarm P_{FA} versus parameter $d = [Q^{-1}(P_{FA}) - Q^{-1}(P_D)]$ (reprinted from [4]).

(2) Optimum Multichannel FH Pulse-Matched Energy Detector

From (4.4), it may be seen that the wideband detector's performance in terms of S/N_0 is proportional to the square root of the spread-spectrum total bandwidth, W_{ss}. Actually, all basic square-law detectors behave in proportion to the square root of the input bandwidth. Thus, if it is somehow possible to effectively reduce W_{ss}, greater S/N_0 sensitivity will be obtained.

The only realistic way to effectively reduce W_{ss} is to subdivide the total bandwidth into, say, K sub-bands or channels, each having bandwidth $W_K = W_{ss}/K$. Each channel then forms the basis of a separate energy detector and the outputs of the K channels are further processed to render the overall detection decision. Figure 4.3 shows the functional configuration wherein each channel has bandwidth W_{ss}/K and is contiguous with respect to those adjacent.

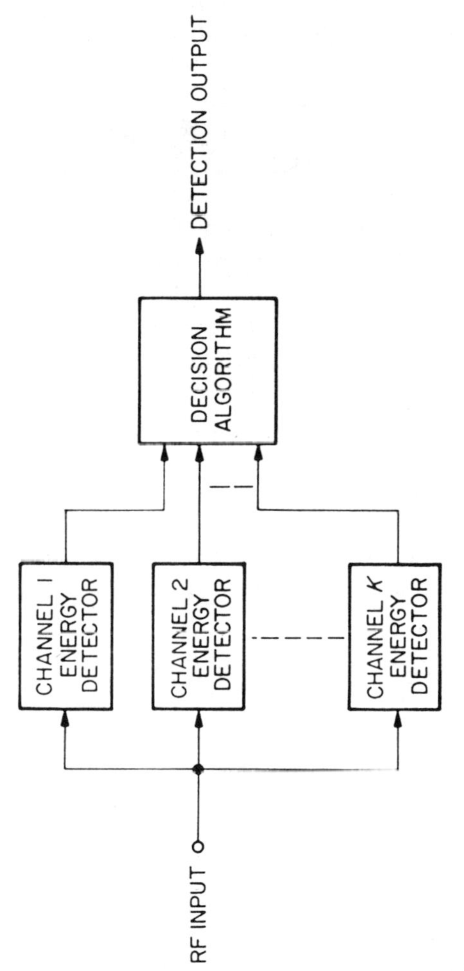

Figure 4.3. Topology of the multiple-channel detector.

It can be shown (see Appendix 4A) that an arbitrary choice of K without regard to the FH frequency cell bandwidth, W_h, and the FH hop period T_h, will lead to performance inferior to that of the wideband detector. The key to superior operation is that the individual channels be matched to the individual hop pulses in both bandwidth and time. Thus, $W_K = W_h$ and $T = T_h$.

An optimum multichannel detector is one having N_T channels (N_T is the total number of hop cells in W_{ss}) and utilizing a likelihood ratio decision algorithm. Figure 4.4 indicates the essential elements. Each channel consists of an energy detector (BPF, squarer, and integrator), followed by scaling. The channel outputs are summed at the end of each hop period and the sums from all N_h hops in the message are multiplied, with the result being compared to a threshold, l, in order to decide if a signal is present at the detector input.

The generalized performance expression for the optimum multichannel detector cannot be obtained due to an inability to specify the output probability distribution functions. When N_h is large (e.g., $N_h > 100$), however, it is possible to closely approximate the true answer by using Gaussian statistics, with the result that S/N_0 is given by [4]:

$$\frac{S}{N_0} = \frac{W_h}{2} I_0^{-1}\left[1 - N_T + N_T \exp\left(d^2/N_h\right)\right] \tag{4.6}$$

where I_0^{-1} is the inverse of the zero-order modified Bessel function of the first kind, and d is given as per (4.5). Since $N_T = W_{ss}/W_h$ and $T_M = N_h T_h$, then letting $W_h T_h = 1$ (as is typical for FH), we arrive at $N_T = W_{ss} T_M / N_h$, which, when substituted in (4.6) results in the alternate expression

$$\frac{S}{N_0} = \frac{W_{ss}}{2N_T} I_0^{-1}\left[1 - N_T + N_T \exp\left(\frac{d^2 N_T}{W_{ss} T_M}\right)\right]. \tag{4.7}$$

Figure 4.5 is a plot of the ratio (in dB) of S/N_0 as determined from (4.4) to S/N_0 of (4.7) versus $W_{ss}T_M$ with the total number of hops N_T in the SS bandwidth as a parameter.[4] For a given $W_{ss}T_M$ and N_T these results illustrate the increase in detectability obtained by the interceptor by using an optimum multichannel detector rather than a wideband radiometer. For example, if $W_{ss}T_M = 8 \times 10^9$, then for $N_T = 10^6$, the optimum detector has an 11.1 dB advantage.[5] If this could be fully realized, it would allow an almost fourfold increase in the detection range over that possible with the wideband radiometer. Clearly, the price for the optimum detector's superior performance is complexity, both in terms of functional operations and the

[4] Note that in comparing the required S/N_0's of the two detectors, it is not necessary to know either the SS bandwidth W_{ss} or the hop rate $R_h = 1/T_h$. Rather the *product* of W_{ss} and the message time T_M, and the total number of hops N_T in W_{ss}, are all that enter the calculation.
[5] This value of $W_{ss}T_M$ is used in [4].

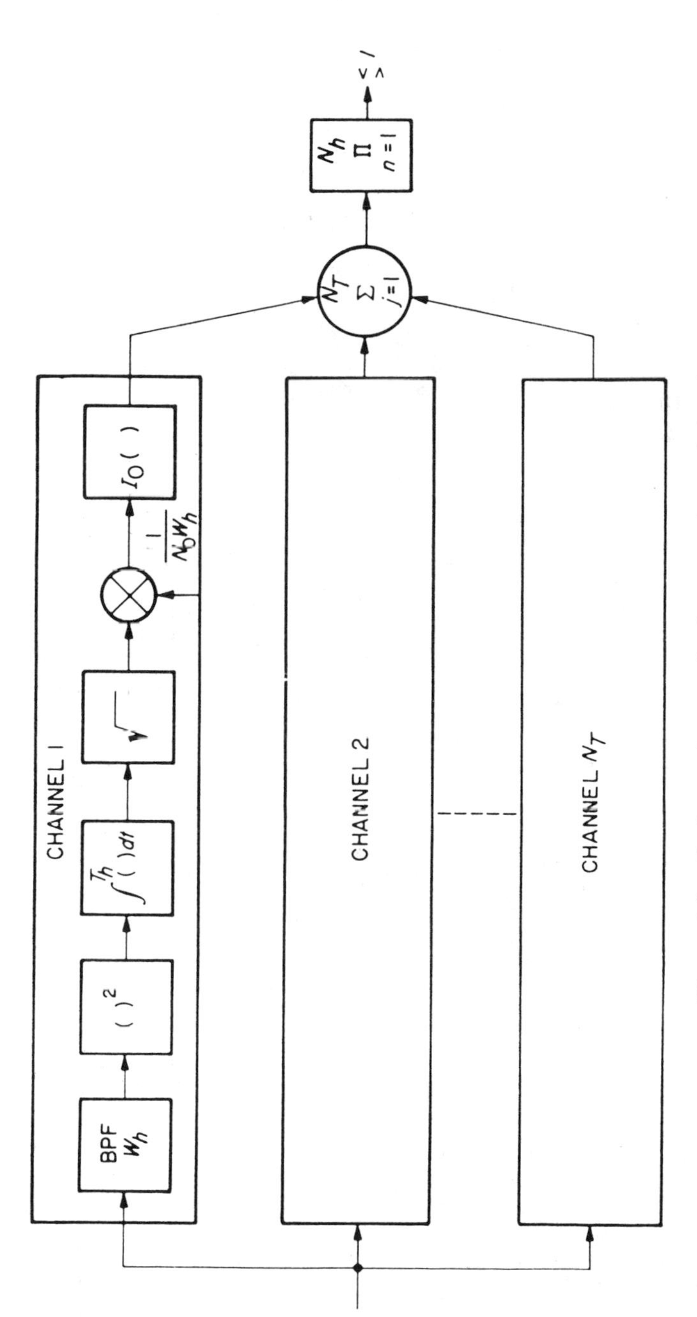

Figure 4.4. Optimum detector for frequency-hopped signals.

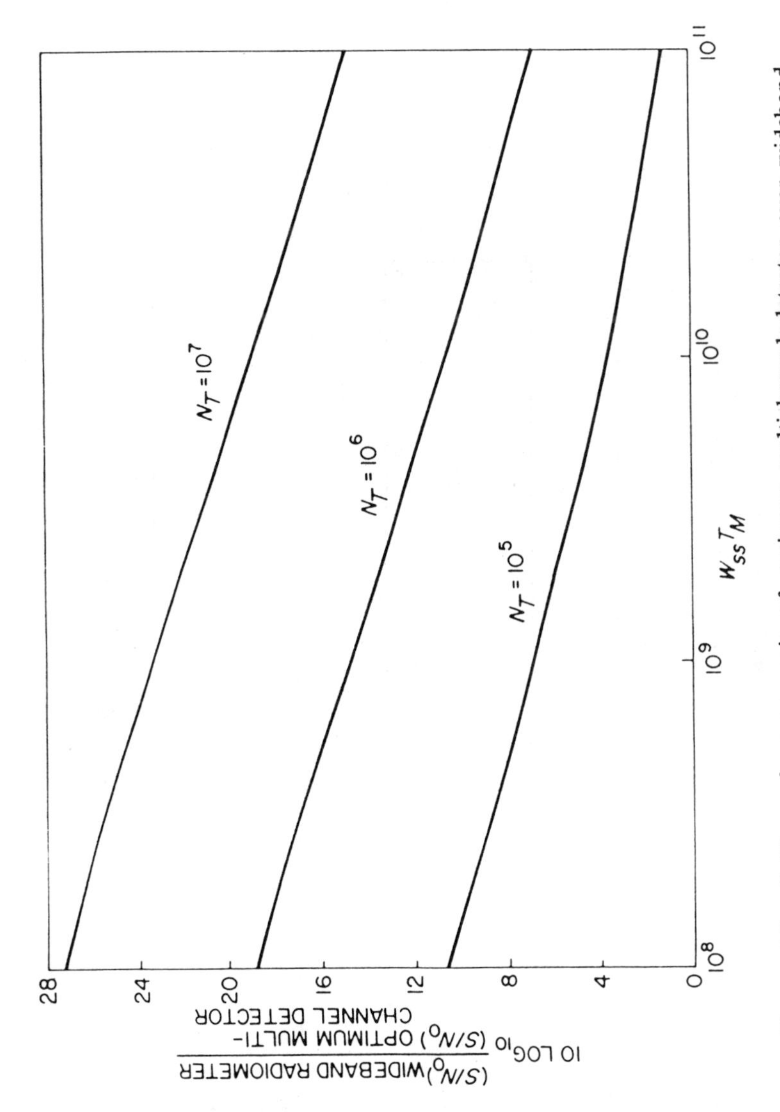

Figure 4.5. S/N_0 performance gain of optimum multichannel detector over wideband radiometer.

number of channels required; for the example above, the detector must have one million channels! Since this seems prohibitive in terms of size, power, and cost (even in the MIC and LSI era), the optimum detector is deemed unfeasible. A more realistic approach is that of the partial-band filter bank combiner. First, we discuss the full-band filter bank combiner in terms of its differences with respect to the optimum multichannel detector.

(3) Filter Bank Combiner (FBC) Detector

Figure 4.6 shows the basic FBC. A comparison with the optimum detector of Figure 4.4 reveals that the energy detector portions are the same but that a decision in each channel relative to a threshold k has replaced the scaling operations. Thus, each channel is allowed to detect the presence or absence of a hop pulse each T_h seconds, with the output of the decision circuit being a logic 1 or 0, respectively. All decisions are subsequently OR'd (i.e., the output of the OR gate is a logic 1 if any of the individual channel decisions are logic 1), and the number of OR output logic 1 states is accumulated over the number of hops in the message duration, i.e., $N_h = T_M/T_h$. The result is finally compared with the threshold l to determine if a message has been detected.

The obvious advantage of the FBC over the optimum multichannel detector is its simpler decision structure obtained for a cost of higher required S/N_0 for the same P_D and P_{FA} performance. Calculation of the FBC S/N_0 requirement cannot be found directly due again to the non-Gaussian nature of the variables, coupled with the fact that the FBC has two decision thresholds, k and l. Computer simulations [3] have found that the "best performance" value of l lies somewhere between five and twenty-five, depending on the values of the other parameters (P_D, P_{FA}, T_h and W_h). A somewhat pessimistic performance bound for the FBC can be obtained by letting $l = 1$, the result being between about 1–2 dB higher in S/N_0 [4]. With $l = 1$, the problem simply reduces to determining the probability of detection and false alarm as a function of the other parameters on a per-channel basis. With the overall message detection and false alarm probabilities being designated as P_D and P_{FA}, respectively, the individual channel probabilities are given by

$$P_{DI} \cong P_D/N_h = P_D N_T/(W_{ss}T_M) \tag{4.8a}$$

$$P_{FAI} \cong P_{FA}/(N_h N_T) = P_{FA}/(W_{ss}T_M) \tag{4.8b}$$

provided that N_T and N_h are sufficiently large. The required S/N_0 may then be calculated using the relationships

$$S/N_0 = \eta d_I \sqrt{W_h/T_h} = \frac{W_{ss}}{N_T}\eta d_I \sqrt{\frac{1}{W_h T_h}} = \frac{W_{ss}}{N_T}\eta d_I \tag{4.9a}$$

$$d_I = Q^{-1}(P_{FAI}) - Q^{-1}(P_{DI}) \tag{4.9b}$$

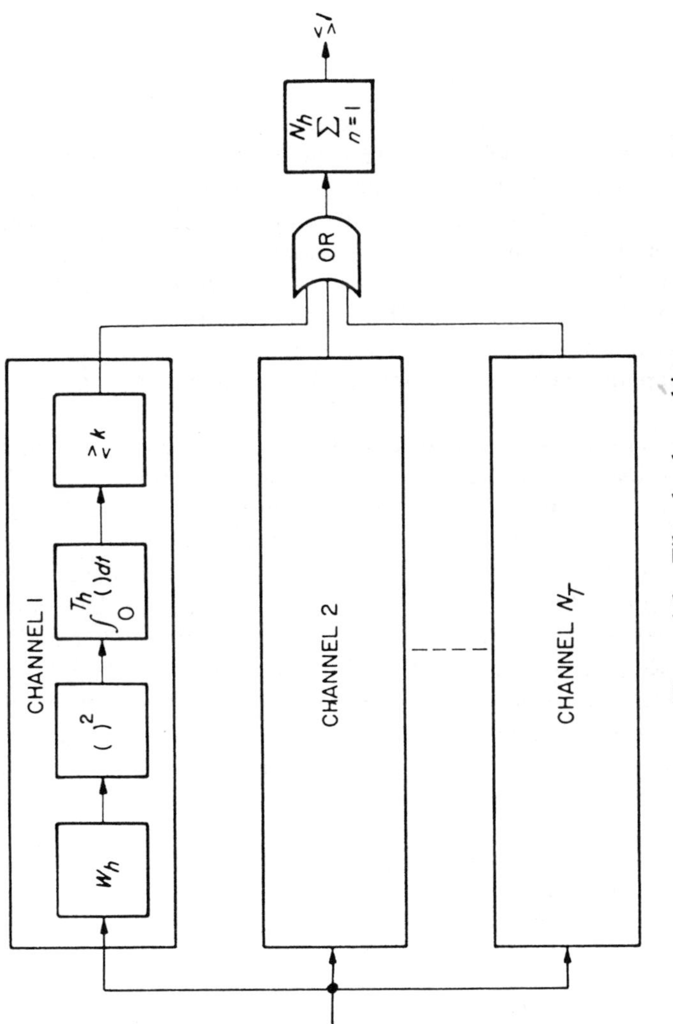

Figure 4.6. Filter bank combiner.

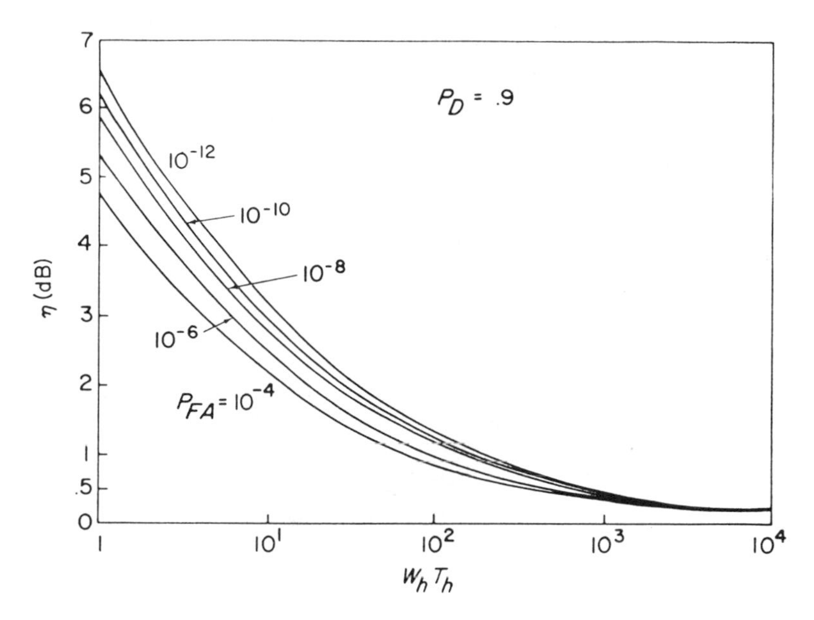

Figure 4.7a. Correction factor η for Gaussian approximation as a function of time-bandwidth product ($P_D = .9$) (reprinted from [4]).

where η is a chi-square correction factor[6] applied to the Gaussian-assumed d_I of (4.9b). Curves of η as a function of P_{DI}, P_{FAI}, and $W_h T_h$ are given in Figure 4.7.

Returning now to the continuing example parameters ($P_D = .9$, $P_{FA} = 10^{-6}$), the $l = 1$ FBC performance as given by (4.9) relative to that of the optimum multichannel detector (4.7) is 3.2 dB worse for $W_{ss}T_M = 8 \times 10^9$ and $N_T = 10^6$. For $N_T = 10^5$ and 10^7, the corresponding performance degradations are 5.1 dB and 2.8 dB respectively. A complete set of curves analogous to Figure 4.5 for the ratio of S/N_0 given by (4.9a) to S/N_0 of (4.7) is hard to come by due to the difficulty in interpolating between the individual graphs in Figure 4.7a–f for different values of P_{DI}. Nevertheless, a coarse examination of the behavior of this S/N_0 ratio over a decade variation in $W_{ss}T_M$ above and below the above sample value reveals a rather insensitive behavior (approximately a $\pm$ 1 dB variation in the ratio for each of these values of N_T). Finally, if l is optimized (somewhere between 5 and 25) with the corresponding adjustments being made for P_{DI} and P_{FAI}, it is

[6] Note that, when $W_h T_h$ is small ($W_h T_h = 1$ in the case at hand), the output of the energy detector cannot be approximated by Gaussian statistics. Use of the Gaussian approximation to the chi-square distribution will yield results which are generally pessimistic in the predicted covertness of the waveform (i.e., the calculated S/N_0 will be less than the true value).

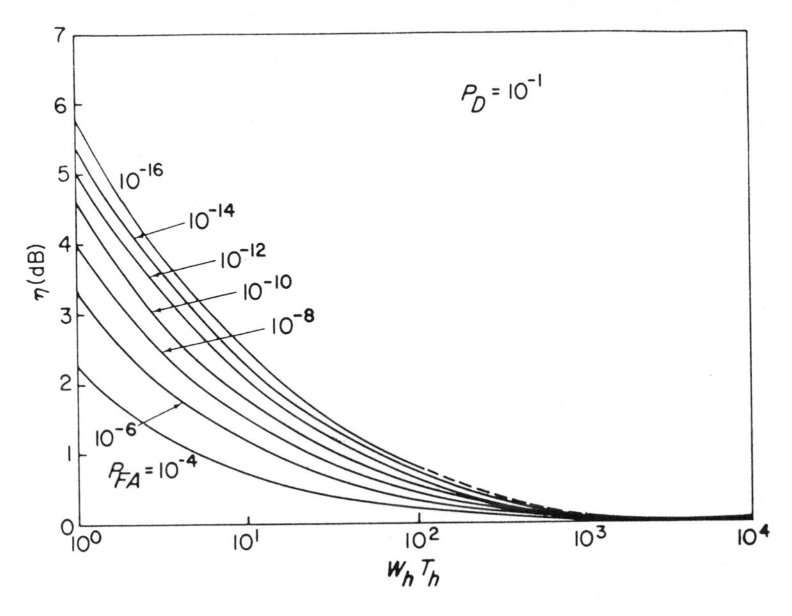

Figure 4.7b. Correction factor η for Gaussian approximation as a function of time-bandwidth product ($P_D = 10^{-1}$) (reprinted from [4]).

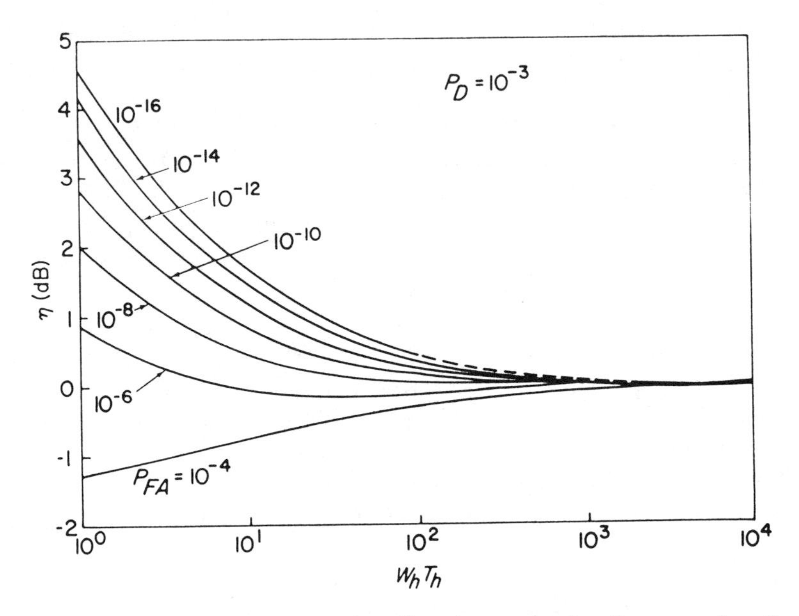

Figure 4.7c. Correction factor η for Gaussian approximation as a function of time-bandwidth product ($P_D = 10^{-3}$) (reprinted from [4]).

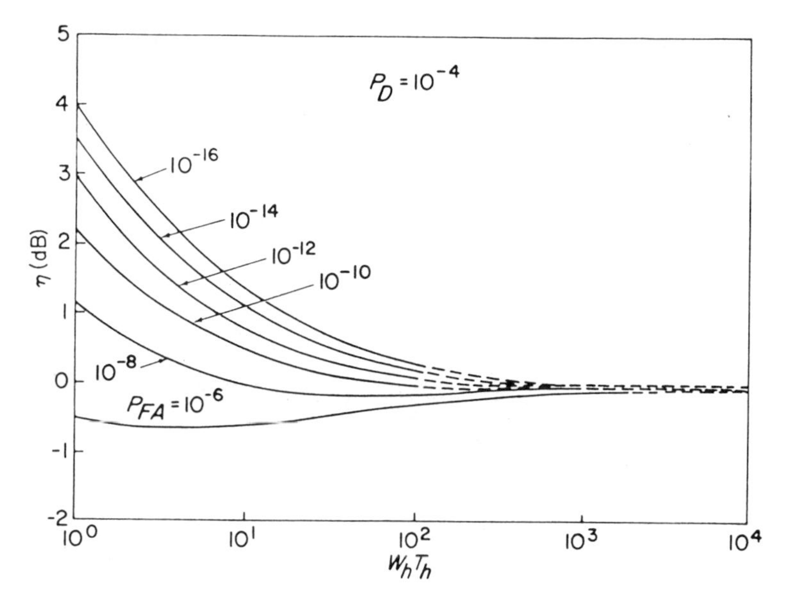

Figure 4.7d. Correction factor η for Gaussian approximation as a function of time-bandwidth product ($P_D = 10^{-4}$) (reprinted from [4]).

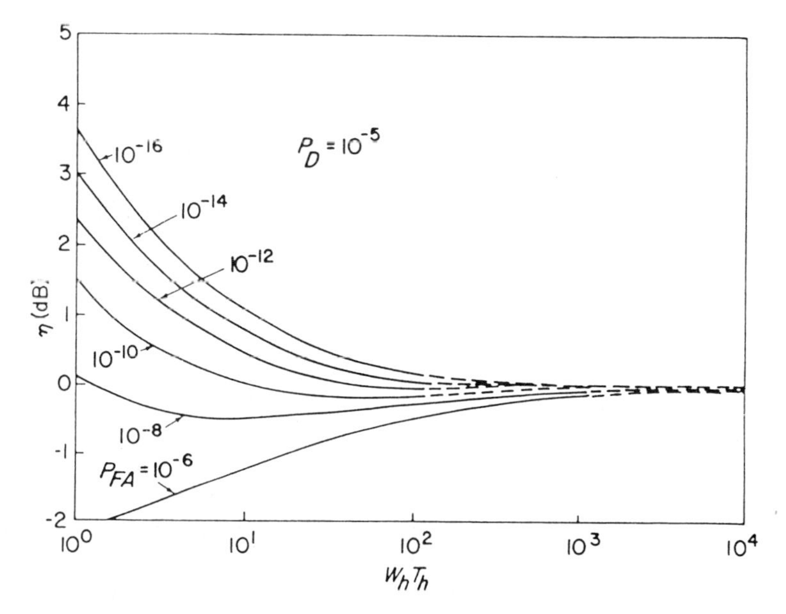

Figure 4.7e. Correction factor η for Gaussian approximation as a function of time-bandwidth product ($P_D = 10^{-5}$) (reprinted from [4]).

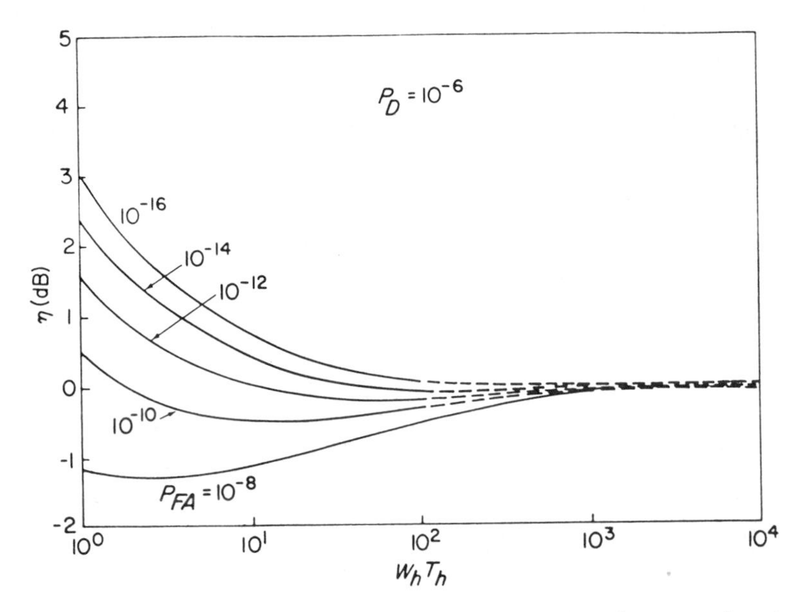

Figure 4.7f. Correction factor η for Gaussian approximation as a function of time-bandwidth product ($P_D = 10^{-6}$) (reprinted from [4]).

expected that the FBC performance may be on the order of only 1.7 dB worse than the optimum detector (1.5 dB better than the $l = 1$ FBC).

At the modest cost of about 1.7 dB of S/N_0 required, it is therefore seen that the reduced complexity FBC is a more practical topology for a multichannel detector. However, even though the individual channels and their output combiner is simplified, one million channels are still required to achieve the above performance. One million less-complex channels, practically speaking, still remains untenable.

(4) Partial-Band Filter Bank Combiner (PB-FBC)

The PB-FBC is simply an FBC with less than the optimum or maximum number of channels. Suppose that $N_T' < N_T$ channels are used, each channel still matched to one of the candidate FH frequencies. The channel reduction factor is defined as $f = N_T'/N_T$.

A new consideration now enters the detector performance. When all N_T channels are implemented, a hop frequency must appear at any given time in one of the channel filters. If only N_T' channels are employed, then, on a per-hop basis, a specific hop frequency will not be covered by the filter bank if it corresponds to a deleted channel. Thus, from hop to hop, it becomes a probabilistic matter as to whether or not the PB-FBC will have a signal within one of its filters. When a signal is present within one of the channels, this condition is known as a "hit." The probability of a hit, assuming that one of the N_T possible hop frequencies may, with equal likelihood, be transmitted on any given hop interval, is $P_{\text{hit}} = f$.

One view of the performance penalty paid for a partial-band detector is to consider what happens to the per-channel detection probabilities P_{DI} and P_{FAI}. If the transmitted message is sufficiently long (for the moment, assume that it is infinite in duration or continuous), then, on the average, the effective per-hop detection probability is $P'_{DI} = P_{DI}P_{\text{hit}}$. The per-channel false alarm probability, however, is unchanged, as it always depends on the absence of a hit. Now, since P_D and P_{FA} are the real measures of performance, using relationships akin to (4.8), the following results are obtained:

$$P'_D = N_h P'_{DI} = (N_h P_{DI}) P_{\text{hit}} \tag{4.10a}$$

$$P'_{FA} = N_h N'_T P_{FAI} = (N_h N_T P_{FAI}) f. \tag{4.10b}$$

But, because $P_{\text{hit}} = f$, it is readily seen that $P'_D = P_D f$ and $P'_{FA} = P_{FA} f$, i.e., the original probabilities are reduced by the channel reduction factor, f. There are only two ways to restore the desired performance: (1) increase the per-channel P_{DI} and P_{FAI} values by $1/f$, which requires a higher S/N_0 relative to the full-band FBC, or (2) increase N_h by $1/f$. This latter fix implies that the communicator's message must therefore be longer by a factor of $1/f$ (which is no problem if the message is continuous) but, since the interceptor has absolutely no control over the message duration, increasing N_h represents an untenable solution.

Use of the PB-FBC should be predicated on its performance being equivalent to the full-band FBC for all conditions except that of a larger S/N_0 requirement. On very short messages, however, the considerations are a bit more complex. What must be factored into the performance criteria is the probability of a given number of hits, n, per message, this being determined by the binomial distribution, viz.,

$$P(n) = \frac{N_h!}{n!(N_h - n)!}(P_{\text{hit}})^n (1 - P_{\text{hit}})^{N_h - n}. \tag{4.11}$$

Defining P^*_{DI} and P^*_{FAI} as the per-channel detection and false alarm probabilities needed to achieve the PB-FBC short message detection and false alarm probabilities, P_D and P_{FA}, the actual P_D conditioned on n is given by

$$P_D(n) = 1 - (1 - P^*_{DI})^n (1 - P^*_{FAI})^{N_h - n} \tag{4.12}$$

whereupon the message detection probability, P_D, is obtained by averaging (4.12) over the probability distribution of (4.11), namely,

$$P_D = \sum_{n=1}^{N_h} P_D(n) P(n). \tag{4.13}$$

Equation (4.13) cannot be easily calculated without the use of a computer;

however, with N_h large and P^*_{FAI} very small, the approximation

$$P_D \cong P_D(\bar{n}) \tag{4.14}$$

is valid, where $\bar{n}$ is the mean of the distribution in (4.11), namely,

$$\bar{n} = \sum_{n=1}^{N_h} nP(n) = N_h f. \tag{4.15}$$

Substituting (4.15) into (4.12) and ignoring the $(1 - P^*_{FAI})^{N_h - n}$ factor gives

$$P_D \cong 1 - \left(1 - P^*_{DI}\right)^{N_h f}. \tag{4.16}$$

Solving for P^*_{DI} yields the desired result

$$\begin{aligned} P^*_{DI} &= 1 - \left(1 - P_D\right)^{1/N_h f} \\ &= 1 - \left(1 - P_D\right)^{N_T/(W_{ss} T_M f)}. \end{aligned} \tag{4.17}$$

The companion relationship for P^*_{FAI} is

$$\begin{aligned} P^*_{FAI} &= P_{FA}/(N_T N_h f) \\ &= P_{FA}/(W_{ss} T_M f). \end{aligned} \tag{4.18}$$

Equations (4.17) and (4.18) are therefore used in lieu of (4.8a) and (4.8b), respectively, for computing the performance of the PB-FBC as per (4.9).

The preceding gives the average or expected performance of the PB-FBC for a single message having N_h hops. It is instructive to examine the conditional detection probability in order to gain an understanding of the true statistical nature of per-message detection using a PB-FBC. For this purpose, it is necessary to return to the numerical example. A recapitulation of the parameter values is:

$$\begin{aligned} P_D &= 0.9 \\ P_{FA} &= 10^{-6} \\ N_T &= 10^6 \\ W_{ss} T_M &= 8 \times 10^9 \\ N_h &= 8000. \end{aligned}$$

Suppose that it is decided that an $N'_T = 1000$-channel PB-FBC is practical (rather than the one-million-channel FBC), then $f = P_{\text{hit}} = N'_T/N_T = 10^{-3}$. The per-channel probabilities calculated using (4.17) and (4.18) become $P^*_{DI} = 0.25$ and $P^*_{FAI} = 1.25 \times 10^{-13}$. (Contrast these numbers with $P_{DI} = 1.25 \times 10^{-4}$ and $P_{FAI} = 1.25 \times 10^{-16}$ for the one-million-channel FBC). Also note that $\bar{n} = N_h f = 8$, i.e., this is the average number of hits per message.

Table 4.1 lists $P(N)$, $P_D(N)$, and the cumulative probability, $\Pr\{n \leq N\}$ as functions of N. The interpretation is that, for any given message of 8000 hops, there could be N hits with probability $P(N)$ and the

Table 4.1
Binomial distribution detection probabilities, $P_D = P_D(\bar{n}) = 0.9$.

N	$P(N)$	$P_D(N)$	$\Pr\{n \leq N\} = \sum_{n=0}^{N} P(n)$
0	0.000334	0	0.000334
1	0.002675	0.250	0.003009
2	0.010712	0.438	0.013722
3	0.028587	0.578	0.042308
4	0.057209	0.684	0.099519
5	0.091581	0.763	0.191098
6	0.122153	0.822	0.313252
7	0.139639	0.867	0.452890
8	0.139656	0.900	0.592547
9	0.124139	0.925	0.716686
10	0.099298	0.944	0.815985
11	0.072199	0.958	0.881843
12	0.048115	0.968	0.936299
13	0.029594	0.976	0.965893
14	0.016900	0.982	0.982793

corresponding conditional probability of detection $P_D(N)$. Note that eight or more hits per message are required to raise $P_D(N)$ to the point where it equals or exceeds the desired $P_D = 0.9$. The probability of this happening is only $\Pr\{n \geq 8\} = 0.55$. (For the full-band FBC, there is no hit conditional statistic so that $P_D = 0.9$ can be expected with unit probability.) The inference, then, is that, if P_D is to be quite close to 0.9 in a single-message basis, a further modification of P_{DI}^* is in order. Say it is desired to equal or exceed $P_D = 0.9$, with a corresponding hit-related probability of 0.9. This requires $P_D(N) \geq 0.9$, which, from Table 4.1 demands that $N \geq 5$. Using these values in (4.12) results in $P_{DI}^* = 0.37$ (rather than 0.25, as above).

Suppose, now, that the PB-FBC is reduced to a single channel. The per-hop hit probability becomes $P_{\text{hit}} = 10^{-6}$ and the probability of one or more hits in the 8000-hop message sequence would be only 7.9×10^{-3}. Clearly, since at least one hit is required for detection, these are very unfavorable odds, and the interceptor would not use a single-channel FBC no matter how high S/N_0 might be. What, then, is a reasonable lower limit on the number of channels, i.e., how small can f be allowed to become? As a minimum, at least one hit per message is needed. In [3], it is suggested that f must be greater than or equal to $1/N_h$. Taking $f = P_{\text{hit}} = 1/N_h$, the probability of one or more hits per message is $1 - (1 - 1/N_h)^{N_h}$. For very large N_h, it can be easily shown that this quantity approaches $1 - e^{-1} = 0.632$. This figure may be only marginally acceptable, as explained previously. If the probability of one or more hits per message is to be, say, 0.9, then P_{hit} will have to be increased from 10^{-6} to 2.87×10^{-4} and the minimum f becomes $f = 2.3/N_h$. Further, on the basis that a single hit is to

Table 4.2

PB-FBC $\Delta S/N_0$ requirements; $P_D = 0.9$, $P_{FA} = 10^{-6}$.

f	Number of Channels	$P_{DI}^{*\#}$	$\Delta S/N_0$ Relative to the Full-Band FBC$^+$
1	1,000,000	1.125×10^4	0 dB
10^{-2}	10,000	0.045	+2.8 dB
10^{-3}	1,000	0.37	+3.8 dB
5×10^{-4}	500	0.536	+4.5 dB
2.88×10^{-4}	288	0.90	+5.6 dB
1.25×10^{-4}	125	0.90@	+5.4 dB

Based on a hit-related probability of 0.9 (see text)
+ The second detection threshold $l = 1$ in all cases
@Hit-related probability is 0.63 (see text)

be adequate for detection, the per-hop channel detection probability must be made equal to the overall detection probability, i.e., $P_{DI}^* = P_D$. Thus, a detection probability of 0.9 will be achieved if a hit occurs, while the probability of no hits per message will be 0.368 for a 125-channel absolute minimum channel PB-FBC, and 0.1 for a PB-FBC that has 288 channels.

Table 4.2 summarizes the $\Delta S/N_0$ requirements for the PB-FBC relative to the full-band FBC as a function of f. As can be seen, the cost is significant, especially for the 1000 or less channel PB-FBC, which represents the range of practical detectors.

A summary of the relative performance of the various detector configurations discussed to this point appears in Table 4.3. What should be deduced is the gross complexity (as measured by the number of channels) versus the

Table 4.3

Performance comparison of detector types using wideband radiometer as reference.

Detector Type	Number of Channels	Required $\Delta S/N_0$	Implementation Notes
Optimum Multichannel	10^6	−11.1 dB	Impractical because of large number of channels
Full-Band Filter Bank Combiner	10^6	−7.9 dB	Impractical because of large number of channels
Partial-Band Filter Bank Combiner	1000 500 125	−4.1 dB −3.4 dB −2.5 dB	Practical but quite complex and costly to build using analog mechanization of the channels
Wideband Energy	1	0 dB	Simplest and least costly of all types to build

performance tradeoff. Taking, for example, the 500-channel PB-FBC as representative of the realizable multichannel class, it can be seen that its S/N_0 performance is 7.7 dB inferior to the optimum detector and only 3.4 dB superior to the wideband detector. In fact, as will be shown in Section 4.2.2.2, even the 3.4 dB advantage virtually disappears when the practical problem of frequency synchronization is considered. Obviously, since the PB-FBC will cost significantly more than the wideband energy detector (see Section 4.2.3), its slight performance advantage is judged insufficient to justify its general use.

4.2.1.3 Signal Structure and Modulation Considerations

In the preceding subsections, the performance of the various detector types was viewed solely from the perspective of pure FH modulation. The effects of using PN and TH modulation in conjunction with FH will now be examined. We begin by briefly examining the effects on the impractical optimum multichannel detector.

When PN modulation is used in conjunction with frequency hopping as in (4.3), the bandwidth of each hop is increased to the PN chip rate $R_c = 1/T_c$. Thus the time-bandwidth product of each hop becomes

$$N \triangleq W_h T_h = T_h R_c > 1. \tag{4.19}$$

The optimum multichannel detector in this case has a structure identical to Figure 4.4 with the operation $I_0(\cdot)$ replaced by $K_N(\cdot)$ where

$$K_N(x) \triangleq \left[\frac{I_{N-1}(Nx)}{(Nx)^{N-1}} \right] 2^{N-1}\Gamma(N). \tag{4.20}$$

The performance of this detector is similarly given by (4.7) with $I_0^{-1}(\cdot)$ replaced by $K_N^{-1}(\cdot)$, i.e.,

$$\frac{S}{N_0} = \frac{W_{ss}}{2N_T} K_N^{-1} \left[1 - N_T + N_T \exp\left(\frac{d^2 N_T}{W_{ss} T_M} \right) \right]. \tag{4.21}$$

For convenience, the function $\frac{1}{2}K_N^{-1}(y)$ (in dB) is plotted against y in dB in Figure 4.8, with N as a parameter. For large values of N, a good approximation to $\frac{1}{2}K_N^{-1}(y)$ is [4]

$$\frac{1}{2} K_N^{-1}(y) \cong \sqrt{\frac{\ln y}{N}} \tag{4.22}$$

which is quite accurate for $\frac{1}{2}K_N^{-1}(y) < \frac{1}{4}(-6 \text{ dB})$ which corresponds to $N \gtrsim 200$ for the range of y plotted in Figure 4.8. Thus, using (4.22) in (4.21) gives the simplified relation

$$\frac{S}{N_0} = \frac{W_{ss}}{N_T} \left\{ \frac{1}{N} \ln \left[1 - N_T + N_T \exp\left(\frac{d^2 N_T}{W_{ss} T_M} \right) \right] \right\}^{1/2}; N > 200. \tag{4.23}$$

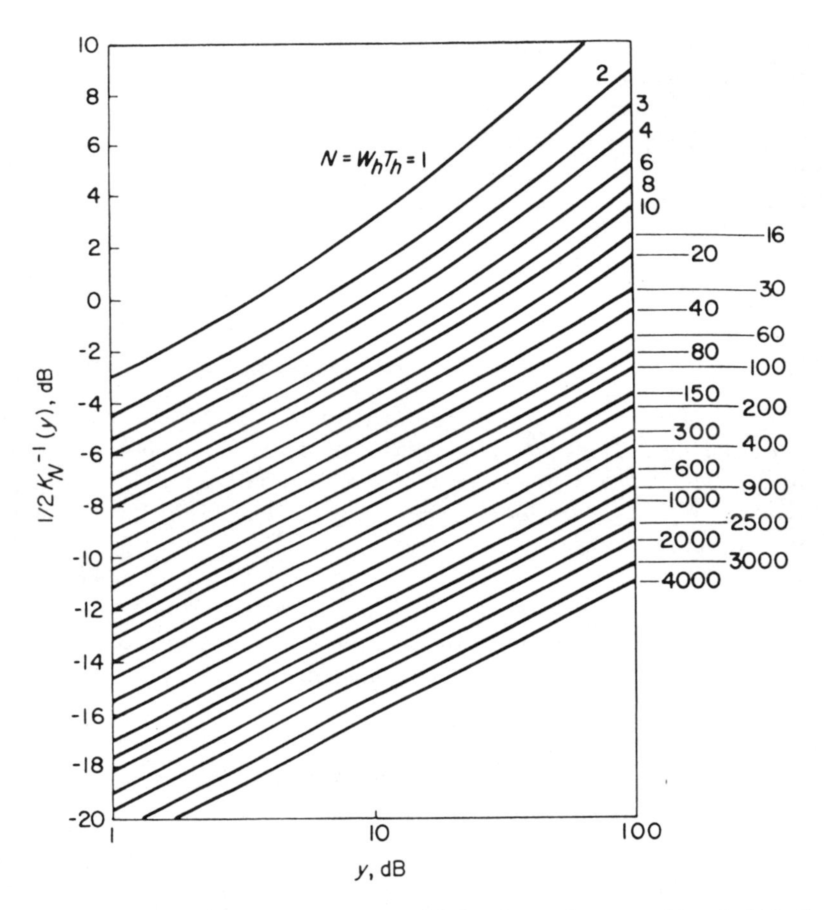

Figure 4.8. Optimum receiver channel weighting factor for several bandwidth-time products (reprinted from [4]).

For the more important practical detector types, namely, the wideband energy detector and the partial-band filter bank combiner, it has previously been seen that the underlying equation of performance is of the form

$$S/N_0 = (\eta d)\sqrt{W_x/T_x} \tag{4.24}$$

where ηd is a function of the desired P_D and P_{FA} together with the statistical (non-Gaussian) nature of the decision quantities, W_x is the detection channel bandwidth, and T_x is the detection integration interval. A wideband detector requires $W_x = W_{ss}$ (total hop bandwidth) and $T_x = T_M$ (total message duration) while, for the PB-FBC, $W_x = W_h$ (hop pulse bandwidth) and $T_x = T_h$ (hop pulse duration). The communicator therefore has three parameters which he may change or influence in some fashion to make detection more difficult for the interceptor, namely, his transmitter power, which directly affects S/N_0, W_x, and T_x.

For the wideband detector, it is clear that restructuring the signal per-hop bandwidth within a fixed total bandwidth of W_{ss} (assumed to be at its maximum value already due to RF channel allocation regulations) has no impact on wideband detector performance. One option of the communicator is to lower his bit or symbol rate by a factor of $\lambda < 1$. This implies that his transmitter power may also be lowered by this same λ factor (ignoring, for the present, the likely increase in non-coherent combining loss in the receiver), meaning that the interceptor's received S/N_0 is also reduced by λ. Now, since $T_x = T_M$ is increased by $1/\lambda$ (the number of bits per message is fixed), the net effective S/N_0 loss to the interceptor is proportional to $\sqrt{\lambda}$, as can be seen by referring to (4.24). It is clear that not quite all of this advantage will be gained if the communicator's non-coherent combining losses are accounted for, but some increase in covertness can be expected from this strategy.

The other option of the communicator as regards the wideband detector is to time hop the message, i.e., to transmit the bits or hop pulses in a time-pseudorandom and non-continuous fashion. Thus, the message transmitter is pulsed on and off in a sequence known only to the communicator. If the transmission is therefore effectively spread in time from T_M to δT_M, $\delta > 1$, the interceptor has no choice but to make his $T_x = \delta T_M$ while, at the same time, his average S/N_0 decreases by $1/\delta$.

Against the wideband detector, then, the communicator may effectively employ a joint strategy of low data rate and TH to the point where he is no longer willing to stretch the total message transmission time beyond some limit (likely dictated by some other operational considerations). The communicator is also frequency hopping over the entire RF band, W_{ss}, but employing further pulse spreading by direct-sequence PN modulation of the instantaneous hop frequencies has no performance effect on the wideband detector.

As concerns the FBC, lowering the communicator's transmitter power as a result of decreasing the data rate (but without altering the hop parameters) can be seen from (4.24) to effectively lower the intercept per-hop detection S/N_0 by λ. On the other hand, the use of TH by the communicator causes the interceptor to raise his ηd because N_h increases, requiring a smaller P_{FAI}^* in order to maintain the specified per-message P_{FA}. However, since ηd is not very sensitive to the increase, the overall effectiveness of this technique is slight. The proper strategy, therefore, is to lower the data rate and corresponding transmitter power as much as possible, again subject to some total transmission time constraint.

Since the PB-FBC operates on the per-hop parameters, the performance being dependent on $\sqrt{W_h/T_h}$, anything the communicator does to increase this quantity directly affects the required intercept S/N_0, forcing it closer to that needed for the wideband detector and discouraging PB-FBC use (especially because of its much higher cost). Now, with pure FH, the per-pulse bandwidth is fixed at $W_h = 1/T_h$. If, for a given T_h, a wider hop pulse bandwidth is desired, it must be brought about by means of additional modulation, namely, PN spreading of the instantaneous hop frequency in accordance with (4.19). Thus the interceptor's S/N_0 requirement appears to increase by $\sqrt{N}$. But it must be remembered that N_T decreases with increasing per-channel bandwidth to $N_{PN} = N_T/N$. This decrease means that the P^*_{FAI} as given by (4.18) is allowed to increase by N. By means of a numerical example, the net effect can be judged. Postulating the 125-channel PB-FBC found in Tables 4.2 and 4.3, suppose that $N = 10$. The required S/N_0 is found to be 2 dB *higher* than that required by the wideband energy detector! (As a point of reference, replacing N_T by $N_{PN} = 10^5$ in (4.21), then making use of Figure 4.8, the optimum multichannel detector still requires 10.1 dB less S/N_0 than the wideband radiometer.)

A general conclusion drawn from this single example is misleading, however. A second example will illustrate that PN spreading of the individual hop frequencies could decrease rather than increase covertness. Suppose that, relative to the ongoing example, the hop rate R_h is reduced by a factor of 20 with all other parameters remaining the same. Then the pertinent system parameters established by the communication are now:

$$W_{ss}T_M = 8 \times 10^9$$

$$N_T = 2 \times 10^7$$

$$N_h = 400 \text{ hops.}$$

The communicator now has two options in terms of signal design: pure FH or FH/PN.

With pure FH, if the interceptor wishes to build a minimum channel PB-FBC, he will have to implement $N_T/N_h = 50{,}000$ channels. Such is probably unjustifiable, so the interceptor opts for the wideband energy detector, which requires the same S/N_0 as before.

Alternatively, assume that the communicator selects FH/PN with a PN code rate such that $N = 10^4$. Then, $N_{PN} = 2000$, meaning that the interceptor could either implement a 2000-channel full-band FBC or a 5-channel minimum-channel PB-FBC (certainly affordable!) The S/N_0 requirements for these two FBCs are, respectively, 5.3 dB and 2.7 dB *below* that of the wideband energy detector. Thus, the interceptor, by virtue of either choice (or any between), is able to better his performance over that of the wideband energy detector. So, for this example, the communicator is seen to lose covertness by selecting FH/PN over pure FH. Of course, it must be conceded that the communicator could be forced to the FH/PN position simply because of the very practical problem of building frequency synthesizers able to produce 2×10^7 frequencies of the required spacing with the necessary accuracy and stability. Nevertheless, the example serves to show that FH/PN is not necessarily superior to pure FH from a sophisticated detector point of view.

As a final point, it should be stated at this juncture that, although the use of PN spreading appears, under appropriate conditions, to doom the PB-FBC to a position of virtual uselessness, the PB-FBC actually attains this distinction on its own when the effects of imperfect frequency synchronization are included in its performance (as discussed in the next section). Thus, the addition of PN spreading will only act to "add icing to the cake." The real value of the PN coding, if it is to have some effective purpose, is to combat jamming of the receiver so that the communicator does not have to increase his transmitter power to overcome the jamming to the same limit as that required when no PN modulation is employed.

4.2.2 Non-Idealistic Detector Performance

4.2.2.1 The Problem of Time Synchronization

The detector performance discussed to this point has been computed on the basis of ideal conditions in that the interceptor has been assumed to have information necessary for perfect time and frequency synchronization. In the case of the former, this is equivalent to saying that the interceptor has exact knowledge of both the time at which a single message transmission originates and the epochs of the individual hop pulses.

In this section, the penalty paid (in increased S/N_0 required) by the interceptor for total lack of time synchronization information is determined. For this more practical or realistic condition, it will be necessary to consider adjunct capabilities to the detectors of Section 4.2.1. Only the wideband energy detector and the FBC will be investigated as they represent the most viable types of detectors useful to the interceptor.

The only continuing assumption will be that the interceptor knows the message duration (T_M) and the hop time interval (T_h). Epochs for the message and its constituent hops are presumed to be unknown. It is also assumed that the interceptor has no means of "learning" so that timing information gleaned from one message transmission will aid in synchronization and detection of a subsequent message (should it occur).

(1) Wideband Detector with Overlapping I & Ds, Each of Duration Equal to that of the Message

Consider, first, a simple modification of the wideband (single-channel) detector wherein the square-law detector output now feeds two T_M-sec integrate and dumps (I & Ds) which overlap $T_M/2$ sec (see Figure 4.9). For this interceptor detector, a signal or noise-only decision will be made every $T_M/2$ seconds.

Assuming with noise only present at the input, an output from either threshold device (corresponding to an I & D output that exceeds the

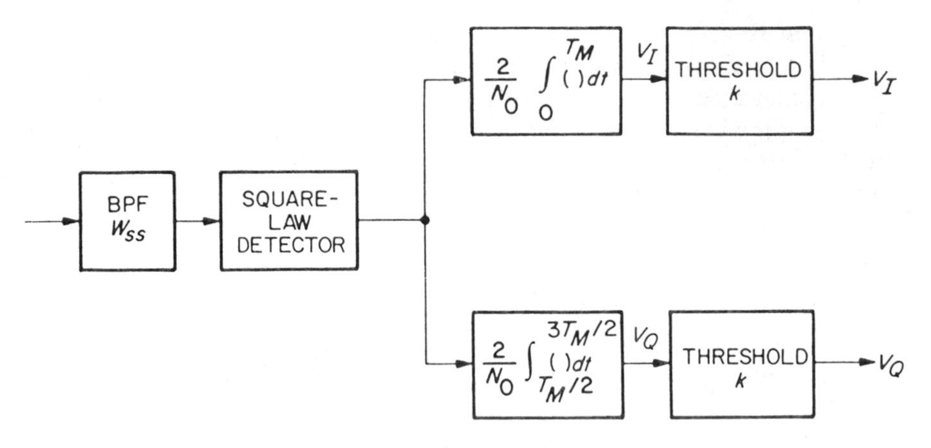

Figure 4.9. Overlapping I & D detector.

threshold k) constitutes a false alarm. The false alarm rate (FAR) is the product of the decision rate $2/T_M$ and the false alarm probability per decision P_{FA}, i.e.,

$$\mathrm{FAR} = \frac{2}{T_M} P_{FA} \tag{4.25}$$

where, as before, for large $W_{ss}T_M$,

$$P_{FA} \cong Q\left[\frac{k - 2W_{ss}T_M}{2\sqrt{W_{ss}T_M}}\right]. \tag{4.26}$$

Thus, to achieve the same false alarm rate as for the basic non-overlapping I & D case, the false alarm probability of (4.26) must be one-half its previous value.

To determine the probability of detection P_D, it is assumed that, with signal-plus-noise present at the input, an output from either threshold device constitutes a true decision, i.e., message detection. When the I & Ds are overlapped as in Figure 4.9, then, in the worst case, three-quarters of the signal energy will be covered by one I & D and three-quarters by the other (assuming that the signal energy is uniformly distributed). This situation is depicted in Figure 4.10.

The above statements can be put into mathematical terms as follows:

$$\begin{aligned} P_D &= \Pr\{V_I > k \text{ or } V_Q > k\} \\ &= 1 - \Pr\{V_I < k \text{ and } V_Q < k\} \end{aligned} \tag{4.27}$$

where, for large $W_{ss}T_M$, V_I and V_Q are jointly Gaussian random variables. For the worst case situation of Figure 4.10, their joint probability density

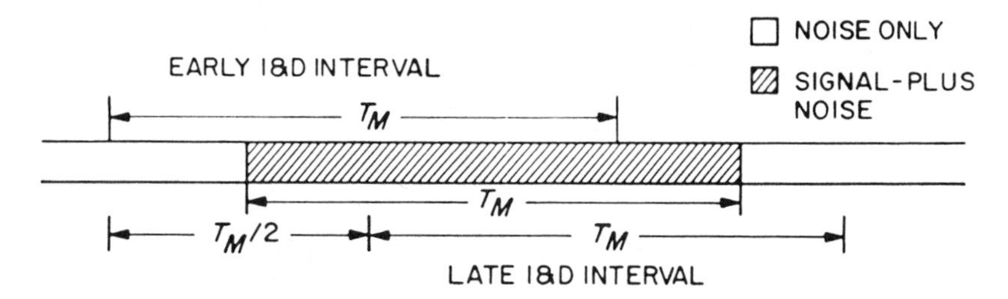

Figure 4.10. Worst case signal misalignment.

function is given by

$$p(V_I, V_Q) = \frac{1}{2\pi\sigma^2\sqrt{1-\rho^2}} \exp\left\{ -\frac{1}{2(1-\rho^2)} \left[\left(\frac{V_I - \mu}{\sigma} \right)^2 + \left(\frac{V_Q - \mu}{\sigma} \right)^2 - 2\rho \frac{(V_I - \mu)(V_Q - \mu)}{\sigma^2} \right] \right\} \tag{4.28}$$

with

$$\rho = \frac{1}{2}\left(\frac{1 + 2\gamma}{1 + \frac{3}{2}\gamma} \right)$$

$$\mu = 2W_{ss}T_M\left(1 + \frac{3\gamma}{4}\right)$$

$$\sigma^2 = 4W_{ss}T_M\left[1 + \frac{3\gamma}{2}\right] \tag{4.29}$$

and

$$\gamma \triangleq \frac{S}{N_0 W_{ss}}. \tag{4.30}$$

The parameter γ in (4.30) represents the signal-to-noise ratio in the input bandwidth.

Using (4.28) the detection probability of (4.27) can be expressed as

$$P_D = 1 - \int_{-\infty}^{k} \int_{-\infty}^{k} p(V_I, V_Q)\, dV_I\, dV_Q \tag{4.31}$$

which unfortunately cannot be obtained in closed form. Nevertheless, P_D can be upper (union) and lower bounded as follows:

$$\begin{matrix} \int_k^\infty p(V_I)\, dV_I \\ \text{or} \\ \int_k^\infty p(V_Q)\, dV_Q \end{matrix} < P_D < \int_k^\infty p(V_I)\, dV_I + \int_k^\infty p(V_Q)\, dV_Q \tag{4.32}$$

or, equivalently,

$$Q\left(\frac{k-\mu}{\sigma}\right) < P_D < 2Q\left(\frac{k-\mu}{\sigma}\right). \tag{4.33}$$

Substituting (4.29) into (4.33) gives the desired result:

$$Q\left(\frac{k - 2W_{ss}T_M\left(1+\frac{3\gamma}{4}\right)}{2\sqrt{W_{ss}T_M\left(1+\frac{3\gamma}{2}\right)}}\right) < P_D < 2Q\left(\frac{k - 2W_{ss}T_M\left(1+\frac{3\gamma}{4}\right)}{2\sqrt{W_{ss}T_M\left(1+\frac{3\gamma}{2}\right)}}\right) \tag{4.34}$$

To determine the S/N_0 required by an interceptor using the overlapped I & D detector of Figure 4.9, for a basis of comparison, the same false alarm rate and detection probability as would be required for a non-overlapped single I & D detector with perfect time synchronization is assumed. Since the overlapped I & D does not have an explicit closed-form expression for P_D, it will be equated to both of the two bounds in (4.34) and thereby a bounding range of values for the required S/N_0 will be obtained.

Proceeding as above, the right-hand side of (4.26) is equated to $P_{FA}/2$, and the threshold k is eliminated between the resulting expression and either the upper or lower bound of (4.34) with the result

$$P_D = C_D Q\left[\frac{Q^{-1}\left(\frac{P_{FA}}{2}\right) - \frac{3}{4}\left(\frac{\lambda}{2\sqrt{W_{ss}T_M}}\right)}{\sqrt{1+\frac{3}{4}\left(\frac{\lambda}{W_{ss}T_M}\right)}}\right] \tag{4.35}$$

where $C_D = 1$ or 2, and

$$\lambda = \frac{2ST_M}{N_0}. \tag{4.36}$$

Since, typically $\lambda \ll W_{ss}T_M$, the square root in (4.35) simplifies to unity. Finally, solving for S/N_0 and substituting the values of 1 or 2 for C_D gives the desired result:

$$\frac{4}{3}\sqrt{\frac{W_{ss}}{T_M}}\left\{Q^{-1}\left(\frac{P_{FA}}{2}\right) - Q^{-1}\left(\frac{P_D}{2}\right)\right\} < \left(\frac{S}{N_0}\right) < \frac{4}{3}\sqrt{\frac{W_{ss}}{T_M}}\left\{Q^{-1}\left(\frac{P_{FA}}{2}\right) - Q^{-1}(P_D)\right\}. \tag{4.37}$$

Recall that the equivalent result for the detector with a single non-overlapping I & D (and perfect synchronization) is given by (4.4) together with (4.5).

As an example of the application of (4.37), consider the parameters of the continuing example of Section 4.2.1 ($W_{ss}T_M = 8 \times 10^9$). For the performance criteria of $P_D = 0.9$ and $P_{FA} = 10^{-6}$, the lower and upper bounds on the S/N_0 requirement for the overlapping I & D detector as found from (4.37) are then, respectively, 0.3 dB and 1.2 dB greater than the S/N_0 requirement for the perfectly synchronized wideband energy detector. Alternately stated, for the above performance parameters and the detector of Figure 4.9, the penalty paid by the interceptor for lack of message time synchronization is between 0.3 and 1.2 dB.

(2) *Wideband Detector with Single (Non-Overlapping) I & D of Duration Equal to Half the Message Duration*

A simpler configuration than that of Figure 4.9 is to maintain the identity of the ideal wideband (single channel) detector but reduce the post-detection I & D interval by a factor of two. Thus, by consecutively integrating over only half the message duration, the interceptor is guaranteed to have one interval which contains signal-plus-noise over its entire duration regardless of his initial epoch. Of course, since the integration interval is now only half as long as before, then, relative to the ideal wideband detector with integration over the full message duration and perfect time synchronization, an S/N_0 penalty of approximately a factor of $\sqrt{2}$ (1.5 dB) will be paid.

In the following, a more exact mathematical formulation of the above conclusion will be developed. The worst case situation from the interceptor's viewpoint occurs when one integration interval (the 0-th) sees full signal and the two adjacent intervals (−1-st and 1-st) each contains signals in only half the interval, as shown in Figure 4.11.

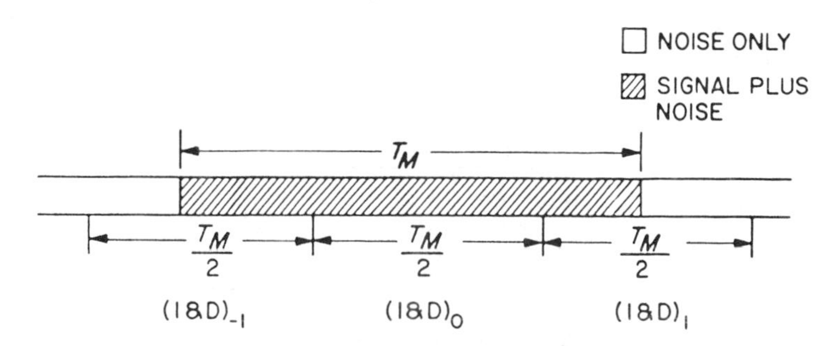

Figure 4.11. Worst case signal condition.

For this case, the probability of detection is

$$\begin{aligned} P_D &= 1 - \Pr\{V_{I_{-1}} < k \text{ and } V_{I_0} < k \text{ and } V_{I_1} < k\} \\ &= 1 - Q\left(\frac{-k+\mu_{-1}}{\sigma_{-1}}\right) Q\left(\frac{-k+\mu_0}{\sigma_0}\right) Q\left(\frac{-k+\mu_1}{\sigma_1}\right) \\ &> 1 - Q\left(\frac{-k+\mu_0}{\sigma_0}\right) = Q\left(\frac{k-\mu_0}{\sigma_0}\right) \end{aligned} \tag{4.38}$$

where (for large $W_{ss}T_M$)

$$\begin{aligned} \mu_{-1} &= \mu_1 = W_{ss}T_M\left(1 + \frac{1}{2}\gamma\right) \\ \mu_0 &= 2W_{ss}T_M(1+\gamma) \\ \sigma_{-1}^2 &= \sigma_1^2 = W_{ss}T_M(1+\gamma) \\ \sigma_0^2 &= 2W_{ss}T_M(1+2\gamma). \end{aligned} \tag{4.39}$$

Since the false alarm probability is still given by (4.26) with, however, T_M replaced by $T_M/2$, then using the lower bound of (4.38) on P_D, together with (4.39), a simple upper bound is obtained on the required interceptor S/N_0, namely,

$$\left(\frac{S}{N_0}\right) < \sqrt{\frac{2W_{ss}}{T_M}}\left\{Q^{-1}(P_{FA}) - Q^{-1}(P_D)\right\}. \tag{4.40}$$

Comparing (4.40) with (4.4) together with (4.5), it is readily observed that the maximum penalty (inferred above) is $\sqrt{2}$ (1.5 dB). Thus, the required S/N_0 falls on the average, between that given by (4.4) and (4.40).

(3) Wideband Detector with a Continuous Integration Post-Detection RC Filter

Perhaps the simplest alternative of all consists of a square-law (envelope) detector followed by an RC filter which acts as a continuous integrator, as shown in Figure 4.12.

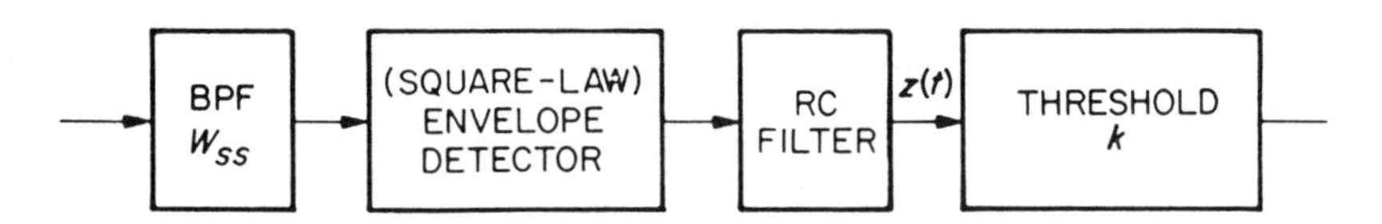

Figure 4.12. Continuous integration detector.

A similar configuration using digital integration is considered in [6]. When noise only is present, the RC filter output is a random process whose instantaneous mean and variance are theoretically constant (independent of time).[7] Furthermore, the instantaneous signal-to-noise ratio (mean-to-standard deviation ratio) is only a function of the ratio of the pre-detection filter bandwidth W_{ss} to the RC filter 3 dB cutoff frequency f_c.

When signal-plus-noise is present, the RC filter output mean and variance become functions of time over the message duration. Furthermore, the mean-to-standard deviation ratio is again a function of W_{ss}/f_c, plus, now, the pre-detection bandwidth signal-to-noise power.

If the noise bandwidth B_N of the RC filter is chosen equal to that of the integrate-and-dump with integration interval equal to the message duration, namely,

$$B_N = \frac{\pi f_c}{2} = \frac{1}{2T_M} \tag{4.41}$$

or, equivalently,

$$\frac{W_{ss}}{f_c} = \pi W_{ss} T_M \tag{4.42}$$

then, for large $W_{ss}T_M$, the RC filter output mean-to-standard deviation ratio becomes

$$\frac{\overline{z(t)}}{\sigma_z} = \begin{cases} \sqrt{W_{ss}T_M}\,; \; -\infty \le t \le t_1 & \text{(noise only)} \\ \sqrt{\dfrac{W_{ss}T_M}{1 + 2\gamma\left(1 - \exp\left[-\dfrac{4}{T_M}(t - t_1)\right]\right)}} \\ \times\left[1 + \gamma\left(1 - \exp\left[-\dfrac{2}{T_M}(t - t_1)\right]\right)\right]; \\ t_1 \le t \le t_1 + T_M & \text{(signal-plus-noise).} \end{cases} \tag{4.43}$$

In (4.43) the parameter t_1 represents the time epoch of the single message duration T_M.

If any threshold crossing by the RC filter output $z(t)$ constitutes an alarm, then for large W_{ss}/f_c (or, equivalently, large $W_{ss}T_M$), it may be assumed that $z(t)$ is a Gaussian process and the false alarm and detection

[7] From a practical standpoint, it is necessary only to assume that the RC filter has been integrating on noise for a period of time which is long relative to the filter time constant.

probabilities are given by

$$P_{FA} \cong Q\left[\frac{k' - 2W_{ss}T_M}{2\sqrt{W_{ss}T_M}}\right]$$

$$P_D(t) = Q\left[\frac{k' - 2W_{ss}T_M\left[1 + \gamma\left(1 - \exp\left[-\frac{2}{T_M}(t - t_1)\right]\right)\right]}{2\sqrt{W_{ss}T_M\left[1 + 2\gamma\left(1 - \exp\left[-\frac{4}{T_M}(t - t_1)\right]\right)\right]}}\right] \tag{4.44}$$

where the normalized threshold k' is related to the threshold k of Figure 4.12 by

$$k' = \frac{2T_M}{N_0}k. \tag{4.45}$$

The normalization in (4.45) is chosen to make (4.33) analogous to the relations derived for the previous I & D detector configurations.

Letting $t = t_1 + T_M$ in (4.44) (the detection probability is maximized if the RC filter output crosses the threshold at the termination of the message), then eliminating k' between P_{FA} and P_D (as before) gives a relationship for the S/N_0 required by the interceptor, namely,

$$\left(\frac{S}{N_0}\right) = \frac{\sqrt{\frac{W_{ss}}{T_M}}\left\{Q^{-1}(P_{FA}) - Q^{-1}(P_D)\right\}}{1 - e^{-2}}. \tag{4.46}$$

Comparing (4.46) with (4.4) together with (4.5) it is observed that, for given values of W_{ss}, T_M, P_{FA}, and P_D, the interceptor pays a "synchronization penalty" of $10\log_{10}(1 - e^{-2}) = 0.63$ dB relative to the ideal wideband detector.

Summing up the expected performance of the wideband energy detector for the condition of unknown message epoch, it is seen that the average S/N_0 performance penalty paid for any one of the three proposed "fixes" amounts to about 0.7 dB, and the maximum penalty does not exceed 1.5 dB. Which of the three approaches should be used by the interceptor will likely be dependent on cost and other operational factors.

(4) Filter Bank Combiner with Overlapping I & Ds, Each of Hop Interval Duration

Analogous to the modification of the wideband detector discussed in (1) of Section 4.2.2.1 and illustrated in Figure 4.9, it is proposed that a filter bank combiner make use of quadrature overlapping I & Ds, each of hop interval duration, as shown in Figure 4.13. In the most general case, channel threshold decisions made on the N_T in-phase I & D outputs are logically

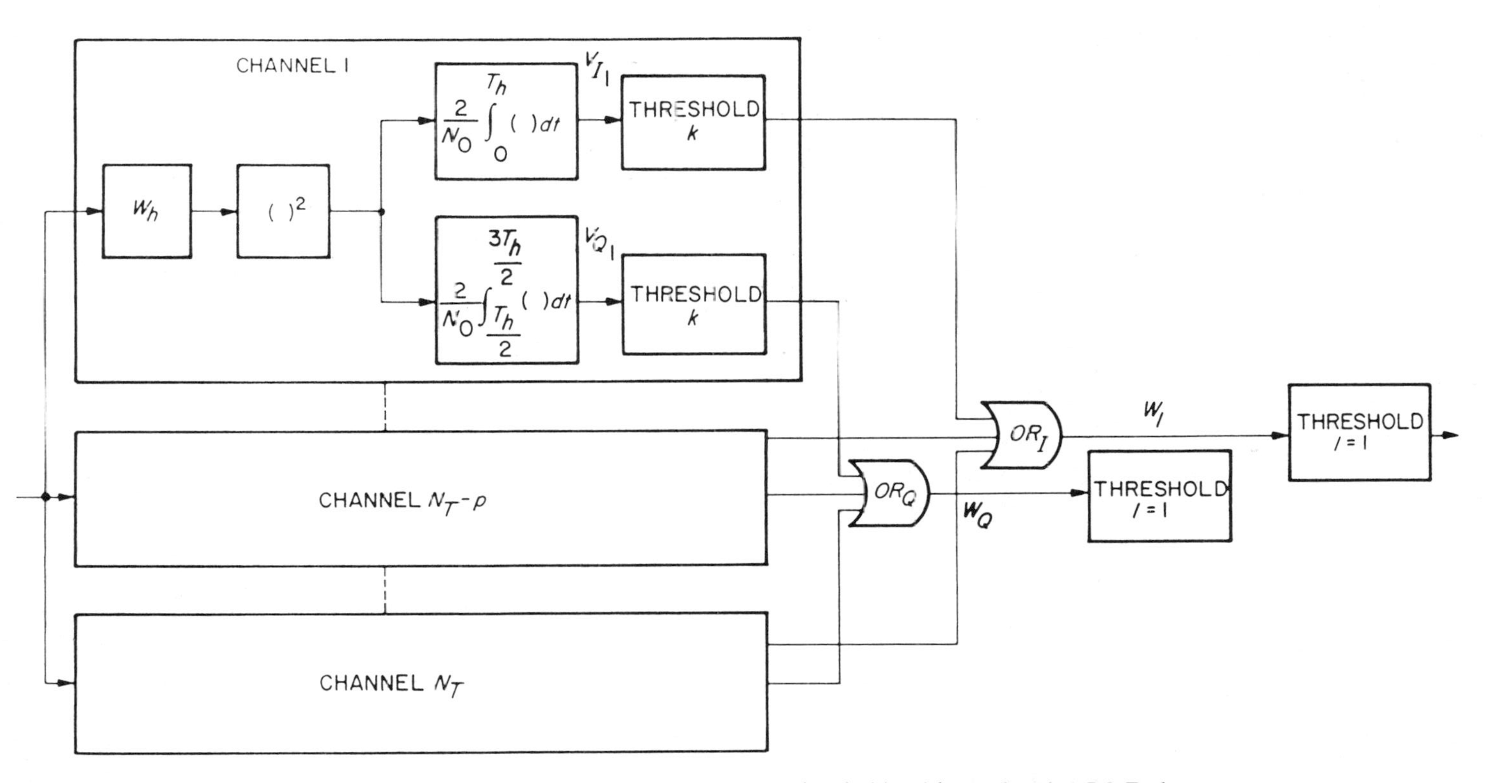

Figure 4.13. Filter bank combiner (unity output threshold) with overlapping I & D detectors.

OR'd, accumulated over a message duration, and compared with an integer threshold, k. A similar situation takes place for the N_T quadrature I & D outputs. If, as has been previously done, one assumes that $l = 1$ for simplicity of analysis, then the accumulators which would normally precede these threshold devices can be eliminated with no loss in generality. This has been done in Figure 4.13.

When noise-only is present, an output from any of the N_T inphase I & Ds which exceeds the channel threshold k will produce an output from the in-phase logical OR and a corresponding output from the in-phase ($l = 1$) threshold device. This constitutes a false alarm and can occur at any integer multiple of the hop time, T_h. Similarly, an output from any of the quadrature I & Ds which exceeds the channel threshold k will produce a false alarm which can occur at any odd multiple of half the hop time. Since potential false alarm decisions are now being made every half-hop interval $(T_h/2)$, the false alarm rate is again the product of the decision rate $(2/T_h)$ and the false alarm probability per decision, P_{FA}. Letting P_{FAI} denote the per-channel, per-hop false alarm probability, i.e., the probability that an individual I & D output exceeds the channel threshold k, then, clearly, P_{FA} and P_{FAI} are related by the familiar binomial equation

$$P_{FA} = 1 - (1 - P_{FAI})^{N_T} \tag{4.47}$$

and the corresponding false alarm rate is given by

$$\text{FAR} = \frac{2}{T_h} P_{FA} = \frac{2}{T_p}\left[1 - (1 - P_{FAI})^{N_T}\right] \tag{4.48}$$

which, for $P_{FAI} \ll 1$, becomes approximately

$$\text{FAR} = \frac{2}{T_h} P_{FAI}. \tag{4.49}$$

To achieve a false alarm rate equal to that of the wideband detector with overlapping I & Ds, (4.49) is equated with (4.25). Then,

$$\frac{2}{T_M} P_{FA} = \frac{2}{T_h} N_T P_{FAI} = \frac{2}{T_M} N_h N_T P_{FAI} \tag{4.50}$$

or

$$P_{FAI} = \frac{P_{FA}}{N_h N_T} = Q\left(\frac{k - 2W_h T_h}{2\sqrt{W_h T_h}}\right). \tag{4.51}$$

Note that (4.51) is the identical equation which relates P_{FA} and P_{FAI} for the "ideal" filter bank combiner (see (4.8b)).

Alternatively, for Figure 4.13 to achieve the same false alarm rate as the "ideal" FBC, the false alarm probability P_{FA} or the per-channel false alarm probability P_{FAI} must be reduced to half its previous value.

To determine the overall probability of detection P_D, it is again assumed that, with signal-plus-noise present at the input, an output from either (unit level) threshold device constitutes a true alarm, i.e., message detection. However, to relate P_D to the per-channel, per-hop detection probability, P_{DI}, namely, the probability that an individual I & D output exceeds the threshold k, is, in general, a difficult task due to the continuing overlap of the inphase and quadrature I & Ds throughout the duration of the message. Nevertheless, through continued application of union bound techniques, upper and lower bounds on P_D are derived assuming a worst case out-of-synchronization condition of 1/4 of a hop interval. In particular, after many simplifying but practical assumptions, it is shown that

$$N_h Q\left(\frac{k - 2W_h T_h\left(1 + \frac{3\gamma_h}{4}\right)}{2\sqrt{W_h T_h\left(1 + \frac{3\gamma_h}{2}\right)}}\right) < P_D < 2N_h Q\left(\frac{k - 2W_h T_h\left(1 + \frac{3\gamma_h}{4}\right)}{2\sqrt{W_h T_h\left(1 + \frac{3\gamma_h}{2}\right)}}\right) \tag{4.52}$$

where

$$\gamma_h = \frac{S}{N_0 W_h}. \tag{4.53}$$

To determine the required S/N_0 using the detector of Figure 4.13 assume for a basis of comparison the same false alarm rate and detection probability as would be required for the ideal filter bank combiner with perfect time synchronization. Since again there is no explicit closed form expression for P_D, it will be equated to either of the two bounds in (4.52) and thereby a range of values of the required S/N_0 will be obtained. Proceeding as before, equating the right-hand side of (4.51) to $P_{FA}/2N_h N_T = P_{FAI}/2$ and eliminating the threshold k between the resulting expression and either the upper or lower bound of (4.52) gives

$$P_D = C_D N_h Q\left[\frac{Q^{-1}\left(\frac{P_{FA}}{2N_h N_T}\right) - \frac{3}{4}\left(\frac{\lambda_h}{2\sqrt{W_h T_h}}\right)}{\sqrt{1 + \frac{3}{4}\left(\frac{\lambda_h}{W_h T_h}\right)}}\right] \tag{4.54}$$

where $C_D = 1$ or 2 and

$$\lambda_h = \frac{2ST_h}{N_0}. \tag{4.55}$$

Since, typically, $\lambda_h \ll W_h T_h$, then simplifying the square root in (4.54) to unity, and solving for S/N_0 by substituting the values of either 1 or 2 for

C_D gives the desired result:[8]

$$\frac{4}{3}\eta_2\sqrt{\frac{W_h}{T_h}}\left\{Q^{-1}\left(\frac{P_{FA}}{2N_hN_T}\right)-Q^{-1}\left(\frac{P_D}{2N_h}\right)\right\} < \frac{S}{N_0} < \frac{4}{3}\eta_1\sqrt{\frac{W_h}{T_h}}\left\{Q^{-1}\left(\frac{P_{FA}}{2N_hN_T}\right)-Q^{-1}\left(\frac{P_D}{N_h}\right)\right\}. \tag{4.56}$$

Recall that the equivalent result for the ideal filter bank combiner with perfect time synchronization is given by (4.9).

Calculating the upper and lower bounds on the S/N_0 requirement for the FBC with overlapping I & Ds (recall that $N_hN_T = W_{ss}T_M$ or $N_h = W_{ss}T_M/N_T$, and $W_hT_h = 1$) and comparing these results with the S/N_0 requirement of a 125-channel partial-band FBC with perfect time synchronization (see Table 4.2), it is concluded that for the parameters of the continuing example, time synchronization loss ranges between 0.3 and 1.4 dB. Note that this result is essentially the same as that obtained for the wideband detector in (1) of Section 4.2.2.1.

4.2.2.2 The Problem of Frequency Synchronization

(1) Doppler Effects

For LPI scenarios in which the interceptor assumes the position of an enemy search aircraft, very significant Doppler shifts over the SS bandwidth can occur due to his velocity. The largest shifts occur for the lowest aircraft altitudes as the aircraft velocity component in the direction of the radiating source is nearly equal to the aircraft velocity. Since typically the interceptor is unable to know his velocity and altitude precisely, and certainly not his range, it should be easily appreciated that a PB-FBC having 125 channels randomly scattered across the frequency band will not have the channel center frequencies coincident with the received hop frequencies. In fact, if a hit occurs, the frequency error can, in many circumstances, be considered to be more or less any value across the filter passband with a uniform probability of occurrence.

(2) Performance of the FBC with Frequency Error

First it should be noted that the performance equation (4.9) for the FBC does not take into account the hop pulse energy lost due to the channel filter. Thus, the effective signal power at the input to the square-law detector

[8] Note that, as in the case of the ideal filter bank combiner, the (S/N_0) result must be multiplied by η, which represents a correction factor from a Gaussian assumption to chi-squared statistics.

following the filter will be reduced by the factor

$$\gamma_0 = \int_{-\infty}^{\infty} |H(f)|^2 T_h \left(\frac{\sin \pi f T_h}{\pi f T_h} \right)^2 df \tag{4.57}$$

where $H(f)$ is the equivalent lowpass transfer function of the bandpass filter.

If, for simplicity, an ideal rectangular-shaped filter characteristic is assumed, viz.,

$$|H(f)| = \begin{cases} 1; & |f| \leq \dfrac{1}{2T_h}, \\ 0; & \text{otherwise} \end{cases} \tag{4.58}$$

then (4.57) simplifies to

$$\gamma_0 = \int_{-1/2T_h}^{1/2T_h} T_h \left(\frac{\sin \pi f T_h}{\pi f T_h} \right)^2 df = \frac{1}{\pi} \int_{-\pi/2}^{\pi/2} \left(\frac{\sin x}{x} \right)^2 dx$$

$$= 0.7737 = -1.1\ dB. \tag{4.59}$$

Because the channel or filter which coincides with a given hop pulse does not pass all of the pulse power, adjacent channels must contain proportional amounts of the "spillover." In particular, the i-th adjacent channel, $i = \pm 1, \pm 2, \pm 3, \ldots$, will contain a signal component with power proportional to

$$\gamma_i = \int_{-(i+1/2)/T_h}^{-(i-1/2)/T_h} T_h \left(\frac{\sin \pi f T_h}{\pi f T_h} \right)^2 df = \frac{1}{\pi} \int_{-(i+1/2)\pi}^{-(i-1/2)\pi} \left(\frac{\sin x}{x} \right)^2 dx. \tag{4.60}$$

Thus, a more exact characterization of the FBC performance than that given in (4.8) and (4.9) is the following.

The per-hop (frame) detection and false alarm probabilities P_{Df} and P_{FAf} (i.e., the probabilities of a one out of the OR circuit in Figure 4.6 under signal-plus-noise and noise-only conditions) are given by

$$P_{Df} = 1 - \prod_i (1 - P_{DI_i}) \tag{4.61}$$

$$P_{FAf} = 1 - (1 - P_{FAI})^{N_T} \cong N_T P_{FAI}, \tag{4.62}$$

where the product over i in (4.61) goes over the N_T FBC channels and P_{DI_i} denotes the individual channel detection probabilities (no frequency error assumed at this juncture). Note that all P_{DI_i} have the same mathematical form, with the signal-to-noise ratio for each channel proportional to γ_i of (4.60) ($i = 0$ corresponds to the hop pulse channel). If, as was previously assumed, the $(\sin x/x)^2$ dependence of the effective power within the

N_T-channel energy detectors is ignored, (4.61) simplifies to

$$P_{Df} = 1 - (1 - P_{DI})(1 - P_{FAI})^{N_T - 1} \cong P_{DI}, \tag{4.63}$$

where P_{DI} and P_{FAI} are the previously defined individual channel detection and false alarm probabilities.

Now since $P_{DI_0} \gg P_{DI_i}$ for $i \neq 0$, the following simplifying assumption can be made:

$$\prod_i (1 - P_{DI_i}) \cong (1 - P_{DI_0}) \tag{4.64}$$

which, when substituted into (4.61), yields

$$P_{Df} \cong P_{DI_0}. \tag{4.65}$$

Comparing (4.63) and (4.65), it is observed that the per-hop detection probability is degraded approximately (in terms of SNR) by γ_0 relative to its value obtained by ignoring the true $(\sin x/x)^2$ spectral nature. Thus, since, for a unit threshold ($l = 1$ in Figure 4.6), the per-hop and overall message probabilities are related by

$$\begin{aligned} P_D &= N_h P_{Df} \cong N_h P_{DI_0} \\ P_{FA} &= N_h P_{FAf} \cong N_h N_T P_{FAI}, \end{aligned} \tag{4.66}$$

then comparing (4.66) with (4.8), (4.9) may be readily modified to include the effect of the channel filter on the required S/N_0, namely,

$$S/N_0 = \frac{\eta}{\gamma_0} d_I \sqrt{W_h/T_h} \tag{4.67}$$

where now

$$\begin{aligned} d_I &= Q^{-1}(P_{FAI}) - Q^{-1}(P_{DI_0}) \\ &= Q^{-1}(P_{FA}/N_h N_T) - Q^{-1}(P_D/N_h). \end{aligned} \tag{4.68}$$

For the partial-band FBC, the results of (4.64) and (4.65) are even better approximations since the remaining channels are far apart from one another and, thus, there is negligible adjacent channel $(\sin x/x)^2$ spillover.

When a frequency error Δf exists between the hop frequency in a given hop interval and the center frequency of the corresponding BPF, the SNR degradations γ_i of (4.59) and (4.60) are simply replaced by

$$\gamma_0(\Delta f T_h) = \int_{-1/2T_h + \Delta f}^{1/2T_h + \Delta_f} T_h \left(\frac{\sin \pi f T_h}{\pi f T_h} \right)^2 df = \frac{1}{\pi} \int_{-\pi[1/2 + \Delta f T_h]}^{\pi[1/2 + \Delta f T_h]} \left(\frac{\sin x}{x} \right)^2 dx \tag{4.69}$$

and

$$\gamma_i(\Delta fT_h) = \int_{-(i+1/2+\Delta fT_h)/T_h}^{-(i-1/2+\Delta fT_h)/T_h} T_h\left(\frac{\sin \pi fT_h}{\pi fT_h}\right)^2 df$$

$$= \frac{1}{\pi}\int_{-(i+1/2+\Delta fT_h)\pi}^{-(i-1/2+\Delta fT_h)\pi}\left(\frac{\sin x}{x}\right)^2 dx. \tag{4.70}$$

Table 4.4 tabulates $\gamma_0(\Delta fT_h)$ versus ΔfT_h. Clearly, the worst case degradation occurs when $\Delta fT_h = 0.50$. For the full-band (N_T channel) FBC at this value of ΔfT_h, two adjacent channels in each hop interval will have identical signal energy, each degraded by $\gamma_0(0.5) = 0.4514$ relative to the total. In this instance, the per-hop detection probability, ignoring the $(\sin x/x)^2$ spillover into the other channels, is given by

$$P_{DF} = 1 - \left(1 - P_{DI_0}(0.5)\right)^2 = 2P_{DI_0}(0.5) - \left[P_{DI_0}(0.5)\right]^2 \tag{4.71}$$

where, in general, $P_{DI_0}(\Delta fT_h)$ denotes the individual channel detection probability in the presence of a frequency offset Δf.

For the partial-band FBC, in each hop interval, it may be assumed that only one channel has signal-plus-noise with the total signal energy degraded by $\gamma_0(\Delta fT_h)$. Thus, the per-hop detection probability for the PB-FBC becomes

$$P_{DF} = 1 - \left[1 - fP_{DI_0}(\Delta fT_h)\right]\left[1 - P_{FAI}\right]^{fN_T-1} \cong fP_{DI_0}(\Delta fT_h) \tag{4.72}$$

where f is the channel reduction factor (previously defined) from the PB-FBC. The result is that a frequency error of Δf will require an effective increase in S/N_0 by a factor of $\gamma_0(0)/\gamma_0(\Delta fT_h)$.

In general, as was previously discussed under (1) of Section 4.2.2.2, the Doppler effects render Δf to a random variable status, which may be taken to be uniformly distributed between $-1/2T_h$ and $1/2T_h$. An average S/N_0

Table 4.4
Frequency offset losses.

ΔfT_h	$\gamma_0(\Delta fT_h)$	$\gamma_0(\Delta fT_h)$ in dB
0	0.7737	−1.1143
0.05	0.7697	−1.1371
0.10	0.7576	−1.2054
0.15	0.7380	−1.3196
0.20	0.7112	−1.4799
0.25	0.6781	−1.6871
0.30	0.6395	−1.9417
0.35	0.5964	−2.2446
0.40	0.5499	−2.5968
0.45	0.5012	−2.9996
0.50	0.4517	−3.4543

modifying factor may thus be obtained by averaging $\gamma_0(\Delta f T_h)$ over the uniform distribution in frequency. This factor is computed to be 1.55 or 1.9 dB and comprises the two components $1/\gamma_0(0) = 1.1$ dB and $1/\overline{\gamma_0(\Delta f T_h)} = 0.8$ dB.

4.2.3 Detector Implementation

In this section, some of the problems of realizing the detector types discussed in Section 4.2.1 are addressed. Since this subject alone could generate an entire chapter unto itself, the present scope will be limited to an assessment of the various general functional circuit topologies that may be employed. In addition, some insight will be given to implementation degradations which can further act to diminish the real effectiveness of the more complex detection approaches.

4.2.3.1 Basic Configurations

(1) Wideband Single-Channel Detectors

Many wideband radiometers have been built to operate in the SHF and EHF frequency bands, and have been used extensively for ground, airborne, and spacecraft applications. As a result, the technology needed for this type of detector is fairly well at hand. From a functional standpoint, a most difficult problem is that of setting and maintaining the receiver threshold value. Proper setting of the comparator threshold voltage relative to the output of the integrator is essential to meeting the specified P_D and P_{FA}. If the threshold is too low, an excessive false alarm rate is obtained while, if it is too high, detection of an actual signal may be missed. Even if the threshold is set properly initially, time, temperature, and voltage variations, and other dynamic conditions, will affect the overall receiver gain such that the initial setting will become incorrect. Further, the receiver effective noise temperature will also change with interceptor altitude and attitude (as the receiving antenna is subjected to varying background temperature due to changing angles and field of view). Thus, some precise, automatic, periodically updating method of threshold determination is needed.

Since the signal to be detected and the noise are uncorrelated but have a definite power ratio for a given P_D and P_{FA} at a specified S/N_0 and W_{ss}, it is necessary only to measure the noise level in the absence of signal in order to derive the independent variable which permits threshold calculation or establishment. Although elementary in principle, the implementation of this concept gives rise to a serious problem. The fact that the noise level must be measured in the absence of signal means that whatever time is taken to accomplish this must be taken from the time available to detect the signal. Switched (Dicke)-type receivers [7] work in this manner by providing a precision noise source which is periodically switched into the receiver in place of the antenna signal and multiplexing the calibration noise and actual signal-plus-noise out of the detector between a noise-level measuring integrator and the signal detection integrator. Typically, the performance penalty paid due to a 50 percent signal duty cycle and front-end switch insertion loss is about 4 dB in required S/N_0, which clearly impairs the interceptor's detection capability.

What then are the possible detector and receiving system alternatives which minimize these disadvantages? One solution would be to continuously measure the received system noise in a band immediately outside of W_{ss}, or to measure noise in a narrowband segment of W_{ss} for which P_{hit} is sufficiently small that an occasional signal pulse will have no significant effect on the measurement. This approach overcomes, to some extent, the problems with the switched (Dicke) method but suffers primarily from the fact that the measurement does not truly characterize the external and internal conditions over the whole bandwidth W_{ss}. Therefore, more than acceptable error in setting the threshold is probable.

In order to provide a means of wideband calibration without incurring the basic switched (Dicke) receiver losses, conventional temperature-measuring radiometers often employ switched parallel channels (e.g., Graham's receiver). Unfortunately, this technique, which is basically a differencing-null method, is inappropriate to the very wideband receivers of the type needed for intercept signal detectors because (1) uniform gain and phase-matching of the channels is very difficult, and (2) the form of the detected signal is not suited to separation into the necessary integration and threshold establishment functions.

Another possible technique would make use of phase orthogonal IF components—one embodying the input signal-plus noise and the other a wideband, locally generated, very stable calibration noise. Just prior to detection, the orthogonal components are phase separated into different detectors. The detector handling the signal-plus-noise component is fed to the integrator and threshold comparator circuits as usual, while the detected calibration noise is used to vary the threshold setting as a function of IF gain changes. Although this technique does not suffer from the 50 percent signal loss of the switched (Dicke) receiver, it still does not account for external, or non-common circuit internal, noise temperature, or gain variations. Maintaining a good quadrature relationship over a very wide IF band may also be quite difficult.

The best approach to threshold determination is based solely on the received signal and noise itself. It must be remembered that, for the general LPI scenario, the communicator's signal is present for only a very short time interval relative to the total intercept search period. Thus, most of the time, a noise-only condition exists against which adaptive statistical measurements may be made to maintain a constant P_{FA} as the statistics slowly change.[9] Since the specified P_{FA} is small (e.g., 10^{-6}), it obviously cannot be

[9]"Slowly" is defined such that the P_{FA}, if uncorrected, would change no more than a factor of 2 upward or a factor of 1/2 downward from one decision period to the next.

measured directly on a short-term basis. However, measurement of the higher order statistical parameters by means of moments or extreme methods, coupled with appropriate predictive formulas, leads to more accurate estimates of P_{FA}. Further, if this is done using reasonably wideband samples, the results can be made virtually insensitive to the presence of signal (whenever such occurs). The result is that the P_{FA} estimates may be directly related to the correct threshold value and the comparator threshold will be continually adjusted to compensate for all external and internal receiver noise temperature and gain changes. Contemporary microprocessor-based algorithms make this method highly viable.

(2) *Channelized Detectors*

In most situations, because of the small practical processing gain achievable at a significant cost over the wideband detector a channelized detector is unlikely to be used. Apart from these considerations, this subsection will investigate channelized detectors from a purely operational topology.

As representative of the considerations involved for channelized detectors, the 125 minimum channel PB-FBC of (4) in Section 4.2.1.2 will be used to illustrate the tradeoffs and problems. Stated explicitly, the task is to receive the total SS band of frequencies and downconvert 125 selected hop frequency positions into W_h-wide channels, each followed by detectors, FH pulse period integrators, and comparators.

The first question that must be answered is: which 125 of the $N_T = 10^6$ possible channels should be selected? If the communicator's FH pattern is essentially random and uniform over the hop frequency set, then it can be rightfully argued that it makes no difference which frequencies are chosen. Whether they are uniformly spaced and contiguous on some 125 W_h-wide sub-band or randomly dispersed across the total SS band should have no effect on the statistical parameter P_{hit}. From an ease of implementation point of view, even without supplying details, it is well conjectured that a receiver built around the contiguous sub-band would be the simplest to realize in terms of downconversion and IF amplification. The uniformly spaced but separated channels would be the second-best choice on the same basis. The communicator also appreciates this and, if he surmises that either approach has been adopted by the interceptor, even if he is not aware of which specific hop channels (uniformly spaced or contiguous) have been chosen, he can likely increase his LPI advantage by structuring the nature of his hop pattern over the *finite* message. Thus, if a contiguous sub-band receiver is being used by the interceptor, the communicator should hop his frequencies over some narrow band (of necessity, still much greater than 125 W_h) or over a small number of non-uniformly separated narrow bands in the hope that none of the frequencies coincide with the interceptor's sub-band. If, on the other hand, the interceptor's receiver is built on the uniformly separated principle, the communicator should hop his frequencies

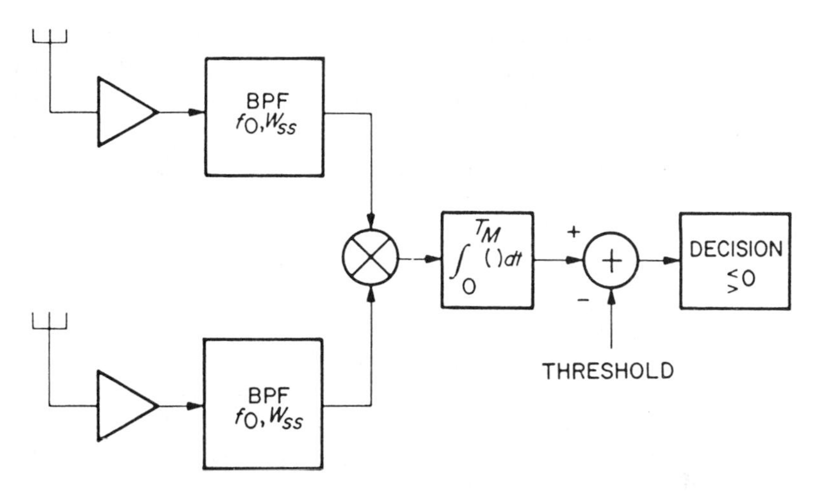

Figure 4.14. Correlation radiometer.

in a pattern that would not allow any frequencies over the message duration to have a separation anywhere near whatever the interceptor's uniform separation distance is expected to be and its multiples.[10] By virtue of such considerations, it appears that the interceptor must employ the randomly dispersed strategy if he is not to give the communicator any *a priori* reason to use some structured hop format over the message duration in order to lower the probability of a hit in the interceptor's channels.

4.2.3.2 Other Possible Feature Detector Configurations

In this section, several additional detector types that have appeared in the literature as applicable to LPI detection are briefly reviewed. One configuration is a variation of the wideband energy detector. Another exploits a specific feature of the communicator's signal in an attempt to detect the FH hop rate. Finally, a method of actually detecting the FH pattern is discussed.

A technique known as the *correlation radiometer* is illustrated in Figure 4.14. This instrument has two independent antennas (that cover the same geometric area) and RF circuits. The result is that, when a signal is present, the signal components from each leg into the multiplier are highly correlated (essentially identical in amplitude and phase) while the noise terms are uncorrelated. Thus, only the cross-correlated signals produce a direct voltage to the integrator. The theoretical advantage of the correlation radiometer over the square-law radiometer is that it requires 3 dB less S/N_0 for the

[10] Large Doppler may modify this strategy somewhat.

same P_D and P_{FA} performance. If two antennas are to be used, however, it is also possible to have each antenna cover one-half of the specified geometric area (3 dB gain increase), which then produces the same S/N_0 performance with two wideband radiometers (operating independently) as that for the correlation radiometer. An advantage of the half-coverage dual-antenna system is that it gives some directional information (say, left versus right) which the correlation radiometer is incapable of since its antennas cover the same overlapping area. The threshold maintenance problem for the correlation receiver is essentially the same as that for the square-law receiver except that the former does not produce a direct voltage which is a function of the noise levels. This slightly simplifies the calculation of the threshold value from the statistical measurements made toward its determination. Overall, the tradeoffs between a correlation receiver and two independent square-law receivers are slight, and system performance and complexity are virtually the same.

One disadvantage of every wideband square-law or correlation type of detector is that it is sensitive to any form of signal, i.e., it will respond equally as well to the communicator's FH signal or to any other extraneous signal irrespective of modulation form and bandwidth (provided that its frequencies fall within (f_0, W_{ss})) as long as it has the same energy content on $(0, T_M)$. For this reason, other types of detectors that are more feature-dependent have been developed. One such configuration is the hop rate detector shown in Figure 4.15. For this receiver, the input band is subdivided into two sub-bands (upper and lower bands), each $W_{ss}/2$ wide. The output of each BPF is square-law detected and the results are differenced. When an FH signal appears at the receiver input, on the average, it spends 50 percent of its time in each sub-band, transitioning randomly at multiples of the hop period. Therefore, the differenced signal appears as (in the absence of noise) a two-level or bipolar waveform. Highpass filtering to remove any direct voltage components and lowpass filtering with a bandwidth on the order of the hop rate yields a narrowband lowpass signal. This signal is delayed by $T_h/2$, and the signal and its delay are multiplied. The result is a process that contains a strong periodic component at the hop rate which, in turn, is detected by, say, a narrowband spectrum analyzer. Although this receiver is capable of making a very accurate measurement of the hop rate, it does so at a large penalty in S/N_0 because it is basically a fourth-law device. (For the widely used system parameters of this section, the S/N_0 would have to be increased by 16 dB in order to achieve an equivalent detectability SNR.) As a result, the FH hop rate detector of Figure 4.15 offers the interceptor no advantage whatsoever in terms of basic detectability. Other rate detection (e.g., PN chip rate or TH rate) receivers may also be realized, but they likewise provide no gain over the wideband energy detector in terms of basic detectability.

Based upon our previous discussion, the implementation of the optimum multichannel receiver of Figure 4.4 is thought to be impractical. There is,

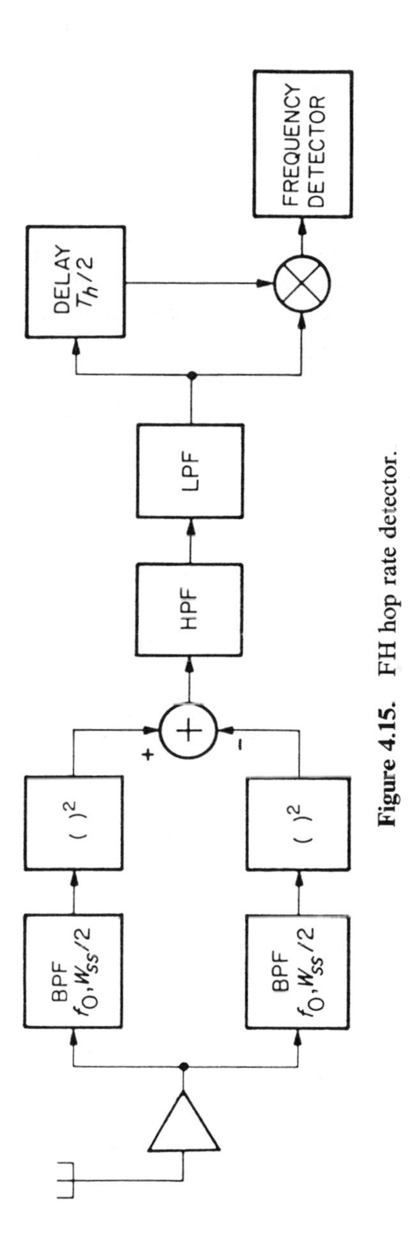

Figure 4.15. FH hop rate detector.

however, a particular mechanization which might make the multichannel detector somewhat more tractable, namely, the *digital spectrum analyzer*.

It may be easily shown that from a detection theoretic point of view, the outputs of a discrete frequency spectrum analyzer at the candidate hop frequencies are equivalent to an optimum non-coherent detection channelized receiver.[11] The spectral values may therefore be compared to appropriate thresholds and detection decisions made akin to the PB-FBC.

Realization of the spectrum analyzer requires that a particular RF frequency band, f_a to f_b, be translated to a lowpass frequency region so that $f_a \rightarrow 0$ and $f_b \rightarrow f_m$, where $f_m = f_b - f_a$. The lowpass waveform (signal-plus-noise) is then sampled at a rate of $2f_m$ samples/second and for a period of T_h seconds to obtain a sample set of $N_s = 2f_m T_h$ samples. A discrete Fourier transform is then calculated using the sample set for each of the candidate hop frequency locations. The magnitude of the Fourier transform at each frequency is compared with a threshold to determine if its spectral value is sufficiently large to indicate the presence of a signal (a hop pulse). This process is repeated for each hop pulse interval T_h.

Figure 4.16 shows functionally the steps involved in the spectrum analyzer algorithm and the pertinent equations of operation. The translation of the bandpass sub-band into the lowpass range $(0, f_m)$ assumes that the candidate hop frequencies are at $f_1 = W_h$, $f_2 = 2W_h$, $f_3 = 3W_h$, etc., with the total number of frequencies (channels) being f_m/W_h.

Consider now a full-band or N_T-channel spectrum analyzer, with the probability of a correct hop pulse decision being 0.9. (For the sake of the following, a message is assumed to be present.) Since, for a full-band spectrum analyzer $P_{\text{hit}} = 1$, on a per-hop basis, the probability of correctly determining the hop pulse frequency is therefore 0.9. Such a receiver would employ a maximum-likelihood decision process, and the required S/N_0 for $N_T = 10^6$ (plus the other example parameters previously cited) is (perfect time synchronization and no frequency error assumed) about the same as that required by a 500-channel PB-FBC for absolute detection; thus, if detection is possible, hop following is also possible provided a 10^6 channel spectrum analyzer can be realized! But it has already been pointed out that a 10^6 channel receiver of any sort is intractable. It would seem then that, even though FH following is theoretically possible, it cannot reasonably be implemented by a spectrum analyzer. There is, however, a technique which offers the potential of a realizable solution without the need for calculating the spectrum at each FH frequency. The method, first proposed by Kleinrock [8], involves time-domain autocorrelation operations on a T_h segment of received signal-plus-noise, and the principles may be summarized as follows.

---

[11] For perfect time and frequency synchronization, such a receiver performs slightly better than the optimum multichannel FH pulse-matched detector introduced in (2) of Section 4.2.1.2.

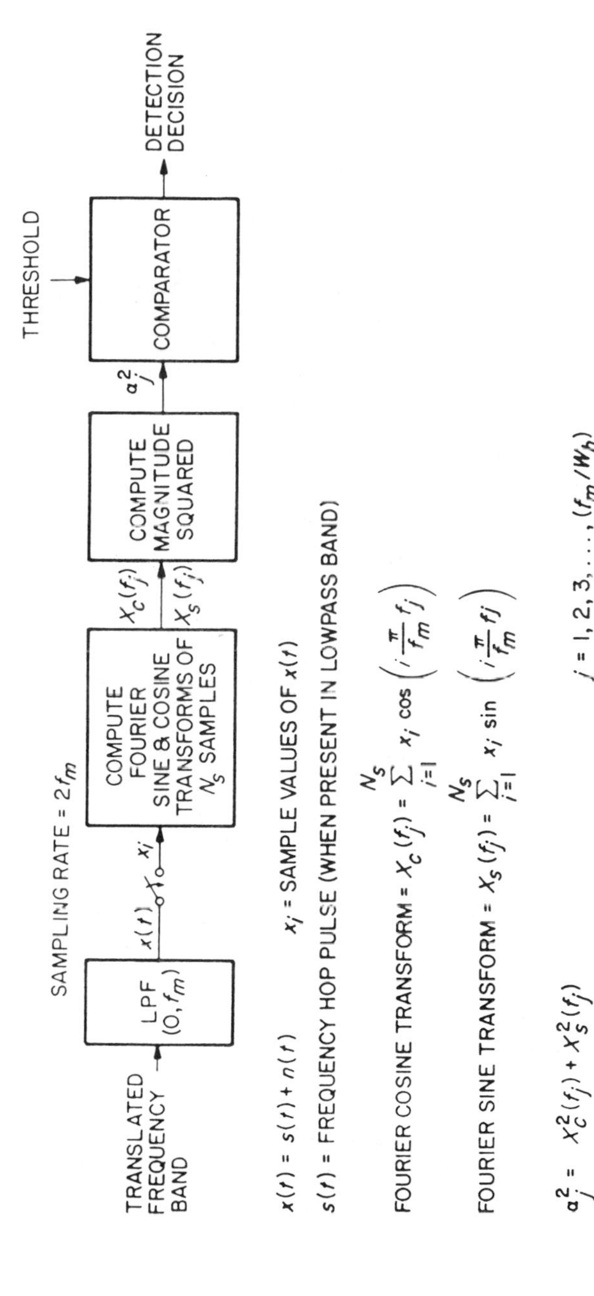

Figure 4.16. Spectrum analyzer operation.

Consider, for the moment, that a finite variance time function $x(t)$ has a power spectrum $S_x(f)$, and that the largest spectral value occurs at a frequency $f = f_{\max}$. Define the normalized autocorrelation function of $x(t)$ by the relationship

$$R_0(\tau) = \frac{\int x(t)x(t+\tau)\,dt}{\int x^2(t)\,dt}. \tag{4.73}$$

Next calculate the autocorrelation function of the autocorrelation function, viz.,

$$R_1(\tau) = \frac{\int R_0(\lambda)R_0(\lambda+\tau)\,d\lambda}{\int R_0^2(\lambda)\,d\lambda}, \tag{4.74}$$

and continue this process again and again. The n-th iteration therefore becomes

$$R_n(\tau) = \frac{\int R_{n-1}(\lambda)R_{n-1}(\lambda+\tau)\,d\lambda}{\int R_{n-1}^2(\lambda)\,d\lambda}. \tag{4.75}$$

Now it can be shown as $n \to \infty$ that the following limiting result is obtained:

$$\lim_{n\to\infty} R_n(\tau) \propto \cos[2\pi f_{\max}\tau], \tag{4.76}$$

that is, after an infinite number of iterations, a pure cosine function is obtained whose frequency corresponds to the location of the spectral maximum of $x(t)$.

As seen, then, it is possible to calculate the location of the largest spectral value without having to calculate the spectrum itself; this is exactly what needs to be accomplished if an FH follower is to be realized. Now the application of the above property to FH following requires that (1) only a finite T_h-second time segment be considered and, (2) an answer be obtained after only a reasonable number of iterations. As a result, some compromise must be allowed in terms of the accuracy of the estimate. Further, even with a T_h-second segment of signal-plus-noise to begin with, each successive iteration theoretically doubles the storage or memory required to hold the result; i.e., after n iterations, $R_n(\tau)$ is generally non-zero over a τ range of $2^{n+1}T_h$. Thus, in order to keep the storage needed at a reasonable size, truncation of the iterated function must be allowed so that $\tau_{\max}$ becomes manageable. This will further reduce the accuracy of the result. Nevertheless, for a desired frequency resolution or accuracy, there exists a procedure which will calculate an estimate of f_{max}, namely, $\hat{f}_{max}$, after only n_0 iterations.

The FH following receiver therefore becomes one which subdivides the received signal-plus-noise into contiguous T_h-second periods and applies the autocorrelation iterative estimator to each segment. The successive frequency estimates are then taken as being representative of the nearest true hop frequency, and the FH pattern (including the MFSK data) used by the communicator may be reconstructed with occasional errors that depend upon S/N_0 and the finite processing limitations previously summarized.

Implementation of an autocorrelation iterating receiver for large SS bandwidths (on the order of GHz) is currently nearly as unrealistic as the full-band spectrum analyzer. To be sure, the total band would have to be subdivided and individual processors applied to each sub-band. Frequency estimates for each sub-band would be obtained along with the normalization factors that would be used to determine which frequency corresponds to the largest spectral value. Present hardware capabilities appear to preclude that such a receiver could be cost effectively constructed. With the rapid advances being made in the surface acoustic wave (SAW), the charge-coupled device (CCD), and very high-speed digital technologies, however, economic feasibility may be only a few years hence. Using one-bit (two-level) quantization (at a sacrifice in required S/N_0), it is possible even with today's circuits to construct a processor capable of handling a 10 MHz frequency range. A 100 MHz range is probable by the mid to late 1980s. With such a capability, only a small number of channels is needed to cover the entire SS bandwidth. Clearly, then, the potential is realistic.

4.3 PERFORMANCE AND STRATEGIES ASSESSMENT

In this final section, an attempt is made to summarize and reconcile the issues and tradeoffs that have been detailed in the foregoing sections. The reader is again reminded that, due to the large number of variables involved, specific but typical examples are being used as the basis for extrapolating general conclusions. So as to broaden this basis and hopefully dispel "what if" type questions or uncertainties, some additional parameter and configuration conditions are explored.

4.3.1 Communicator Modulation and Intercept Detectors

Section 4.2 contained a very detailed examination of intercept detector types from both practical (or attainable) performance (as measured by the S/N_0 required) and implementation (assessed by functional and circuit complexity) perspectives. Using a fixed set of system parameters, the relative merits of four well-known detectors (optimum multichannel, full-band filter bank combiner (FB-FBC), partial-band filter bank combiner, wideband energy or radiometer) were compared, and it was observed that only the minimum channel partial-band filter bank combiner (PB-FBC) and the wideband energy detector have utility. Further, the minimum channel PB-FBC would be employed only when its S/N_0 performance advantage over the wideband radiometer justifies its complexity as reflected by the cost of mechanizing the number of channels needed.

To further strengthen these earlier conclusions, the performance of these same detectors will now be calculated for several different hop rates and in addition PN spreading of the hop pulses. The results are tabulated in Table 4.5. To repeat an earlier observation, in comparing the S/N_0 requirements of various intercept detectors, relative to, say, that of the wideband energy detector as a reference, it is not necessary to specify the SS bandwidth W_{ss}, the message duration T_M, or the hop rate $R_h = 1/T_h$. Rather, the product of W_{ss} and T_M, the total number of hops N_T in W_{ss}, and, if a partial-band configuration, the fractional number of channels f used in the implementation are all that are needed to perform the calculations. If PN spreading is used in hybrid with the assumed FH modulation, then one must, in addition, specify the ratio of PN code chip rate R_c to the hop rate. In Table 4.5 the PN code chip rate is held constant as the hop rate is varied over two decades (the effects of varying the chip rate will be discussed toward the end of this section). Thus, the ratio R_c/R_h also varies over two decades.

The central column in Table 4.5 repeats the numbers tabulated in Table 4.3 for FH modulation, with the modification that the time and frequency asynchronous losses derived in Sections 4.2.2.1 and 4.2.2.2, respectively, have been added. All other entries also include losses for lack of time and frequency synchronization. A double crosshatched line has been placed to separate the practical versus impractical detector realizations as measured by the number of channels required. As can be seen, only two entries represent a potential gain over the wideband energy detector; these are further reviewed in the following paragraphs.

For R_h such that $N_T = 10^6$, a 125-channel PB-FBC is capable of achieving a lower S/N_0 threshold than a wideband energy radiometer of a mere 0.5 dB. Considering the complexity of a 125-channel PB-FBC relative to that of the one-channel wideband detector, the gain is clearly not worth the cost. Thus, the interceptor will opt to use the wideband radiometer.

There is another pure-FH entry in Table 4.5 that warrants some review, namely, the minimum channel PB-FBC requiring 12,500 channels with R_h chosen to give $N_T = 10^7$. The 10.2 dB performance advantage over the wideband energy detector is very significant, and some form of implementation is therefore tempting. Postulating that mechanization of 12,500 channels is out of the question, even for a 10.2 dB S/N_0 advantage, it may be logically asked: Is there some implementable realization that can attain some of the gain?

Since it is mandatory that 12,500 channels be equivalently manifest, the only choice is to construct a PB-FBC with fewer real channels, say, by a

Table 4.5

A comparison of detector performance as a function of hop rate and FH versus FH/PN ($W_{ss}T_M = 8 \times 10^9$).

Detector Type		$R_c/R_{h1} = 1000$ R_{h1} ($N_T = 10^7$)		$R_c/R_{h2} = 100$ R_{h2} ($N_T = 10^6$)		$R_c/R_{h3} = 10$ R_{h3} ($N_T = 10^5$)	
		No. of Channels	$\Delta S/N_0$ (dB)	No. of Channels	$\Delta S/N_0$ (dB)	No. of Channels	$\Delta S/N_0$ (dB)
Optimum	FH	10^7	−17.5	10^6	−9.1	10^5	−1.9
Multichannel	FH/PH	10^4	−7.3	10^4	−3.7	10^4	+0.2
FB-FBC	FH	10^7	−14.6	10^6	−5.9	10^5	+3.3
	FH/PN	10^4	−5.0	10^4	+0.1	10^4	+5.3
Minimum Channel PB-FBC	FH	12,500	−10.2	125	−0.5	2	+9.0
($f = 1.25 \times 10^{-3}$)	FH/PN	13	−2.1	2	+3.7	1	+10.4
Wideband Energy	FH FH/PN	1	0	1	0	1	0

(Includes Average Time and Frequency Asynchronous Losses)

Table 4.6
Hopped-channel PB-FBC performance.

Detector	$1/K$	No. of Channels	$\Delta S/N_0$ (dB)
PB-FBC	1	12,500	−10.2
PB-FBC	0.1	1,250	−2.4
PB-FBC	0.01	125	+6.1
Wideband Energy	1	1	0

factor of $1/K$, and further reduce the integration time in each channel by the same factor so that the $12{,}500/K$ channels may be "hopped" to different (unique) sub-band locations K times per hop pulse interval. Table 4.6 summarizes the results of such a strategy. As can be seen, a reduction of the number of channels by a factor of 10 (to 1250 channels) decreases the gain from 10.2 dB to 2.4 dB, while another factor of 10 decrease (to 125 channels) causes worse performance than the wideband energy detector by 6.1 dB. Thus, the attempt is in vain. There is just no way the the minimum channel requirement can be ignored. This being the case, the communicator need never fear that the PB-FBC will ever be used by the interceptor as long as the required number of minimum channels is forced (by design) at low hop rates to be above some threshold (say, greater than 100) for which the cost per dB of advantage is untenable.

Turning now to the FH/PN performance entry in Table 4.5 for the minimum channel PB-FBC at R_h corresponding to $N_T = 10^7$, the 2.1 dB advantage over the wideband radiometer requires only 13 channels. This therefore represents a situation where the interceptor might indeed justify the PB-FBC. A good strategy for the communicator should be to avoid designing an FH/PN system with the subject parameters. If such a low hop rate is deemed necessary, the communicator should avoid PN spreading, at least at such a high chip rate. Table 4.7 shows the level of PB-FBC performance which may be expected if a lower chip rate is employed with the above hop rate. Again it can be seen that the tradeoff is a better intercept S/N_0 requirement, but at the expense of a significantly increased number of minimum channels. Thus, although the interceptor might opt to build a 13-channel detector when the PN chip rate is 1000 times the hop rate, he will likely refrain from a 125-channel unit when the chip rate is 100 times the hop rate, in favor of some more economical approach.

Having now reviewed a rather wide range of FH and FH/PN parameters, it appears reasonable to conclude that:

1. For any of the pure FH cases, the interceptor will be forced to the wideband energy detector,
2. PN spreading of the FH pulses is not essential to the prevention of channelized detector usage, nor does it directly add to the state of LPI.

Table 4.7
Performance of a minimum channel PB-FBC for a fixed hop rate and different PN chip rates; $N_T = 10^7$.

Detector	R_c/R_h	No. of Channels	$\Delta S/N_0$ (dB)
PB-FBC	1000	13	−2.1
PB-FBC	100	125	−6.0
PB-FBC	10	1,250	−8.9
Wideband Energy	Any	1	0

Restating, then, the basic strategy that should be employed by the communicator:

1. He should choose FH or FH/PN parameters so that any channelized detector requires larger S/N_0 than that for the wideband radiometer, or
2. He should choose FH or FH/PN parameters so that, if any channelized detector requires lower S/N_0 than that for the wideband radiometer, it is uneconomical to build because of the large minimum number of channels needed.

No channelized detector can be expected to be used against pure FH provided that the hop cell bandwidth is set equal to the hop rate and all possible hop frequencies are employed (i.e., can be synthesized).

4.3.2 Anti-Jam Measures

The basis for good AJ performance was covered in Volumes I and II. It was established there that both spread-spectrum modulation and error-correction coding must generally be used jointly in order to maximize jamming immunity. Table 4.8 tabulates for two different hop rates the maximum J/S ratios that may be tolerated for some typical cases of interest.[12] Each J/S entry has been calculated against the most effective jammer type and, therefore, represents the worst case jamming environment. As large a J/S ratio as possible is the desired condition that will, in turn, foster the most favorable LPI state.

Without coding, it is clear that FH/PN at the lower hop rate R_{h1} gives the best results. With coding, either FH or FH/PN at R_{h1} emerges the winner. Since, with error-correction coding, the highest levels of performance are attained for all conceivable jamming situations, it should be preferred. Whether or not PN spreading is employed is unimportant as it gains nothing when the hop rate is low.

[12] The numerical entries for this table may be calculated from the theoretical results presented in Chapter 2, Volume II.

Table 4.8
Maximum J/S ratios as a function of modulation and coding methods.

Modulation Technique / Error Correction Coding Technique	Maximum J/S $= (W_{ss}/R_b)/(E_b/N_0) = (N_T/3R) \times (R_h/R_s)/(E_b/N_0)$ for $P_b = 10^{-4}$			
	FH/8-ary MFSK		FH/PN/8-ary MFSK	
	$N_T = 10^7;\ R_{h1}/R_s = 8$	$N_T = 10^6;\ R_{h2}/R_s = 80$	$N_T = 10^7;\ R_{h1}/R_s = 80$	$N_T = 10^6;\ R_{h2}/R_s = 80$
No Coding ($R = 1$)	59.3 dB $\rho = .085$ PB-MTJ	59.1 dB FB-NJ	62.9 dB $\rho = .59$ PB-NJ	59.1 dB FB-NJ
$R = 1/2$ Convolutional Coding	63.0 dB $\rho = .60$ PB-NJ	59.1 dB FB-NJ	63.0 dB $\rho = .60$ PB-NJ	59.1 dB FB-NJ
Dual-3 Convolutional Coding	65.3 dB FB-NJ	59.7 dB $\rho = .93$ PB-MTJ	65.3 dB FB-NJ	61.8 dB FB-NJ

ρ = Fraction of Total Band Jammed
PB-MTJ = Partial-Band Multitone Jamming
PB-NJ = Partial-Band Noise Jamming
FB-NJ = Full-Band Noise Jamming
R_b = Data Bit Rate
$E_b = ST_b$ = Energy Per Information Bit
$R_s = R_b/3$ = Data Symbol Rate
R_h/R_s = Number of Hops Per Symbol

4.3.3 Optimum LPI Modulation / Coding Conditions

Having now reviewed the intercept detectability and AJ performance of the various modulation and coding methods, a final conclusion may be drawn. The use of FH/PN versus pure FH has been shown to be of no advantage and, since it represents additional communication system complexity, especially in terms of receiver acquisition and tracking functions, FH becomes the recommended SS approach.

The remaining issue is the choice of hop rate. Three criteria may be applied. The first involves a restatement of the conditions which preclude the interceptor's use of a channelized detector; namely, for finite duration messages, it is essential to minimize the number of hop slots per message relative to the total number of possible hop slots $N_T = W_{ss}/R_h$. To satisfy the first criterion:

$$\text{Hop Rate} < (\text{Total FH Slots}) \div (100 \times \text{Message Time}).$$

A second hop rate criterion is dictated by the number of hops per coded symbol that must be employed to obtain good AJ protection, namely:

$$\text{Hop Rate} \geq 4 \times (\text{Symbol Rate}).$$

Thus, the first two criteria, respectively, bound the hop rate to upper and lower values. The third criterion involves minimization of the message receiver non-coherent combining loss. Clearly, the fewer the number of hops per symbol, the lower the non-coherent combining loss and, therefore, the lower the communicator's EIRP. This criterion demands that the lowest possible hop rate be selected. However, since a lower limit is dictated by the second criterion, this limit becomes the optimum hop rate for all considerations.

4.4 FURTHER DISCUSSION

The material presented in this chapter has focussed on providing a systems viewpoint of the tradeoffs required between the communicator/receiver and the interceptor for communication in an LPI environment. Emphasis has been placed on determining the system design parameters necessary for communicating in the presence of *practical* interceptor detectors, nevertheless pointing out their relation to optimal structures.

In the recent literature, several authors [9], [10], [11] have taken a more formal maximum-likelihood approach to the LPI communications problem, both from the standpoint of estimating the unknown synchronization parameters associated with the communicator's modulation (e.g., carrier phase, chip or hop epoch) and determining the optimum interceptor detector structures given none, some, or all of this synchronization knowledge. In particular, Polydoros and Weber [9] determine synchronous and asynchronous (with respect to the chip or hop offset of the spread-spectrum modulation), coherent and non-coherent (with respect to the carrier phase) detectors for both direct sequence and frequency-hopped modulations. All of these structures fall into the category of feature-extraction detectors, since in the absence of all knowledge except carrier frequency, the wideband radiometer is the obvious choice and is in fact an asymptotically optimum device as the predetection SNR decreases to zero. The following represents a summary of the results obtained in [9].

Let $y(t)$ denote the signal received by the interceptor which, when the communicator is transmitting, is the sum of signal plus noise and otherwise consists only of noise. For a direct-sequence spread-spectrum modulation, application of the generalized likelihood ratio test leads to the following decision rules. Assuming both chip timing epoch and carrier phase are known (a very idealistic assumption), then the *generalized coherent synchronous radiometer* is an implementation of the decision rule:

$$\text{if } \sum_{i=1}^{N} \ln\cosh y_i \begin{array}{l} > \eta, \quad \text{decide signal present} \\ < \eta, \quad \text{decide signal absent} \end{array} \tag{4.77}$$

where η is the detection threshold,

$$y_j = \int_{(j-1)T_c}^{jT_c} y(t)\,dt \tag{4.78}$$

and N is the number of chips, each of duration T_c, in the observation time T used to define the likelihood ratio test. If the "ln cosh" non-linearity is approximated by a square-law device as is appropriate at low predetection SNR, then the resulting structure is just a *synchronous coherent energy detector or radiometer*.

Relaxing the assumption of known carrier phase leads to the *optimal non-coherent detector* satisfying the decision rule:

$$\text{if } \sum_{\substack{i=1 \\ i\varepsilon G \text{ or } \bar{G}}}^{2^{N-1}} I_0\left(\frac{2\sqrt{S}}{N_0} R_i\right) \begin{array}{l} > \eta, \quad \text{decide signal present} \\ < \eta, \quad \text{decide signal absent} \end{array} \tag{4.79}$$

where

$$R_i = \sqrt{e_{ci}^2 + e_{si}^2} \tag{4.80}$$

with

$$e_{\left[\begin{smallmatrix} c \\ s \end{smallmatrix}\right] i} = \sum_{j=1}^{N} r_{\left[\begin{smallmatrix} c \\ s \end{smallmatrix}\right] j} c_{ij} \tag{4.81}$$

and

$$r_{\left[\begin{smallmatrix} c \\ s \end{smallmatrix}\right] j} = \int_{(j-1)T_c}^{jT_c} r(t) \begin{bmatrix} \cos\omega_0 t \\ \sin\omega_0 t \end{bmatrix} dt; \quad j = 1, 2, \ldots, N. \tag{4.82}$$

Here ω_0 is the carrier radian frequency and c_{ij} denotes the j-th binary element ($+1$ or -1) of the i-th PN code pattern $c_i(t)$. In general, the index

i ranges over the N-dimensional space corresponding to the 2^N possible patterns (arrangements) of the N binary symbols within the $T = NT_c$-second observation interval. However, it can be shown that insofar as the decision rule is concerned, it is sufficient to divide the above space into two disjoint complementary subsets (G and $\overline{G}$), each having 2^{N-1} elements, and sum only over those elements in either G or $\overline{G}$. The rule for the subdivision is that, for each possible PN code vector $\boldsymbol{c}_i = (c_{i1}, c_{i2}, \ldots, c_{iN})$, its negative (complement) belongs to the other subset. If as before the non-linearity "I_0" is approximated by its low SNR equivalent $I_0(x) = 1 + x^2/4$, then a *synchronous non-coherent energy detector* results.

For detection of frequency-hopped signals, it can be shown that the optimal *synchronous non-coherent detector* is an implementation of the decision rule

$$\text{if } \sum_{n=1}^{N_h} \ln\left(\sum_{m=1}^{N_T} I_0(R_{mn}) \right) \begin{matrix} > \eta, & \text{decide signal present} \\ < \eta, & \text{decide signal absent} \end{matrix} \tag{4.83}$$

where, analogous to (4.80), R_{ij} is the envelope of the signal in the j-th hop frequency slot and the i-th hop time interval, N_h is the number of hop frequency slots in the spread-spectrum bandwidth, and N_T is the total number of hop time intervals in the observation. We note that the detector corresponding to (4.83) is equivalent to Figure 4.4 since in deriving (4.83) the log-likelihood ratio test was actually employed. Applying this same test in deriving Figure 4.4 would have resulted in the inclusion of a logarithm non-linearity between the summer and product blocks in this figure. However, since the logarithm of a product is identical to the summation of the logarithms, we obtain the equivalence with (4.83).

While the above results that have been reported in [9] are only for synchronous structures, they are not purely of academic interest since they can be used to derive upper bounds on performance for any practical asynchronous system. Furthermore, as the authors point out, the same maximum-likelihood approach can be used to derive asynchronous optimal and suboptimal detector structures.

In [10], Krasner addresses the general problem of optimum detection of digitally modulated signals (a train of unknown symbols modulated onto a single or quadrature carriers) in the context of the LPI application, i.e., low symbol SNR, unknown symbol epoch, unknown carrier phase. By not restricting the symbol set to be binary and allowing various choices for the correlation properties of the symbol set, e.g., antipodal (balanced), orthogonal, or biorthogonal, the direct-sequence and frequency-hopping spread-spectrum modulations occur as special cases. Again the structures that are developed result from application of the maximum-likelihood theory to testing the hypothesis of signal plus noise against the null hypothesis of noise alone. As such, the presence of information modulation on the signal when present is of no consequence. Analogous to [9], optimal detectors for the coherent and non-coherent carrier cases are derived, here, however, in the presence of unknown symbol epoch (asynchronism). Performance comparisons are made in terms of output SNR between the optimal structures and the classical wideband radiometer.

Also considered in [10] are the effects on the maximum-likelihood structures produced by (1) assuming that the signal of interest is formed by passing the "ideal" digitally modulated signal through a band-pass filter that may severely distort the waveform and (2) assuming the presence of correlation among the symbols in the transmitted sequence. The practical significance of the assumptions in (1) and (2) are that filtering is often intentionally performed on spread-spectrum type signals to make them appear more "noise-like," whereas sequences of correlated symbols naturally come about when modulations such as minimum-shift-keying (MSK) are employed to produce desirable spectral shaping.

While all of the structures that are developed in [10] assume a uniform *a priori* probability distribution on the input symbols, a simple modification, e.g., a non-linear weighting of each of the terms contributing to the sum in (4.79), can be performed to make the results applicable to other distributions.

In [11], Krasner continues his work in [10] by developing maximum-likelihood estimators of carrier phase and symbol epoch for quadriphase modulated signals, again under the assumption that the symbol sequence is unknown and that the presence of data information on these symbols is of no interest to the receiver. As in [10], the case of interest is low-symbol SNR and the resulting maximum-likelihood structures that are derived are further simplified to correspond to this case. The effects of filtering and correlated symbols are also considered.

Finally, we wish to point out the existence of an excellent tutorial style article by Glenn [12] (also presented at MILCOM'82 but not included in the proceedings), which identifies the key system parameters and their interrelation in determining the LPI performance of airborne command post/satellite links operating at super high frequency (SHF) and extremely high frequency (EHF).

4.5 REFERENCES

[1] G. M. Dillard, "A moving-window detector for binary integration," *IEEE Trans. Inform. Theory*, IT-13, no. 1, pp. 2–6, January 1967.

[2] R. A. Dillard, "Vulnerability of low detectability communication to energy detection," Naval Electronic Laboratory Center, San Diego, California, January 26, 1971.

[3] J. D. Edell, "Wideband noncoherent frequency-hopped waveforms and their hybrids in low-probability-of-intercept communications," Naval Research Laboratory, Washington, D.C., Technical Report No. 8025, November 8, 1976.

[4] D. G. Woodring, "Performance of optimum and suboptimum detectors for spread spectrum waveforms," Naval Research Laboratory, Washington, D.C., Technical Report No. 8432, December 1980.
[5] R. A. Dillard, "Detectability of spread spectrum signals," *IEEE Trans. Aerospace and Electronic Systems*, AES-15, no. 5, pp. 526–537, July 1979.
[6] J. E. Ohlson, "Efficiency of radiometers using digital integration," *Radio Science*, vol. 6, no. 3, pp. 341–345, March 1971.
[7] M. Skolnik, ed., *Radar Handbook*, New York: McGraw-Hill, 1970.
[8] L. Kleinrock, "Detection of energy peak of an arbitrary signal," MIT Lincoln Laboratory, Lexington, Mass., Technical Report No. 325, August 23, 1963.
[9] A. Polydoros and C. L. Weber, "Optimal detection considerations for low probability of intercept," *MILCOM'82 Conference Proceedings*, Boston, Mass., pp. 2.1-1–2.1-5, October 17–20, 1982.
[10] N. F. Krasner, "Optimal detection of digitally modulated signals," *IEEE Trans. Commun.*, COM-30, no. 5, pp. 885–895, May 1982.
[11] N. F. Krasner, "Maximum likelihood parameter estimation for LPI signals," *MILCOM'82 Conference Proceedings*, Boston, Mass., pp. 2.3-1–2.3-4, October 17–20, 1982.
[12] A. B. Glenn, "Low probability of intercept," *IEEE Commun. Mag.*, vol. 21, no. 4, pp. 26–33, July 1983.

APPENDIX 4A: CONDITIONS FOR VIABLE MULTICHANNEL DETECTOR PERFORMANCE

Assume that a K-channel detector is to be realized by arbitrarily dividing the total signal bandwidth W_{ss} into K contiguous non-overlapping bands. As such, a hit is guaranteed in one of the K channels for each hop. The required per-channel S/N_0 is given by

$$\left(\frac{S}{N_0}\right)_K = (d_K \eta_K) \sqrt{\frac{W_K}{T_K}}, \tag{4A.1}$$

where the K subscript denotes the per-channel parameters. Now, the term $(d_K \eta_K)$ is a function of the per-channel P_{DI} and P_{FAI} and the Gaussian assumption correction factor,* and $W_K = W_{ss}/K$. This leaves only T_K to be specified.

Clearly, the larger T_K is, the lower the $(S/N_0)_K$ required. The minimum T_K that could be used is $T_K = T_h$, the hop pulse period. However, since the individual channels are, by definition, not matched in bandwidth to that of the hop pulses, this would be a very poor choice. Intuitively, it can be seen that T_K should be "matched" to the presence of hop pulses in each channel; i.e., the channel integrator is enabled (integrates) when a pulse is present and is disabled (holds) when a pulse is absent. But the detector has no idea

*The factor η, which represents a correction from a Gaussian assumption to chi-squared statistics, is discussed in (3) of Section 4.2.1.2.

when the various hits in each channel will occur; thus, the "matched" strategy is totally impractical. There is no recourse, then, but to make $T_K = T_M$. Therefore,

$$\left(\frac{S}{N_0}\right)_K = \frac{1}{\sqrt{K}} d_K \eta_K \sqrt{\frac{W_{ss}}{T_M}}. \tag{4A.2}$$

Now the single-channel wideband radiometer (which occurs if $K = 1$) has its performance given by:

$$\left(\frac{S}{N_0}\right)_{WB} = d_{WB} \eta_{WB} \sqrt{\frac{W_{ss}}{T_M}}. \tag{4A.3}$$

If it is assumed that $W_{ss}T_M \gg 1$ and $W_{ss}T_M/K \gg 1$, then η_{WB} and η_K can both be conveniently taken as unity. Substituting (4A.3) into (4A.2) gives

$$\left(\frac{S}{N_0}\right)_K = \left(\frac{d_K}{d_{WB}}\right)\left[\frac{1}{\sqrt{K}}\left(\frac{S}{N_0}\right)_{WB}\right]. \tag{4A.4}$$

Now, assume for the moment that the (S/N_0) input to the K channel radiometer is exactly $(S/N_0)_{WB}$. On the basis of equal energy division between the K channels, the available $(S/N_0)_K$ is

$$\left(\frac{S}{N_0}\right)_K (\text{available}) = \frac{1}{K}\left(\frac{S}{N_0}\right)_{WB}. \tag{4A.5}$$

Further, taking $d_K = d_{WB}$ (as a bounding worst case assumption), by comparing (4A.5) with (4A.4), it is readily seen that the *available* $(S/N_0)_K$ is a factor of $1/\sqrt{K}$ lower than that *required* by (4A.4). Clearly, then, if parity is to be achieved between the two detectors, it is necessary that $d_K = d_{WB}/\sqrt{K}$. Suppose the per-channel P_{DI} and P_{FAI} of the K-band detector are defined as:

$$P_{DI} = P_D/K \tag{4A.6}$$

$$P_{FAI} = P_{FA}/K. \tag{4A.7}$$

The requirement then becomes:

$$\left[Q^{-1}(P_{FA}/K) - Q^{-1}(P_D/K)\right] \stackrel{?}{=} \left[Q^{-1}(P_{FA}) - Q^{-1}(P_D)\right]/\sqrt{K} \tag{4A.8}$$

Although the validity of (4A.8) cannot be readily established, recourse to Figure 4.2 or to numerical examples, shows that equality will not be obtained and that the inequality

$$\left[Q^{-1}(P_{FA}/K) - Q^{-1}(P_D/K)\right] > \left[Q^{-1}(P_{FA}) - Q^{-1}(P_D)\right]/\sqrt{K} \tag{4A.9}$$

must hold. [Example: With $P_D = 0.9$, $P_{FA} = 10^{-6}$, and $K = 10$, (4A.9) becomes, specifically, 5.8 dB > 2.8 dB.]

The conclusion, then, is that a K channel detector of the form postulated above requires a higher S/N_0 than the simple single-channel wideband radiometer. A manifest reason for this is that the channels are not matched to the times when signal is present within them. This is a necessary criterion for any detector that is going to outperform the wideband radiometer. (In theory, the partial-band FBC meets this criterion and, as a result, its performance is generally superior.)

Chapter 5

MULTIPLE ACCESS

Spread-spectrum signals[1] examined in this book are designed to combat intentional jamming interference in radio channels. Thus, to any spread-spectrum transmitter/receiver pair that is communicating in a network of radios, other spread-spectrum signals can be collectively regarded as a jamming signal and, provided their numbers are not too large, each such link should be able to achieve reliable communication with this unintentional mutual interference.

This chapter presents a somewhat tutorial discussion of the performance of spread-spectrum communication systems in some generic networks where there are several spread-spectrum signals of the same type occupying the same time and frequency. Specifically, we examine two basic questions concerning multiple access communications:

1. Point-to-Point: How well can a receiver detect and decode a spread-spectrum signal from one radio transmitter when there is interference from several other spread-spectrum radios?
2. Multipoint-to-Point: How well can a receiver simultaneously detect and decode several spread-spectrum signals transmitted from spatially separated radios?

For the point-to-point channel, multiple access is achieved only at baseband using a multiplexer and demultiplexer at the transmitter and receiver, as shown in Figures 5.1 and 5.2. The corresponding multipoint-to-point system is illustrated in Figures 5.3 and 5.4. Here multiple access can be achieved at radio frequencies.

The above questions arise in military digital radio networks. We assume throughout that *in these networks spread-spectrum signals are used primarily to combat intentional jamming*. Since they are designed to combat channel interference of all kinds, they have certain multiple access capabilities as well as some tolerance to mutual interference.

[1] In this chapter we examine DS/BPSK and FH/MFSK signals.

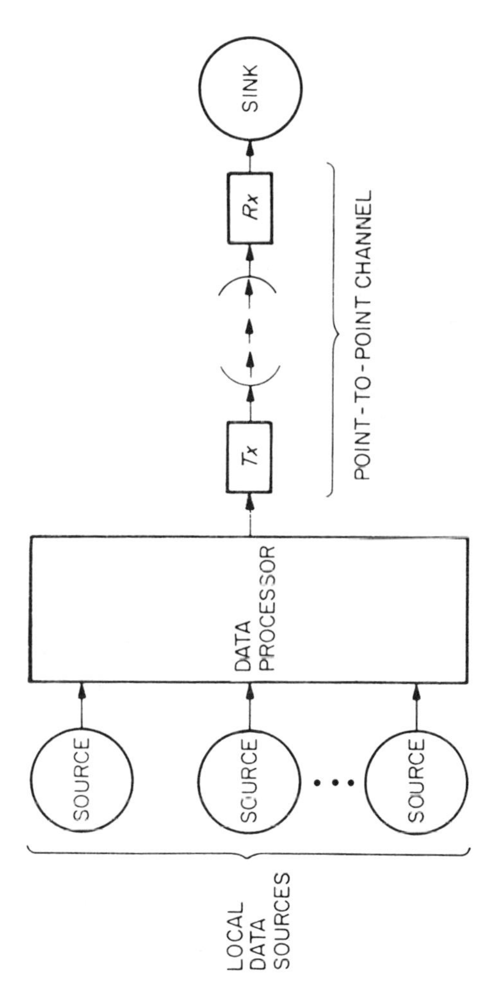

Figure 5.1. The multiplexer channel.

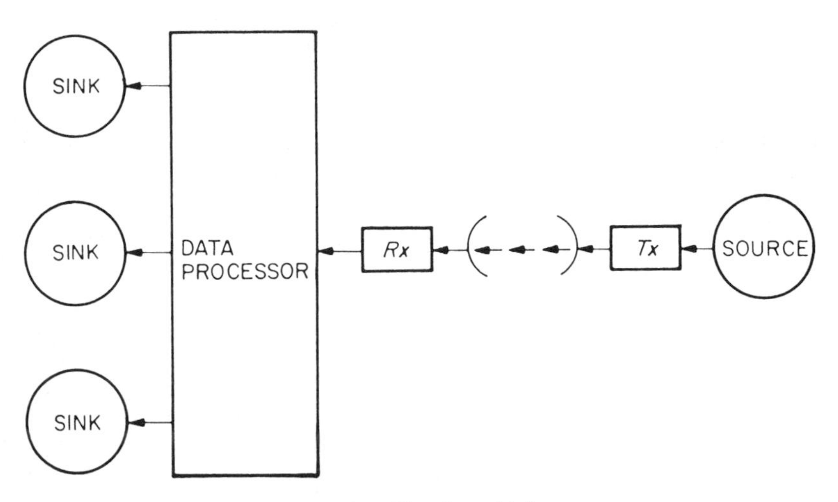

Figure 5.2. The demultiplexer.

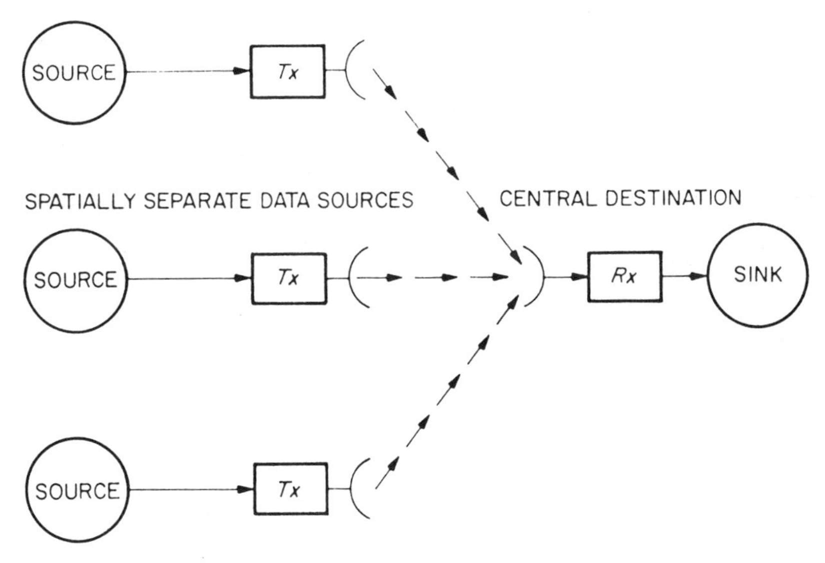

Figure 5.3. Distributed multiple access channel.

Military digital radio network design principles are not as well understood or developed as those for commercial digital networks. For one thing there is a much wider variety of military network types compared with commercial networks. Radios here are often mobile, subject to jamming and physical attack, and must operate in all types of environments [1]–[3]. In addition, to reduce vulnerability terrestrial tactical digital radio networks

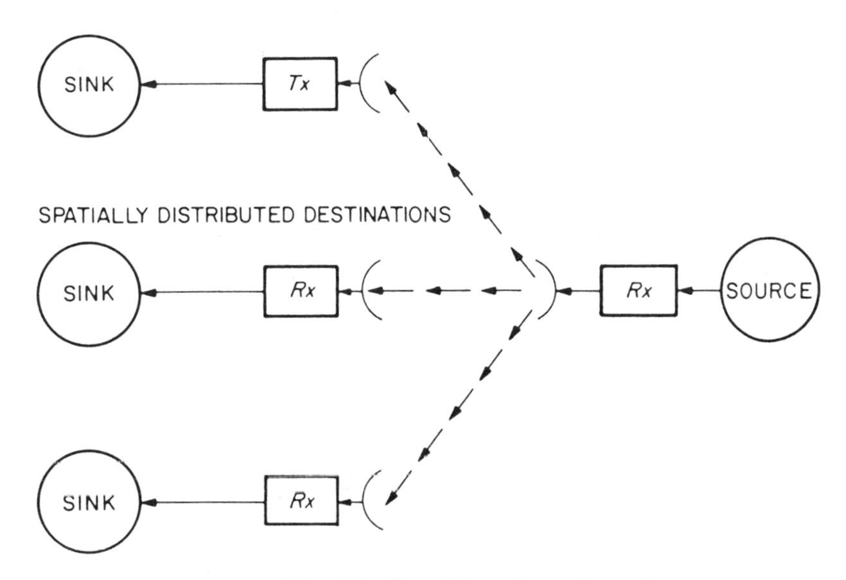

Figure 5.4. Distributed broadcast channel.

often require distributed network control. Other higher level networks, such as a satellite network, may have centralized network control [4]. To motivate the multiple access analysis of this chapter we first briefly describe two generic military digital radio networks. After this we discuss mutual interference and multiple access techniques in general, followed by the examination of the two questions raised above on mutual interference and multiple access with spread-spectrum signals.

5.1 NETWORKS

There are many different types of military communication networks and these are often interconnected to form parts of larger networks resulting in layers of communication networks. To place in some context and to motivate the mutual interference and multiple access problems that we examine in this chapter, consider two generic examples of radio and satellite communication networks where some or all terminals may be mobile.

5.1.1 Decentralized (Point-to-Point) Networks

Consider a collection of mobile radios scattered across some terrain. Assume each radio has an omni-directional antenna with no prior knowledge of the location of other radios. All radios use spread-spectrum signals for combatting intentional jamming where each radio has a unique key that generates a PN sequence assigned to it and can also generate the PN

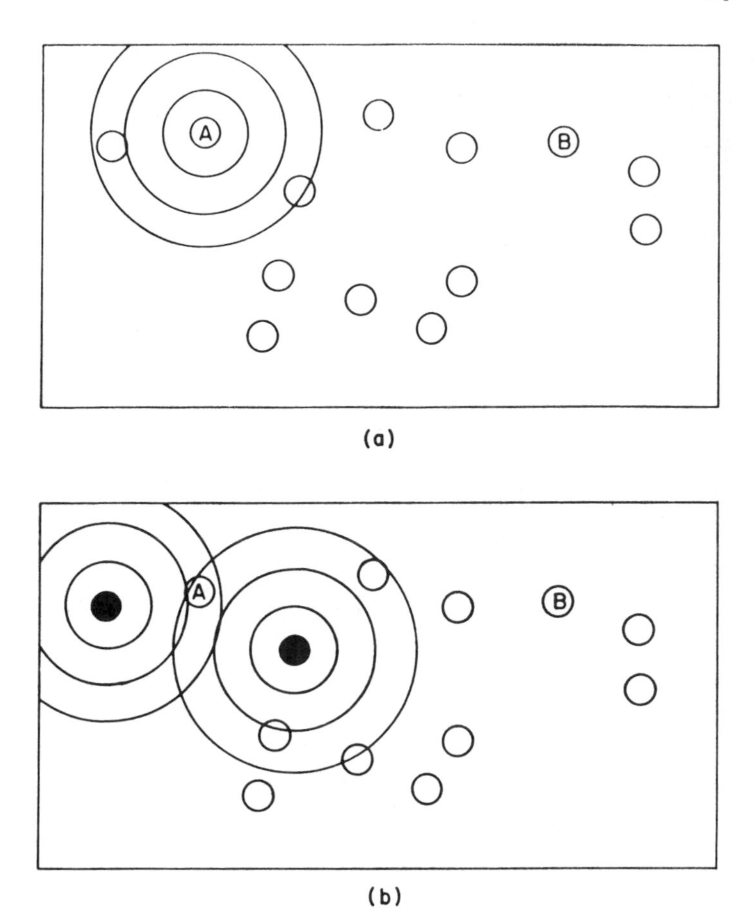

Figure 5.5. Illustration of flooding.

sequence assigned to some of the other radios. Acquisition and synchronization of these PN sequences is assumed throughout this chapter. Also there is enough processing capability and memory in each radio to maintain and update knowledge of the overall network connectivity between radios. Assume there is no central controller and each radio is within range of some subset of all radios in the terrain.

Consider only point-to-point communication between any two radios. Specifically, for the generic mobile digital radio network described, how does one radio communicate digital data to another radio? Since we do not assume full connectivity among radios, this is a multihop communication network. That is, a communication link between two radios in this network typically requires other radios to act as relays.

One brute force method, called "flooding" [3], [5]–[7], is illustrated in Figure 5.5. Suppose Radio A wants to send a message to Radio B but has no knowledge of the location of Radio B or any other radio in the network.

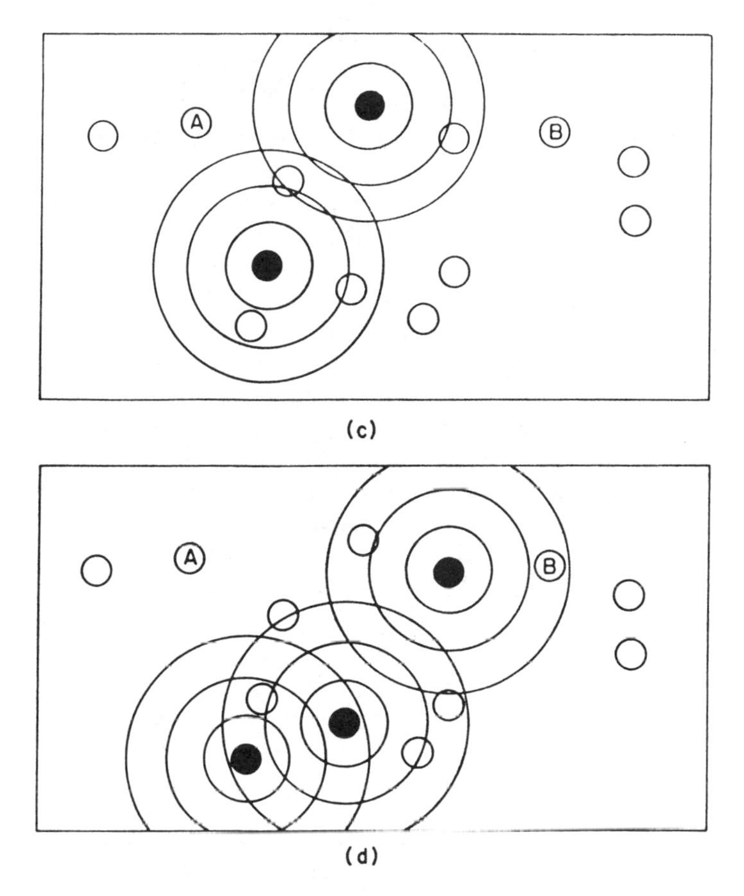

Figure 5.5. (continued)

Assume all other radios have a common key that generates a common pseudorandom sequence used for spread-spectrum signalling. Radio A transmits the message in an omni-directional signal that also identifies the destination Radio B and source Radio A. This signal can be received by all radios within some range, assuming all radios use the common key. The protocol for radios in this network is to retransmit the same message only once right after first receiving it. Hence, as shown in Figure 5.5(a), Radio A first transmits the message. In Figure 5.5(b) only radios marked in dark first receive Radio A's transmission and retransmit the same message. In Figure 5.5(c) radios that received the signal for the first time in the second transmission are shown. These in turn retransmit the same message with the final result that Radio B receives the message as shown in Figure 5.5(d). Retransmissions, however, may continue until each radio has received and transmitted the message once.

In this flooding technique a single radio may receive the same signal simultaneously from several other radios. This is the same as receiving a signal from a single transmitter in a multipath channel. If the relative delays between the different signals are greater than a "chip" time, then the receiver can resolve this difference and detect only one signal. Typically, in mobile digital radio systems real multipath would occur and techniques for handling it are required (see Chapter 1, Volume II).

There are several variations of the flooding scheme [3], [5]–[7]. For instance, each radio may retransmit the same message more than once. However, a maximum number of hops for a flooding signal might be set requiring each retransmission to update a "hop count" which is also transmitted. If a radio receives a signal with a count equal to a predetermined value, it will not retransmit it. Another approach is for each radio that receives a signal to wait a random length of time before retransmission. If it receives another copy of the same signal while it is waiting, it does not retransmit the signal.

The "flooding" technique is clearly an inefficient way for Radio A to send a message to Radio B. It results in excessive transmission by other terminals and few messages can be sent across the network at the same time. However, it may be useful to broadcast a short emergency message to many terminals.

In order for Radio A to more efficiently transmit a message to Radio B, it needs to know the connectivity of radios in the network so that it can route a message through the network. This means that somehow all radios must learn about how the radios in the network are connected to each other. Thus there are two problems:

1. How do radios learn of their connectivity in the network?
2. When network connectivity is known, how should a radio transmitter route messages through the network?

One approach is to assume there is a common network key that is used to generate a common pseudorandom sequence for the purpose of handling network overhead traffic. This sequence is used by the radios to learn how the radio network is connected. Here the flooding technique can be utilized with one radio sending a "route-finding" packet and each other radio adding its own identification to the packet before retransmitting it. Then whenever a radio receives such a signal it learns the sequence of radios that transmitted it. With enough such retransmissions each radio can obtain some knowledge of how the radio network is connected. For a time-varying mobile radio network this route-finding flooding technique is repeated periodically as the network changes.

Given a network connection table stored in memory, a radio can now transmit a message to any other radio by first selecting a route through the network based on this knowledge [8]–[27]. Now rather than use the common network key, the radio can route a message to the next radio in a multihop route by transmitting a spread-spectrum signal with the unique key for that specific radio. To all other radios this signal would appear only as small additional interference since such signals are designed to combat jamming. Only the radio that is receiving signals with its own unique spread-spectrum carrier would receive the transmitted signal and relay it on to the next radio in the designated route. This next hop in the route is again done by transmitting a spread-spectrum signal using the key unique to this next radio. Destination and routing information is assumed to be attached to the message.

It is common practice in communication networks to acknowledge the receipt of messages. The failure to receive an acknowledgment causes a retransmission of the message. In multihop networks, where messages are relayed one or more times, acknowledgments may be used for each relay (hop-by-hop), from the final destination to the source (end-to-end), or both.

The above generic decentralized network might represent terrestrial digital radios in a tactical battlefield environment where radios may drop out of the network due to jamming and/or direct attack. Centralized network control may make such a network system too vulnerable. Hence we have considered here a system with minimal network control and synchronization requirements.

5.1.2 Centralized (Multipoint-to-Point) Networks

Military communication satellites are usually processing satellites that can despread, demodulate, decode, reformat, and route through various downlink antenna beams the uplink spread-spectrum signals from various mobile and stationary terminals [4]. Generally, such a satellite is the central node in a star network as sketched in Figure 5.6 where the satellite serves as the

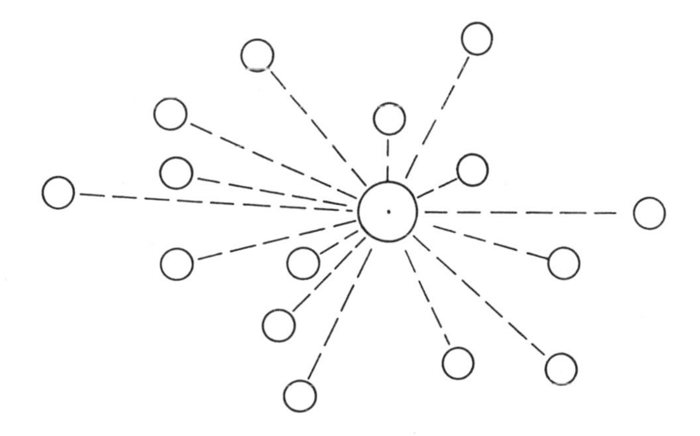

Figure 5.6. Star network.

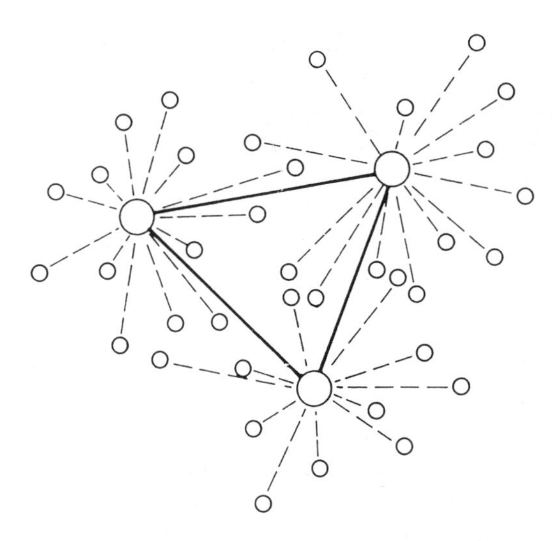

Figure 5.7. Fully connected star networks.

central controller for the network. This type of radio network is the opposite extreme from the terrestrial radio network described in the previous section.

For the star network the central node provides time synchronization[2] for each radio, typically through a feedback loop where each radio terminal adjusts its time reference based on feedback from the central node. Here we can expect some basic time reference available to all radios. For this case we consider the performance of various spread-spectrum multiple access schemes where several coordinated radios transmit signals to the central node. This is a multipoint-to-point system where the central node simultaneously receives signals from many radios.

A generalization of the star network is shown in Figure 5.7. Here there are several star networks with the central nodes forming a fully connected higher order network. This could represent a single processing satellite where each star network can represent a separate antenna beam, a separate frequency band, a separate spread-spectrum carrier, or any combination of these. Each network may also represent separate satellites with cross links that may or may not be fully connected. There is the possibility that any radio terminal will be able to switch from one star network to another.

The star network presents the multiple access problem of how several physically separated radios simultaneously transmit spread-spectrum signals to a single central node. We shall examine various techniques for doing this and evaluate their performance.

[2] The central node's signal may also provide a stable frequency reference.

5.2 SUMMARY OF MULTIPLE ACCESS TECHNIQUES

In a radio communication network where many radios communicate among themselves, there must be some means of sharing the available channel capacity. This means dividing up the overall channel into sub-channels and then assigning these to radios. Typically, there are more radios than available sub-channels but only a fraction of all radios have messages to transmit at any given time. The assignment of sub-channels to radios can be fixed or vary in time according to some policy.

Coordinating the assignment of sub-channels to various radios often requires that network control information flow in the network. This uses some of the available capacity. Ideally, one would like to assign sub-channels to those radios that have a message to transmit. A *fixed assignment* scheme (which can also change in time in a fixed manner) does not require much network capacity for coordination but it does not account for the random time-varying data transmission requirements of each radio. A real-time assignment of sub-channels upon demand by radios, called *demand assignment*, takes more network capacity and is more complex [28]–[36]. Demand assignment schemes require setting aside some channel capacity for transmitting requests and responding to these requests by one or more controllers. This can also be done by having a controller *poll the radios* to see if any one or more of them want to transmit messages [37]–[41]. One approach that takes little network coordination is for each radio to grab a sub-channel whenever it has a message to transmit. This is called *random access* [42]–[51]. Two or more radios, however, may use the same sub-channel at the same time causing "collisions" and these must somehow be resolved [52]–[56].

The simplest way to divide up the total radio channel capacity is to use frequency division multiple access (FDMA) [57]. Here the available frequency band is divided into disjoint sub-bands where any two radios can communicate using a sub-band or frequency. There would be no interference between radio signals whose spectra occupy disjoint parts of the total available frequency band.

If we restrict spread-spectrum signals to a sub-band of the total available frequency band, then the signal's anti-jam capability is reduced. Therefore, FDMA is not a good idea for spread-spectrum signals. Instead of dividing the available channel capacity using FDMA, a natural choice for spread-spectrum signals is to divide the available channel capacity into different spread-spectrum carriers. That is, instead of assigning a frequency to a radio, assign a spread-spectrum carrier which is specified by a pseudorandom sequence. The pseudorandom sequence is in turn determined by a pseudorandom sequence generator key and its initial state. Thus, rather than assign a frequency to a radio we can assign a key to the radio that uses spread-spectrum signals. This is referred to as *spread-spectrum multiple access* (SSMA) [1]–[4], [58]–[62].

Assigning a key to a spread-spectrum radio is analogous to assigning a frequency to a conventional narrowband radio. The primary difference is that signals of different frequencies in an FDMA system are orthogonal functions of time, whereas spread-spectrum signals with different keys in an SSMA system have some time cross-correlation. When regarded as random processes, however, spread-spectrum signals with different keys are often designed to be statistically independent and are orthogonal in the statistical sense of being uncorrelated random processes. This means that the expectation of the time cross-correlation is zero.

It is possible for M signals of bandwidth of W Hz and T seconds to be orthogonal (zero time cross-correlation) for $M \leq 2WT$ (coherent) and $M \leq WT$ (non-coherent). These orthogonal signals can, in fact, be generated using the same waveforms as spread-spectrum signals discussed in previous chapters but with specific assigned chip sequences. For DS/BPSK waveforms, for example, using orthogonal binary sequences as the chip sequences will result in orthogonal signals. For FH/MFSK waveforms hopping sequences can be chosen so that during a chip time (hop time) no two signals hop to the same part of the spread-spectrum frequency level. This is true as long as the chip sequences are time synchronized among all radios.

If we relax the chip synchronization requirement, we can use chip sequence generators specifically designed to yield low time cross-correlations between signals for all relative time delays. Gold sequences and Bent sequences discussed in Chapter 5 of Volume I result in signals using DS/BPSK waveforms that have low time cross-correlations [63]–[76]. For FH/MFSK waveforms, Reed-Solomon codewords have been proposed [77]–[82] as hopping sequences that yield low time cross-correlation.

Signals with the same form as spread-spectrum signals discussed in earlier chapters but designed to have low time cross-correlation require the use of specific chip sequences to be assigned to radios. When these are used to divide the available channel capacity we refer to this as code division multiple access (CDMA). *We distinguish*[3] *this CDMA technique from SSMA where in SSMA we assume the chip sequences are statistically independent when regarded as random processes*. That is, for SSMA we assume pseudorandom sequences are well modelled as i.i.d. sequences and different keys result in independent pseudorandom sequences. The SSMA system thus uses spread-spectrum signals that are uncorrelated in the statistical sense where the expectation of the time cross-correlation of any two signals is zero. We define CDMA signals as those designed to have low time cross-correlations where the signals are not statistically independent. Generally, CDMA signals with sequences of long periods behave like SSMA signals [65].

[3] To our knowledge this distinction between CDMA and SSMA has not been used before.

Another common way to divide up the total radio channel capacity is to use time-division multiple access (TDMA) [57]. Here time is divided into disjoint slots where any two radios communicate using assigned time slots. This can be done with signals that occupy the entire signal bandwidth or with each sub-band of an FDMA system.

In principle, TDMA is equivalent to FDMA with time rather than frequency being the primary variable that is divided into segments. In practice, however, TDMA systems are more flexible than FDMA systems. TDMA systems require some means of maintaining a common time reference among all radios, which usually means that some network control signal must be used. Flexibility is achieved with TDMA since time slots can be easily changed without requiring hardware changes in the radio system. Also a radio can receive data from many other radios with only one receiver since their transmission time slots do not overlap.

Just as a single frequency in an FDMA system can be used in a TDMA mode, a spread-spectrum carrier can be used in a TDMA mode. That is, several radios can use the same pseudorandom sequence determined by a key but each transmitting a spread-spectrum signal at disjoint assigned time slots. Using disjoint time slots as in a TDMA format, however, is not necessary when using spread-spectrum signals. When two radios use the same spread-spectrum carrier (same pseudorandom sequence specified by the same key) but have a relative delay between them of greater than a chip time T_c, a radio can pick out either one of the two radio transmissions. For DS/BPSK spread-spectrum signals, for example, this is like a multipath channel where (recall from Chapter 1 in Volume II) at the receiver each received multipath signal component can be separated. Essentially, we can have a matched filter[4] with outputs that have separated signal correlation peaks due to the relative time delay of the separate signals. These matched filter output peaks resulting from different signals will not overlap if time delays between signals using the same key are greater than a chip time. Here the receiver must sample the matched filter outputs at times corresponding to one of the transmitted signals. It is interleaved with others but can be separated by selecting appropriate samples. This is illustrated in Figure 5.8.

FH/MFSK spread-spectrum signals using the same key but separated by more than a chip time (hop time) also can be separated at the receiving radio. Here the FH/MFSK radio receiver merely needs to be synchronized with the intended transmitted signal.

For spread-spectrum signals the notion of TDMA has a new form. Here we merely require spread-spectrum signals using the same key to use fixed time delays relative to each other where time delay slots are spaced every

[4] This may be implemented using a pseudorandomly time-varying surface acoustic wave (SAW) matched filter [83]–[86].

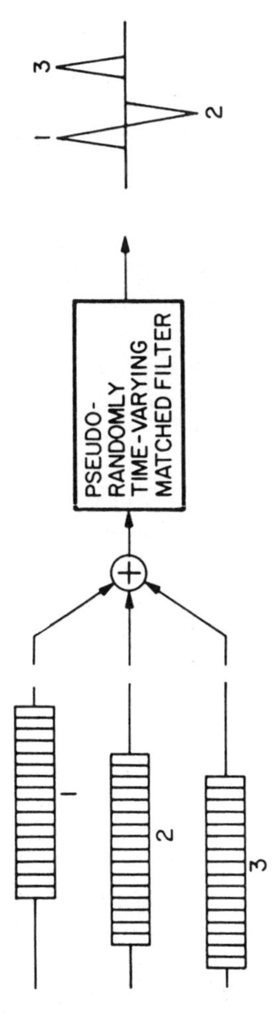

Figure 5.8. Resolving time shifted spread-spectrum signals sharing common PN sequence.

chip time interval. This is due to the fact that despreading the received radio signal at the receiver essentially filters out all signals except the one signal that is synchronized with the receivers. For many terrestrial military radio applications, however, maintaining time accuracy up to a chip time interval may be too difficult. This is especially true of DS/BPSK systems where chip times are usually much smaller than the chip (hop) time of FH/MFSK systems.

Random access is like a TDMA scheme except here each radio transmits a signal whenever it has a message to send without regard for other radios in the network. The Aloha random access scheme [42] is the simplest in that there are no restrictions on when a radio can transmit. In this scheme a radio transmits any time it has a message and listens for an acknowledgment from the receiving radio. If there is no acknowledgment, it retransmits the message after a random delay. Slotted Aloha [45] is a scheme where the random transmissions are restricted to fixed time slots. This implies that all radios must maintain a time reference. In carrier sense multiple access (CSMA) [44] techniques the radio senses the channel before transmitting and delays transmission if it is already being used. There are several variations on the CSMA technique [45]–[51]. The more complex random access techniques allow more efficient utilization of the channel but also require more side information in the form of time synchronization and/or channel measurements.

Since spread-spectrum signals are generally difficult to detect (see Chapter 4, Volume III), CSMA schemes are not useful for most spread-spectrum carriers. Slotted Aloha requires time synchronization among radios which is often difficult to achieve. Also, with spread-spectrum signals the notion of non-overlapping time slots is not useful since these signals do not have "collisions" even when using the same spread-spectrum carriers and the same time interval as long as their relative time delays are greater than the chip time. With pure Aloha random access, two spread-spectrum radio signals can cause a "collision" at a receiving radio only if they both use the same key and transmit with relative delays of less than the chip time. Otherwise, these signals interfere with each other like independent jamming interference. If pure Aloha random access is to be used, this suggests that all radios must transmit with random delays and receiving radios must be able to acquire and synchronize over the range of possible transmission delays. These delays can be small compared with data bit time intervals in DS/BPSK systems.

Finally, note that there are ways to divide up a channel using antenna techniques. Adaptive multiple spot beam antennas are used in satellites [87]–[89], for example, not only to separate uplink and downlink signals[5] but also to null out undesirable interference such as intentional jamming.

[5] Signals from terminals that are in different spot beam areas can be separated.

Antennas can also use polarization division where electromagnetic fields can be polarized into separate channels.

5.3 SPREAD-SPECTRUM MULTIPLE ACCESS WITH DS/BPSK WAVEFORMS

When a transmitter and receiver use a DS/BPSK waveform to communicate, all the interference in the channel can be approximated as additive white Gaussian noise. This was shown to be a good approximation in Chapter 1 of Volume II, provided the pseudorandom sequence used is statistically independent of the interference signal. In fact, for many CDMA systems where signals are not independent, the Gaussian approximation is also justified, although the resulting variance may be different [65]. In this section we assume radios in a network where different keys have statistically independent pseudorandom sequences associated with them and that each sequence is modelled as a sequence of independent equal probable binary random variables. We refer to this case as SSMA as opposed to CDMA where different keys correspond to sequences designed to have low cross-correlation properties. Our assumption here is that the primary purpose in using DS/BPSK waveforms is to combat jamming and the multiple access capability is a secondary additional property we can use for multiple access in digital radio networks.

Throughout this section assume that pseudorandom sequence acquisition and synchronization can be easily achieved by the intended receiver. This discussion is limited to the idealized assumption that the receiver for the desired DS/BPSK signal is perfectly synchronized in frequency, phase, chip epoch, and bit epoch. Also assume all radios are asynchronous and there is no network control or common time reference among the radios. As stated earlier for our example distributed radio network each radio has a unique key or pseudorandom sequence assigned to it as well as a common network key shared by all radios. During certain known fixed times the network key is used by all radios. Otherwise, each radio uses its own unique key for receiving DS/BPSK transmissions and each radio can transmit DS/BPSK waveforms with the key corresponding to some other radios. In this context we examine SSMA properties of DS/BPSK waveforms.

5.3.1 Point-to-Point

The analysis of Chapter 1 of Volume II applies directly to the point-to-point communication system where the interference or jamming signal is due to other users in the radio network. Suppose that while a transmitter and synchronized receiver are communicating, the interference in the channel is due to L other radio transmitters of power

$$J_\ell; \quad \ell = 1, 2, \ldots, L \tag{5.1}$$

at the receiver in question while the intended signal has power S. Then the effective bit energy-to-jammer-noise ratio is

$$\frac{E_b}{N_J} = \frac{PG}{J/S} \tag{5.2}$$

where

$$PG = N \tag{5.3}$$

is the number of chips per data bit and

$$J = \sum_{\ell=1}^{L} J_\ell. \tag{5.4}$$

As an example suppose the $K = 7$ rate $R = 1/2$ convolutional code with soft decision Viterbi decoding is used with the DS/BPSK waveform. To achieve 10^{-6} bit error probability we require the bit energy-to-noise ratio of (see Figure 1.7 of Chapter 1 in Volume II)

$$E_b/N_J = 5 \text{ dB}. \tag{5.5}$$

Also suppose the number of chips per data bit is

$$\begin{aligned} N &= 1000 \\ &= 30 \text{ dB}. \end{aligned} \tag{5.6}$$

This means the point-to-point DS/BPSK radio link in question can communicate effectively as long as the total interference power satisfies

$$\frac{\sum_{\ell=1}^{L} J_\ell}{S} \leq 316.23. \tag{5.7}$$

That is, up to 316 radios of equivalent power (at the receiver) as the intended transmitter signal can be simultaneously transmitting DS/BPSK waveforms. In practice, of course, some radios will be closer[6] than others and the power levels will be unequal at the receiver. This is the "near-far" problem encountered in terrestrial radio networks. Also some of the interference may be due to multipath components of the intended signal. In this example all these interferences must have total power that is no more than 316 times the intended signal power at the receiver.

The analysis here is based on the continuous jammer of power J. In a radio network, interference in any point-to-point link will vary randomly in time. Here assume the maximum interference power is less than the prescribed value. In general a coded or uncoded spread-spectrum DS/BPSK system designed to combat continuous jamming will have the same performance bound (see Section 1.2, Chapter 1, Volume II) as a BPSK signal in

[6]If an interfering radio is very close it can drive the receiver front end to saturation and effectively block all transmissions. The analysis here assumes no saturation has taken place.

white Gaussian noise with bit energy-to-noise ratio given by (5.2). If γ is the bit energy-to-noise ratio that achieves a desired bit error probability, then the total interference in the channel must be bounded by

$$J = \sum_{\ell=1}^{L} J_\ell \leq \left(\frac{N}{\gamma}\right) S. \tag{5.8}$$

Figure 5.9 illustrates the special case where

$$J_\ell = S; \ \ell = 1, 2, \ldots, L \tag{5.9}$$

plotting the maximum number of equal power interference signals at the receiver that can be tolerated as a function of the number of pseudorandom sequence chips N per information bit, called the processing gain (PG). This is parameterized by the required bit energy-to-noise ratio γ, which varies with the bit error probability requirement, the choice of coding technique, and the decoding metric. Since we assume maximum power for the total interference in giving γ, we can use standard error probability curves for the additive white Gaussian noise channel to determine the required value of γ

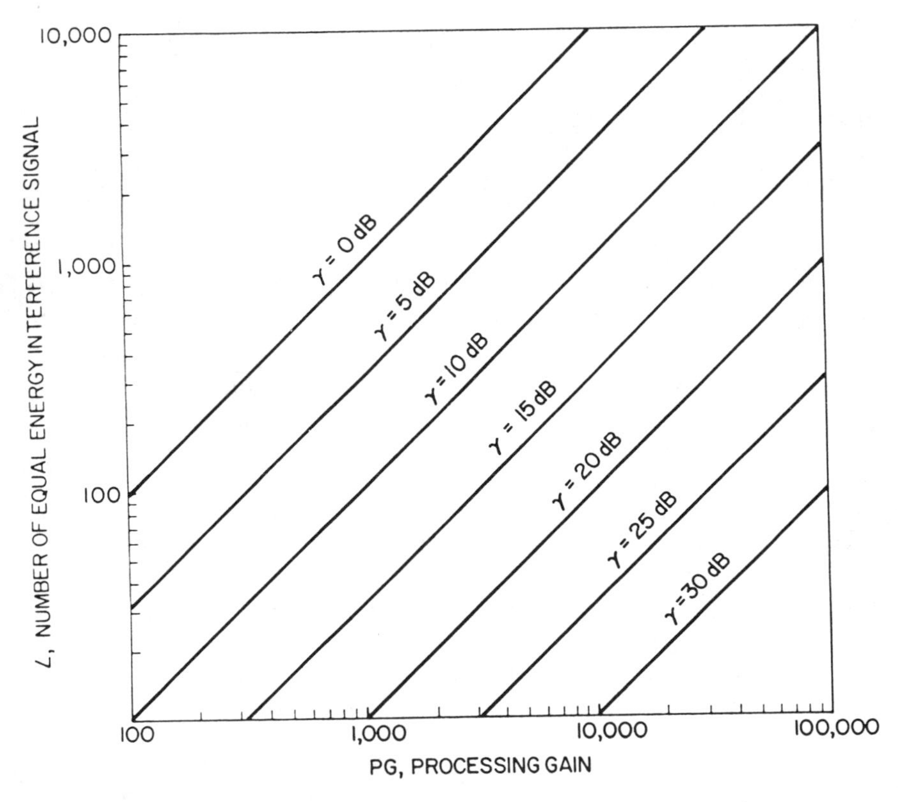

Figure 5.9. Simultaneous transmissions versus process gain.

to achieve a desired coded or uncoded bit error probability. Keep in mind that these results assume no background or receiver noise. This must ultimately be considered for some cases, as described in Chapter 3 of Volume I. Background noise can be added directly to the equivalent interference.

The point-to-point SSMA analysis for DS/BPSK waveforms is the same as that of the continuous jammer case covered in Chapter 1 of Volume II. For CDMA where pseudorandom sequences are designed to have low cross-correlation the multiple access performance will improve somewhat [63]–[76]. For the CDMA case the SSMA results here can be viewed as a bound on performance. Generally, when the number of CDMA signals is large the SSMA results presented here are close [65].

The results here generalize directly to fading channels. With Rayleigh fading the bit energy-to-noise ratio becomes

$$E_b/N_J = \frac{PG}{\bar{J}/\bar{S}} \tag{5.10}$$

where $\bar{J}$ is the average interference power and $\bar{S}$ is the average signal power. The curves used to determine γ, the required bit energy-to-noise ratio for a given bit error probability, would be obtained from analysis assuming Rayleigh fading (see Chapter 1 in Volume II). Otherwise, Figure 5.9 can still be applied. As with pulse jamming, because the real time bit energy-to-noise ratio varies in time, with the use of coding, care must be taken to distinguish between using side information to obtain the maximum-likelihood metric or a simpler non-optimum metric. With suboptimum metrics (no side information about real time bit energy-to-noise ratio) hard decision channel quantization can outperform soft decision channel quantization [90].

5.3.2 Conventional Multipoint-to-Point

Consider the possibility of two or more radios transmitting simultaneously to a single radio terminal in a network. For a conventional FDMA system this would be possible if the transmitting radios use different frequencies and the receiving radio terminal has separate receivers each tuned to one of the transmitting frequencies. For DS/BPSK waveforms the analogous system is where the transmitting radios use different keys and the receiving radio terminal has separate receivers each using a key with a pseudorandom sequence synchronized to the corresponding transmitting radio. Here a key in the SSMA system is similar to a frequency in the FDMA system. This is illustrated in Figure 5.10.

A radio terminal capable of receiving several signals of different frequencies in an FDMA system or DS/BPSK waveforms of different pseudorandom sequences in an SSMA system is often too complex and costly. This is because the receiving radio terminal essentially consists of several separate receivers. Conventional TDMA systems get around this problem since a

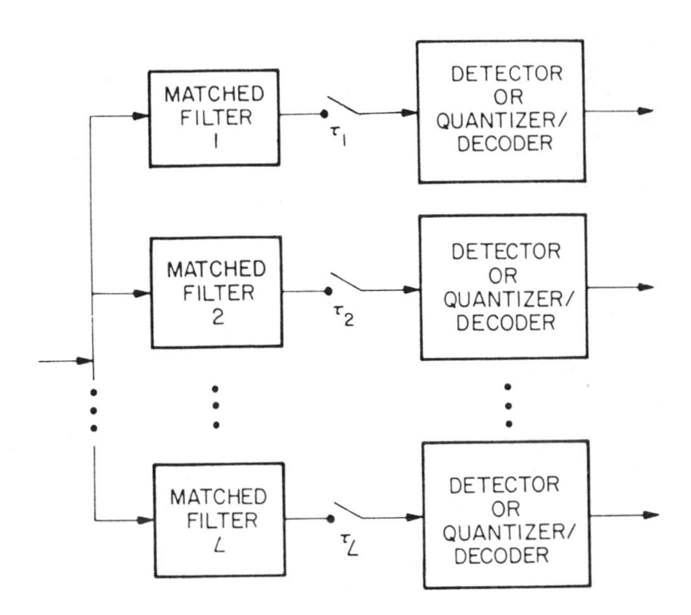

Figure 5.10. Transmissions with different keys.

single radio receiver can sequentially receive each of the transmitted radio signals that occupy non-overlapping time intervals. However, TDMA receivers must operate at higher burst rates to achieve the same overall throughput. In addition, time synchronization must somehow be maintained among the radios in the network. Acquisition and synchronization must also be done by the receiver for each separate radio transmission burst and this reduces the overall efficiency by requiring extra overhead bits in each burst.

Similar to conventional TDMA, a radio terminal in an SSMA system using DS/BPSK waveforms can simultaneously receive transmissions from several radios using a single receiver. Suppose all radios transmitting to the same receiving radio terminal use the unique key associated with this radio. Instead of transmitting in non-overlapping time intervals as in TDMA systems, each transmitting radio introduces a unique time shift in its DS/BPSK transmission which is a multiple of the basic chip time. At the receiving radio terminal these time-shifted DS/BPSK signals all using the same pseudorandom sequence appear like components of a multipath channel output with one radio transmission. If the receiving radio knows the time shifts used by the transmitting radios, then it can correlate delayed versions of the common pseudorandom sequence with the received radio signal to resolve the various transmitted signals (see Section 1.6, Chapter 1, Volume II).

If each coded bit consists of N_C chips then correlation is done for each N_C chip sequence corresponding to a coded transmitted bit of each radio transmitter. The N_C chip correlator can be realized with a time-varying matched filter using a SAW device [83]–[86]. With a matched filter the various transmitted DS/BPSK signals will appear as peaks of energy at the filter output. The peaks are roughly two chip time in width and separated from each other by the relative delays of the radio signal shifts at the receiving radio. This is illustrated in Figure 5.8 where we show one coded bit from three radios and the time-varying matched filter output. Note that there is a unique sample point in every coded bit time interval for each of the transmitting radio signals. These samples correspond to the usual correlator outputs in the DS/BPSK receiver except that with the use of a single matched filter, correlator outputs for all transmitted radio signals can be obtained at once. The sample sequence for each transmitting radio is then decoded separately.

Figure 5.11 illustrates the difference between receiving signals with different keys and a common key. For the uncoded case the detector is a simple hard quantizer. Also here we assume known phase and bit time epoch for each signal.

The receiving radio terminal described here uses one matched filter followed by a sampling circuit and individual decoders for each transmitted signal. We assumed that the relative time shifts of each transmitted signal were known at the receiving radio terminal which samples the match filter output at the correct time. For DS/BPSK waveforms it is usually impracti-

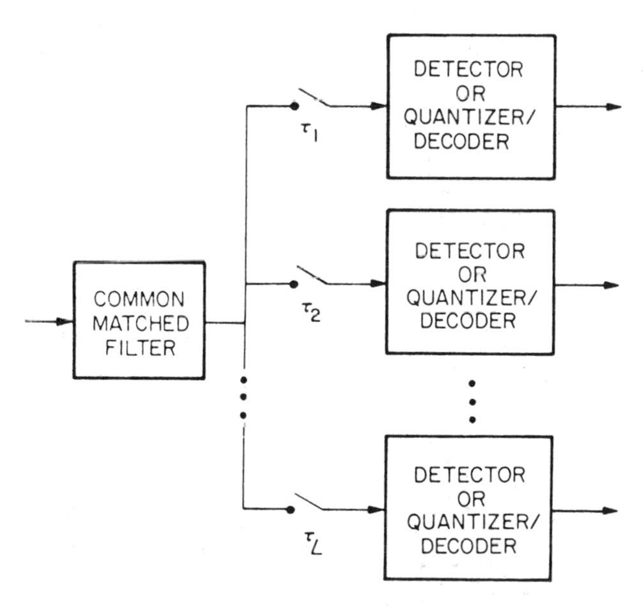

Figure 5.11. Transmissions with a common key.

cal for radio transmitters to accurately time shift their transmissions so that they are within a prescribed chip time at the receiving radio terminal. A more practical approach is to have each radio transmission introduce a random shift within a time interval and have the receiver system estimate appropriate sample times. This requires some sample time estimation scheme at the matched filter output. In addition, this introduces the possibility that two or more transmitting radios will have relative time shifts less than a chip time interval, with the result that their matched filter output sample times will coincide and cause "collisions." The probability of such collisions is determined in a manner analogous to the Aloha random access scheme. It depends on the number of simultaneous transmitting signals and the number of chip time slots in the random time shift interval. Generally, this probability is very small for DS/BPSK signals of interest.

The multipoint-to-point SSMA system described here requires radio terminals to have more digital signal processing capability in order to simultaneously receive from several radio transmitters. However, it requires the use of only one key or pseudorandom sequence in a time-varying matched filter. Without collisions the bit error probability for each transmitted data sequence is the same as in the point-to-point system described in the previous section. Here the interference is due to all other simultaneously transmitted radio signals, including those using the same key.

5.3.3 Optimum Multipoint-to-Point

In this section we present the theoretically optimum multiple access receiver when L radios transmit simultaneously to one radio terminal. Assume each transmitting radio uses a different key for its DS/BPSK waveform and all L radios transmit uncoded data at a rate of one data bit every T_b seconds. As illustrated in Figure 5.3, the distributed multiple access channel has asynchronous spatially separate radios transmitting simultaneously to a single destination radio.

It was first pointed out by Shnidman [91] that intersymbol interference and crosstalk between multiplexed signals are essentially identical phenomena. Kaye and George [92] have worked out this idea by investigating the transmission of multiplexed signals over multiple channel and diversity systems. Savage [93] analyzed such systems using random coding bounds where signal addresses were randomized. Van Etten [94] and Schneider [95] began looking at optimal detector techniques. The optimal multiple access detector for the system presented here was studied by Verdu [96], [97] and is based on earlier work on optimal receivers for channels with intersymbol interference [98]–[104]. We follow the work of Verdu in this section.

During the time interval $[kT_b, (k+1)T_b]$ each of the L radios will begin transmission of its k-th data bit using a DS/BPSK waveform. Since there is no time synchronization among the radios, assume the l-th radio transmits a data bit sequence using a continuous sequence of pulses of the form

$$
\begin{aligned}
s_l\left(t; d_k^{(l)}\right) &= A_l d_k^{(l)} c_l(t-\tau_l)\cos\left[\omega_0(t-\tau_l)+\theta_l\right]; \\
kT_b + \tau_l &\le t < (k+1)T_b + \tau_l \\
k &= \cdots -1, 0, 1, 2, \cdots .
\end{aligned} \tag{5.11}
$$

Here $d_k^{(l)} \varepsilon \{-1, 1\}$ is the k-th data bit of the l-th radio. The pseudorandom sequence waveform is given by $c_l(t-\tau_l)$ (see Chapter 1, Volume II). Parameters A_l, τ_l and θ_l depend on the propagation conditions of the radio channel as well as the radio transmitter.

Figure 5.12 shows a sketch of the k-th pulse $s_l(t; d_k^{(l)})$ of the l-th radio that transmits the k-th data bit $d_k^{(l)}$. This pulse occupies the time interval $[kT_b + \tau_l, (k+1)T_b + \tau_l]$. The actual transmission of this radio is a continuous sequence of such pulses. However, we focus here on the pulse related to the k-th data bit because we are interested in the sum of such pulses from all L radios. This is given by

$$
x_k(t; \boldsymbol{d}_k) = \sum_{l-1}^{L} s_l\left(t; d_k^{(l)}\right) \tag{5.12}
$$

which is sketched in Figure 5.13. Here define

$$
\boldsymbol{d}_k = \begin{bmatrix} d_k^{(1)} \\ d_k^{(2)} \\ \vdots \\ d_k^{(L)} \end{bmatrix} \tag{5.13}
$$

as the k-th data vector consisting of the k-th bits from all L radios. Note that due to the arbitrary delays $\tau_1, \tau_2, \ldots, \tau_L$ this waveform begins at $kT_b + \min\{\tau_l\}$ and ends at $(k+1)T_b + \max\{\tau_l\}$, which is confined to the interval $[kT_b, (k+2)T_b]$.

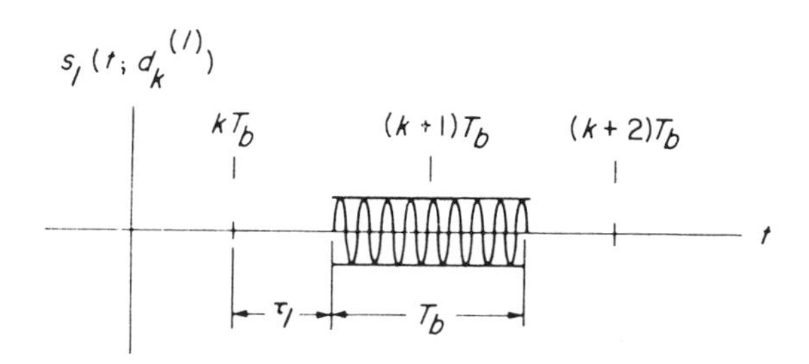

Figure 5.12. Single radio pulse.

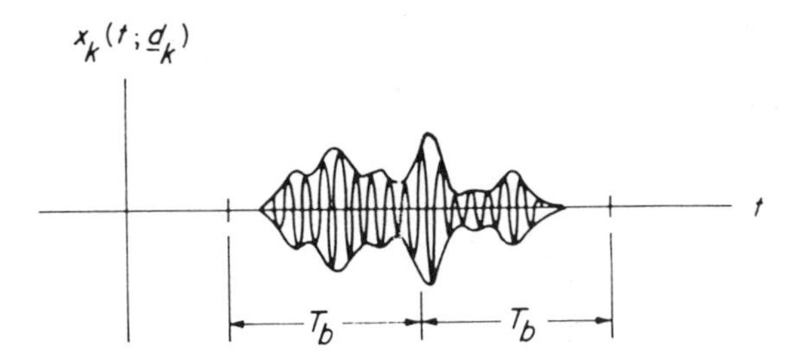

Figure 5.13. L radio pulses.

The composite signal from all L radios consists of a continuous sequence of pulses $x_k(t; \boldsymbol{d}_k)$, denoted

$$x(t) = \sum_k x_k(t; \boldsymbol{d}_k). \tag{5.14}$$

Note that these pulses are spaced T_b seconds apart, whereas each pulse has length greater than T_b seconds but less than $2T_b$ seconds. Transmission of such overlapping pulses is commonly referred to as *intersymbol interference*.

Based on the above discussion now model the set of L asynchronous radios of Figure 5.3 as a set of time synchronous radios followed by arbitrary delays as shown in Figure 5.14. Mathematically the transmitted signals are the same. Now, however, we have the final equivalent model of Figure 5.15 where we start with a vector source that outputs data vector $\boldsymbol{d}_k$ at time kT_b followed by a modulator and an additive white Gaussian noise channel with intersymbol interference. The signal at the receiving radio is

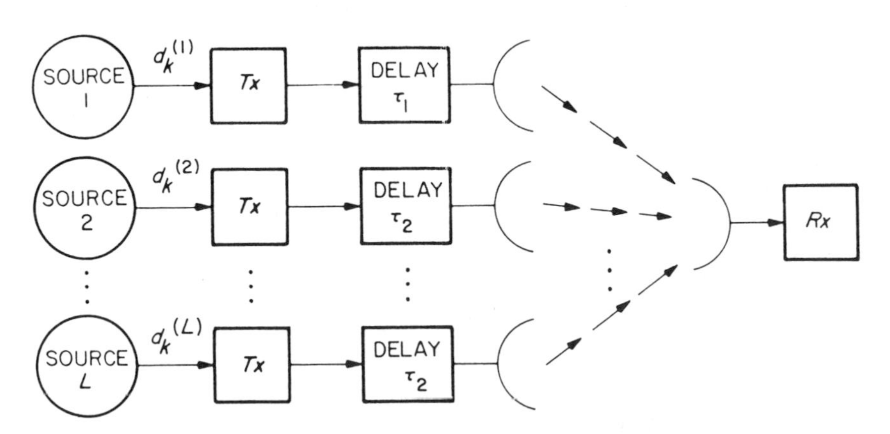

Figure 5.14. Equivalent synchronized radios.

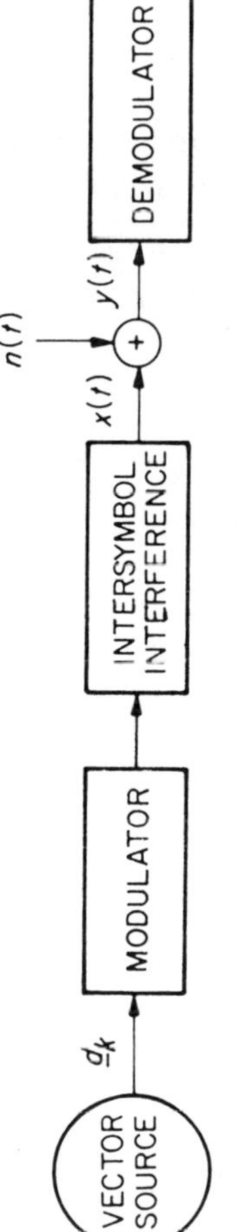

Figure 5.15. Intersymbol interference channel model.

given by

$$y(t) = x(t) + n(t) \tag{5.15}$$

where $n(t)$ is white Gaussian noise of single-sided spectral density N_o. Here we introduce receiver noise in the analysis.

Now consider the optimum receiver or demodulator. Assume that the receiver has acquired and accurately synchronized estimates of the signal parameters $\{A_l\}$, $\{\tau_l\}$, and $\{\theta_l\}$. Thus the receiver has complete knowledge of the transmitted radio signals except for the data vector sequence $\{\boldsymbol{d}_k\}$. The goal of the receiver is to estimate this data vector sequence given the received radio signal $\{y(t), -\infty < t < \infty\}$.

The optimum receiver will examine each data vector sequence such as $\{\hat{\boldsymbol{d}}_k\}$, which has the corresponding signal

$$\begin{aligned} \hat{x}(t) &= \sum_k x_k(t; \hat{\boldsymbol{d}}_k) \\ &= \sum_k \sum_{l=1}^{L} s_l(t; \hat{d}_k^{(l)}), \end{aligned} \tag{5.16}$$

and determine its likelihood as a transmitted data vector sequence. It uses the maximum-likelihood (ML) criterion based on minimizing [103]

$$\int_{-\infty}^{\infty} [y(t) - \hat{x}(t)]^2 \, dt \tag{5.17}$$

or maximizing

$$\int_{-\infty}^{\infty} y(t)\hat{x}(t) \, dt - \tfrac{1}{2}\int_{-\infty}^{\infty} \hat{x}^2(t) \, dt. \tag{5.18}$$

Thus, given the received radio signal $\{y(t), -\infty < t < \infty\}$, the optimum ML receiver chooses the data vector sequence $\{\hat{\boldsymbol{d}}_k\}$ that maximized (5.18).

Note that

$$\begin{aligned} &\int_{-\infty}^{\infty} y(t)\hat{x}(t) \, dt \\ &= \sum_k \sum_{l=1}^{L} \int_{-\infty}^{\infty} y(t) s_l(t; \hat{d}_k^{(l)}) \, dt \\ &= \sum_k \sum_{l=1}^{L} \hat{d}_k^{(l)} \int_{kT_b+\tau_l}^{(k+1)T_b+\tau_l} y(t) A_l c_l(t-\tau_l) \cos[\omega_0(t-\tau_l) + \theta_l] \, dt \\ &= \sum_k \sum_{l=1}^{L} \hat{d}_k^{(l)} y_k^{(l)} \end{aligned} \tag{5.19}$$

where

$$y_k^{(l)} = \int_{kT_b+\tau_l}^{(k+1)T_b+\tau_l} y(t) A_l c_l(t-\tau_l) \cos[\omega_0(t-\tau_l) + \theta_l] \, dt \tag{5.20}$$

is the matched filter output sampled at time $(k + 1)T_b + \tau_l$ for the filter matched to the l-th pseudorandom DS/BPSK waveform. Thus the required (sufficient statistics) received radio signal components are the L matched filter output samples.

The energy term

$$\int_{-\infty}^{\infty} \hat{x}^2(t)\,dt \tag{5.21}$$

depends on the cross-correlation properties of the L pseudorandom waveforms and the particular data vector sequence $\{\hat{\boldsymbol{d}}_k\}$ being examined (see Verdu [96]). This results in the overall decision rule based on

$$\int_{-\infty}^{\infty} y(t)\hat{x}(t)\,dt - \tfrac{1}{2}\int_{-\infty}^{\infty} \hat{x}^2(t)\,dt = \sum_k m_k(y_k; \hat{\boldsymbol{d}}_k, \hat{\boldsymbol{d}}_{k-1}) \tag{5.22}$$

where $m_k(y_k; \hat{\boldsymbol{d}}_k, \hat{\boldsymbol{d}}_{k-1})$ is some metric[7] and

$$y_k = \begin{bmatrix} y_k^{(1)} \\ y_k^{(2)} \\ \vdots \\ y_k^{(L)} \end{bmatrix} \tag{5.23}$$

is the vector of sampled matched filter outputs. The metric at time k depends on $\hat{\boldsymbol{d}}_k$ and $\hat{\boldsymbol{d}}_{k-1}$ because only the pulse $x_{k-1}(t; \hat{\boldsymbol{d}}_{k-1})$ interferes with the transmission during the k-th pulse $x_k(t; \hat{\boldsymbol{d}}_k)$.

By defining $\hat{\boldsymbol{d}}_{k-1}$ as the state at time k we can model the L radio signals as a finite state process described by a trellis diagram where there are 2^L states. The process of finding the data vector sequence $\{\hat{\boldsymbol{d}}_k\}$ that maximizes (5.22) can be implemented using the Viterbi algorithm [103]. This system is illustrated in Figure 5.16.

Verdu [96] took examples and evaluated upper and lower bounds on their bit error probabilities for this optimum maximum-likelihood receiver. These bounds were derived as a function of the L signal parameters $\{A_l\}$, $\{\tau_l\}$, and $\{\theta_l\}$. Then the results were averaged over uniform probability distributions for $\{\theta_l\}$ and $\{\tau_l\}$ and for the worst case choice of the delays $\{\tau_l\}$. Figure 5.17 shows Verdu's example of $L = 2$ equal energy ($A_1 = A_2$) radios transmitting to a single receiver. The chip sequence here was periodic with a three chip period and $N = 3$ chips per data bit as shown. Except at low values of E_b/N_0, the optimum ML receiver is able to demodulate both signals as well as if there was only one DS/BPSK radio transmitting. The conventional receiver here has the form of Figure 5.10 as compared with the optimum receiver shown in Figure 5.16. This result is similar to the comparison of conventional and maximum-likelihood receivers for channels

[7] This metric may be time varying because of the pseudorandom sequences used.

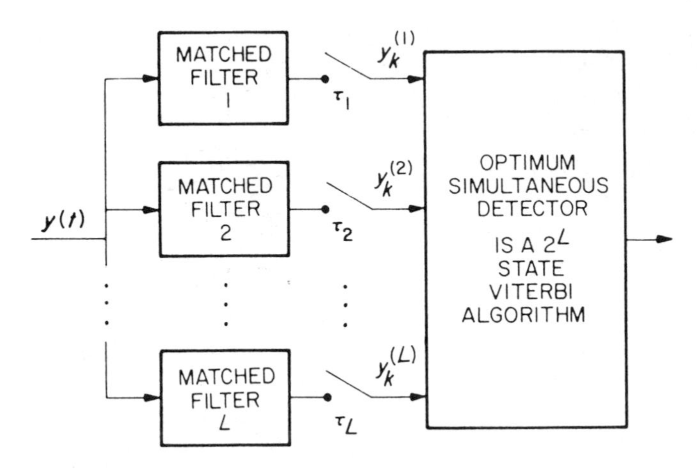

Figure 5.16. Optimum detector.

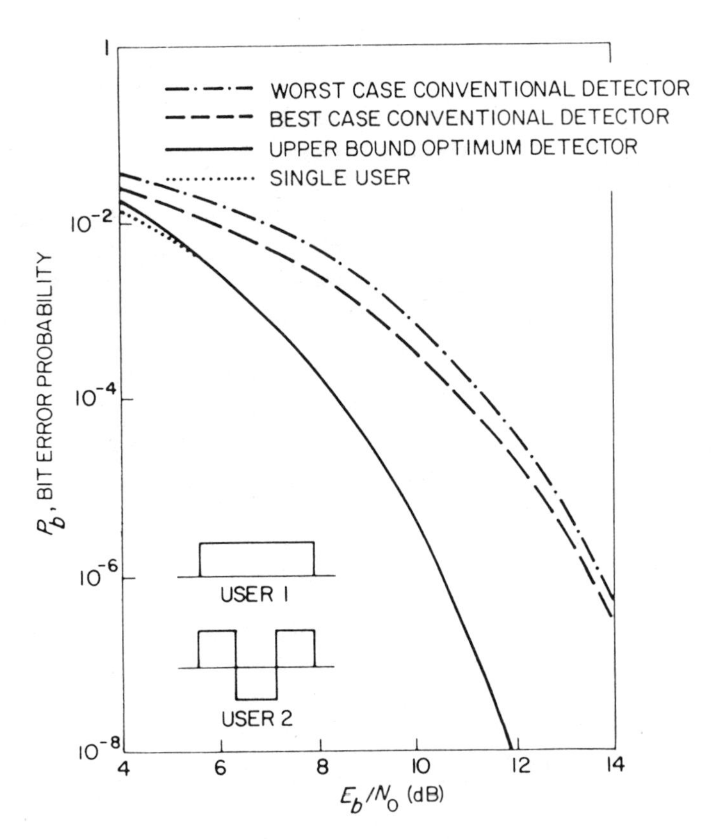

Figure 5.17. $N = 3,\ L = 2$ example.

with intersymbol interference. Other examples considered by Verdu include $L = 3$ equal power radios using $N = 31$ chips per data bit and an $L = 2$ case with unequal signal powers. These examples also show that the optimum maximum-likelihood receiver can achieve the same performance as the single radio transmitter case for high signal-to-noise ratios.

At high signal-to-noise ratios the optimum maximum-likelihood receiver in these examples can reliably determine the transmitted data from all simultaneously transmitting radios. This is not surprising since we assumed complete information about the signal parameters $\{A_l\}$, $\{\tau_l\}$, and $\{\theta_l\}$. Also we assumed no quantization of the matched filter output samples $\{y_k\}$ or of the metrics used in the Viterbi algorithm. In practice some quantized metrics must be used and little or no side information may be available regarding signal parameters. The optimum receiver results presented here serve as a theoretically achievable limit or baseline with which we can compare practical uncoded systems.

5.4 SPREAD-SPECTRUM MULTIPLE ACCESS WITH FH / MFSK WAVEFORMS

SSMA systems using FH/MFSK waveforms can take a wider range of forms compared with systems using DS/BPSK waveforms. This is due to the fact that a wide variety of detector functions and decoder metrics can be used here including metrics that allow for side information regarding the channel conditions (see Chapter 2, Volume II). In addition, with FH/MFSK waveforms, M is a parameter which can be increased until the entire spread-spectrum frequency band consists of one large MFSK signalling band with no hopping.

For point-to-point communication we exploit the fact that interference due to other radio signals resembles multitone jamming. In general worst case multitone jamming with the same total interference power will result in greater performance degradation than this unintentional interference due to other FH/MFSK signals. *Therefore, earlier results on multitone jamming can be used to upper bound bit error probabilities in the FH/MFSK SSMA system.*

For point-to-multipoint SSMA with FH/MFSK waveforms there exists the possibility of considering synchronous radio transmitters. In practice, with FH/MFSK waveforms, hop time intervals are generally much larger than the chip time intervals in DS/BPSK waveforms. Thus we can have some networks with radios transmitting FH/MFSK waveforms where the hopping is synchronized.

5.4.1 Point-to-Point

Consider here the performance of point-to-point communication between two radios using FH/MFSK waveforms in a network of other similar radios. Between the transmitter and receiver assume ideal synchronization where the receiver knows the frequency pattern and hop time epoch of the desired FH/MFSK signal. As usual non-coherent detectors are used. Throughout this discussion the other users may or may not have synchronized hop times. *All hopping patterns are assumed to be independent when different keys are used and each hopping pattern is modelled as a sequence of i.i.d. random frequency variables uniformly distributed over some uniformly spaced set of points across the spread-spectrum frequency band.* This is the SSMA system as opposed to a CDMA system where specific hopping patterns with low mutual interference is used [77]–[82] primarily for multiple access applications. In military networks the primary requirements are to use waveforms with anti-jam (AJ) and low probability of intercept (LPI) capabilities.

Suppose the point-to-point link using an FH/MFSK waveform has interference in the radio channel due to L other radio transmitters of power distribution given by (5.1) at the radio receiver in question while the intended signal has power S. *The L interfering signals appear as multiple tones of different powers randomly hopping across the band much like a multitone jammer. We now upper bound the bit error probability by assuming that a multitone jammer has the same total power J given by* (5.4) *and uses this in a worst case multitone strategy.* Generally, this means the jammer would take equal size tones and distribute them according to some strategy as discussed in Section 2.2, Chapter 2, Volume II.

With the worst case multitone jammer the effective bit energy-to-noise ratio is again given by (5.2), where the processing gain is the total spread-spectrum bandwidth divided by the link data rate in bits per second. Figure 5.9 again illustrates the special case where all L interference signals have the same power at the receiver. The only difference between using Figure 5.9 for the DS/BPSK system and the FH/MFSK system is the choice for the required bit energy-to-noise ratio γ to be used. For DS/BPSK this is based on the additive white Gaussian noise channel, whereas for FH/MFSK systems it is based on the worst case multitone jammer.

The multitone jammer analysis of Chapter 2 in Volume II assumes ideal jammer state information and conventional chip energy detector outputs. What this means is that during a hop time interval, in the MFSK sub-band of the intended transmitted signal, the receiver has M energy detectors. If a jamming tone is also present along with the transmitted signal in this sub-band, then this fact is used by the receiver when it takes a weighted sum of energy detector outputs to make decisions. If this same type of receiver is used in the radio network with interference due to other radios, the resulting required bit energy-to-noise ratio γ would be less than that for the worst case multitone jammer. The number of users L in Figure 5.9 would then be a lower bound when the required value of γ is taken from the worst case multitone jamming analysis.

With FH/MFSK waveforms many other detectors and metrics are possible. Against intelligent jammers, combining chip energies without jammer state information is not effective. This is because such a pure "soft decision" receiver without jammer state information is vulnerable to a jammer strategy where high jammer power can be concentrated on a small number of symbols of a coded transmission sequence and lead to a large number of decoding errors. One approach to alleviating this problem is to quantize the chip energy detector outputs into a finite number of threshold levels, but the disadvantage of this is that optimum threshold settings require AGC, which is difficult to maintain in a jamming environment.

An example of a detector that does not require AGC is one that makes hard M-ary decisions based on the largest chip energy detector output or that outputs an erasure symbol [105]–[108]. Reed-Solomon codes have been proposed for these systems with M-ary symbols that can correct twice as many erasures as hard decision errors. Various techniques for the detector to select a hard decision or make an erasure decision have been proposed including taking advantage of the fact that for asynchronous radios the interfering tone usually does not overlap completely in time with the intended signal [109], [110].

An alternative approach, called list detection, was discussed in Section 2.7.3 in Chapter 2 of Volume II. With this technique, demodulator energy outputs are ranked in magnitude from the highest to the lowest, and metrics are assigned according to position in the ranking rather than the magnitude. The process of rank-ordering is equivalent to partitioning the M-dimensional observation space of demodulator outputs into regions corresponding to the different ordered lists. In this sense list detection is like soft-decision quantization because it creates a discrete memoryless channel with more outputs than inputs as seen by the encoder/decoder. Note that list detection does not depend on thresholds which are difficult to maintain during jamming.

List detection has been considered previously [111], [112] for the AWGN channel where performance is inferior to threshold quantization. More recently, Viterbi [113] has presented an interference mitigation technique which is a variant of list detection, and results show that robust performance is achieved against tone jamming with simple receiver implementation (see Section 2.7.2, Chapter 2, Volume II). Following the analysis of Section 2.7.3 in Chapter 2 of Volume II, we present results of Crepeau [114] and Crepeau et al. [115] for the evaluation of cutoff rates against worst case multitone jamming using the list detector. The metrics associated with list detector outputs are the maximum-likelihood metrics with or without jammer state information. Here jammer state information is in the form where the receiver knows which of the M frequencies contain some signal or interference energy. In the multiple access context we say that the receiver has "collision compensation" information since this is used to change or compensate the metric assigned to the list detector outputs. Our multiple access results are thus given for the cases with collision compensation (CC) and without collision compensation.

For M-ary alphabets, the cutoff rate R_0 can be defined by[8]

$$R_0 = \log_2 M - \log_2 [1 + (M-1)D] \tag{5.24}$$

with the Chernoff parameter, D, given for $\hat{x} \neq x$ by

$$D = \min_{\lambda \geq 0} E\{\exp \lambda [m(y, \hat{x}) - m(y, x)] | x \text{ sent}\} \tag{5.25}$$

where $m(y, x)$ is the decision metric evaluated for the channel output y, and the transmitted code symbol x. For MFSK, the channel output is the set of energy detector outputs $y = (e_1, e_2, \ldots, e_M)$. The list decision metric is defined by

$$m(y, x) = N_{L_x} \tag{5.26}$$

where L_x is the position on the list where the symbol x placed (symbol with the highest energy places first) and N_ℓ is the "score" awarded to the symbol placing ℓ-th on the list.

For an arbitrary set of scores, $\boldsymbol{N} = (N_1, N_2, \ldots, N_M)$, R_0 is evaluated using ($\hat{x} \neq x$),

$$\begin{aligned} D &= \min_{\lambda \geq 0} \sum_{\ell=1}^{M} \sum_{k=1}^{M} e^{\lambda(N_k - N_\ell)} P\{L_x = \ell, L_{\hat{x}} = k | x \text{ sent}\} \\ &= \min_{\lambda \geq 0} \frac{1}{M-1} \sum_{\ell=1}^{M} \left[\sum_{k=1}^{M} e^{\lambda(N_k - N_\ell)} - 1 \right] q_\ell \end{aligned} \tag{5.27}$$

where $q_\ell = P\{L_x = \ell | x \text{ sent}\}$. Here we used the symmetry condition, for $\hat{x} \neq x$,

$$P\{L_{\hat{x}} = k | x \text{ sent}, L_x = \ell\} = (M-1)^{-1}(1 - \delta_{\ell,k}). \tag{5.28}$$

We can simplify the list metric by choosing to rank only the L^* detector outputs with the highest energies. Each of the remaining $M - L^*$ unranked symbols would then be given a common score. This "list-of-L^*" metric specializes to the hard decision metric for $L^* = 1$. By direct differentiation, we obtain conditions for selecting the list scores, $\boldsymbol{N}$, so as to maximize R_0 for the list-of-L^* metric ($1 \leq L^* \leq M$). The resulting list scores and cutoff rate are [111]

$$N_k = \begin{cases} \log q_k; & k = 1, 2, \ldots, L^* \\ \log\left(\dfrac{q_0}{M - L^*}\right); & k = L^* + 1, \ldots, M \end{cases} \tag{5.29}$$

[8]A symmetric, memoryless channel is assumed.

and

$$R_0 = \log_2 M - 2\log_2\left(\sum_{l=1}^{L^*}\sqrt{q_l} + \sqrt{(M - L^*)q_0}\right) \tag{5.30}$$

where q_0 is the probability that the transmitted symbol will be off the list of L^*. The ordering distribution $\{q_l\}$ will depend upon E_c/N_J and the jamming format encountered, which we shall examine next.

Suppose that a tone jammer divides his power, J, equally so as to jam a fraction ρ of the total number of hopping frequencies. Furthermore, suppose that the jammer has perfect knowledge of the communicator's frequency slots and positions his tones randomly among these slots. Then, defining β as the signal-to-jamming-tone power ratio, the number of slots that the jammer jams is $N^* = \beta(J/S)$. Denoting[9] the time per bit by T_b, the total number of hopping frequencies is $N_T = W_{ss}T_bR = R(W_{ss}/R_b) = (E_c/N_J)(J/S)$, so that $\beta = \rho(E_c/N_J)$ where $S/J \le \beta \le E_c/N_J$. Let $T_{\hat{x}} = 1$ indicate that the symbol $\hat{x}$ was hit by the jammer ($T_{\hat{x}} = 0$ otherwise), then the energy detector outputs for the transmitted symbol, x, and any $\hat{x} \neq x$ are given by

$$e_x = \begin{cases} E_c, & T_x = 0 \\ (1 + 2\sqrt{\beta}\cos\theta + \beta)\dfrac{E_c}{\beta}, & T_x = 1 \end{cases}$$

$$e_{\hat{x}} = \begin{cases} 0, & T_{\hat{x}} = 0 \\ \dfrac{E_c}{\beta}, & T_{\hat{x}} = 1 \end{cases} \tag{5.31}$$

where θ is the relative phase angle between the information and jamming tones. Letting n_J denote the number of MFSK symbols, other than x, hit by the jammer during a hop, then

$$q_\ell = \sum_{n=0}^{M-1}\binom{M-1}{n}\rho^n(1-\rho)^{M-1-n}[(1-\rho)q_\ell(n,0) + \rho q_\ell(n,1)] \tag{5.32}$$

where $q_\ell(n_J, T_x) = P\{L_x = \ell | x \text{ sent}, n_J, T_x\}$.

First, consider the case where the information tone is not hit ($T_x = 0$). If $\beta > 1$, then x places first on the list. If $\beta < 1$, then x places $(n_J + 1)$-th. However, sufficiently near $\beta = 1$, the ordering of x and the n_J jammed symbols will be determined by noise sources not modelled here (e.g., receiver noise). Consequently, at $\beta = 1$, we assume that x can place

[9] We define R = code rate in bits per MFSK chip, R_b = data rate in bits per second, $N_J = J/W_{ss}$, and the normalized cutoff rate $r_0 = R_0/\log_2 M$.

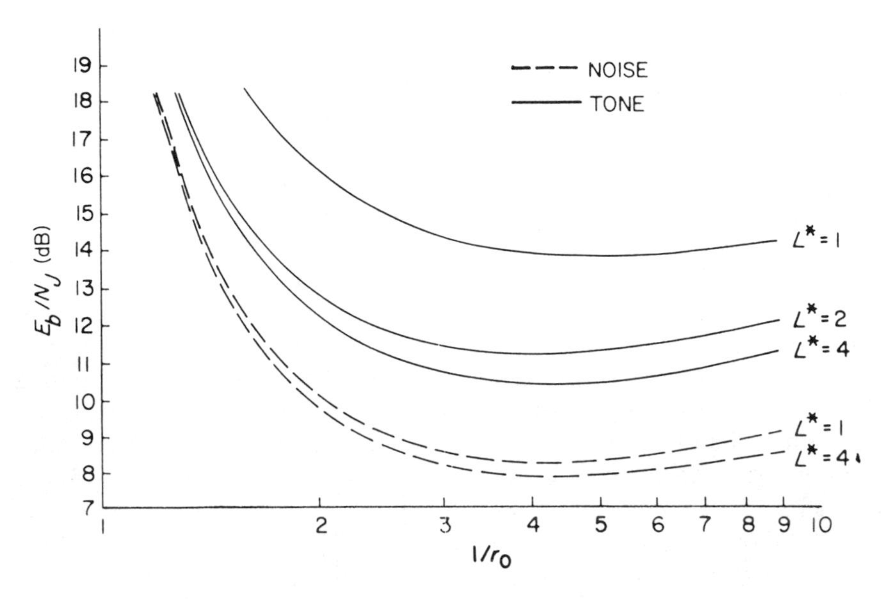

Figure 5.18. Minimum E_b/N_J for list detection (4 FSK).

anywhere among the n_J jammed tones with equal probability so that

$$q_\ell(n,0) = \begin{cases} \delta_{l,n+1}; & \beta < 1 \\ 1/(n+1), \quad 1 \le l \le n+1; & \beta = 1 \\ \delta_{l,1}; & \beta > 1. \end{cases} \tag{5.33}$$

Next, consider the case when x is hit by the jammer ($T_x = 1$). Assume that the relative phase angle, θ, is uniformly distributed over $(-\pi, \pi)$. Notice from (5.33) that when $\beta \ge 4$, x always places first on the list. However, when $\beta < 4$ and $|\theta| > \theta_c = \cos^{-1}(-\sqrt{\beta}/2)$, x places $(n_J + 1)$-th. Thus, averaging over θ we obtain

$$q_\ell(n,1) = \begin{cases} \dfrac{(\pi - \theta_c)}{\pi}\delta_{\ell,n+1} + \dfrac{\theta_c}{\pi}\,\delta_{\ell,1}; & \beta \le 4 \\ \delta_{\ell,1}; & \beta > 4. \end{cases} \tag{5.34}$$

Worst case tone jamming with no jammer state information results for $4 \le M \le 32$ are given in Figures 5.18 through 5.21 by solid curves. Dashed lines correspond to worst case partial-band noise jamming.

Here the code rate is set at the cutoff rate, $R = R_0$. For $E_c/N_J > 4$ dB, worst case performance results when the jammer places slightly more power in his tones than the communicator's tone (i.e., $\beta = 1^-$) so that x places $(n_J + 1)$-th when $T_x = 0$. For $E_c/N_J \ll 4$ dB, β is small and θ_c near $\pi/2$ so that when $T_x = 1$, x places first or $(n_J + 1)$-th with about equal probability. In this situation, if the jammer were to jam all slots, then x

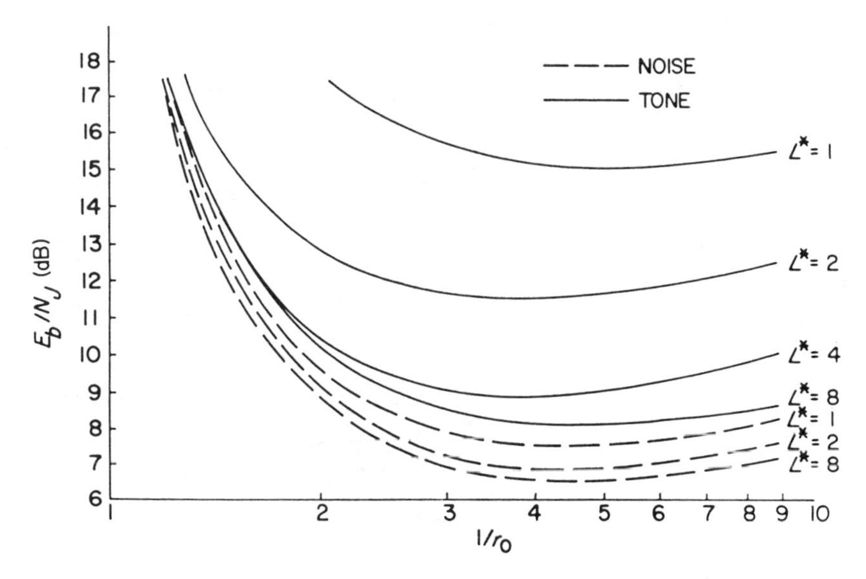

Figure 5.19. Minimum E_b/N_J for list detection (8 FSK).

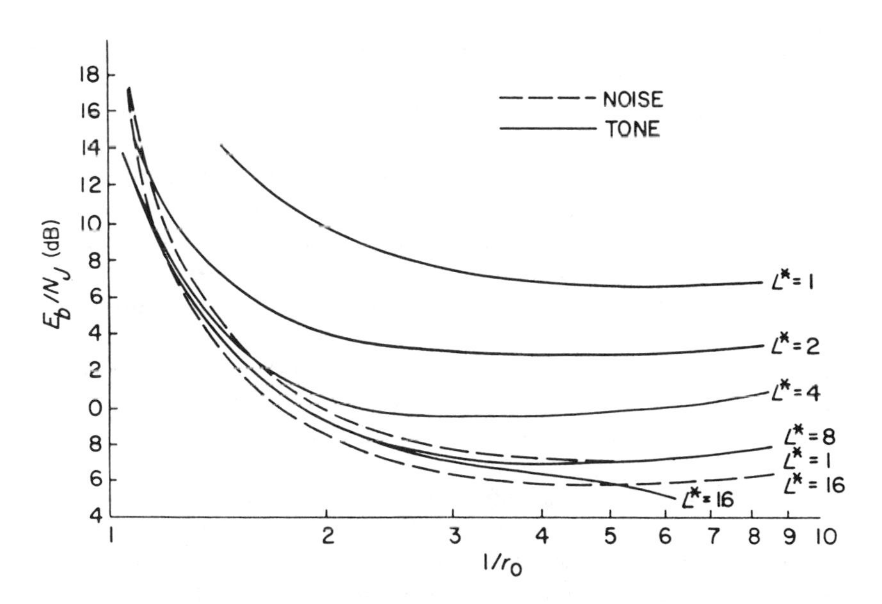

Figure 5.20. Minimum E_b/N_J for list detection (16 FSK).

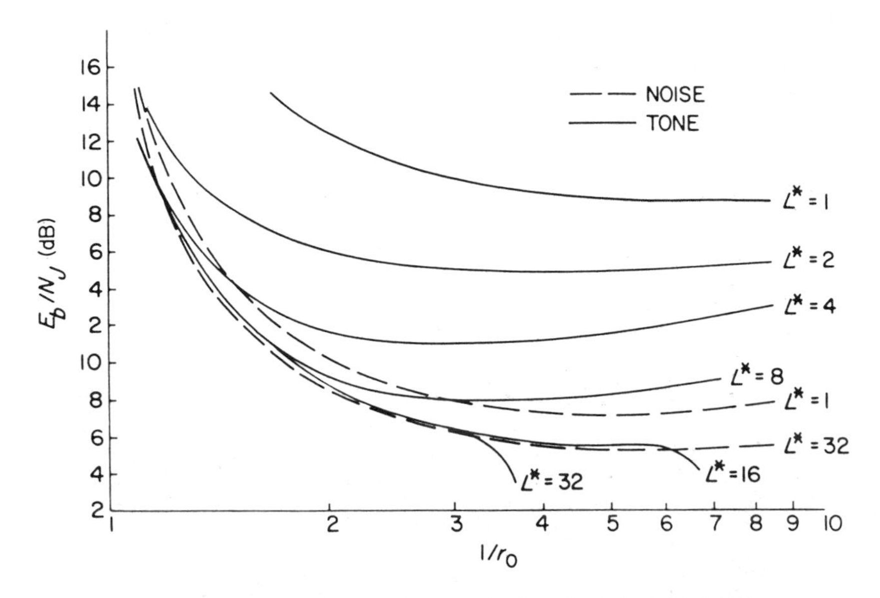

Figure 5.21. Minimum E_b/N_J for list detection (32 FSK).

always places either first or last with about equal probability and $r_0 = 1 - 1/\log_2 M$, which approaches 1 for large M. Consequently, at low E_c/N_J, the best strategy for the tone jammer is in general not full band ($\rho = 1$) jamming, as it was for the noise jammer.

The worst case tone jamming results for list metrics specifies the required bit energy-to-noise ratio for coded systems. Here we can find γ and use this in Figure 5.9 to obtain a lower bound on the maximum number of simultaneous equal energy radio transmitters that can be tolerated in a radio network. In a radio network environment list detectors can be quite effective, especially for large alphabet size M, while being robust against jamming. The metrics used here, however, do depend on some knowledge of the channel statistics in the form of probabilities q_k; $k = 1, 2, \ldots, L^*$. In a network such channel statistics may be available at each radio along with the connectivity of the radios in the network.

Figure 5.22 illustrates the effectiveness of the list metric for larger alphabet size $M = 32$. We compare the full list ($L^* = M = 32$) metric with the energy metric (EM), which is near optimum for the additive white Gaussian noise channel, and the hard decision metric (HDM). The probability q_ℓ that the transmitted signal is ℓ-th on the list is plotted in Figure 5.23 for the worst case partial-band noise jammer when $M = 8$. Note that q_ℓ for $\ell = 2, 3, \ldots, 8$ are not too far apart. This result is contrasted with the worst case tone jammer results shown in Figure 5.24, which show a much wider divergence in the values of q_ℓ for $\ell = 2, 3, \ldots, 8$. Against tone jamming there is more information in the list detector outputs.

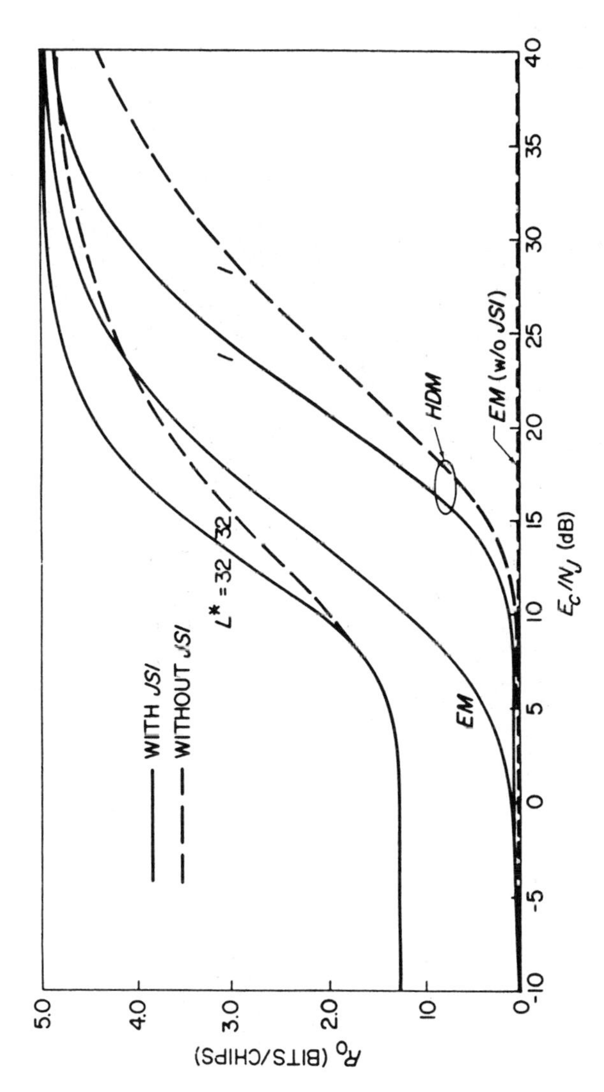

Figure 5.22. R_0 versus E_c/N_J against worst case tone jamming ($M = 32$).

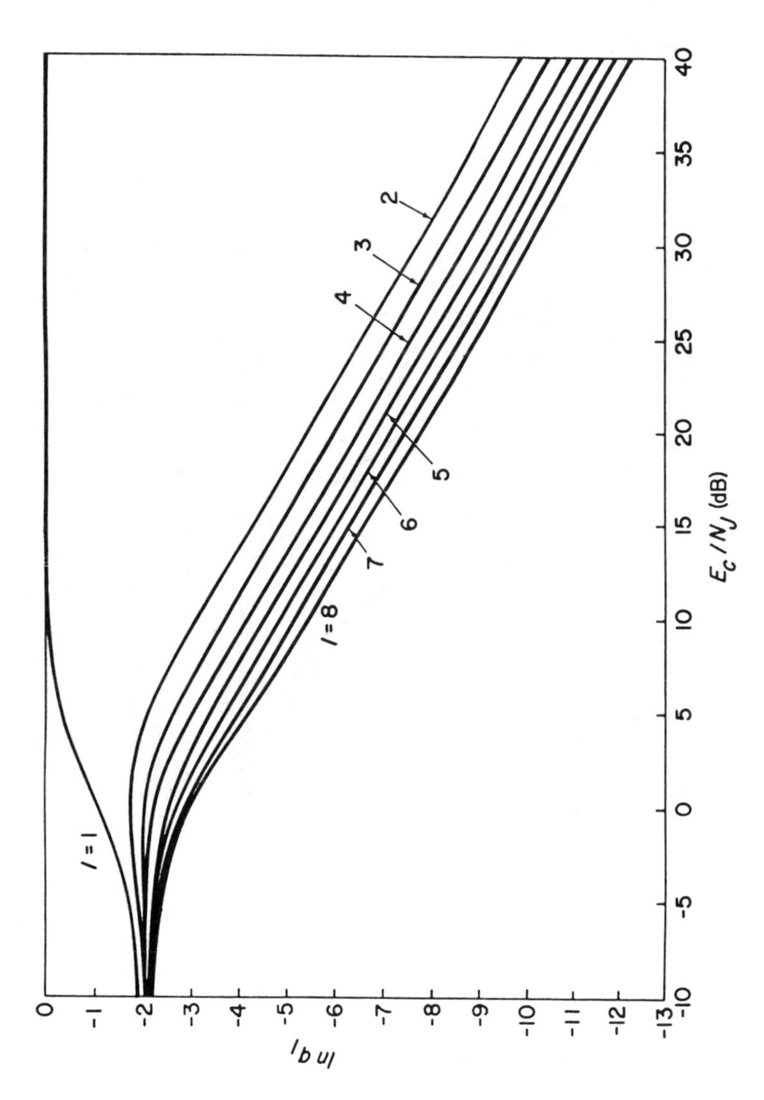

Figure 5.23. $\ell n q_\ell$ versus E_c/N_J against worst case PB noise jamming ($M = 8$).

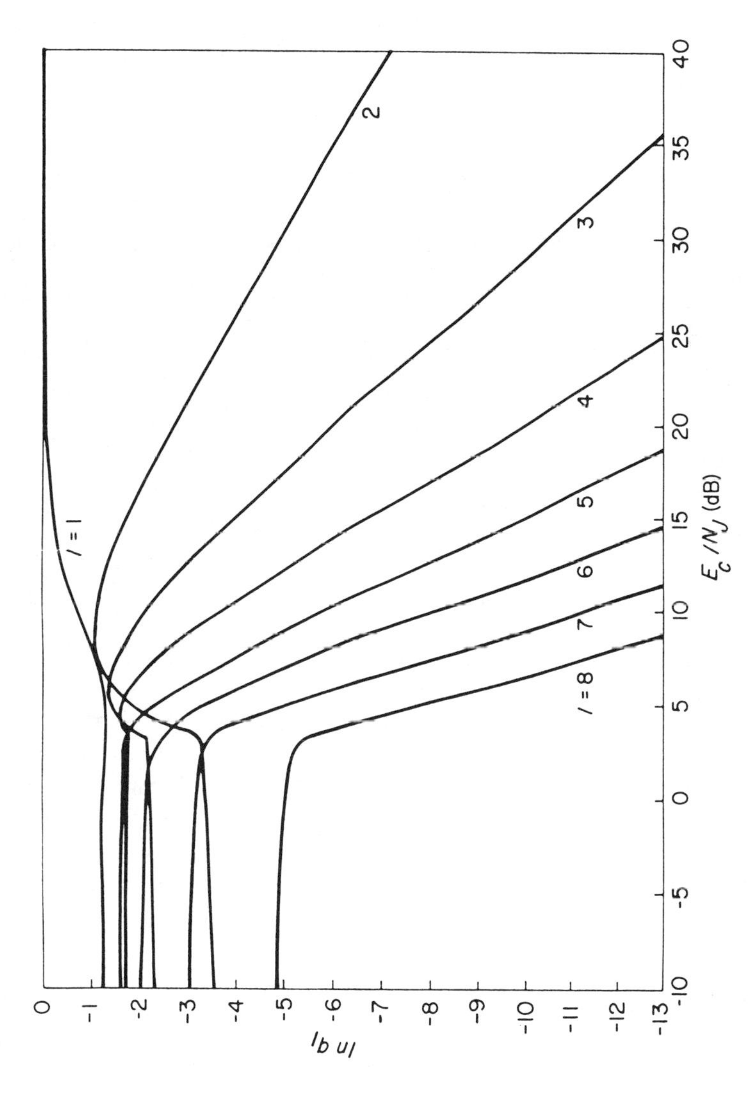

Figure 5.24. $\ell n q_\ell$ versus E_c/N_J against worst case tone jamming ($M = 8$).

Rather than assume the worst case multitone jammer, Creighton [116] studied the list detector with maximum-likelihood metrics when there are L simultaneously transmitting radios with FH/MFSK signals of equal power at the receiver. He assumed the following:

1. All FH/MFSK signals have the same power level at the receiver.
2. Over a chip time interval, the average power of the sum of tones at a given frequency equals the sum of their average powers.
3. All radios are time synchronized and have signals hopping at the same time.
4. All hopping patterns are independent of each other and consist of independent uniformly distributed hop frequencies.
5. The performance is limited by mutual interference and receiver noise can be ignored.

With these assumptions the following parameters were selected:

m = diversity or number of MFSK chips for each M-ary symbol

L^* = list size

L = number of simultaneously transmitting radios

Two types of maximum-likelihood metrics were selected. The first metric assumes only knowledge of the probabilities $\{q_k\}$ and uses the metric defined by (5.29). The second metric assumes that additional side information is available in the form of knowing the number of M chip energy detector outputs that consist of one or more tones.[10] This can vary from chip to chip and is assumed to be measured at the chip energy detectors and provided along with the ordered list of L^* largest energy detector outputs. This side information changes the probabilities $\{q_k\}$ to conditional probabilities which can change from chip to chip. The corresponding maximum-likelihood metric is referred to as the "collision compensation" metric. It is the same as (5.29) with $\{q_k\}$ replaced by conditional probabilities where the condition is on the number of the M chip frequencies with some signal input.

Under these assumptions Creighton [116] first examined the bit error probability with diversity alone, which is given by the bound

$$P_b \leq \frac{M}{2} D^m \tag{5.35}$$

where D is given by (5.27) and the energy per chip is related to the energy

[10] This is equivalent to knowing how many chip energy detectors had no input tones.

Table 5.1

Maximum number of users—$PG = 30$ dB.

Channel	Metric		List-of-L^* without Collision Compensation					List-of-L^* with Collision Compensation				
		M	2	8		32		2	8		32	
	P_b	m \ L^*	1,2	1	8	1	32	1,2	1	8	1	32
No Fading	10^{-2}	2	32	42	115	33	170	87	72	170	43	180
	10^{-4}	4	16	31	80	31	170	45	47	110	39	190
	10^{-6}	4	6	11	27	12	58	20	22	50	17	68
Fading	10^{-2}	4	14	13	68	6	125	98	35	190	11	220
	10^{-4}	8	7	9	47	5	100	48	22	115	8	155
	10^{-6}	8	3	4	18	3	42	26	11	62	5	82

per bit by

$$mE_c = (\log_2 M) E_b. \tag{5.36}$$

Here the energy-per-bit-to-equivalent-noise ratio is

$$\begin{aligned} \frac{E_b}{N_J} &= \frac{PG}{J/S} \\ &= \frac{PG}{L-1}. \end{aligned} \tag{5.37}$$

Tables 5.1 and 5.2 summarize the number of allowable simultaneously transmitting radio signals under these conditions. Here $L^* = 1$ corresponds to the hard decision M-ary channel. The fading cases are assumed to be Rayleigh fading, which is independent from chip to chip.

As stated throughout this book, when channel interference is unpredictable, as with jamming waveforms, optimum detectors and decoding metrics are not known. The detectors and metrics given here require different amounts of side information regarding the channel. In theory, we could have a perfect system with perfect side information. For example, suppose the receiver knew exactly the intended signal's power level. Then it could distinguish it from all other signals since in practice no two signals will have the same power level at the receiver. Generally, there is a tradeoff between performance, complexity, and amount of side information required. One would like to have detectors and metrics that are robust in the sense that they minimize the degradation due to the worst conditions in the channel and are not sensitive to channel parameters and do not require much side information.

Table 5.2

Maximum number of users—$P_b \leq 10^{-4}$.

Channel	Metric		List-of-L^* without Collision Compensation					List-of-L^* with Collision Compensation				
		M	2	8		32		2	8		32	
	PG (dB)	m \ L^*	1, 2	1	8	1	32	1, 2	1	8	1	32
No Fading	20	4	3	4	9	4	17	5	6	12	5	20
	30	4	16	31	80	31	170	45	47	110	39	190
	40	2	30	45	115	37	200	160	150	320	93	350
Fading	20	8	1	1	5	1	12	5	3	11	1	13
	30	8	7	9	47	5	100	48	22	115	8	155
	40	4	13	16	96	10	240	270	98	560	32	590

5.4.2 Conventional Multipoint-to-Point

The point-to-point system covered in the previous section assumed all radios used independent hopping patterns and that during each hop an MFSK chip is transmitted. There the frequency hopping radios may or may not be synchronized. Now suppose L radios use FH/MFSK waveforms to simultaneously transmit data to a single radio terminal.

A brute force approach to the point-to-multipoint design is to have a radio terminal with L separate receiver systems where the ℓ-th system receives the ℓ-th radio transmitter signal using the ℓ-th random frequency hopping pattern. This means there are L frequency synthesizers at the receiving radio terminal where each one is synchronized to one of the L transmitting radios.

One approach to reducing the complexity of the receiving radio's terminal is to require all radios to transmit synchronously such that at the receiving radio terminal all transmitted radio signals hop at the same time. In addition, suppose all L radios use the same hopping pattern but with frequency offset so that after dehopping (using one frequency synthesizer) the L transmitted radio signals appear in non-overlapping MFSK sub-bands. These can then be detected using a conventional FDMA receiver system. This is illustrated in Figure 5.25 where W_{ss} is the total spread-spectrum frequency band and W_{MA} is the frequency range used for the L MFSK signals in an FDMA mode. Here the multiple access band is generally much smaller than the spread-spectrum frequency band

$$W_{MA} \ll W_{ss} \tag{5.38}$$

and it is hopped around once every chip time T_c. Thus, we have here a

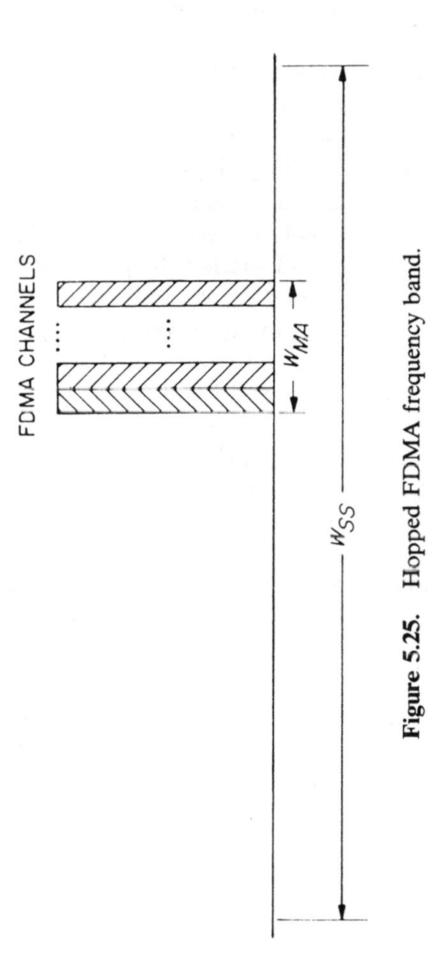

Figure 5.25. Hopped FDMA frequency band.

conventional FDMA system with MFSK waveforms but the frequency band W_{MA} is hopping over a wide frequency range once[11] every chip time T_c.

With L radios transmitting synchronized FH/MFSK waveforms with the same frequency hopping pattern, the receiving radio terminal's front end requires only one frequency synthesizer to dehop all the transmitted signals simultaneously. For the first part of this section we shall assume this type of multipoint-to-point system. We shall, however, examine alternative ways in which the L radios can use the multiple access frequency band of W_{MA} Hz.

Assume for the multiple access frequency band that there are M_o frequency slots where tones of duration T_c are orthogonal. This is roughly $M_o = W_{MA}T_c$ for non-coherent chip waveforms. The simplest approach to dividing up the available capacity of frequency W_{MA} Hz and T_c seconds is to use FDMA as discussed above and sketched in Figure 5.25. If there are more possible transmitting radios than available FDMA slots using MFSK waveforms,[12] then there must be some means of sharing these slots, as discussed earlier in Section 5.2. Demand assignment or polling schemes are possible but these require some central control capabilities. Another approach which requires no control is to allow each user to randomly hop *within* the available non-overlapping MFSK frequency sub-bands in an SSMA mode. These systems will be discussed next.

Goodman, Henry, and Prabhu [117] extended a technique first proposed by Viterbi [118] for multiple access by low rate mobile users employing a satellite transponder. They suggested that each radio be assigned a unique address of m symbols belonging to $\{0, 1, \ldots, M-1\}$ where $M = M_0$, the number of orthogonal tone positions in the frequency band of W_{MA} Hz. An M-ary symbol is transmitted by each radio by sending m MFSK chips using the unique address as follows: Let the ℓ-th radio's m symbol address be

$$R_1^{(\ell)}, R_2^{(\ell)}, \ldots, R_m^{(\ell)} \tag{5.39}$$

where $R_k^{(\ell)} \in \{0, 1, \ldots, M-1\}$ and $M = M_o$. If X is an M-ary data symbol, then the transmitted m chip sequence of the ℓ-th radio is

$$Y_k^{(\ell)} = X + R_k^{(\ell)} \text{ modulo } M. \tag{5.40}$$

This is then sent as an MFSK chip sequence after frequency hopping.[13] After dehopping, the receiver hard quantizes each of the M chip energy detector outputs. That is, at the output of each of the M energy detectors a decision is made as to the presence or absence of a transmitted MFSK chip tone as follows: Any set of chip energy detector outputs $(e_1, e_2, \ldots, e_M)$ is

[11] Slower hopping schemes where several MFSK chips (tones) are transmitted during each hop, are not effective against partial-band or multitone jammers unless interleaving is also used to create independent channel statistics for each chip.

[12] Although there may be many radios, each radio may be transmitting only a small fraction of the time.

[13] For commercial applications frequency hopping may not be used.

hard quantized to $(n_1, n_2, \ldots, n_M)$ where

$$n_k = \begin{cases} 1, & \varepsilon_k \geq \delta \\ 0, & \varepsilon_k < \delta \end{cases} \qquad k = 1, 2, \ldots, M \tag{5.41}$$

for some decision threshold δ. Naturally, with noise and multipath a decision of a tone being present at a frequency may be made when none has been transmitted (false alarm) as well as a decision of no tone being present when in fact a chip tone was transmitted at the frequency (miss).

Each chip time there are M hard quantized bits. The receiver examines the sequence of m such outputs to make decisions as to which symbols were transmitted. The decision rule for the receiver is to choose the data symbol associated with an address pattern as given by (5.40) which has the greatest number of entries or detected tones. For example, suppose $m = 5$ and the address sequence for the ℓ-th radio is

$$0, 1, 2, 3, 4 \tag{5.42}$$

with $M = 8$ as the number of possible tones. If $X = 6$ is the 8-ary data symbol, then the transmitted sequence is (see (5.40))

$$6, 7, 0, 1, 2. \tag{5.43}$$

Suppose the sequence of 5 chip energy detector hard quantized outputs is given by the array

	1st	2nd	3rd	4th	5th
7	0	(1)	1	0	1
6	(1)	0	0	1	1
5	0	0	0	0	0
4	1	0	0	0	0
3	0	0	0	1	0
2	1	1	0	0	(0)
1	0	1	0	(1)	0
0	0	1	(1)	1	1

The only possible output sequences the ℓ-th radio could transmit are

Symbol		Sequence
0	⟶	0, 1, 2, 3, 4
1	⟶	1, 2, 3, 4, 5
2	⟶	2, 3, 4, 5, 6
3	⟶	3, 4, 5, 6, 7
4	⟶	4, 5, 6, 7, 0
5	⟶	5, 6, 7, 0, 1
6	⟶	6, 7, 0, 1, 2
7	⟶	7, 0, 1, 2, 3

(5.44)

By checking the detector output patterns we see that the sequence 6, 7, 0, 1, 2 corresponding to $X = 6$ had the greatest number of entries. This is the circled chip energy detector output sequence shown.

Under this hard quantized detector output with the above pattern decision rule, errors will occur when noise and other users combine to form allowed sequences with more entries than the sequence that was actually transmitted.

The multiple access scheme just described assumes that, given the output pattern of m chip sequence of M hard decision bits, the receiver first checks for the possible sequences of the 1st radio and makes a data symbol decision for it. Then it independently checks the same output pattern for possible sequences of the 2nd radio and makes a data symbol decision for it. It does this L times for the L radios that are transmitting. Here each data symbol decision is independent of each other even though the output pattern of the m chip sequence of M quantized bits for making decisions is the same. This is illustrated in Figure 5.26.

Goodman et al. [117] has shown that for $M = 625$ and $m = 19$ with perfect transmission where the only degradation is mutual interference, an error rate of less than 10^{-3} can be maintained with up to 209 simultaneous transmitting radios. Transmission impairments, consisting of white Gaussian noise and frequency-selective Rayleigh fading with an average signal-to-noise ratio of 25 dB, reduced the number of simultaneous users to about 170. This exceeded the capacity of the original frequency-hopped, phase-shift-keying, spread-spectrum system proposed by Cooper and Nettleton [119]–[121]. Haskell [122] did computer simulations to compare the performance of randomly chosen address sequences with chirp sequences and those found by Einarsson [123]. His results show that the chirp and Einarsson address sequences were equivalent and somewhat better than random address sequences but the differences diminish as the number of symbols $M = M_o$ increases.

The case where each radio transmitter uses a random address sequence is essentially the spread-spectrum example where each transmitter uses the FH/MFSK waveform with diversity of degree m. The only difference here is that we have L radios simultaneously transmitting at all times in the same M-ary sub-band of total bandwidth W_{MA}. The examples here assume that each chip energy detection output is hard quantized. Certainly, more information is maintained for making decisions if the chip energy detector outputs are quantized into more levels. Another possibility is to form an ordered list of the chip energy detector outputs and use it for making decisions. One could then account for the differences in received signal strengths from different radios. Weaker signals will consistently fall lower on the list. Creighton [116] has examined the use of list detectors with various metrics for this SSMA system.

The address sequence is essentially the simplest repeat m coding. With more powerful codes we can achieve somewhat better performance. Greater

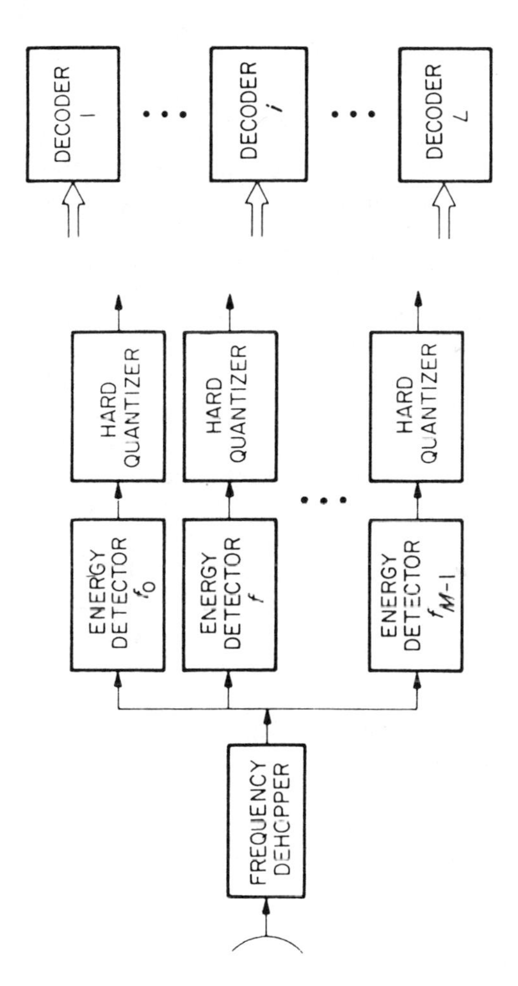

Figure 5.26. Independent decoders.

improvements, however, can be achieved by changing detectors and metrics, and taking advantage of side information in the decoding process.

The system proposed by Goodman et al. [117] certainly is not as efficient as pure FDMA. However, it allows random access with no overall control. With low duty cycle users this means many users can access a single receiving radio terminal with no overall control other than hop synchronization. To make this system more efficient Haskell [122] and Timor [124], [125] have proposed schemes that make use of information derived while decoding the messages of other users to reduce interference of a given transmitted radio signal. For the same example above with 209 simultaneous users Timor's scheme achieves 450 users. In the next section we examine the general question of optimum receivers for multipoint-to-point radios using FH/MFSK waveforms.

5.4.3 Optimum Multipoint-to-Point

We examine the same system as in the previous section where L radios using FH/MFSK waveforms transmit to a single receiving radio terminal. These radios are hop synchronized at the receiving radio and they use the same hopping pattern. Thus the hopping at the transmitters and dehopping at the receiving radio can be ignored since they are transparent to the analysis. Also assume all L radios transmit MFSK waveforms in the same frequency band (after dehopping) and the hard quantized chip energy detectors are the channel outputs upon which decisions are based.

In the previous section the receiver had the form shown in Figure 5.26. Here each transmitted radio signal was decoded independently where the ℓ-th decoder investigated the set of possible sequences of m M-ary symbols that the ℓ-th transmitter could have sent. We now examine what can be done when the decoder decodes all L signals simultaneously.

To illustrate the optimum receiver take the simplest case of $L = 2$ radios each transmitting binary symbols where $M = 2$. Let f_0 and f_1 represent the two possible transmitted frequencies by the two radios. Ignoring hopping and dehopping, the set of possible frequencies and the corresponding hard quantized chip energy detector outputs are:

Inputs Frequency		Detector Outputs	
Radio 1	Radio 2	Output for f_0	Output for f_1
f_0	f_0	1	0
f_0	f_1	1	1
f_1	f_0	1	1
f_1	f_1	0	1

If we take the conventional approach illustrated in Figure 5.26, the second transmitting radio is regarded as channel interference to the link between the first transmitting radio and the receiving radio. To this link the

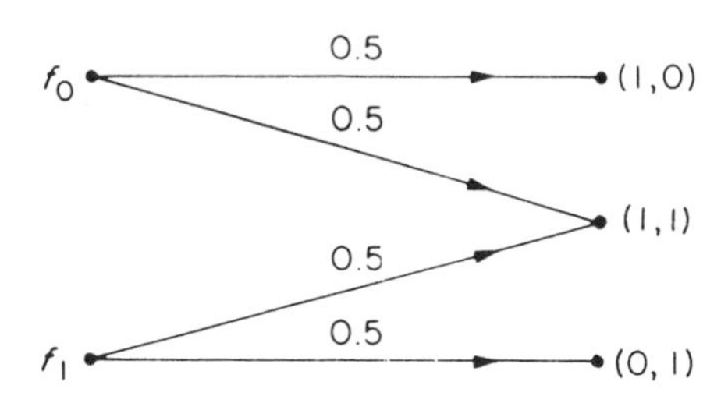

Figure 5.27. Binary erasure channel.

interference channel is as shown in Figure 5.27, where we assume all binary symbols are equally likely to occur. Each time the second radio sends a frequency different from the first radio, which occurs with probability .5, the receiver detector hard quantized output for the two detectors is (1, 1). Essentially, there is no information about what frequency the first radio transmitted when this occurs and we might as well have "erased" the output. This is the binary erasure channel which has channel capacity [103]

$$C_{BEC} = .5 \text{ bits/symbol.} \tag{5.45}$$

This is the maximum data rate possible between the first transmitting radio and the receiving radio. By symmetry this is also the channel between the second transmitting radio and the receiving radio when the first transmitting radio's signal is regarded as interference.

Since the channel capacity of the interference channel in Figure 5.27 is 1/2, codes of this rate, in principle, can achieve any arbitrarily small bit error probability. Suppose the first radio uses such codes and the receiver decodes with no errors. Then the receiver knows exactly the first radio's transmitted coded symbols and can use this to determine exactly the symbols transmitted by the second radio. Thus the second transmitting radio achieves reliable communication without any coding and sends data at rate

$$R_2 = 1.0 \text{ bits/symbol.} \tag{5.46}$$

The rate 1/2 coded first radio sends data at rate

$$R_1 = .5 \text{ bits/symbol.} \tag{5.47}$$

The above example is an illustration of how an optimum decoder simultaneously decodes the signals from both radios. Such multiple access communication systems were first studied by Shannon [127] in 1961. In 1971, Ahlswede [128] determined the capacity regions for the two-user and three-user multiple access channels with independent sources, and van der Meulen [129] put forward a limiting expression and simple inner and outer bounds on the capacity region for the two-user multiple access channel. Liao [130] studied the general L-user multiple access channel with

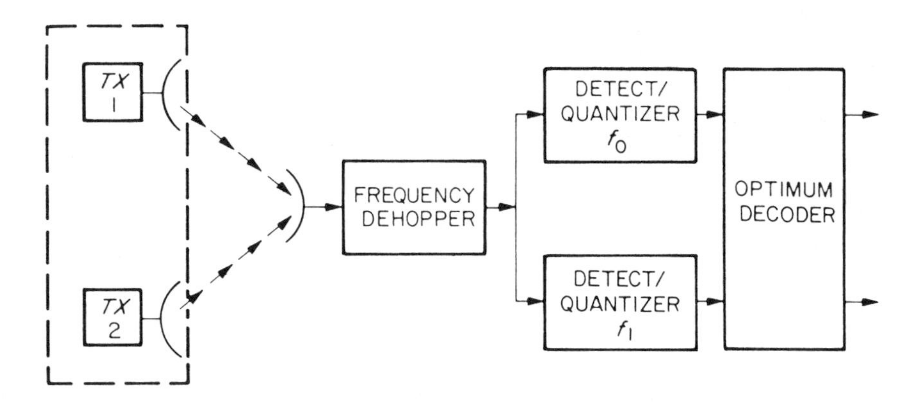

Figure 5.28. Optimum decoder.

independent sources. He formulated the capacity region for this channel and proved the fundamental coding theorem. An extensive survey on the information-theoretic aspects of multiple access channels has been assembled by van der Meulen [131], [132].

As sketched in Figure 5.28, the optimum detector simultaneously decodes both radio signals. It regards the two transmitting radios shown as a single radio with a vector data symbol consisting of two binary data symbols. Thus there are four possible inputs and three possible outputs. The optimum decoder examines all possible sequences of vector data symbols and compares them with the channel output pattern of hard quantized energy detector outputs. The resulting channel is shown in Figure 5.29.

Since the two transmitting radios are spatially separated, the codes used in this channel are restricted. Liao [130], and then Slepian and Wolf [133], gave formulas for the capacity region for this discrete memoryless channel

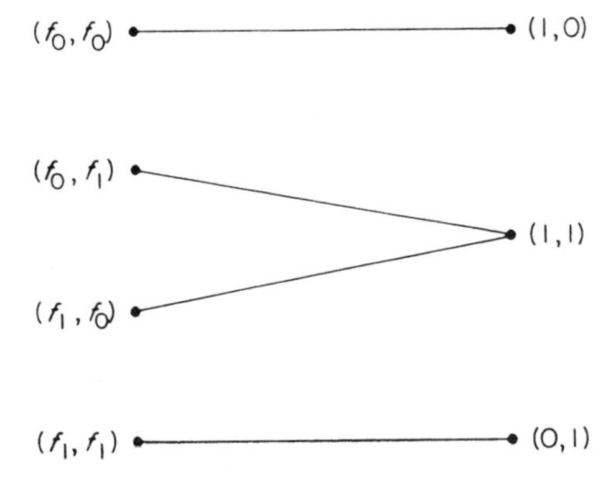

Figure 5.29. Channel for optimum decoder ($M = 2$, $L = 2$).

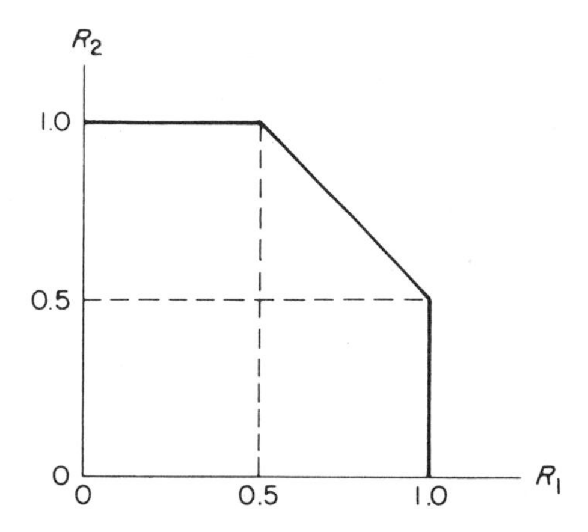

Figure 5.30. Optimum decoder capacity region.

with independent encoding of the two message sources. Their results are shown in Figure 5.30, which gives the data rates of the two transmitting radios that can be simultaneously achieved while maintaining arbitrarily small bit error probabilities. The rates $R_1 = .5$ and $R_2 = 1.0$ illustrated above represent one achievable point in this capacity region.

It is interesting to compare the optimum case of the previous example with pure TDMA. Suppose in a TDMA mode the first radio transmits ρ fraction of the time while the second radio transmits at $1 - \rho$ fraction of the time. Since there would be no interference there are no errors and the average data rates are

$$R_1 = \rho \text{ bits/symbol} \qquad (5.48)$$
$$R_2 = 1 - \rho \text{ bits/symbol}$$

or

$$1 = R_1 + R_2. \qquad (5.49)$$

This defines the capacity region for pure TDMA and is shown in Figure 5.31. Note that the *simultaneously transmitting radios with optimum decoding can achieve higher data rates than pure TDMA*.

Construction of specific codes for the two-radio channel has been investigated by several authors [134]–[138]. Chang and Weldon [139] and Chang and Wolf [140] extended these results to the general case of L-users and M frequencies. The use of trellis codes for these multiple access channels has also been investigated [141]–[147].

Figures 5.32 to 5.34 show the multiple access channels for $L = 3$, $M = 2$; $L = 2$, $M = 3$; and $L = 2$, $M = 4$. For arbitrary L and M there are M^L inputs and the number of outputs is given by

$$\sum_{k=1}^{\lambda} \binom{M}{k}, \qquad \lambda = \min\{L, M\}. \qquad (5.50)$$

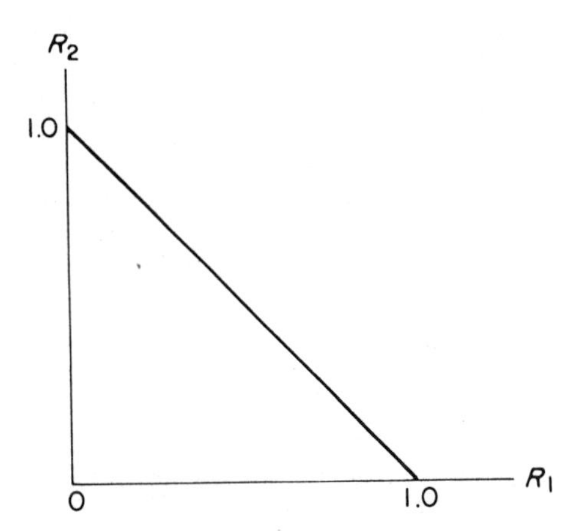

Figure 5.31. Pure TDMA capacity region.

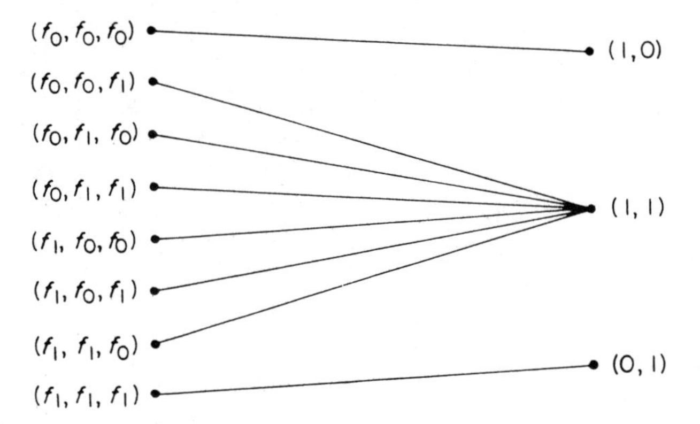

Figure 5.32. Channel for optimum decoder ($M = 2$, $L = 3$).

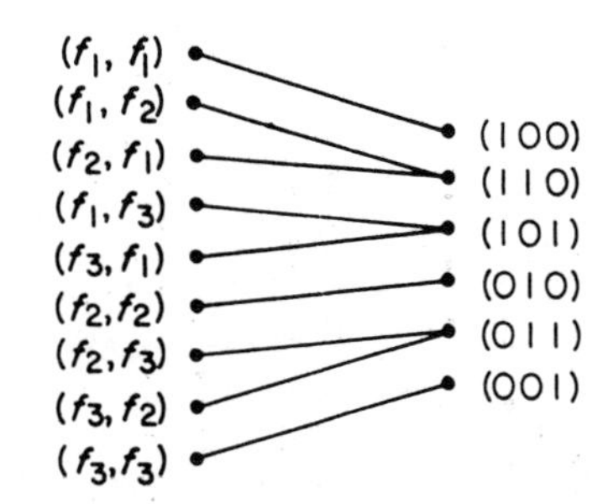

Figure 5.33. Channel for optimum decoder ($M = 3$, $L = 2$).

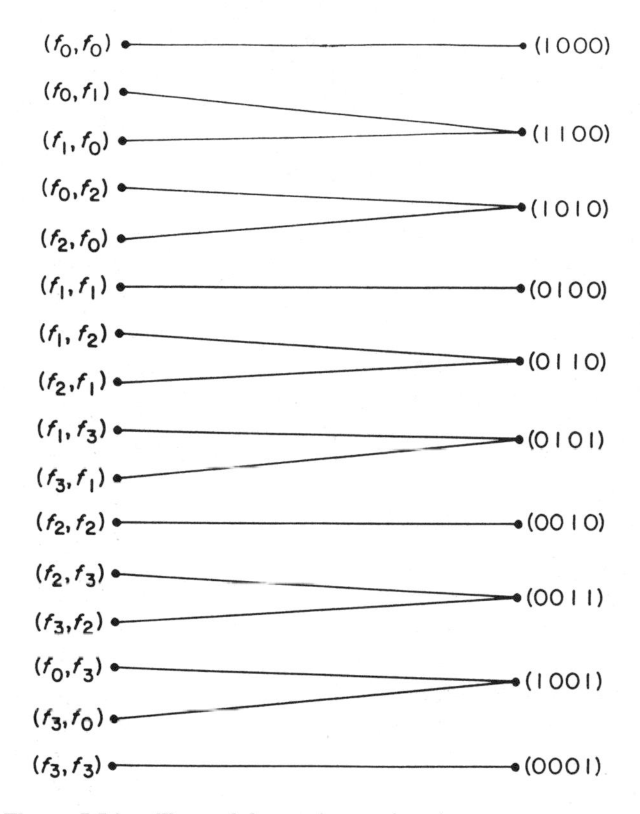

Figure 5.34. Channel for optimum decoder ($M - 4$, $L = 2$).

The overall system, however, is almost the same as that described by Goodman et al. [117] and discussed in the previous section. The major difference here is that all transmitted signals are decoded simultaneously by regarding all L transmitting radios as a single composite multiple frequency tone transmitting radio. The L separate data sources are viewed as a single L dimensional vector source and the optimum receiver compares all possible sequences of these vector data symbols with the channel output sequence. In this case it looks for the vector sequence of greatest agreement with the channel output sequence.

This section examined only the special case where the chip energy detector outputs were quantized to one bit. Generalization to multiple level quantization is possible but will require AGC, which is difficult to maintain in a jamming environment. List detectors with various metrics have been studied by Vo [148] for these multiple access systems. In the list detector, side information regarding the L transmitting radio's signal tone energies at the receiving radio can be incorporated in the decision process. The optimum decoder again treats all L data sources as a single L dimensional vector source and compares all possible transmitted vector data sequences with the total channel output sequence. The metric used for making this comparison depends on the kind of detectors used and the available side information. As an example, consider $L = 8$ identical multiple access transmitters where there are $M = 32$ orthogonal tone frequencies available. Pure FDMA is achieved when each user is given two tones where we have $L = 8$ non-overlapping BFSK signals. Assuming the use of coding, Vo [148] has shown that the overall throughput is higher than FDMA when all $L = 8$ users use all 32 tones (32-FSK) with list detectors and maximum-likelihood metrics. This improvement over pure FDMA is even greater when the multiple access signals have different power levels which are known to the optimum multiple access receiver.

5.5 DISCUSSION

Spread-spectrum techniques are currently being incorporated into most military communication systems. One of the most active areas of research and new developments is in military communication networks [149]–[152]. In this chapter we presented an overview of the possible applications of spread-spectrum waveforms in a network environment with an emphasis on some theoretically optimum systems under ideal conditions. In practice, particularly in a mobile radio environment, there are many practical problems. Turin [153], for example, has examined experimental multipath fading data for mobile radios and developed more complete channel models. His results show that the multipath fading problems can result in worse performance than one expects with the idealized case presented here [154]–[157].

Our purpose here was to examine various types of multiple access systems using spread-spectrum waveforms. The ideal optimum receiver for multipoint-to-point systems in particular may not be practical today but does serve as a baseline with which to compare practical system designs. Also as our ability to do more complex signal processing at higher speeds develops, we can approach the idealized system designs discussed in this chapter. We are just beginning to understand and develop a new generation of spread-spectrum radios for military communication networks.

5.6 REFERENCES

[1] The MITRE Corporation, *Definition of Network Management Problems for Large Ground Data Networks*, MTR-79W00001, Charles F. Swett, Contract No. F19628-81-C-0001, Washington Operations, McLean, VA, February 1979.

[2] The MITRE Corporation, *A Survey of Routing Algorithms for Distributed Digital Radio Networks*, MTR-81W00074, Richard W. Carpenter, Contract No. F19628-81-0001, Washington Operations, McLean, VA, March 1981.

[3] The MITRE Corporation, *Channel Access Methods for Distributed Digital Radio Networks*, MTR-81W00273, Richard W. Carpenter, Contract No. F19628-82-C-0001, Washington Operations, McLean, VA, January 1981.
[4] Session 25, "Advanced space technology for next-generation MILSATCOM system," *MILCOM '82*, Boston, MA, October 1982.
[5] P. Baran, *On Distributed Communications: I. Introduction to Distributed Communications Networks*, The RAND Corporation, RM-3420-PR, August 1964.
[6] B. W. Boehm and R. L. Mobley, "Adaptive routing techniques for distributed communications systems," *IEEE Trans. Commun.*, COM-17, no. 3, pp. 340–349, June 1969.
[7] J. W. S. Liu, "Distributed routing and relay management in mobile packet radio networks," *Proc. Compcon Fall 80*, pp. 235–243, September 1980.
[8] E. W. Dijkstra, "A note on two problems in connection with graphs," *Numerische Mathematik 1*, pp. 269–271, 1959.
[9] L. R. Ford and D. R. Fulkerson, *Flow in Networks*, Princeton, NJ: Princeton University Press, 1962.
[10] R. W. Floyd, "Algorithm 97 shortest path," *Communications of the ACM*, vol. 5, no. 6, p. 345, June 1962.
[11] L. Kleinrock, *Communication Nets: Stochastic Message Flow and Delay*, New York: McGraw-Hill, 1964.
[12] S. E. Dreyfus, *An Appraisal of Some Shortest Path Algorithms*, The RAND Corporation, RM-5433-1-PR, September 1968.
[13] L. Fratta, M. Gerla, and L. Kleinrock, "The flow deviation method: An approach to store-and-forward communication network design," *Networks*, vol. 3, pp. 97–133, 1973.
[14] H. Rudin, *On Routing and "Delta Routing": A Taxonomy of Techniques for Packet-Switched Networks*, IBM Zurich Research Laboratory, RZ 701, June 1975.
[15] W. D. Tajibnapis, *Message-Switching Protocols in Distributed Computer Networks*, Ph.D. Dissertation, The University of Michigan, 1976.
[16] D. B. Johnson, "Efficient algorithms for shortest paths in sparse networks," *Journal of the Association for Computing Machinery*, vol. 24, no. 1, pp. 1–13, January 1977.
[17] R. G. Gallager, "A minimum delay routing algorithm using distributed computation," *IEEE Trans. Commun.*, COM-25, no. 1, pp. 73–85, January 1977.
[18] W. D. Tajibnapis, "A correctness proof of a topology information maintenance protocol for a distributed computer network," *Communications of the ACM*, vol. 20, no. 7, pp. 477–485, July 1977.
[19] T. E. Stern, "A class of decentralized routing algorithms using relaxation," *IEEE Trans. Commun.*, COM-25, no. 10, pp. 1092–1102, October 1977.
[20] J. L. Kennington, "A survey of linear cost multicommodity network flows," *Operations Research*, vol. 26, no. 2, pp. 209–236, March-April 1978.
[21] F. C. Schoute and J. M. McQuillan, "A comparison of information policies for minimum delay routing algorithms," *IEEE Trans. Commun.*, COM-26, no. 8, pp. 1266–1271, August 1978.
[22] J. M. McQuillan, G. Falk, and I. Richer, "A review of the development and performance of the ARPANET routing algorithm," *IEEE Trans. Commun.*, COM-26, no. 12, pp. 1802–1811, December 1978.

[23] R. Dial et al., "A computational analysis of alternative algorithms and labeling techniques for finding shortest path trees," *Networks*, vol. 9, no. 3, pp. 215–248, Fall 1979.

[24] D. R. Shier, "On algorithms for finding the k shortest paths in a network," *Networks*, vol. 9, no. 3, pp. 195–214, Fall 1979.

[25] P. M. Merlin and A. Segall, "A failsafe distributed routing protocol," *IEEE Trans. Commun.*, COM-27, no. 9, pp. 1280–1287, September 1979.

[26] J. M. McQuillan, I. Richer, and E. C. Rosen, "An overview of the new routing algorithm for the ARPANET," *Sixth Data Communications Symposium*, pp. 63–68, November 1979.

[27] Y. W. Ma, "A Shortest Path Algorithm with Average Execution Time $0(\sqrt{n}\log n)$," Ph.D. Dissertation, Department of Electrical Engineering and Computer Sciences, University of California, Berkeley, 1980.

[28] W. K. Crowther, R. Pettbert, D. Walden, S. Ornstein, and F. Heart, "A system for broadcast communication: Reservation-Aloha," in *Proceedings 6th Hawaii International Systems Science Conference*, January 1973.

[29] L. Roberts, "Dynamic allocation of satellite capacity through packets reservation," National Computer Conference, *AFIPS Conference Proceedings*, vol. 42, 1973.

[30] R. Binder, "A dynamic packet-switching system for satellite broadcast channels," *Proc. ICC 1975*, San Francisco, CA, June 1975.

[31] I. Rubin, "Integrated random-access reservation schemes for multi-access communication channels," UCLA-ENG-7752, July 1977.

[32] J. W. Mark, "Global scheduling approach to conflict free multiaccess via a data bus," *IEEE Trans. Commun.*, COM-26, no. 9, pp. 1342–1352, September 1978.

[33] I. M. Jacobs, R. Binder, and E. V. Hoversten, "General purpose packet satellite networks," *Proc. IEEE*, vol. 66, no. 11, pp. 1445–1467, November 1978.

[34] J. E. Wieselthier and A. Ephremides, "A new class of protocols for multiple access in satellite networks," *IEEE Trans. Automatic Control*, vol. Ac-25, pp. 865–879, October 1980.

[35] A. Nilsson and C. J. Graff, "Packet radio communication system architecture in a mixed traffic and dynamic environment," Computer Networking Symposium, IEEE Catalog No. 80CH1586-7, December 10, 1980.

[36] E. P. Greene and A. Ephremides, "Distributed reservation control protocols for random access broadcasting channels," *IEEE Trans. Commun.*, COM-29, no. 5, pp. 726–735, May 1981.

[37] F. A. Tobagi and L. Kleinrock, "Packet switching in radio channels: Part III —Polling and (dynamic) split-channel reservation multiple access," *IEEE Trans. Commun.*, COM-24, no. 8, pp. 832–844, August 1976.

[38] A. K. Agrawala and R. L. Larsen, *Efficient Communication for Local Computer Networks-Coordinated Access Broadcast*, TR-639, NAS5-24092, February 1978.

[39] J. F. Hayes, "An adaptive technique for local distribution," *IEEE Trans. Commun.*, COM-26, no. 8, pp. 1178–1186, August 1978.

[40] I. Chlamtac, W. R. Franta, and K. D. Levin, "BRAM: The broadcast recognizing access method," *IEEE Trans. Commun.*, COM-27, no. 8, pp. 1183–1189, August 1979.

[41] L. Kleinrock and M. O. Scholl, "Packet switching radio channels: New conflict-free multiple access schemes," *IEEE Trans. Commun.*, COM-28, no. 7, pp. 1015–1029, July 1980.

[42] N. Abramson, "The aloha system," in *Computer Networks*, N. Abramson and F. Kuo, Ed., Englewood Cliffs, NJ: Prentice-Hall, 1973, pp. 501–517.

[43] S. S. Lam, *Packet Switching in a Multi-Access Broadcast Channel With Application to Satellite Communication in a Computer Network*, Ph.D. Dissertation, University of California, Los Angeles, CA, UCLA-ENG-7429, April 1974.

[44] F. A. Tobagi, *Random Access Techniques for Data Transmission Over Packet-Switched Radio Networks*, Ph.D. Dissertation, University of California, Los Angeles, CA, UCLA-ENG-7499, December 1974.

[45] L. G. Roberts, "Aloha packet system with and without slots and capture," *Computer Communications Review*, vol. 5, pp. 28–42, April 1975.

[46] L. Kleinrock and S. Lam, "Packet switching in a multi-access broadcast channel: Performance evaluation," *IEEE Trans. Commun.*, COM-23, pp. 410–423, April 1975.

[47] S. S. Lam and L. Kleinrock, "Packet switching in a multi-access broadcast channel: Dynamic control procedures," *IEEE Trans. Commun.*, COM-23, no. 9, pp. 891–904, September 1975.

[48] L. Kleinrock and F. A. Tobagi, "Packet switching in radio channels: Part I—Carrier sense multiple-access modes and their throughput-delay characteristics," *IEEE Trans. Commun.*, COM-23, no. 12, pp. 1400–1416, December 1975.

[49] F. A. Tobagi and L. Kleinrock, "Packet switching in radio channels: Part II—The hidden terminal problem in carrier sense multiple-access and the busy-tone solution," *IEEE Trans. Commun.*, COM-23, no. 12, pp. 1417–1433, December 1975.

[50] G. Fayolle, E. Gelenbe, and J. Labetoulle, "Stability and optimal control of the packet switching broadcast channel," *Journal of the Association for Computing Machinery*, vol. 24, no. 3, pp. 375–386, July 1977.

[51] F. A. Tobagi, "Packet switching in radio channels: Part IV—Stability considerations and dynamic control in carrier sense multiple access," *IEEE Trans. Commun.*, COM-25, no. 10, 1103–1119, October 1977.

[52] J. I. Capetanakis, *The Multiple Access Broadcast Channel: Protocol and Capacity Considerations*, Report ESL-R-806, M.I.T., Cambridge, MA, March 1978.

[53] R. G. Gallager, "Conflict resolution in random access broadcast networks," 1978 AFOSR Workshop in Communication Theory and Applications, Provincetown, MA, pp. 74–76, September 1978.

[54] J. I. Capetanakis, "Tree algorithms for packet broadcast channels," *IEEE Trans. Inform. Theory*, IT-25, no. 5, pp. 505–515, September 1979.

[55] P. A. Humblet and J. Mosely, "Efficient accessing of a multiaccess channel," *IEEE Conference on Decision Control*, Albuquerque, NM, December 1980.

[56] J. L. Massey, "The capacity of the collision channel without feedback," *IEEE Int. Symposium on Information Theory*, Les Ares, France, June 21–25, 1982.

[57] J. L. Spilker, Jr., *Digital Communications by Satellite*, Englewood Cliffs, NJ: Prentice-Hall, 1977.

[58] The MITRE Corporation, *JTIDS Net Access via Distributed Reservation*, J. C. Seaquist, Contract No. F19628-79C-0001, Bedford Operations, Bedford, MA, October 1978.

[59] R. R. Boorstyn and A. Kershenbaum, *Research in Network Management Techniques for Tactical Data Communication Networks*, Polytechnic Institute of New York, NY, October 1979 to September 1980.

[60] R. R. Boorstyn and A. Kershenbaum, "Throughput analysis of multihop packet radio," *ICC 1980 Conference Record*, vol. 1, pp. 1361–1365, 1980.

[61] J. E. Wieselthier, "Spread spectrum multiple access issues in the HF intra task force communication network," *5th MIT/ONR Workshop on C^3 Systems*, Naval Postgraduate School, Monterey, CA, August 1982.

[62] J. E. Wieselthier and A. Ephremides, "A distributed reservation scheme for spread spectrum multiple access channels," GLOBECOM '83, San Diego, CA, November 1983.

[63] M. B. Pursley, "Evaluating performance of codes for spread spectrum multiple-access communications," in *Proc. 12th Annual Allerton Conf. on Circuit and Systems Theory*, pp. 765–774, October 1974.

[64] J. L. Massey, and J. J. Uhran, "Sub-baud coding," *Proc. 13th Annual Allerton Conference on Circuit and Systems Theory*, pp. 539–547, October 1975.

[65] K. Yao, "Error probability of asynchronous spread spectrum multiple-access communication systems," *IEEE Trans. Commun.*, COM-25, pp. 803–809, August 1977.

[66] M. B. Pursley, "Performance evaluation for phase-coded spread spectrum multiple-access—Part I: System analysis." *IEEE Trans. Commun.*, COM-25, pp. 795–799, August 1977.

[67] N. E. Bekir, *Bounds on the Distribution of Partial Correlation for PN and Gold Sequences*, Ph.D. Dissertation, Department of Electrical Engineering, University of Southern California, Los Angeles, CA, January 1978.

[68] N. E. Bekir, R. A. Scholtz, and L. R. Welch, "Partial period correlation properties of PN sequences," in *Proc. Nat. Telecommunications Conf.*, pp. 35.1.1–4, December 1978.

[69] M. B. Pursley and H. F. A. Roefs, "Numerical evaluation of correlation parameters for optimal phases of binary shift-register sequences," *IEEE Trans. Commun.*, COM-27, pp. 1597–1604, October 1979.

[70] D. E. Borth, M. B. Pursley, D. V. Sarwate, and W. E. Stark, "Bounds on error probability for direct-sequence spread spectrum multiple-access communications," in *1979 Midcon Professional Program*, vol. 15: Spread Spectrum Communication System Concepts, November 1979.

[71] D. V. Sarwate and M. B. Pursley, "Cross-correlation properties of pseudorandom and related sequences," *Proc. IEEE*, vol. 68, pp. 593–619, May 1980.

[72] M. B. Pursley, D. V. Sarwate, and W. E. Stark, "On the average probability of error for direct-sequence spread spectrum multiple-access system," in *Proc. 1980 Conf. Information Sciences and Systems*, pp. 320–325, 1980.

[73] K. T. Wu, and D. L. Neuhoff, "Average error probability for DS-SSMA communication system," *Proc. 18th Annual Allerton Conf. on Communication, Control, and Computing*, pp. 359–368, October 1980.

[74] K. T. Wu, "Average error probability for DS-SSMA Communications: The Gram-Charlier expansion approach," *Proc. 19th Annual Allerton Conf. on Communication, Control, and Computing*, pp. 237–246, October 1981.

[75] M. B. Pursley, D. V. Sarwate, and W. E. Stark, "Error probability for direct-sequences spread spectrum multiple-access communication—Part I: Upper and lower bounds," *IEEE Trans. Commun.*, COM-30, pp. 975–984, May 1982.

[76] E. A. Geraniotis and M. B. Pursley, "Error probability for direct-sequences spread spectrum multiple-access communications—Part II: Approximations," *IEEE Trans. Commun.*, COM-30, pp. 985–995, May 1982.

[77] R. C. Singleton, "Maximum distance Q ~ ary codes," *IEEE Trans. Inform. Theory, IT-10, pp. 116–118, April* 1964.

[78] L. I. Bluestein and R. L. Greenspan, "Efficient approximation of orthogonal waveforms," Group Report 1964-48, M.I.T., Lincoln Laboratory, November 3, 1964.

[79] I. S. Reed, "kth order near orthogonal codes," *IEEE Trans. Inform. Theory*, IT-17, pp. 116–117, January 1971.

[80] G. Solomon, "Optimal frequency-hopping sequences for multiple-access," *Proc. 1973 Symposium on Spread-Spectrum Communications*, vol. 1, AD-915, pp. 33–35, 1973.

[81] R. M. Marsareau and T. S. Seay, "Multiple access frequency hopping patterns with low ambiguity" *IEEE Trans. Aerospace and Electronic Systems*, AES-17, no. 4, pp. 571–578, July 1981.

[82] T. S. Seay, "Hopping patterns for bounded mutual interference in frequency hopping multiple access," *MILCOM '82*, Boston, MA, October 1982, paper 22.3.

[83] J. H. Cafarella, "Advanced SAW-based signal processing for packet communications," *MILCOM '82*, Boston, MA, October 1982, paper 10.6.

[84] W. Skudera, W. Novick, and D. Mains, "SAW spread spectrum remote control link," *MILCOM '82*, Boston, MA, October 1982, paper 12.1.

[85] D. M. Grieco and J. K. Gutman, "The SEEK TALK spread spectrum acquisition using a SAW matched filter," *MILCOM '82*, Boston, MA, October 1982, paper 17.3.

[86] T. J. Goblick, W. B. Goggins, D. H. Hurlburt, P. G. McHugh, and N. W. Spencer, "A spread spectrum burst communication system using SAW convolvers," *MILCOM '82*, Boston, MA, October 1982, paper 18.5.

[87] R. E. Conley, "MILSTAR—A military communication system," *MILCOM '82*, Boston, MA, October 1982, paper 31.5.

[88] S. B. Heppe, "Viewpoints on control of military satellite communications, *IEEE Commun. Mag.*, vol. 21, no. 4, July 1983.

[89] TRW Electronic Systems Group, "30/20 GHz low data rate ground terminal design study," Final Report to NASA Lewis Research Center, Document Number 3-6-T-9-F2 on Contract Number NAS3-23341, June 1983.

[90] O. Yue, "Hard-limited versus linear combining for frequency-hopping multiple-access systems in a Rayleigh fading environment," *IEEE Trans. Veh. Technol.*, VT-30, pp. 10–14, March 1981.

[91] D. A. Shnidman, "A generalized Nyquist criterion and optimum linear receiver for a pulse modulation system," *Bell Syst. Tech. J.*, vol. 46, pp. 2163–2177, November 1967.

[92] A. R. Kaye and D. A. George, "Transmission of multiplexed PAM signals over multiple channel and diversity systems," *IEEE Trans. Commun. Technol.*, COM-18, pp. 520–526, October 1970.

[93] J. E. Savage, "Signal detection in the presence of multiple-access noise," *IEEE Trans. Inform. Theory*, IT-20, pp. 42–49, January 1974.

[94] W. Van Etten, "Maximum likelihood receiver for multiple channel transmission systems," *IEEE Trans. Commun.*, COM-24, no. 2, pp. 276–283, February 1976.

[95] K. S. Schneider, "Optimum detection of code division multiplexed signals," *IEEE Trans. Aerospace and Electronic Systems*, AES-15, no. 1, pp. 181–185, January 1979.

[96] S. Verdu, *Minimum Bit-Error-Rate Detection of Asynchronous Multiple-Access Communications*, Coordinated Science Laboratory Technical Report.

[97] S. Verdu, "Optimum sequence detection of asynchronous multiple-access communications," *IEEE 1983 Int. Symposium on Information Theory*, St. Jovite, Canada, September 1983.

[98] J. K. Omura, "Optimal receiver design for convolutional codes and channels with memory via control theoretical concepts," *Information Sciences*, vol. 3, pp. 243–266, 1971.

[99] H. Kobayashi, "Correlative level coding and maximum-likelihood decoding," *IEEE Trans. Inform. Theory*, IT-17, pp. 586–594, January 1971.

[100] G. D. Forney, "Maximum likelihood sequence estimation of digital sequences in the presence of intersymbol interference," *IEEE Trans. Inform. Theory*, IT-18, no. 3, pp. 363–378, May 1972.

[101] L. K. Mackechnie, "Receivers for channels with intersymbol interference," (Abs.) *IEEE 1972 Int. Symposium on Information Theory*, Asilomar, CA, p. 82.

[102] G. D. Forney, "The Viterbi algorithm," *Proc. IEEE*, vol. 61, no. 3, pp. 268–278, March 1973.

[103] A. J. Viterbi and J. K. Omura, *Principles of Digital Communication and Coding*, New York: McGraw-Hill, 1979.

[104] J. K. Omura, "Performance bounds for Viterbi algorithms," *Proc. 1981, IEEE Int. Commun. Conf.*, Denver, CO, pp. 2.2.1–5.

[105] M. B. Pursley, "Coding and diversity for channels with fading and pulsed interference," *Proc. Sixteenth Annual Conference on Information Sciences and Systems*, Princeton University, pp. 413–418, March 1982.

[106] B. Hajek, "Recursive retransmission control—Application to a frequency-hopped spread-spectrum system," *Proc. Sixteenth Annual Conference on Information Sciences and Systems*, Princeton University, pp. 116–120, March 1982.

[107] E. A. Geraniotis and M. B. Pursley, "Error probabilities for slow-frequency-hopped spread-spectrum multiple-access communications over fading channels," *IEEE Trans. Commun.*, COM-30, pp. 996–1009, May 1982.

[108] M. B. Pursley, "Throughput of frequency-hopped spread-spectrum communications for packet radio networks," *Proc. Seventeenth Annual Conference on Information Sciences and Systems*, Johns Hopkins University, pp. 550–556, March 1983.

[109] J. E. Wieselthier and A. Ephremides, "A scheme to increase throughput in frequency hopping multiple access channels," *Proc. Seventeenth Annual Conference on Information Sciences and Systems*, Johns Hopkins University, p. 379, March 1983.

[110] J. E. Wieselthier and A. Ephremides, "Throughput increase in frequency hopped multiple access channels by means of discrimination against partially overlapping interference," Submitted to *IEEE Trans. Commun.*

[111] K. L. Jordan, Jr., "The performance of sequential decoding in conjunction with efficient modulation," *IEEE Trans. Comm. Tech.*, COM-14(3), 283–297, June 1966.

[112] J. M. Wozencraft and R. S. Kennedy, "Modulation and demodulation for probabilistic decoding," *IEEE Trans. Inform. Theory*, IT-12, pp. 291–297, July 1966.

[113] A. J. Viterbi, "A robust ratio-threshold technique to mitigate tone and partial-band jamming in coded MFSK systems," *MILCOM '82*, Boston, MA, October 18–20, 1982.

[114] P. J. Crepeau, "Generalized list detection for coded MFSK/FH signaling on fading and jamming channels," NRL Report 8708, Naval Research Laboratory, Washington, DC, June 1983.

[115] P. J. Crepeau, M. A. Creighton, and J. K. Omura," Performance of FH/MFSK with list metric detection against partial band noise and random tone jamming," *MILCOM '83*, Washington, D.C., October 31–November 2, 1983.

[116] M. A. Creighton, *Analysis of List Decoding Metrics for Jamming and Multiple Access Channels*, Ph.D. Thesis, University of California, Los Angeles, CA, 1985.

[117] D. J. Goodman, P. S. Henry, and V. K. Prabhu, "Frequency-hopped multilevel FSK for mobile radio," *Bell Syst. Tech. J.*, vol. 59, no. 7, September 1980.

[118] A. J. Viterbi, "A processing satellite transponder for multiple access by low-rate mobile users," National Radio Science Meeting, November 6–9, 1978, Boulder, Colorado, Commission C, Session 3.

[119] G. R. Cooper and R. W. Nettleton, "A spread spectrum technique for high capacity mobile communication," *IEEE Trans. Vehic. Tech. J.*, VT-27, pp. 264–275, November 1978.

[120] P. S. Henry, "Spectrum efficiency of a frequency-hopped DPSK mobile radio system," *Proc. IEEE Vehic. Tech.*, VT-28, pp. 327–332, November 1979.

[121] O. Yue, "Frequency-hopping multiple-access, phase-shift-keying systems in a Rayleigh fading environment," *Bell Syst. Tech. J.*, vol. 59, no. 6, pp. 861–879, July–August 1980.

[122] B. G. Haskell, "Computer simulation results on frequency-hopped MFSK mobile radio-noiseless case," *Proc. Nat. Telecommun. Conf.*, Houston, TX, December 1980.

[123] G. Einarsson, "Address assignment for a time frequency-coded spread spectrum system," *Bell Syst. Tech. J.*, vol. 59, no. 7, pp. 1241–1255, September 1980.

[124] U. Timor, "Improved decoding scheme for frequency-hopped multilevel FSK system," *Bell Syst. Tech. J.*, vol. 59, no. 9, pp. 285–296, November 1980.

[125] U. Timor, "Multistage decoding of frequency-hopped FSK system," *Bell Syst. Tech. J.*, vol. 60, no. 4, pp. 471–483, April 1981.

[126] U. Timor, "Multitone frequency-hopped MFSK system for mobile radio," *Bell Syst. Tech. J.*, vol. 61, no. 10, pp. 3007–3017, December 1982.

[127] C. E. Shannon, "Two-way communication channels," *Proc. 4th Berkeley Symp. Math. Stat. Prob.*, vol. 1, pp. 611–644, 1961. Reprinted in *Key Papers in the Development of Information Theory*, D. Slepian, ed., New York: IEEE Press, 1974, pp. 339–372.

[128] R. Ahlswede, "Multi-way communication channels," *Proc. 2nd. Int. Symp. Inform. Theory*, Tsahkadsor, Armenia, USSR, pp. 23–52, 1971.

[129] E. C. van der Meulen, "The discrete memoryless channel with two senders and one receiver," *Proc. 2nd Int. Symp. Inform. Theory*, Tsahkadsor, Armenia, USSR, pp. 103–135, 1971.

[130] H. Liao, "A coding theorem for multiple access communications," presented at Int. Symp. on Inform. Theory, Asilomar, CA, 1972. Also Ph.D. Dissertation, *Multiple Access Channels*, Deptartment of Electrical Engineering, University of Hawaii, 1972.

[131] E. C. van der Meulen, "Advances in multiple-user communication channels," *Proc. 1975 IEEE-USSR Joint Workshop Inform. Theory*, Moscow, USSR, December 1975.

[132] E. C. van der Meulen, "A survey of multi-way channels in information theory: 1961–1976," *IEEE Trans. Inform. Theory*, IT-23, pp. 1–37, January 1977.

[133] D. Slepian and J. K. Wolf, "A coding theorem for multiple access channels with correlated sources," *Bell Syst. Tech. J.*, vol. 52, pp. 1037–1076, September 1973.

[134] T. Kasami and S. Lin, "Coding for a multiple-access channel," *IEEE Trans. Inform. Theory*, IT-22, pp. 129–137, March 1976.

[135] E. J. Weldon, Jr., and K. P. Yiu, "Coding for a multiple access channel," presented at Int. Symp. Inform. Theory, Ronneby, Sweden, 1976.

[136] E. J. Weldon, Jr., "Coding for a multiple access channel," *Inform. Contr.*, vol. 36, no. 3, pp. 256–274, 1978.

[137] T. Kasami and S. Lin, "Bounds on the achievable rates of block coding for a memoryless multiple-access channel," *IEEE Trans. Inform. Theory*, IT-24, pp. 187–197, March 1978.

[138] H. C. A. van Tiborg, "An upper bound for codes in a two-access binary erasure channel," *IEEE Trans. Inform. Theory*, IT-24, pp. 112–116, January 1978.

[139] S. C. Chang and E. J. Weldon, Jr., "Coding for T-user multiple-access channels," *IEEE Trans. Inform. Theory*, IT-25, pp. 684–691, November 1979.

[140] S. C. Chang and J. K. Wolf, "On the T-user M-frequency multiple-access channel with and without intensity information," *IEEE Trans. Inform. Theory*, IT-27, no. 1, pp. 41–48, January 1981.

[141] R. L. Peterson, *Tree, Trellis, and Convolutional Coding for Multiple-Access Channels*, Department of Electrical Engineering, Illinois Institute of Technology, Technical Report EE, 7808-32-02, August 1978.

[142] P. R. Chevillat, *N-User Trellis Coding for a Class of Multiple-Access Channels*, IBM Research Report, Zurich, Switzerland, RZ 928 (#31790), November 1978.

[143] D. J. Costello and R. L. Peterson, "Binary convolutional codes for a multiple-access channel," *IEEE Trans. Inform. Theory*, IT-25, pp. 101–105, January 1979.

[144] R. L. Peterson and D. J. Costello, Jr., "Error probability and free distance bounds for two-user tree codes on multiple-access channels," *IEEE Trans. Inform. Theory*, IT-26, pp. 658–670, November 1980.

[145] P. R. Chevillat, "N-user trellis coding for a class of multiple-access channels," *IEEE Trans. Inform. Theory*, IT-27, pp. 114–120, January 1981.

[146] J. K. Omura and R. Sorace, "Coding for a multiple access channel," 1979 *NTC Record*, 1979, pp. 23.4.1–23.4.7, Washington, DC.

[147] R. Sorace, *Analysis of Noncoherent Multiple Access Communication Channels*, Ph.D. Dissertation, University of California, Los Angeles, CA, 1981.

[148] Q. Vo, *Optimal Detection of Multiple Access Spread Spectrum Signals*, Ph.D. Dissertation, University of California, Los Angeles, CA, 1985.

[149] R. E. Kahn et al., "Advances in packet radio technology," *Proc. IEEE*, vol. 66, pp. 1468–1496, November 1978.

[150] P. Sass, "Army spread-spectrum—Evolution or revolution," MILCOM '82, Boston, MA, October 1982, paper 4.1.

[151] P. Sass, "Why is the army interested in spread spectrum?" *IEEE Commun. Mag.*, vol. 21, no. 4, pp. 23–25, July 1983.

[152] K. Brayer, "Implementation and performance of survivable computer communication with autonomous decentralized control," *IEEE Commun. Mag.*, vol. 21, no. 4, July 1983.

[153] G. Turin, "Introduction to spread spectrum antimultipath techniques and their application to urban digital radio," *Proc. IEEE*, vol. 68, no. 3, March 1980.

[154] G. L. Turin et al., "Urban vehicle monitoring: Technology, economics and public policy," Vol. II: Technical Analysis and Appendices," report prepared under DHUD contract H-1030, October 1970.

[155] G. L. Turin et al., "A statistical model of urban multipath propagation," *IEEE Trans. Veh. Technol.*, VT-21, pp. 1–9, February 1972.

[156] G. L. Turin et al., "Simulation of urban vehicle-monitoring systems," *IEEE Trans. Veh. Technol.*, VT-21, pp. 9–16, February 1972.

[157] G. L. Turin, "Simulation of urban radio propagation and of urban radio communication systems," *Proc. Int. Symp. Antennas and Propagat.*, Sendai, Japan, pp. 543–546, August 1978.

VOLUME I INDEX

VOLUME II INDEX

VOLUME III INDEX